Elements of
ECOLOGY

Elements of
ECOLOGY

GEORGE L. CLARKE

Harvard University
and
Woods Hole Oceanographic Institution

Revised Printing with Subject Guide to New References

John Wiley & Sons, Inc., New York · London · Sydney

Contribution No. 704 from the Woods Hole Oceanographic Institution
Library of Congress Catalog Card Number: 54-12205

To

M. S. C.

Preface

"Live Alone and Like It" is a slogan that no living thing can adopt. Every plant and animal is subject to both the living and the non-living influences of its surroundings. Every organism depends upon its environment to supply it with vital materials and energy. Every living being must share its world with members of its own species and with members of other species—be they friend or foe.

Man is no exception. Man is surrounded by many kinds of living things, and he must derive his needs from the world around him. Man must learn to live in adjustment with his fellow men, and with the plants and animals of his environment, and to use his natural resources judiciously, or he will be exterminated.

Obviously, then, the interrelations of the organism and its environment are crucial; and ecology, which is the study of these interrelations, is of great significance. Yet few books are available which deal with the general principles of the whole subject. Most of the books in the field of ecology treat primarily either "plant ecology" or "animal ecology." But animals cannot get along without plants, and plants are almost always vitally influenced by animals. Man is dependent upon both.

Accounts of the flora and fauna of various regions and descriptions of a variety of habitats have long been available. Early ecologists have investigated the effects of environmental factors on the activities of living things. But not until relatively recently have we realized that plants and animals also react on their surroundings in such a way that they form a reciprocating and integrated system with their environment. The modern ecologist focuses his attention on the dynamic interplay of the forces in the living community.

The purpose of this book is to bring together in one place and in a simple way the elements of ecology with special emphasis on the modern viewpoint of the science. It is desired to stress the unity of ecology and the necessity for including the influence of both plants and animals as well as the physical forces as part of the environment. The subject is old, but efforts to crystallize the basic principles in any exact way are relatively new. The potential scope of ecology is very great, and no attempt at any exhaustive treatment of the subject is made here. Rather, this book presents an introductory account of the fundamental relationships of ecology upon which an understanding of the life of the individual and of the community depends. Since many of these relationships are seen in a relatively simple form in the marine environment, many illustrations are taken from marine habitats.

The book is written primarily for students in ecology. It is also intended as background material for those interested in conservation, forestry, agriculture, fisheries, wildlife management, and other branches of "applied ecology." The general biology student should also derive value from the book since a knowledge of the principles governing the real lives of animals and plants in nature is a vital backdrop for problems in physiology, morphology, genetics, and evolution. Furthermore, it must be remembered that every one of us is an organism with an environment and that each of us forms part of the environment for other living beings. The general reader, as well as the biology student, is interested to know how the world of life works. Populations of men follow many of the same laws as populations of microbes. The need for a knowledge of the proper adjustment among men and between man and his natural environment was never greater than it is today.

The material of the book is drawn in large part from a course in ecology given by the author at Harvard University. Many ideas and illustrations have been derived from discussions with colleagues at Harvard University, the Woods Hole Oceanographic Institution, and elsewhere, and acknowledgment is made of this material. I am also indebted to W. C. Allee, S. A. Cain, J. T. Curtis, R. W. Dexter, W. H. Drury, E. H. Graham, D. R. Griffin, H. C. Hanson, A. G. Huntsman, S. C. Kendeigh, B. H. Ketchum, P. C. Lemon, D. Merriman, R. S. Miller, E. W. Moore, E. T. Moul, O. Park, T. Park, H. M. Raup, A. C. Redfield, F. A. Richards, G. A. Riley, J. H. Ryther, P. S. Sears, J. G. Steel, H. C. Stetson, and J. M. Teal for reading parts of the manuscript and offering helpful criticisms. I am particularly grateful to Marion S. Clarke, Donald Kennedy, and J. E. G. Raymont for assistance in preparing the manuscript and for many valuable suggestions.

GEORGE L. CLARKE

August, 1954

Contents

Chapter 4 · WATER   90

Chapter 5 · TEMPERATURE   129

Chapter 6 · LIGHT

185

Chapter 7 · OXYGEN AND CARBON DIOXIDE

242

Contents

1

Viewpoint of Modern Ecology

Every living thing is surrounded by materials and forces which constitute its environment and from which it must derive its needs. Contact with the environment is inescapable. Protoplasm, the essential constituent of an organism, is a dynamic substance, requiring a continuous exchange of energy and materials. In order to remain alive the organism, too, must secure energy and materials, and these can be procured only by exchange with the outside world. Thus the animal or plant cannot live completely sealed in an impervious skin or shell but requires from its surroundings: (1) a supply of energy; (2) a supply of materials; (3) a removal of waste products. The exchanges that the organism has with its environment may be thought of as an "external physiology," and they are just as essential as its internal physiological adjustments.

The supplying of the vital needs of the organism is by no means the only action of the environment. Since the animal or plant must leave its borders open to foreign trade, as it were, the possibility exists that harmful materials will enter the organism or destructive influences act upon it. For example, algae in a river must be sufficiently permeable to take in the water needed for their metabolism, but, if they drift into the sea, the higher salinity will cause a fatal loss of water from their tissues. Animals in the environment of these algae tend to add materials to the water which serve as plant nutrients, but these same animals may also feed upon the algae and eventually destroy the population.

In order for the life of an organism to continue, the environment must be satisfactory on two counts: (1) it must provide the minimum requirements for life; (2) it must contain no influence incompatible with life. If there is too little water, as in the Sahara Desert, or too little oxygen, as at the top of Mt. Everest, or if nutrients are not available, as on rocky plateaux, animals or plants cannot obtain their minimum needs.   In other situations an ample supply of food and light may be found, but the temperature may be so high as to exclude all life.   This is true in some hot springs.   Certain soils of southwestern United States are completely devoid of vegetation because of the excessive amounts of salts or "alkali."   Death Valley on the Dieng Plateau in Java is populated with plants but no animal life can exist because of high concentrations of carbon dioxide issuing from subterranean crevices.   Such influences are prohibitory to life and others are harmful without being lethal.   In a complex natural situation it is not always easy to discover the particular role each factor plays, but we can be certain that in every situation dealings with the environment are inescapable.

THE MEANING OF ECOLOGY

The study of these interrelations of plants and animals with their environment constitutes the science of ecology.   The environment includes the influences of other plants and animals present as well as those of the physical features.   In order to investigate the exchanges and interdependencies involved, it is necessary to have a knowledge both of the organisms themselves and of the environments inhabited by them.   The ecologist must know the material with which he works. He must have a grasp of the classification and the structure of plants and animals, and he must understand what makes them tick.   At the same time the ecologist must be thoroughly aware of the nature of the environment—both living and non-living.   He must be familiar with the different types of terrain on land and with the different qualities of water in the ocean, lakes, and rivers.   He must appreciate the special environmental conditions provided by the various kinds of vegetation.   He must have a knowledge of the circulation of water and air and of the dynamic processes going on in the soil.   But the taxonomy, morphology, and physiology of organisms and the physiography of land and sea, although providing a necessary background, do not form the central core of ecology.   The ecologist focuses his attention primarily on the *interrelationships* between the organism and its environment:

$$\text{Ecology}$$
$$\swarrow \downarrow \searrow$$
$$\text{Organism} \longleftrightarrow \text{Environment}$$

The word "ecology" comes from the Greek "oikos," meaning "home" or "estate"—hence, ecology is the study of the home, or how the household of nature is kept in order. Interestingly enough, although ecology comes from the same root as our word "economics," the subject that we now call ecology was not given a name until a century later. Man, being egocentric, began this type of study in his immediate surroundings. Not until long afterwards did he realize that man's economics is but a special case of the broader subject. In the words of Wells, Huxley, and Wells (1939), "Ecology is really an extension of economics to the whole world of life." Economics and sociology might be thought of as the "ecology of man" in a broad sense. The realization that the relations of man to his environment, both physical and social, form a distinct and most important study is reflected in the increasing use of the term *human ecology* in sociology and in other fields.

Our goal in ecology is to understand the interrelations of organisms and their environments *under natural conditions*. Many biologists of all sorts have tended to lose this point of view. As Elton (1939) stated, "The discoveries of Darwin, himself a magnificent field naturalist, had the remarkable effect of sending the whole zoological world flocking indoors, where they remained hard at work for fifty years or more, and whence they are now beginning to put forth cautious heads again into the open air!" Laboratory tests and field experiments are, of course, used in studying the reactions of animals and plants as an aid to understanding their actual and possible behavior under natural conditions. Modern ecology thus goes beyond the mere description of the habitat, or the listing of its inhabitants, to an analysis of causal relationships and a coordinated understanding of constructive and destructive processes in the community.

THE MEANING OF ENVIRONMENT

In referring to the natural environment one tends to think first of the broad aspects of the landscape, such as water, soil, desert, or mountain. These types of environment can be more exactly described in terms of physical influences—differences in moisture, temperature, texture of material, and the like—and of biological influences. Other organisms form part of the environment just as much as the soil or the rocks. No animal can live entirely as a hermit; every animal must have other organisms within its range to serve as food. All animals are dependent directly or indirectly upon green plants. Many plants are dependent upon animals—those that require pollination by insects, for example. Some green plants could live independently for a time, deriving their energy from the sun and their nutrients from the soil, but, as soon as seedlings start to grow, relations of competition appear.

Every organism thus has other organisms as a necessary, or an un-avoidable, part of its environment. Animals and plants compete with each other, devour, or aid one another. Fellow inhabitants cannot be disregarded as part of the environment, as is clearly apparent in a thick stand of trees (Fig. 1.1) or in the slum conditions of

Fig. 1.1.   Grove of giant redwoods near Crescent City, California, showing the intense competition of the trees with each other and their profound influence on the conditions beneath the forest canopy.

a sea-bird rookery (Fig. 1.2). In other situations the effects of the presence of other animals and plants are more subtle. Although such influences cannot be photographed, they are often just as crucial, and the environment must be understood to include both physical and biological influences whether conspicuous or obscure.

Allan D. Cruickshank, National Audubon Society

FIG. 1.2. Gannet rookery on Bonaventure Island, Quebec, showing the keen competition for nest sites.

The Critical Environment

Are the necessary dealings of the organism with the environment usually successful? Can all living things find their needs in the outside world and avoid dangers? In most instances a large fraction of the young plants and animals produced are unable to cope with the environment, and relatively few survive. A striking example of the magnitude of natural mortality is found in the accompanying data from a study of the growth of mackerel eggs and young off the east coast of the United States (Sette, 1943).

Stage of Young Mackerel	Duration	Mortality
Spawning to 10-mm length	40 days	14% per day
Transition to post-larva	few days	30% per day
Post-larva to 50-mm length	40 days	10% per day

These values show that mortality was high throughout development and that a particularly critical period occurred during the transition to the post-larval stage. Out of each million mackerel eggs spawned in the area of this investigation *only four survived* on the average to reach a size at which the young fish could forage for themselves effectively. Others would, of course, succumb before they grew to spawning size.

The U. S. Fish and Wildlife Service estimated that early in 1944 there were roughly 125 million ducks in North America. These ducks ordinarily produce 10 to 16 eggs per pair. If all the adults and all the eggs produced in 1944 had survived, there would have been about 900 million ducks inhabiting the continent in 1945. Actually the population was not significantly larger at the next census, early in 1945, with again about 125 million ducks present. This means that something like 775 million ducks had died during the year. The sportsman's kill, which is estimated from licenses and bag reports, was about 20 million during 1944, or less than 3 per cent of the total mortality (Griscom, 1947). Again it is obvious that a very large portion of this bird population died during the year, and most died of "natural causes"—not by the hand of man.

One process developed during the course of evolution that acts to insure the survival of species in the face of this high mortality is the production of huge numbers of young. The prodigious fertility of nature is a measure of the destructive action that is received from the environment. In species in which each pair produces thousands or millions of eggs or seeds, only two survive on the average to reach the adult condition as long as the population is not continually increasing. Many examples could be given of the huge excess number of young that are produced and the small number that survive (Fig. 1.3). Insects are notoriously prolific. The queen termite in an African species after only one mating is reported to lay eggs at the rate of one every few seconds and to continue egg laying at this terrific pace for the rest of her life. A calculation shows that at this rate each termite queen would lay approximately 30,000 eggs per day or 100 million in her lifetime (Wheeler, 1923). According to estimates, an oyster may discharge 500 million ripe eggs in one spawning. If all these eggs developed into mature oysters and all subsequent progeny survived, after only four generations we would have a pile of oysters about eight times the size of the earth!

Plants also have the capacity to reproduce at very high rates, and, if all spores or seeds grew to maturity, plant populations would increase with tremendous rapidity. Pine trees liberate such quantities of pollen that a yellowish dust is often deposited on all surfaces in the vicinity. A tropical American orchid of the genus *Maxillaria* is reported to produce as many as 1,756,000 seeds per capsule. Spores are produced in astronomical numbers by many lower plants. A conservative estimate made for the downy mildew, *Sclerospora*, which attacks maize in the Philippines, indicates that as many as 6 billion conidia (spores) are liberated from the fungi parasitizing a single maize plant during one night. Since discharge of conidia continues night after night for months, the intensity of the reproductive capacity of these species surpasses the imagination (Weston, 1923).

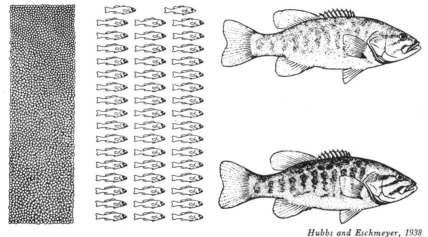

Hubbs and Eschmeyer, 1938

Fig. 1.3. Schematic representation of natural mortality in small-mouthed black bass. Only a few fish survive to maturity from hundreds of eggs laid.

The adaptations of some plants and animals are more specifically perfected to their environments, and their reproductive rates can consequently be relatively low, but even slow breeders tend to increase. If the elephant produces only six young in its life time, as has been estimated, these creatures would nevertheless eventually increase to such numbers, if all progeny survived, that they would cover the whole surface of Africa. An even slower breeding rate is exhibited by the California "big trees" (*Sequoia gigantea*) which do not produce their first seeds until they are 175 or 200 years old! And yet even this species has the capacity to enlarge its population.

Since no species of plant or animal goes on increasing indefinitely, we are forced to the conclusion that, whether reproduction rate is fast or slow, supernumerary individuals are killed off. Usually most of the young produced die at an early age. In the terms of the insurance salesman, their life expectancy is low. Man is a notable exception. Civilization has brought about an increasingly higher life expectancy in man—and with economic and sociological consequences to which we must adjust.

The great majority of plants and animals in nature die young, not because of flaws in their internal mechanism, but because of their failure to cope successfully with the external world. When fish eggs are raised under the best conditions in a hatchery, most of them survive; very few die because of a mechanical or a physiological breakdown in their embryological development. When seeds are sown in a well-prepared greenhouse bed, germination of most of the population is expected. On a bag of grass seed, you will usually find a statement that tests of the seed have shown a germination of 80 to 95 per cent. In a laboratory culture the larvae of a marine copepod were raised to the adult stage with an 80 per cent survival, although a survival of less than 0.5 per cent would have been sufficient to maintain the population on the basis of the number of eggs laid (Johnson and Olson, 1948). In the laboratory the copepod was protected from predators, diseases, and the exigencies of the physical and chemical factors of its usual environment, which would normally have killed off more than 995 out of every 1000 young animals.

Of course, some individuals are born with congenital flaws in their anatomy or physiology. Little information exists on the frequency with which lethal genes occur in wild populations, but their influence is probably very slight. Studies of wild fruit flies indicate that only about 20 per cent of the eggs laid fail to develop into adult insects because of genetic causes. Most of these "lethals" succumb because the genetic changes cause failures in their relations to the environment, rather than failures in their internal adjustments.

The few animals or plants that have escaped death long enough to reach maturity are leading a very precarious existence. A sword of Damocles hangs over their heads! The threat is ever present that the action of the environment may become a little more severe and wipe the population out. This sometimes happens. A striking example of wholesale destruction of a bird population occurred in Minnesota when hundreds of Lapland longspurs were killed during a late winter storm (Fig. 1.4). Another illustration of mass mortality is the suffocation of fish under the ice of a lake (Fig. 1.5). In these instances certain physical features of the environment became too severe and the entire local population was killed.

Sometimes a biological influence goes beyond tolerable limits. Older residents of northeastern United States tell of Sunday excur-

T. S. Roberts, Minnesota Museum of Natural History

FIG. 1.4. Dead Lapland longspurs on the frozen surface of a Minnesota lake after a late winter storm.

Prescott, 1939, AAAS Pub. No. 10

FIG. 1.5 Masses of dead fish washed ashore after the breakup of the ice in Lake East Okoboji in northwestern Iowa. Bass, perch, carp, and other fish were killed by the depletion of oxygen under the ice following the decay of a heavy growth of algae.

sions into extensive groves of edible chestnut trees to gather nuts. Now an edible chestnut tree is a rarity because a blight on this species, caused by a fungus, spread throughout the northeastern states and wiped out the chestnut groves between 1910 and 1930.

If the slight, but crucial, increase in the destructive action of the environment extends beyond a local area to the whole range of a species, its effect becomes much more serious, and it may even result in the extinction of the species. This, too, has happened, not once, but many times. Within the memory of man such species as the Labrador duck and the passenger pigeon have become extinct; many more, such as the American bison, would have been entirely wiped out if it were not for protected preserves. No one knows how many species during the ages failed to meet the challenge of the environment. We do know that about 21,000 species of extinct vertebrates and an even larger number of extinct higher plants have been described. If we add to this figure a guess as to the number of extinct vertebrates and higher plants whose remains were never found, and of the extinct species of invertebrates and of lower plants, we shall have some impression of the precariousness of existence in this world.

As if the destructive action of the environment were not serious enough under natural conditions, man has added immeasurably to it as civilization has "advanced." As will appear many times in our further discussions, man need not necessarily be the destroyer. With an adequate understanding of ecological principles he can utilize many natural resources without impairing them. In some instances the abundance and variety of the natural fauna and flora have improved as a result of man's activities. If we include cultivation, a very great development of plant and animal life has, of course, been brought about by the hand of man. Unfortunately the intelligent use of biological resources has not been the rule. Whole populations of animals and birds have been slaughtered for their fur or their feathers. Grasslands have been ruined, forests have been cut down (Fig. 1.6).

Besides direct devastation of much of our natural vegetation and wildlife, we have wrought even more harm through causing serious pollution of lakes, rivers, and harbors, irreparable damage to the soil, and loss of ground-water reserves (Fig. 1.7). The sad story of man's destruction of his own natural resources throughout the world has been effectively told. The need for intelligent conservation and the steps being taken in the United States to achieve it have been summarized by Gustafson, Guise, Hamilton, and Ries (1949), by G. H. Smith (1950), and others. Suffice it here to stress once more the fact that animals and plants in nature are living dangerously. The natural

U. S. Forest Service

Fig. 1.6.   Advanced degree of land destruction near Leadville, Colorado, where forest has been ruined by clear-cutting, and the complete removal of trees has resulted in gullying and serious soil erosion.

U. S. Soil Conservation Service

Fig. 1.7.   Soil erosion and consequent farm abandonment in Oklahoma, showing disastrous economic and sociological effects of agricultural practices carried on without regard to the ecological limitations of the region.

environment causes the death of most young organisms brought into the world, and sometimes it may vary so as to kill all members of a population. Man is an unavoidable part of the environment. With intelligence he may help guard the danger spots—he may even improve the productivity of natural environments. Without intelligence man accelerates destruction.

In the preceding examples of mass mortality and extinction the devastating action which the environment can have, with and without the presence of man, is obvious to all. For every spectacular instance of this sort, there are thousands of instances in which no cataclysmic destruction is taking place, but in which the forces of the environment are nevertheless exerting a crucial influence in some subtle or obscure manner.

This undercover work of the agents of the environment may perhaps be most easily appreciated first in its action on individual species. The geographical range of each species, for example, is controlled by the pruning action of external forces. Every species is pressing against its boundaries and is always tending to extend its range. It is held in check by the physical and biological factors of the environment which kill off those individuals which spread out too far—into areas where conditions are no longer tolerable. During periods when no unusual fluctuations occur at the limits of the range inhabited by a species, the destructive effect of the environment may not be spectacular because ordinarily only a few individuals are eliminated at any one time or place.

The environment may thus control crucially, but quietly, the geographical range of a species. Fluctuations in the environment may even allow the limits of distribution to change somewhat as conditions vary without a particularly noticeable mortality. One example of that possibility is found in the commercial fishery records for the landings of the weakfish along our middle Atlantic coast. This fish, which is sold in New York markets as "sea trout," was caught only in waters south of Cape Cod previous to 1895. During that year and in succeeding seasons weakfish were taken north of the Cape, and by 1901 the catch was large enough to support a regular fishery. By 1907, however, the numbers of this fish had dropped again to such a low figure that the fishery was abandoned, and never established again north of Cape Cod. There was no dramatic change in the ocean waters around the Cape during those six years. Some subtle, unnoticed variation in the ecological conditions allowed the weakfish to extend its range a short distance for a little while, and then caused the northern limit of the species to be drawn back again.

However, the environment sometimes changes so as to allow huge variations in the numbers of organisms, such as plagues of mice or insect pests, as will be discussed later. More generally, however, the fluctuations in the surroundings and in the abundance of plants and animals are less violent. In the great majority of these unspectacular oscillations it is nevertheless the environment that is exerting the vital control of the numbers of each species. In order to discover the causes of fluctuations, which are sometimes of great economic importance, a clear understanding of the essential relations between the organism and its environment must be obtained.

The everyday action of the environment in curtailing the geographical spread and the abundance of organisms has other significant effects. The production of more young plant seedlings and young animals than can survive causes a continual struggle for existence, with the resulting survival of the fittest. These are essential factors in the evolutionary process—as was pointed out by a prominent "ecologist" by the name of Darwin, long before the term ecology came into common use. Through its influence on the individual the environment indirectly controls the natural community. It determines the complexion of the whole population by determining which species can exist in each area and the relative numbers of each. Through the control of feeding, growth, and other activities of each living component, the environment regulates the dynamic operation of the community.

THE DEVELOPMENT OF ECOLOGY

The Ecology of Plants and of Animals

The term "oecology" was first used by the German zoologist Haeckel in 1869. The word did not appear again until 1895, when a report on ecological plant geography was published by Warming, a Danish botanist. The term in its modern spelling was taken up again later by the zoologists. In those early days and for a long period thereafter botanists and zoologists were often working quite separately. It is not surprising, therefore, that plant ecology and animal ecology tended to develop independently, but it is unfortunate that this division into two separate fields tended to persist. We have now come to realize that a proper understanding of the ecology of animals necessarily involves a consideration of the plants of the environment, and that a study of the ecology of plants would be incomplete without including the influence of animals. However, ecologists, and biologists in general, have been slow to point out that many of the principles of ecology are the same for both plants and animals.

The modern ecologist strives to understand the fundamental influence of the factors of the environment and to delineate such general concepts as limiting action, competition, population growth, and the like. These principles may be applied to the plants or to the animals of the region under investigation, but for many concepts, such as those of the food chain and the dynamics of energy exchange, both the plants *and* the animals *must* be considered. The term ecology thus necessarily includes the interrelations of all kinds of organisms with the environment.

The Ecology of Habitats and of Individuals

In the early development of the subject, one group of ecologists concentrated on the relations of the habitat. They strove toward a better description of the habitat and of the influences of the habitat on the plants and animals that lived there. First the physical features and then the biological influences were investigated. The study of the habitat and its effects is often spoken of as *habitat ecology*.

The work of other early ecologists, instead of beginning with a description of environments, took its departure from an investigation of the individual plant or animal. Attention was focused on the needs and the reactions of the organism and the influence of environmental factors upon it. Thus was developed a study of the ecology of the individual, or to use a specially coined term, *autecology*.

The Ecology of Populations and of Communities

While the habitat ecologists were hard at work, other biologists with ecological leanings were turning their attention to the fact that new interrelations appear when groups arise. No animal or plant lives as a completely isolated individual. When groups of the same species are formed new effects appear. A simple example will illustrate this point. Suppose that 100 trees are growing as individuals widely spaced in a pasture. The shade from each of these trees will move around during the course of the day so that the ground beneath the trees will receive direct sunlight at least for a time each day. On the other hand, if these same 100 trees were growing close together in a grove, the shadow of one would overlap that of the next, with the result that continuous shade would exist underneath. The effect of the trees in the grove on temperature of the soil, evaporation, and wind conditions would be entirely different from that produced by widely spaced trees. The interdependencies resulting from an aggregation of individuals of the same species may become very complex, as for example in an insect colony. The size of a population of animals or plants and its rate of growth are regulated by the reactions of the members of the population to each other and to the environment. The study of these and similar relationships of groups of organisms is termed *population ecology.*

When several species of plants and animals are present, as is usual in a natural community, still further complications arise. In the example cited above a very different vegetation would exist beneath the 100 trees growing as isolated individuals from that found on the floor of a dense grove. The species of animals associated with the plants will also differ widely in the two situations. Widely varying combinations of plants and animals coexist in the many different habitats of the world. It is found that certain species live together in mutual adjustment, and these are spoken of as a natural community. The study of the relationships of the animals and plants making up a community is termed *community ecology* or, again to use a coined term, *synecology.*

The development of the different viewpoints in ecology mentioned above is due in part to the fact that the plant ecologist and the animal ecologist have tended to work rather independently. The community of plants is perhaps more obvious than the community of animals. With plants the vegetation as a whole is often more striking, whereas with animals the individuals tend to be considered first. Since animal communities were generally less apparent, they were delineated at a later date. The result of these influences was that animal and plant communities were first thought of and studied quite separately.

As ecology developed, it came to be realized that the animals of an area do not constitute a community entirely distinct from the plants of that area. It is true that in some situations, as for example in the desert, the interrelations between the animals and the plants may be less critical than the dependence of both upon the physical factors of the environment. Nevertheless, because of the fundamental dependence of animals upon green plants and the influences commonly effective in the reverse direction, the plants and animals of a region should be considered as one integrated community. The animal taxonomist lists the fauna in a region and the plant taxonomist records the flora. The fauna and flora together are spoken of as the *biota* of the region. In an analogous fashion the modern ecologist considers the integrated community of plants and animals as the *biotic com-*

munity. It cannot be emphasized too strongly that the community exists because of the suitable reactions of the individuals which make up the community. Therefore, no sharp line exists between the ecology of the individual and community ecology. All the foregoing concepts will be discussed more fully and illustrated in subsequent chapters.

The Ecological Complex

We have traced the development of the concept of the biotic community as the complete assemblage of interdependent plants and animals inhabiting an area. As a further step it came to be realized that the physical conditions of the area must be considered for the community just as for the individual. The organisms interact with each other and also with the physical conditions that are present. Thus organisms and the physical features of the habitat form an *ecological complex*, or, more briefly, an *ecosystem*.

In ecology, as in other subjects, the descriptive view appeared first. Lists of the animals and plants present in characteristic situations were prepared, and values were reported for the physical and chemical conditions of the areas. In time all the important habitats became subjects of special study, including the forests, the grasslands, the deserts, the mountains, and the aquatic regions. Investigations of certain definite habitats gave rise to such sciences as forestry, oceanography, and limnology. In other instances studies of special types of environment were not given specific names.

As various characteristic environments and their biotas were investigated more intensively, the realization developed that the ecological complex should not be viewed as a static group of animals and plants with the accompanying climatic conditions. The ecosystem is not a museum group remaining immovable and unchanged as generations of observers pass by the plate glass windows. The community cannot continue to exist without exchanges and interdependencies any more than the individual plant or animal can. The community, as well as the individual organism, is "something happening." Thus the functional viewpoint gained momentum as modern ecology developed. Sears (1939) neatly emphasized this point by stating, "When the ecologist enters a forest or a meadow, he sees not merely what is there, but what is happening there."

As the action of the environment was studied in further detail it was found convenient to list its influences as ecological factors. The student may have at first gained an impression of all the factors of the environment impinging upon the organism in a one-sided action. With further understanding of the natural situation, however, it came to be realized that not only do these factors affect the organism, but also the organism affects its environment. This reciprocal action is seen first of all in relation to the physical features of the habitat. For example, light plays a part in controlling the growth of trees, and at the same time the trees control the amount of light beneath them. Similarly, the dissolved nutrients and oxygen in pond water affect the growth of the aquatic organisms that live there, but the very activity of these organisms in turn modify these factors. The growth of plants depletes the supply of nutrient salts. The respiration of animals consumes oxygen and increases the amount of carbon dioxide in the water. Thus the environment receives materials from the organisms living in it and loses material to them as they grow. The fact that regular changes in the environment are brought about by the life activities of the inhabitants was especially emphasized in a series of Lowell Institute lectures given by A. C. Redfield in 1941, which he entitled *The Physiology of the Environment.*

The animals and plants modify the biological features of their environment just as they do the non-living factors. In thinking of the activity of a carnivore, such as a fox preying on rabbits, we realize first perhaps the influence of the predatory action in killing the rabbits and depleting their numbers. But by turning the picture around it becomes clear that the abundance of rabbits also influences the fox population. A rapid growth of the individual foxes and a high rate of reproduction is made possible if the supply of rabbits for food is large, but the number of foxes may be drastically curtailed if rabbits become extremely scarce. In the same way when we observe a flock of sheep in a pasture, we tend to think first of the activity of the sheep in grazing down the grass. It is also true, however, that the sheep's sharp teeth are clipping off tree seedlings which may be sprouting in the turf and the animals are adding manure to the pasture. If it were not for the presence of the sheep, the continued existence of the turf would often no longer be possible. In many situations trees would seed in, and as a forest grew up the turf would be killed off. Clearly the sheep and the plants of the turf form an integrated system.

The concept that organisms and their environment form a reciprocating system represents the viewpoint of most modern ecologists. In every natural situation the environment affects the organisms present and to a greater or lesser extent, the organisms affect the environment. The accompanying terms were proposed by Clements to describe the several aspects of the foregoing relationships.

$$\text{``Action''} = \text{habitat} \rightarrow \text{organism}$$

$$\text{``Reaction''} = \text{organism} \rightarrow \text{physical factors}$$

$$\text{``Co-action''} = \text{organism} \rightarrow \text{organism}$$

The community, which Sears (1950) aptly refers to as "the living landscape," maintains itself as a working unit with all the necessary exchanges going on, more or less in balance, but in a dynamic and not a static balance. The functional concept of the community and of the two-way reaction between the environment and its inhabitants carries us far beyond the descriptive view. The improvement gained from this modern approach in ecology is analogous to the better understanding of the conditions inside an individual animal or plant that is obtained when the physiologist's viewpoint and technique are added to those of the anatomist. Modern ecology might thus be thought of as the "physiology" of the ecological complex in the sense that it deals with the functional aspects of the interactions, exchanges, and adjustments of the members of the community and of their environment.

THE SCOPE OF ECOLOGY

Taylor (1936) has said "Ecology is the science of all the relations of all the organisms to all their environment." Since the plant and animal inhabitants may be very abundant and diverse, and since environmental conditions are extremely variable, the possible scope of ecology becomes very great. The central task of ecology, however, is to delineate the general principles under which the natural community and its component parts operate. These may then be applied to the interpretation of the activities of the particular plants and animals present under the existing specific conditions of a given stiuation.

Although the fauna and flora of an area must be identified and enumerated, and although the physical forces at work in the area must be recognized, neither an account of the biota, nor a description of the habitat constitutes an ecological investigation. Similarly, if a man arises at daybreak and makes a list of the birds he sees without any consideration of the relation of the occurrence of these species to other factors, he is not an ecologist. Modern ecology is concerned with the *functional interdependencies* between living things and their surroundings. Ecology is primarily a field subject. Nevertheless, a knowledge of the principles and problems of ecology should be acquired before attempting to evaluate a natural situation, where the multiplicity of ecological activities may be bewildering. Many ecological relationships can be effectively analyzed under the simplified and controlled conditions of the laboratory.

Because of a lack of understanding of ecological principles the efforts of well-intentioned conservationists and agriculturalists are frequently badly misdirected. A story is told of certain sheep ranchers who became convinced that coyotes were robbing them of their young sheep. As a result, the community rose up and by every possible means slaughtered all the coyotes that could be located for miles around. Following the destruction of the coyotes, the rabbits, field mice, and other small rodents of the region increased tremendously and made serious inroads upon the grass of the pastures. When this development was realized, the sheep men executed an about-face, abruptly stopped killing the coyotes, and instituted an elaborate program for the poisoning of the rodents. The coyotes filtered in from surrounding areas and multiplied, but finding their natural rodent food now scarce they were forced to turn to the young sheep as their only available source of food!

An understanding of ecological principles provides a background for further investigations not only into the fundamental relationships of the natural community but also into sciences dealing with particular environments such as the forest, soil, ocean, or inland waters. Many practical applications of ecology are found in agriculture, biological surveys, game management, pest control, forestry, and fishery biology. Knowledge of ecology is critically important for intelligent conservation whether in relation to soil, forest, wildlife, water supply, or fishery resources.

Ecology is significant also in a wider sense for us as citizens. It gives us an insight into how the world works. In addition, man himself is a most important element in the environment. Man almost always has a modifying influence, and, without proper regulation, he often has a destructive effect. Man is himself an organism with an environment, and this fact has been particularly emphasized in the development of *human ecology*. A knowledge of the general principles of ecology thus provides a background for the understanding of human relations just as a study of general zoology is necessary as a groundwork for medicine. Like other animals man is influenced by the physical features of his environment, he is absolutely dependent upon other species, and he must adjust to other individuals of his own species.   At the moment man is suffering from lack of these adjustments.

APPROACH TO THE STUDY OF ECOLOGY

The study of ecology is best begun through the analytical approach. This involves the delineation of the individual influences of the environment and the recognition separately of the various activities of the organisms present as steps toward building an understanding of the entire dynamic interaction between the complete environment and its inhabitants.

The fundamental relationships are most readily grasped by analyzing the simplest situations first.   Contrast, if you will, the ecological dependencies of an alga living near the surface in the open ocean with those of a tree growing on land.   The tissues of the alga receive their energy supply directly from the sun and they carry on their interchange of materials directly with the surrounding water, which is uniform and extremely constant in respect to the ecological factors concerned.   The tree, on the other hand, is partly in the light and partly in the dark.   Part of the tree is surrounded by the atmosphere with its widely fluctuating temperature and humidity; part is in the soil, where it is subject to a very different temperature and is alternately flooded with air and with water.   The part of the tree that is above ground must deal with one set of organisms, and the part of the tree below ground is concerned with an almost entirely different set.

Another reason for adopting the analytical approach is that this procedure is more likely to reveal limiting factors.   All animals and plants tend to grow, to reproduce, and to disperse until checked by some influence of the environment.   The factor that first stops the growth or spread of the organism is called the *limiting factor*.   It is not always easy to single out the limiting factor, and sometimes two or more factors combine to provide the limiting influence.   Nevertheless, it is extremely desirable whenever possible to determine what agent or agents control the natural tendency of the plants and animals present to increase in size, numbers, and range.   In the investigation of any natural area correlations will be found between features of the environment and the activities of organisms present.   Analysis of the action of individual influences at work in the habitat is necessary in determining which of the correlated factors are actually causal factors.   Suppose, for example, that we discovered a correlation between the occurrence of the factor A and organism B.   Should we conclude that A causes B?

$$A \rightarrow B$$

It might very well be that no direct causal relation exists between A and B whatsoever, but that both are controlled by a third influence, C.

Or factor A may influence C, which in turn influences B, thus:

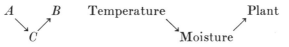

In considering the factors of the environment separately in order to distinguish and to measure the influence of each, we must remain thoroughly aware that in nature the factors are never acting alone. Animals and plants are subject to many influences at the same time, and the effect of one factor is often modified by action of other factors. The "real life" of the organism, on which its growth, distribution, and multiplication depend, necessarily involves the simultaneous and continuing impact of all existing factors and also influences that occurred at earlier stages in the organism's experience.

An important difference exists in the extent to which factors can be modified by living organisms. Some features of the environment are largely unaffected by the activities of the organisms present; these are *unmodifiable* or *conservative factors*. The salinity of the ocean is an example of a conservative factor. The volume of the ocean is so great that, although animals and plants living in it are continually adding or withdrawing salts, the amounts have an immeasurably small effect upon the total salt content of the water. The *modifiable* or *non-conservative factors* of the environment are susceptible to change caused by the inhabitants of the area. The oxygen in a small pond, for example, may be so depleted by the respiration of a large population of fish that an unfavorable or even a lethal condition for the fish is produced; or the concentration of oxygen in the pond may be increased by the photosynthesis of algae a modification that will benefit the fish. Heather (*Calluna*) tends to increase greatly the acidity of the soil in which it is growing, and this condition favors the further development of this plant, but it is unfavorable to most other plants. Through modification of its own environment, heather often comes to dominate the vegetation in large areas, as may be seen in Jutland.

No sharp division exists between modifiable and unmodifiable factors. All gradations exist, and a given factor may be modifiable in some situations or for some organisms and quite unmodifiable for others. In the succeeding chapters the more general, often unmodifiable, factors will be scrutinized first, and will be followed by a discussion of the more commonly modifiable factors. This will lay the foundation for a consideration in the later chapters of the composition and functioning of the community as a whole.

2

The Medium

The first of the physical features of the environment to be considered will be the medium—that is, the material which immediately surrounds the organism and with which it has its all-important exchange. At first sight one might think that many diverse media exist. Some organisms live in the soil, and some in ponds; some thrive in manure piles, and others enjoy a successful existence in the blood stream of vertebrate animals. Certain nematodes live in vinegar, and a fly larva of the genus *Psilopa* grows in petroleum. Once during a departmental gathering at Cambridge University a member of the staff entered the room waving a journal in which the habits of this larva were reported. "Look here," he said, "in this report an insect is described which lives in petroleum. The first thing you know it will parasitize our motor cars!"

The medium in each of the above examples, and indeed that for organisms in every natural situation, is either a liquid or a gas, and it is usually air or water. Although animals and plants inhabiting soil or mud may at first appear to be exceptions, a closer scrutiny shows that a film of air or water around each organism is actually the material in immediate contact with it. An enlarged view of the small animals living in the wet sand of the seashore shows that their essential exchange is with the water percolating between the sand grains and that the medium for these animals is sea water, not sand (Fig. 2.1). The term medium is thus used in a strict sense and is distinguished from the *substratum*, or surface on or in which the organism lives.

The existence of air and water as the fundamental media divides the world into two major environments: terrestrial and aquatic. The media are not completely isolated from each other, however; some of the atmospheric gases are dissolved in all natural waters, and some moisture is present almost everywhere in the atmosphere. Differences in the amount of intermixture play a part in subdividing the terrestrial environment into arid and humid climates and the aquatic environment into stagnated and aerated water. Transition areas of special interest exist—such as swamps and the tidal zone—where sometimes one medium and sometimes the other dominates the scene. Dams built by beavers occasionally result in the flooding of large tracts of

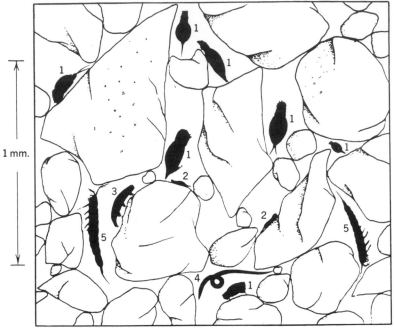

Pennak, 1939, AAAS Pub. No. 10

FIG. 2.1. Enlarged diagram of sand in a beach habitat showing water-filled spaces between the grains. 1 = rotifers, 2 = gastrotrichs, 3 = tartigrade, 4 = nematode, 5 = harpacticoid copepods.

land, transforming them from terrestrial to aquatic habitats (Fig. 2.2); conversely, the growth of vegetation often tends to fill up a shallow pond, gradually converting it into a swamp, and eventually into dry land. Ordinarily, however, the medium is a highly independent factor, for rarely do the activities of organisms cause a change from one basic medium to the other.

CONTRASTING QUALITIES OF AIR AND WATER

The two fundamental media are very different in nature, and this difference has important ecological consequences. Air is composed of 79 per cent nitrogen, 21 per cent oxygen, 0.03 per cent carbon dioxide, and several other gases in much smaller quantities. These gases are not chemically combined, but exist as a simple physical mixture. Water, by contrast, consists primarily of a single compound, H_2O. There is nothing especially unusual about the physical and chemical properties of air and the gases of which it is composed.

Fig. 2.2.   Pond formed by beaver dam (left foreground), showing beaver house (right center) and trees felled and stripped by the beavers.   Cochetopa National Forest, Colorado.

Water, on the other hand, is a unique substance from the ecological viewpoint. H. B. Bigelow, formerly director of the Woods Hole Oceanographic Institution, when lecturing on oceanic biology once stated: "The most important fact about the ocean is that it is full of water!"

The unusual qualities of water are discussed in detail by Henderson (1924) in his classic book, *The Fitness of the Environment*. Suffice it here to mention a few of the attributes of water that have a special ecological importance. In the first place water is the most abundant substance of the earth's surface, covering more than 70 per cent of the area of the globe. Because the oceans are about $2\frac{1}{2}$ times more extensive than the land, and because they are habitable throughout their depth, the sea provides more than 300 times the living space. Water has a higher specific heat, latent heat of fusion, and latent heat of evaporation than any other common substance. These facts play a very important role in the heat regulation of organisms themselves and in the resistance of natural environments to temperature change.

Another characteristic of water having crucial ecological significance is its relatively high freezing point. Because of the large amount of heat which must be given up before water can turn to ice and because of restricted stirring, oceans and lakes freeze only at the surface. Even ponds rarely freeze to the bottom. The temperature of the medium, therefore, can drop only to 0°C in fresh-water environments, or to a few degrees lower in the ocean. The biological reactions of a great many plants and animals can still go on perfectly well at temperatures down to the freezing point of water.

Another unusual quality of water is its power as a solvent; no other common substance compares with water in this respect. Many kinds of material can pass into, through, and out of the body of an organism in aqueous solution. Water provides a transporting medium that is versatile as a solvent but not too active chemically. Very considerable solution would take place if sulphuric acid ran in our rivers or coursed through our veins, but such a solvent would profoundly alter the materials that it carried. Furthermore, the extent of ionization of solutes in water is extremely high, providing the possibility of a great variety of radicals and of chemical recombination. Water has the highest surface tension of any common substance except mercury. This high surface tension has many ecological influences, involving the movement of water into and through organisms as well as the rise of ground water in the soil.

Many of the foregoing differences and special qualities of air and water will be referred to again in connection with other factors of the environment. Confining ourselves for the moment to the simple physical differences between the two fundamental media, let us explore the ecological effect of the difference in density of air and water. The densities of representative natural waters and of air, and the approximate average density of protoplasm are as tabulated.

Pure water	1.000 g/cc at 4°C
Pond water	1.001
Sea water (at salinity of 35‰)	1.028
Air (at sea level)	0.0013
Protoplasm	1.028

The density of protoplasm is closely similar to that of sea water and only slightly greater than that of fresh water, but it is more than 850 times greater than that of air. Associated with this difference in density are important differences in the pressure, inertia, viscosity, and mobility of the media.

PRESSURE

The difference in the densities of the media results in a great difference in the rate of change of pressure at increasing altitudes in the atmosphere and at increasing depths in the water. Near the earth's surface a rise of 300 m (1000 ft) in altitude results in a reduction of pressure of about 25 mm Hg, or a relatively slight change in

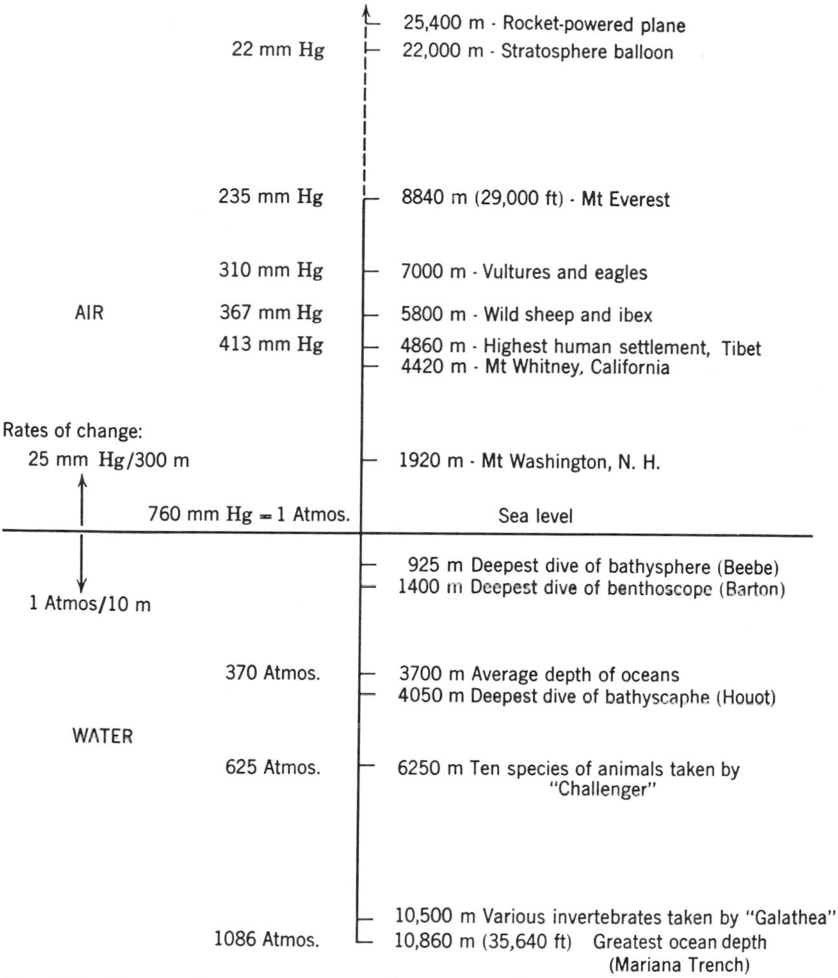

	22 mm Hg	25,400 m · Rocket-powered plane 22,000 m · Stratosphere balloon
	235 mm Hg	8840 m (29,000 ft) · Mt Everest
	310 mm Hg	7000 m · Vultures and eagles
AIR	367 mm Hg	5800 m · Wild sheep and ibex
	413 mm Hg	4860 m · Highest human settlement, Tibet 4420 m · Mt Whitney, California

Rates of change:
25 mm Hg/300 m

1920 m · Mt Washington, N. H.

760 mm Hg = 1 Atmos.   Sea level

1 Atmos/10 m

925 m Deepest dive of bathysphere (Beebe)
1400 m Deepest dive of benthoscope (Barton)

370 Atmos.   3700 m Average depth of oceans
4050 m Deepest dive of bathyscaphe (Houot)

WATER

625 Atmos.   6250 m Ten species of animals taken by
"Challenger"

10,500 m Various invertebrates taken by "Galathea"
1086 Atmos.   10,860 m (35,640 ft)   Greatest ocean depth
(Mariana Trench)

FIG. 2.3.   Range of pressure in air and water in relation to the distribution of life.

pressure. In contrast, for every increase of 10 m (33 ft) in depth in the water, pressure is increased by 760 mm Hg, or 1 atmosphere. The tremendous pressures existing at the average depth of the ocean and in the ocean deeps are indicated in Fig. 2.3. At a depth of only 900 m in the ocean Beebe's bathysphere was subjected to a total pressure on its whole surface of more than 7000 tons. It is not surprising that in his explorations of the earth man has not been able to descend into the ocean to depths much greater than 4 km, whereas he has ascended in the atmosphere to heights of more than 22 km. What are the ecological effects of these differences in pressure and in the rates of pressure change in the two media?

Pressure Reduction with Altitude

The reduction of pressure with altitude seems to be of little importance for plants, invertebrate animals, and the lower vertebrates. Insects have been subjected experimentally to a reduction of pressure from 760 mm Hg to 0.0001 mm Hg without harmful effect. Similarly, frogs have withstood reduction of pressure down to 100 mm Hg. Beetles reach the highest meadows in the Himalayas and earthworms are found up to the snow line in the Andes. In most situations it is not the reduced pressure which limits the altitude at which plants and cold-blooded animals can exist. The distribution of these organisms up the sides of mountains is ordinarily stopped by other adverse factors, such as low temperature, unsuitable soil, or lack of food, long before the influence of the reduced pressure is felt.

For warm-blooded vertebrates the reduction of pressure with altitude becomes important primarily because of the lesser amount of oxygen present. It is true that at very high altitudes the thinness of the air renders flying more difficult, but the chief limitation imposed on birds, and also on mammals, is the impairment of respiration. Distinctly harmful effects are observed for man when the pressure of the atmosphere has been reduced to about half that normal at sea level. The highest permanent human settlement occurs in Tibet at an altitude of about 5000 m. Even the best adapted of other mammals are not found living permanently much higher than this altitude (Hesse, Allee, and Schmidt, 1951, Ch. 24). Although vultures and eagles have been reported at about a thousand meters higher, they probably remain at such altitudes for only short periods of time. Insects, which often abound near the rocky or snow-covered peaks of mountains, are undoubtedly blown there by the wind, as they could not survive long under the conditions of the low temperature and lack of food.

Pressure Increase with Depth

If the relatively slight reduction in pressure with altitude in air is important to some organisms, the tremendously greater increase in pressure with depth in water might be expected to have serious consequences to all aquatic organisms. When early calculations were made of the magnitude of the pressure at the bottom of deep lakes, and particularly of the ocean, it was believed that the stupendous pressures would annihilate all living beings, so that the greatest depths in the aquatic environment must be lifeless. This conclusion seemed at first to be confirmed by the early explorations, but, with the improvement of gear for investigating the bottom of the deep sea, animal life was gradually discovered at greater and greater depths in all the ocean basins (Fig. 3.5). In 1951 the Danish *Galathea* Expedition trawled 17 sea anemones, 61 sea cucumbers, 2 bivalves, and 1 crustacean from a depth of about 10,500 m off the Philippine Islands. At this depth the pressure is 1050 atmospheres, or about 1 ton on each square centimeter, but this terrific weight of water does not crush the organisms living at that depth because the pressure is the same inside their bodies as outside.

When most deep-sea animals are brought to the surface, they are dead or dying. The popular opinion is that they have been killed by a violent release of pressure. In reporting the work of the research vessel *Atlantis*, a newspaper once stated: "The sudden change of pressure when deep-sea fish are brought to a higher level in the ocean causes them to explode. The fragments are then put together again!" Fish with air cavities within their bodies do indeed expand when they are brought to a higher level, but most fish inhabiting the ocean abyss have no air bladders. Their death is due primarily to injury from the nets and to the change in temperature experienced in being brought to the surface.

The effect of the pressure changes in the aquatic environment is very different for organisms with and without air cavities. Aquatic plants that live at levels considerably below the surface stratum and the great majority of deep-sea animals do not have gas-filled spaces in their bodies. Since any cavities in these organisms are completely filled with fluids, no mechanical deformation is caused by pressure changes because the watery tissues are only slightly compressible.

The Medium

Green plants are confined to relatively shallow subsurface depths because of their need for light. Many types of animals, on the other
hand, display a very great vertical range in their distribution.

Several species of invertebrates are found at depths extending from
near the surface in the *littoral zone* down to 4000 m or even 5000 m
in the *abyssobenthic zone* (Fig. 2.4). Although the individuals of
these bottom-living forms do not travel far, the species as a whole
have become adapted to this great vertical range over a period of

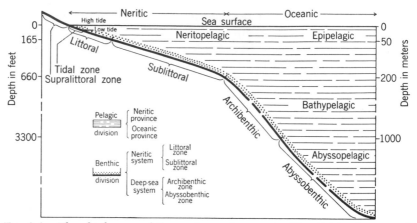

Fig. 2.4. The chief zones of the marine environment. The division between the
neritic and oceanic provinces occurs at the edge of the continental shelf where
depth is about 200 m. The lower limit of the archibenthic zone occurs between
800 and 1100 m. The littoral zone forms the upper part of the neritic benthic
zone and usually receives strong wave and current action and sufficient light for
plant growth. The depth of its lower limit is variable but is often in the neighborhood of 40 to 60 m. These divisions also apply in a general way to lakes.
(Modified from *The Oceans* by Sverdrup et al., 1942, copyright Prentice-Hall,
Inc., N. Y.)

time. In certain other kinds of marine animals the individuals are
known to change level over considerable distances and hence are
able to withstand correspondingly great pressure changes. Some
species of fish move downward as much as 400 m during the day and
swim up again to their former level each night, thus subjecting themselves twice daily to a pressure change of 40 atmospheres. Certain
small planktonic Crustacea similarly carry out diurnal vertical migrations of 200 m to possibly 600 m in amplitude (Waterman, Nunnemacher, Chace, and Clarke, 1939).

The foregoing is not to imply that most species of marine organisms
do not have definite vertical limits to their distribution. Many species

are confined to relatively narrow zones, but these restrictions of range are probably due primarily to other factors, such as temperature, light, or food. Nevertheless very great changes in pressure have been shown experimentally to alter the rates of certain physiological reactions; and a variety of invertebrate animals, fishes without swim bladders, and bacteria are inactivated, or killed, when subjected in pressure chambers to several hundred atmospheres, although the effect is much reduced if the temperature remains nearly constant (Zobell and Oppenheimer, 1950). Thus, although moderate pressure changes do not ordinarily harm such organisms, great changes may exert certain subtle influences on their life processes. Whether or not such physiological action of pressure actually limits the vertical range of aquatic organisms in their natural habitats has not yet been ascertained.

For animals with air-filled cavities, such as fish possessing swim bladders and diving birds and mammals, the rapid increase in pressure with depth in the aquatic environment is a serious matter. The swim bladder of a fish supplies buoyancy, and a fish with this air cavity is similar in its flotation to the Cartesian diver of the physicists. When the fish moves downward, the bladder is compressed, and when it moves toward the surface, the bladder expands. Gas must be removed from the swim bladder, or added to it, in order for the fish to maintain control of its buoyancy equilibrium. If the fish moves upward so fast that gas cannot be removed from the swim bladder at a rate sufficient to compensate for the reduction in pressure, the contained gas will continue to expand and the fish will rise toward the surface at an accelerating rate. If movement toward the surface continues, the swim bladder will eventually burst, and the expanding gas, now in the body cavity, will force the stomach to protrude from the mouth, the intestine from the anus, and the eyes from their sockets. Presumably, under ordinary conditions, an early stage of internal volume change stimulates the fish to return to its former level. The pressure factor thus definitely limits the vertical range of fish with swim bladders as well as the speed with which they can move from one depth to another (Jones, 1952).

For diving mammals and birds the problem of breathing is added to that of the increased pressure. When a human diver descends into the water in a flexible diving suit he must withstand the increased pressure, but air is supplied to him through a hose or by means of an "aqualung." Pressure alone prevents the diver from descending more than 100 m or so. Whales, seals, and diving birds are forced to go without a renewal of oxygen during the period of their dive. Whales apparently withstand the great pressures by allowing their lungs to be completely flattened and the air that was in them to be forced into the strong, boxlike larynx. How a mammal swimming vigorously can get along for more than a few minutes without a renewal of its oxygen supply has been a matter for speculation for generations. Evidence obtained primarily from the study of seals indicates that these diving mammals can store an increased amount of oxygen in their tissues and that this oxygen is reserved for the brain, heart, and other vital organs by cutting off the circulation to other parts of the body. The muscles build up an oxygen debt that is paid off when the animal surfaces again (Scholander, 1940). Too rapid ascent may result in the formation of gas bubbles in the blood, but the fact that the whale, unlike the human diver, has only one lungful of air during the dive presumably reduces the danger from absorbed nitrogen.

The depth and duration of the whale's dive have been hotly contested by captains of whaling ships and others for many years. It seems probable that whales dive to 200 or 400 m regularly. Seemingly indisputable evidence for an even greater dive was furnished by the discovery of a sperm whale that had become entangled at a depth of about 1000 m in a submarine cable running between two of the Caribbean Islands. At this depth the pressure is about 100 atmospheres (or over 100 kg per sq cm), and evidently the mechanism of the whale is adapted to withstand pressures as great as this. Whales ordinarily stay submerged for twenty minutes or so, but when harpooned they may disappear from the surface for one to two hours. Such dives, accompanied as they are by violent swimming, are a striking demonstration of the ability of these animals to remain active for long periods without renewal of oxygen.

SUPPORT AND RESISTANCE TO MOTION

The difference in density of the two elemental media, air and water, also influences the degree to which they provide support and resistance to motion. Since water has nearly the same density as protoplasm, whereas air is very much less dense, water furnishes much more buoyancy than air.

Effects on Structure and Size

Since terrestrial organisms are very much heavier than their surrounding medium, they would tend to collapse from their own weight if it were not for special supporting structures. On land only very

small organisms and such animals as earthworms and slugs can maintain their shape without skeletal material of some sort. The woody
tissue characteristic of the higher plants provides rigidity against the
force of gravity. The bones and muscles of the larger land animals
are similarly arranged primarily to provide support (Thompson,
1942).

Generally speaking, the weight of an organism tends to increase as
the cube of its linear dimensions, but the strength of supporting
columns increases only as the square of the dimensions. As a result
animals and plants are definitely limited as to size. Since land plants,
once established, do not require locomotion, they can have a much
larger amount of rigid supporting tissue than animals. Hence the
plant kingdom holds the record for size on land. The giant redwoods
of California (Fig. 1.1) attain heights well over 100 m (record height:
365 ft), and the trunks alone are estimated to weigh as much as 500
or 600 tons. In the animal kingdom few modern species attain a size
as great as 6 or 7 tons, although the dinosaurs of the past were somewhat larger. Possibly *Brontosaurus* would have tipped the scales at
30 or 40 tons, but *Brontosaurus* came to an unhappy end, no doubt
in part because of its ungainly size.

In the water environment, since all parts of the organism tend to be
buoyed up by the medium, supporting structures may be greatly reduced or entirely lacking. Woody tissue is needed for support by
few aquatic plants. When an elaborate skeleton is present in aquatic
animals, it usually occurs for purposes other than support. For many
crustaceans and mollusks the hard tissues serve primarily as protection; in other forms, such as fish, the skeleton is used chiefly for
the attachment of muscles of propulsion. Many aquatic organisms
such as the jellyfish have no skeleton at all. It is true that the jellyfish
is a weak and sluggish organism but the octopus and the giant squid
are decidedly vigorous, and yet the skeletons of the latter are reduced
to horny pens and a few cartilages in the head region. An octopus
kept in an aquarium at the Bermuda Biological Station was so successful in getting out of his tank in spite of a weighted lid that he was
named Houdini.

In the plant kingdom even the algae can grow to tremendous sizes.
The giant kelp *Nereocystis*, common off the west coast of the United
States, may grow to a length of more than 35 m, and *Macrocystis* is
reported to attain an even greater size. Such plants have no woody
tissue whatsoever, but the water buoys up the extended parts of the
organism. Animals in the sea today attain sizes larger than ever
existed on land. By weighing the parts of a blue whale being cut up

on the deck of a factory ship Hjort (1937) obtained the tabulated values, which do not include the blood and viscera.

Muscles	56.	tons
Bones	23.	
Blubber	26.	
Tongue	3.	
Heart	0.6	
	108.6	

If a whale becomes stranded on the beach, the weight of its body prevents breathing by crushing the lungs, and its great strength is of little avail for getting it back into the water since its muscles of propulsion are adapted exclusively for swimming in the open sea.

Effects on Locomotion through Medium

Differences in the viscosity, mobility, and inertia of air and water have profound effects upon the resistance of the medium to the motion of organisms through it. In general the resistance of water is very much greater than that of air but the actual value depends upon the size and shape of the organism, the viscosity of the medium, and the speed of locomotion. The coefficient of viscosity of water is 60 times that of air at the same temperature. The result is that an important resistance to locomotion is felt at very much lower speeds in water than in air. Animals whose living depends upon rapid swimming through water must be thoroughly streamlined. In the mackerel, for example, not only is the body almost perfectly streamlined but also the fins fold back into grooves and the surfaces of the eyes conform exactly to the contour of the head.

Another result of this great difference in the resistance of air and water is that really high speeds can be attained by animals only in the air environment, and even at low speeds very much more effort is required to move through water than through air. The speed record for the animal kingdom is probably held by the duck hawk, whose flight has been clocked at 288 km per hr (180 miles per hr). Several other species of birds can fly at speeds greater than 160 km per hr, but no running animal can approach these velocities. The gazelle and the antelope are credited with speeds of 96 km per hr, and the cheetah can do 112 km per hr (70 miles per hr) over short distances. These catlike animals are employed by the natives in Africa to bring down antelope for them. The natives steal up as close as possible to a herd of antelope in an old Ford and then release the cheetah for the last short dash.

In the aquatic environment fish of the mackerel tribe are the fastest swimmers and attain speeds as great as 48 km per hr (30 miles per hr). The flying fish has been reported to attain 56 km per hr just before its take-off. Anyone who has watched a flying fish, however, will remember that in the last moments before the fish leaves the water most of its body is in the air, with only the tail sculling violently in the surface like an outboard motor.

Even the method of propulsion is controlled to a large extent by the elemental difference in the nature of the air and water media. Since the density, viscosity, and inertia of air are so low, most animals cannot use the air alone for propulsion but must obtain a purchase on the earth's surface. Only birds, insects, and a few other animals can propel themselves wholly in air. In the aquatic environment, on the other hand, the majority of animals swim in the free water, and those for which speed is important do not use the substratum for effective locomotion. The lobster, for example, pokes around on its walking legs, but to make a sudden dash it uses swift strokes of its tail, letting its legs leave the bottom entirely. Because of the relatively great inertia of the water medium, some animals, such as jelly fish and scallops, can propel themselves in one direction by pumping water in the opposite direction—an early version of "jet propulsion." The squid can dart backwards with remarkable rapidity by ejecting water from its siphon.

Passage of Medium through Organism

Sometimes the medium must move through the organism instead of, or in addition to, the movement of the organism through the medium. Because of the great mobility of air, this medium can move in and out of the cavities of an animal or plant with relative ease, but water does not circulate as freely. Special adaptations are required to carry water to the tops of trees, including root pressure, transpiration, and the tensile strength of fine water columns. The movement of the water through the tracheids of the plant is relatively slow. Even in aquatic plants direct water exchange by osmosis or colloidal imbibition requires considerable physical force.

Although large expenditure of work is necessary, some aquatic animals do succeed in causing water to flow through relatively simple respiratory or feeding chambers. But water could not possibly be pumped into and out of a finely branched system of tubules like the tracheae of the insects with sufficient speed to meet respiratory needs. No doubt partly for this reason relatively few kinds of insects have succeeded in establishing themselves in the aquatic environment. Most of these remain in the water for only a portion of their lives— usually the larval stage. Insects living completely submerged possess tracheal gills or other special devices for obtaining oxygen without taking water into the tracheae. Many fresh-water species are adapted to come to the surface for air. In the marine environment *Halobates* lives on the surface of the ocean as a "water strider," and several dipterans inhabit shallow areas as larvae, but only one insect, the midge *Pontomyia natans,* is known to complete its entire life cycle submerged in sea water.

Existence of Plankton

The relatively high density of the water medium not only tends to buoy up parts of the body but also in some instances supports the whole body and thus allows certain organisms to float at various depths in the free water. This fact makes possible the existence of *plankton*—plants and animals that live suspended in the ocean and inland water bodies and that drift about either because they are non-motile or because they are too small or too weak to swim effectively against the currents (Figs. 2.5 and 2.6). The term plankton is derived from a Greek word meaning "wanderer," and many organisms in this category, or plankters, spend their whole lives drifting in the water. Both animal and plant plankton is found in practically all natural waters, frequently in enormous abundance and variety. Other categories of life in the aquatic environment are the *benthos,* which consists of the organisms living on or in the bottom material, and the *nekton,* which is composed of the strong-swimming animals. The benthos and the nekton have their counterparts on land, but the permanent plankton represents an important category of life that is totally absent from the air environment.

Certain planktonic animals and plants live permanently suspended in the water by actual flotation. This method of support is not possible in the air. Pollen grains, seeds, and spores, commonly spoken of as "floating" in the air, are not actually doing so, but are sinking at a slow rate—often retarded by various feathery structures. In the water actual flotation is possible for forms that contain air cavities or light materials such as fats or oils. The brown alga *Sargassum* is provided with gas-filled bladders, and the Portuguese man-of-war, a siphonophore, has a pneumatic "sail." Many fish eggs float by virtue of droplets of oil. Some pelagic diatoms completely counterbalance the weight of their siliceous shells by means of a cell sap which is lighter than water so that these organisms have no tendency to sink.

In addition to the truly floating forms many other kinds of plants and animals sink so slowly that they are able to lead a planktonic

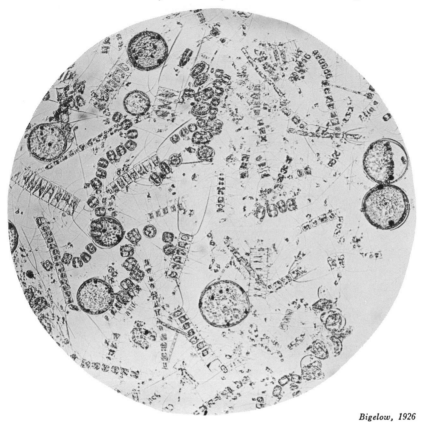

Bigelow, 1926

FIG. 2.5. Marine phytoplankton. Photomicrograph of several common genera of oceanic diatoms. The largest cell is approximately 0.05 mm in diameter.

life. In the air environment the sinking rate of the smallest organisms, such as bacterial spores, is extremely slow, but eventually all particles settle out. In the water, however, the sinking rate of some organisms, including many multicellular animals, is so retarded that a small amount of swimming allows the organisms to maintain their position. In other instances the amount of sinking may be inconsequential before the organism is brought up to the surface again by vertical currents.

Sinking rate is also controlled in part by size and shape. It might be said that one of the simplest ways of reducing sinking speed is to be small because with reduction in volume the surface—and hence surface friction—becomes relatively greater. Any departure from the spherical shape increases the surface of an organism. Unicellular forms like the pelagic *Globigerina* which are bristling with spines

Bigelow, 1926

Fig. 2.6. Marine zooplankton. Photomicrograph of common copepods, chaetognaths, and medusae. The euphausiid "shrimp" is approximately 2.5 cm (1 in.) long.

graphically illustrate this fact (Fig. 2.7). Most multicellular animals that live a planktonic life also are liberally provided with long antennae, spines, and bristles of a great variety of shapes. The effect of these changes in the morphology of planktonic organisms, combined with differences in density, in reducing the sinking rate is illustrated in Table 1.

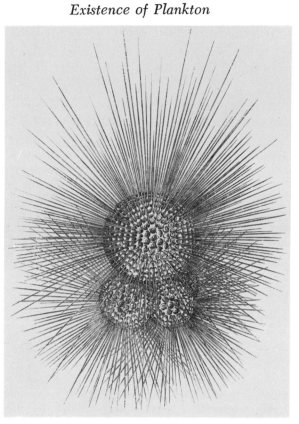

Murray and Hjort, 1911, copyright Macmillan & Co.

FIG. 2.7. *Globigerina bulloides,* a planktonic protozoan belonging to the order Foraminifera. The largest sphere of the shell is about 0.5 mm in diameter.

TABLE 1

COMPARISON OF SINKING RATES OF THREE TYPES OF PLANKTON ORGANISMS
WITH THOSE OF SPHERICAL SAND AND SILT PARTICLES

	Length or Diameter (millimeters)	Sinking Rate (meters per day)
Sand grain	1.0	8600.
Copepod (*Calanus*)	3.0	576.
Silt particle	0.01	14.5
Diatom (*Nitzschia*)	0.020	0.050
Bacteria	0.001	0.132

Since the density of the water environment is closely similar to that of organisms living in it, the reader will not be surprised to learn that slight changes in the former often have important consequences in the vertical distribution of plankton. Differences in the density of fresh water and sea water at three temperatures within the biological range are shown in Table 2. As a result of these density differences,

TABLE 2

SAMPLE VALUES FOR THE DENSITY OF WATER AT DIFFERENT TEMPERATURES

Temperature °C	Fresh Water (g/cc)	Sea Water (salinity 35‰) (g/cc)
0	0.999	1.0281
4	1.000	1.0278
30	0.995	1.0217

relatively sharp stratification of water masses may come into being in lakes and in oceanic areas. If other influences do not interfere, warmer water tends to remain over colder water, and fresher water tends to float on top of the more saline.

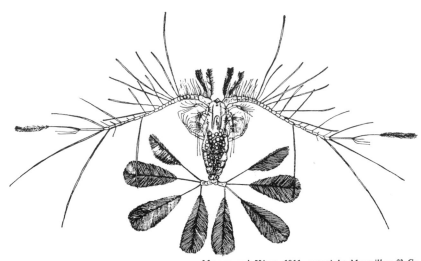

Murray and Hjort, 1911, copyright Macmillan & Co.

FIG. 2.8. *Calocalanus pavo,* a tropical planktonic copepod. The length of the crustacean's body is about 2.5 mm.

Although the differences in density shown in Table 2 may seem very small, they are sufficient to influence profoundly the circulation of water in lakes and in the ocean, and to make the difference between floating and sinking for planktonic organisms. Plankton sometimes tends to sink through the upper stratum of less dense water, but to stop sinking when it reaches a stratum of higher density below.

In such a situation plankton and detritus accumulate and form a "false bottom" that provides a potentially rich feeding zone.

Important changes in viscosity also occur as temperature is altered. At 25°C the viscosity of water is only half that at 0°C. Since at higher temperatures the effect of the decreased viscosity is added to that of the lower density, the rate of sinking tends to be greater. Probably as an adaptation to this difference through natural selection many planktonic organisms in warmer waters are more profusely provided with bristles and other feathery structures tending to retard sinking (Fig. 2.8). Certain planktonic diatoms and dinoflagellates also show a graded difference in the length of spines in tropical and

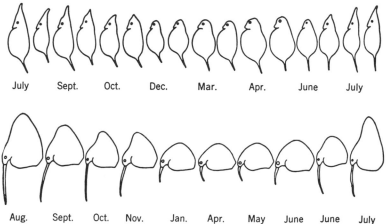

July　　Sept.　　Oct.　　Dec.　　Mar.　　Apr.　　June　　July

Aug.　Sept.　Oct.　Nov.　Jan.　Apr.　May　June　June　July

Redrawn from Wesenberg-Lund, 1910

FIG. 2.9. Cyclomorphosis in *Daphnia cucullata* (upper) and *Bosmina coregoni* (lower), showing seasonal changes in body form.

polar areas. Whether such geographical variants should be divided into separate species may not be settled until controlled culturing experiments are undertaken.

In some plankters the body form changes with the season of the year. This phenomenon, known as *cyclomorphosis*, is strikingly exhibited by the increased size of the "helmet" and length of spines in certain Cladocera during warm months (Fig. 2.9). These changes produce increase in body surface and were originally believed to be entirely an adaptation to the lower density and viscosity of warmer water, but subsequent work has shown that factors other than temperature also influence body form (Brooks, 1946). In all such relationships the ecologist must distinguish between actual causal factors and possible beneficial results. For a further discussion of plankton in relation to flotation the reader may refer to Sverdrup et al. (1942) and Welch (1952).

TRANSPORTATION BY MEDIUM

Another significant action of the medium is its action in providing transportation for plants and animals. Certain requirements such as light can often reach the organism without the movement of either the organism or the medium. Most necessities, however, are not adequately provided for unless either the organism or the medium moves. Put in simplest terms the needs for mobility are: (1) to provide materials for metabolism and growth; (2) to remove waste products; (3) to bring male and female elements together; (4) to distribute progeny; (5) to avoid unfavorable conditions.

Either the organism must be able to forage and to distribute itself effectively, or else some mobile agent must be available. Fortunately, both media are mobile, but their potentialities for providing transportation differ considerably. Air moves much more readily and much faster than water, but water can carry heavier objects in suspension. The composition of air remains relatively constant, but the water medium contains widely varying amounts of ecologically important substances.

Movement of the air medium ranges from local wind currents of beneficial nature to violent and destructive gales. Animals and plants in some areas are subject to strong winds which vary in direction from day to day, whereas in other regions, such as the trade-wind belts, the wind blows almost constantly from one quarter with corresponding unidirectional influence. Air movement also indirectly affects other factors such as temperature, rainfall, and evaporation. The circulation of the atmosphere controls the weather and provides for the transport of moisture from the sea to the land.

Movement of the water medium similarly varies from small-scale, sporadic circulation, generated by local wind and waves, to larger and stronger currents. Plants and animals living in ponds and lakes are regularly subject to wind-driven currents. In fresh-water streams the one-way transport of water is a matter of vital concern to all the inhabitants. Along the sea coast, on the other hand, the tidal currents are characteristically reversible or oscillatory. Farther offshore the permanent currents are encountered, and these are parts of the great current systems of the ocean which include a rotary circulation in each of the ocean basins (Fig. 2.10). Two well-known oceanic currents of great ecological significance in the northern hemisphere

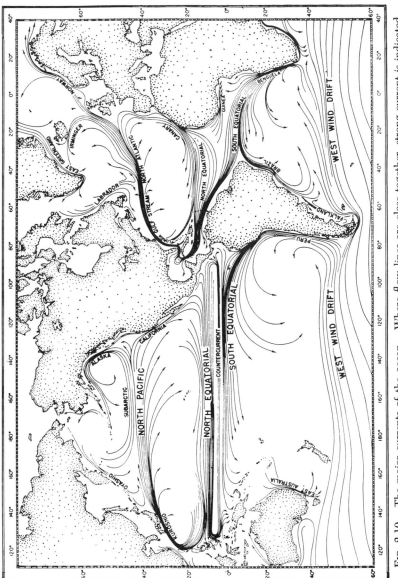

FIG. 2.10. The major currents of the ocean. Where flow lines are close together, strong current is indicated.

43

are the Gulf Stream, which carries water of tropical origin northward along the east coast of the United States and thence northeastward toward northern Europe, and the Japanese Current, which brings relatively warm water to the Aleutians and the Alaskan coast.

Sessile Existence

Since both air and water are practically always on the move, the possibility exists that animals and plants might live a lazy existence, remaining in one place and letting the medium bring their needs to them. The desirable features of such a tranquil life might appeal to many of us. But since air can carry only the smallest and lightest particles, no free-living animal on land can obtain sufficient solid food by air transport. There are no completely sessile animals in the terrestrial environment. A few land animals, such as the spider and the ant lion, lie in wait for the prey which flies or crawls to their traps, and other forms, such as the dung beetle and the wood borer, live within their food material, but even for these animals some locomotion is necessary.

The needs of land plants, on the other hand, are such that most of them can be brought by mobile agents. The carbon dioxide and oxygen exchange of the plant is readily taken care of by the movement of the air. Mineral nutrients needed by the plant are also carried to it, but in most situations these materials are brought by the soil water so that we are really dealing with a special case of the mobility of water. However, certain epiphytes, such as the bromeliads and Spanish mosses, live in the crotches of trees or even on telephone wires where absolutely all their needs reach them by means of air transport. These "air plants" obtain mineral nutrients from rain water and from dust particles which lodge in their crevices. For many species the wind plays an essential role also in reproduction and in distribution.

In the water environment the transport by the medium of the needs of both plants and animals is quite an ordinary occurrence. Most multicellular plants in aquatic habitats lead a completely sessile existence, allowing the water to bring them the oxygen, carbon dioxide, and food materials that they require. The algae absorb their nutrients directly from the free water, but the vascular plants generally obtain these materials through their roots from the water in the mud.

Large numbers of aquatic animals enjoy a sedentary life. Many groups of sessile animals, such as the sponges, coelenterates, bivalves, and barnacles, are extremely abundant in the water environment, but are entirely unrepresented on land. These forms can remain permanently attached to the bottom, allowing food particles to be brought to them by the water. Many of these animals are characterized by radial symmetry, since food may be brought from any direction, a radial arrangement of feeding appendages around the animal's mouth is efficient. Only when locomotion is required is it particularly desirable to have a head and a tail end with attendant bilateral symmetry. Colonial existence is also possible among sessile organisms but would be very clumsy for forms that require active locomotion.

In aquatic plants and animals the male reproductive cells are carried to the egg cells by water movement, or both are discharged into the surrounding medium where currents bring them together to accomplish fertilization. The young of sessile organisms are effectively removed from the neighborhood of the adults during the larval stage. The planktonic larvae, carried far and wide by the currents, accomplish the dispersal of the species and the colonization of new areas.

Many marine and fresh-water animals grow more effectively in a current than in quiet water, and some forms can live only where the water is moving rapidly. Certain caddis fly larvae (*Hydropsyche*) living on stream bottoms construct funnel-shaped nets with openings upstream into which food particles drift. The larva of the mayfly (*Chirotenetes*) braces itself on the bottom with its head upstream and spreads its hairy prothoracic legs like a net with the result that particles of food in the flowing water are funneled into the animal's mouth (Morgan, 1930). The term *current demand* has been used for the dependence of certain forms, particularly stream forms, on a movement of the water, but in some situations the precise reason that a current is necessary is not clear. The larva of the black fly (*Simulium*), for example, will not develop in quiet water even though plenty of oxygen and other obvious needs are available.

Distribution by Medium

If the needs are not brought to the organism, the organism must go after them—either by its own locomotion or by hooking a ride on something else. The transportation service of the environment is of particular value to the seeds or larvae of sessile organisms and for those motile organisms that are small or feeble and hence would be very slow in getting around under their own steam.

Transport by Air. No organism can live permanently floating in the air, but this medium is often useful in the sporadic and intermittent transport of terrestrial organisms (Wolfenbarger, 1946). The smallest forms, such as the bacteria, can be transported effectively by even a slight movement of air. ZoBell calculated that if bacteria were released at a height of 33 m when the wind velocity was as low as 16 km per hr (10 miles per hr), the microbes would be carried 4800 km before they reached the ground. The heights to which small organisms may be carried by turbulence is illustrated by a record of fungal spores collected on plates exposed from an airplane at an altitude of 3600 m. The rapid transport by air of spores causing diseases in both plants and animals represents an ever-present threat to economically important populations. New strains of wheat rust, for example, seem to be brought in by the wind almost as fast as resistant types of wheat are developed.

Many of the earth's most abundant types of higher plants, such as the conifers, depend largely upon wind pollination. Pollen grains are regularly transported hundreds of miles by the wind, and pollen has been detected in the air over the ocean more than 1000 miles from land. The seeds of orchids and of certain other groups are so small that they are carried by the wind almost as effectively as pollen grains and spores. Hairy structures, such as the familiar "parachutes" of the dandelion, make possible the wind transport of larger seeds over considerable distances, and wings, bladders, etc., such as those of the maple and elm, enable many of the heavier seeds of these trees to be blown far enough from the parent plants to avoid immediate competition (Siggins, 1933). In the grasslands and desert regions yet another bizarre method for transport is encountered in the tumbleweed, the spherical upper portion of which breaks off and rolls for miles before.the wind, scattering the seeds as it goes.

Wind also plays a significant role in the distribution of animals, particularly of insects. The wings of flying insects provide the lift, and even ordinary winds provide horizontal translocation which may carry them very great distances (Gislen, 1948). Elton (1939) found certain aphids and flies alive over Spitzbergen after a wind drift over the ocean of about 1300 km. Stronger winds carry flightless insects, spiders, and other small invertebrates in either the active or the encysted condition. Strong prevailing or seasonal winds in certain situations tend to exert a regular influence on the distribution of insects. Along the northern shore of the Gulf of Mexico, human inhabitants are pestered by mosquitoes regularly blown many kilometers inland from the salt marshes by the onshore breeze, and Garrett-Jones (1950) reported mass wind-borne invasions of areas as much as 47 km from the mosquitoes' breeding places in Egypt. As compared with oceanic currents, however, winds tend to be irregular, and insects, as well as other flying land animals, can often migrate against the wind, as has been shown to be true for the monarch butterfly (Williams et al., 1942). Consequently, regular transport by the medium generally plays a far smaller part in the lives of land animals than in the lives of the denizens of the sea.

Occasionally the geographical range of an insect pest is extended by wind action. A classical example of such an occurrence is presented by the spread of the gypsy moth in New England. This foreign insect escaped from cages in which experiments were being conducted in the vicinity of Medford, Mass., in 1869. Since the female of the species is flightless, one might suppose that the insect would be confined to the immediate neighborhood of its point of introduction, or at least would spread very slowly. However, the species has a special way of "thumbing a ride" on the wind. The newly hatched caterpillars in their first instar are provided with especially long hairs. When they crawl to the tops of trees and spin long threads, they are soon blown off and are carried considerable distances before they reach the ground. The caterpillars climb again to the tree tops and the process is repeated. By this means, to the detriment of the oak forests, the gypsy moth was spread throughout New England within a few years. It even succeeded in crossing Cape Cod Bay, a distance of about 40 km.

The lifting power of the wind during hurricanes and tornadoes is well known and provides an exceptional opportunity for the transport of larger animals and plants in unexpected directions. Although in most regions hurricane winds are rare, over the centuries they may nevertheless have made possible the introduction of new species to islands and other locations which would ordinarily be inaccessible to the forms concerned. If the new arrivals become established and if they are predatory or infectious or if they compete successfully, though passively, with the native species, they may completely upset the ecological adjustments of the existing community.

It has long been recognized that the fauna of the Greater Antilles in the West Indies has been derived in the evolutionary sense principally from the Central American fauna. No convincing evidence has been brought forward, however, that land bridges ever connected these islands with the mainland of Central America. How the amphibians, rodents, snakes, and other species of this general size ever reached the islands remained a mystery until Darlington (1938) pointed out the possibility of transport by the hurricanes which so frequently cross this area.

The exceptional lifting power of certain atmospheric disturbances is illustrated by the "rain of fishes" which occurred in 1947 at Marksville, La., and is described by an eye witness (Bajkov, 1949). On the morning of October 23, fish ranging between 5 and 23 cm in length fell on the streets and in the yards, mystifying the citizens of the town. There were areas along the main street in which the abundance of fish averaged one to every square meter. The fish belonged to the fresh-water species native to the local ponds. Although no large wind storm occurred, numerous small "devil duster" tornadoes had been noticed in the area. At Marksville the majority of fish were dead when picked up from the ground, but it is perfectly possible that many of them would have survived had they fallen in water. Stocking of remote ponds by dumping fish from airplanes has often been successfully accomplished. Transport by local violent air currents may therefore explain the introduction of fish into land-locked ponds or lake systems not connected with other fresh-water areas in which the species occurred.

Transport by Water. Since water has a much greater buoyant effect than air, transport by the water medium is of vital concern to many more kinds of plants and animals than transport by air. Transport by currents plays an important role in distribution in both inland waters and the sea. However, we find the fresh-water organisms do not utilize this transportation system to nearly as great an extent as marine organisms. This difference may be partially explained by the fact that fresh water is less dense and hence less buoyant. Also, inland waters are less permanent. Since fresh-water bodies often dry up, or freeze, their currents cannot always be relied upon for transportation.

Correlated with the foregoing facts, we find that many types of animals whose marine species have free-living larvae are represented in fresh water by species with a much shorter larval life. In fresh water there are many more species in which the eggs or young remain attached to the adult, as in the copepod, *Cyclops,* and the crayfish, or are retained within a brood pouch as in the Cladocera (Fig. 2.11).

If stream animals make use of the water transport system, they must have some method for getting back upstream again. Some of the devices serving this purpose are most intriguing. The larvae of mussels are provided with special hooks with which they attach themselves to the gills of fish. Some of the fish that are thus parasitized eventually wander upstream where the maturing larvae drop off and metamorphose into adult mussels. Other stream forms resort to the formation of resistant spores that may be carried by birds or blown by the wind.

Oysters and other benthonic animals remain established in tidal rivers and estuaries although the planktonic larvae might be expected to be carried away since the net water movement is always toward the sea (Ketchum, 1951). In some situations the denser, more saline water near the bottom tends to move predominantly into the estuary whereas the greater flow in the surface strata is seaward. Observations in certain estuaries indicate that the older oyster larvae tend to drop to the bottom on the ebb tide and to rise into the water on the

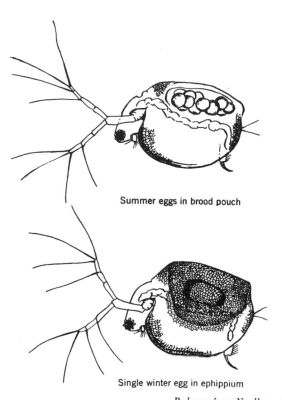

Summer eggs in brood pouch

Single winter egg in ephippium

Redrawn from Needham and Lloyd, 1937

FIG. 2.11.   *Ceriodaphnia reticulata* showing eggs developing in the brood pouch.

flood tide (Carriker, 1951). In this manner a sufficient number of young oysters work their way upstream to repopulate the upper regions of the estuary. In barnacles the problem is solved by the fact that, although the younger larvae are found in the upper water layers, the larvae approaching the setting stage tend to concentrate at deeper levels where the net drift carries them up the estuary (Bousfield, 1954).

In the ocean many more groups are influenced by the transporting action of the water. This affects not only the varied permanent planktonic population but also the planktonic larvae of the benthos and of the nekton. Species having planktonic larvae are much more numerous in the marine environment than in fresh water. The planktonic life of marine larvae also tends to be longer, often with many more stages. Certain euphausiid crustaceans, for example, have five larval stages including about twenty moults before reaching the adult condition.

So characteristic are the planktonic forms of many water masses that they are sometimes used in tracing the currents. Members of the permanent plankton which live in specific water masses must go wherever the water goes, like Mary's lamb. Such species are termed *current indicators.* Russell (1939) has shown, for example, that the "Channel water" ordinarily occupying the English Channel is populated by a plankton community of which the chaetognath, *Sagitta setosa,* is a characteristic member. Occasionally, however, a mass of "mixed oceanic and coastal water" moves into the Channel from the region south of Ireland, and its presence is revealed by the abundance of another species, *Sagitta elegans.* A third species, *Sagitta serratodentata,* is an indicator for the "pure oceanic water" which is found to the west of the water mass tagged by *S. elegans.*

The Gulf weed *Sargassum,* which can be seen by any traveler crossing the southern part of the North Atlantic ocean, is an indicator for water of tropical origin. This plant begins life attached to the bottom around certain of the West Indian Islands (Parr, 1939). It is torn up by storms and drifts out to sea where it continues to grow vegetatively for years. Masses of *Sargassum* clumped together gave rise in the past to the legend of the Sargasso Sea where ships were supposed to become hopelessly entangled in the seaweed. You will remember that, in crossing the Atlantic, Columbus was encouraged by the presence of drifting seaweed to keep on, believing that he had seen an indisputable sign of the proximity of land. It is fortunate that Columbus did not realize that *Sargassum* may be carried hundreds or even thousands of miles from shore by the currents of the ocean.

The matter of transport by ocean currents should not be left without mention of the classical example of the eel. For generations the people of Europe wondered where eels came from. Young elvers ascended their rivers in the spring, and mature eels left their rivers in the fall after several years' life in fresh water. No one knew where or when the eels spawned. Finally, it was discovered that a small, flat planktonic organism, long thought to be another species entirely, was the larva of the eel. The Danish marine biologist, Johannes Schmidt, then set out to find the spawning ground from which the larvae came. Little did he know, when he began, that his search would require many years of work and thousands of miles of exploration before he answered the question. By plotting the occurrence of smaller and smaller larvae, Schmidt (1925) gradually traced the drift of the larvae back to its point of origin southeast of Bermuda (Fig. 2.12). Here the eels spawn apparently deep in the water, since no

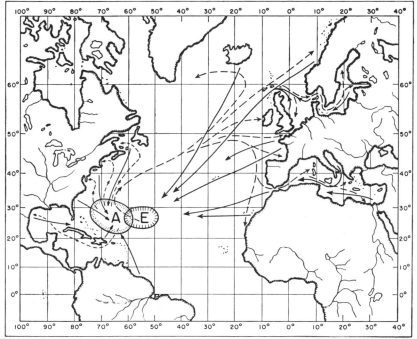

Redrawn from Schmidt, 1925

FIG. 2.12. Migrations of the eel. Dotted lines indicate drift of larvae from breeding areas of American eel (A) and European eel (E). Solid lines indicate return migration of the adult eels.

one has seen them. The newly hatched larvae drift into the Gulf Stream and after three years are carried to the European shore, where they metamorphose into elvers and enter the rivers. The mature eels make the return trip under their own locomotion, although how they find their way across two or three thousand miles of ocean is a complete mystery.

The American species of eel breeds in an area that overlaps the spawning zone of the European eel. The Gulf Stream circulation similarly plays an essential role in carrying its larvae northward. Nevertheless, no record exists of European eels entering an American river, or of American eels being found in Europe. The metamorphosis of the American eel takes place at the end of one year when it is opposite the American shore. At this time it is ready to respond to some influence which orients it toward the mouths of the rivers. However, its European cousin, mingled with it in the plankton, is not yet responsive to shore influences and continues drifting with the Gulf Stream water until it reaches the European coast. The eventual arrival of the two species of eel on opposite sides of the Atlantic is a spectacular illustration of the integration of the action of the environment with genetic differences in the timing of responses.

Harmful Transport

In our discussion of the favorable results of transport by the medium in some natural situations we must not lose sight of the fact that this influence, like most others, may also produce harmful effects under different circumstances. Some terrestrial organisms benefit by the distribution provided by the wind, but a great many others are carried into regions where they cannot possibly survive. Many land animals and plants are blown out to sea or over lakes, where they fall into the water. Insects and birds permanently established in windy regions have been forced to develop reactions that protect them from being blown away. The insect fauna of islands and mountain regions frequently includes a disproportionate number of wingless species. Although in some circumscribed situations flightless forms may have survived chiefly from lack of need of flight (Darlington, 1943), it is probable that certain flying species have been positively eliminated from many exposed islands by wind action.

Inhabitants of rapid streams are frequently swept down into sluggish rivers or into lakes in which conditions are unfavorable for them. Fresh-water forms are carried into the ocean, where usually they are quickly killed by the change in salinity. Similar harmful transport occurs in the marine environment. All the Arctic organisms that are carried southward by the Labrador Current are killed when the water in which they are living is mixed with warmer water in the vicinity of the Grand Banks. All tropical phytoplankton and zooplankton which are swept by eddies out of the northern edge of the Gulf Stream succumb as a result of excessive cold.

Other examples of the destructive action of currents may be on a smaller scale but of considerable economic importance. In many coastal regions the planktonic larvae of cod, haddock, and other commercially important fish are normally carried by currents from the areas where they are spawned to offshore banks suitable for the feeding of the juvenile stages when they take to the bottom. There is evidence that occasionally unusual eddies carry the young stages beyond the banks into the open ocean. When the developing fish are ready for bottom life, they find no suitable bottom within reach, and whole populations may perish as a result. A practical application for an understanding of these ecological relations is involved in the intelligent establishment of hatcheries both on the coast and inland. Before large amounts of the taxpayer's money are spent, some assurance should be gained that the young fish released will be carried by the existing currents to areas suitable for their further development.

ABRASIVE ACTION OF MEDIUM

The abrasive action of the medium and of the material carried by it, sometimes referred to as "molar" action, is another aspect of the ecological influence of the medium. If the medium is air, this action means the mechanical force of the wind and the grinding action of sand, dust, snow, and other materials driven by it. In the water, even stronger abrasive action is produced by waves, currents, and particularly by stones, sand, ice, and the like, carried by the water.

Even the wind by itself can influence the growth form of plants in exposed regions. The buttresses at the base of the ceiba trees in the flat country of Cuba have been shown to develop to the greatest extent in directions tending to support the trunk against the most frequent winds (Fig. 2.13). In the Texas Panhandle it is said that on a normal day a man can expectorate a mile and a quarter! The sand carried by winds in such exposed areas produces an abrasive effect which can be resisted only by plants with tough cuticle like the cacti and many grasses. In mountain regions the amount of strong wind to which the vegetation may be subjected is not always appreciated. For example, on Mt. Washington, only 1920 m high, the weather station recorded a wind velocity of more than 120 km per hr (75 miles per hr) on 85 days between October, 1940, and March, 1941. The average wind speed for the period was 61 km per hr, with a maximum of 219 km per hr. The all-time high for Mt. Washington was reached during

Photo from J. H. Welsh

FIG. 2.13.   Buttresses at the base of a ceiba tree near Soledad, Cuba.   The great leverage action of the wind, which the buttresses help to resist, can be imagined from the height and size of a similar tree seen in the left background.

the early part of the hurricane of 1938 when the anemometer indicated a wind velocity of 343 km per hr.   The instrument then blew away.

The continued pressure of even moderate winds blowing predominantly from one direction frequently produces a training action on the branches of the trees.   In addition, branches whipped about by the wind on the exposed side of the trees knock off one another's growing buds. These effects, augmented by excessive evaporation on the windward side, often produce extremely asymmetrical growth. "Flag-form" trees with the upper branches restricted to one side of the trunk are commonly found on exposed mountain ridges. Groves of trees in windy lowlands are often similarly wind-trained, the more protected individuals growing many times higher than those on the exposed side. The outline of such a grove presents a smoothly rising contour (Fig. 2.14). Along the sea coast the harmful action of salt

FIG. 2.14. Live oaks on wind-swept shore at Morehead City, N. C. Wind action has stunted the trees on the exposed side of the grove at the left.

spray is added to the other effects of the wind in progressively restricting growth toward the exposed beach and in causing a zonation of the species present (Oosting and Billings, 1942). At high elevations in the mountains low temperatures act with the severe winds to produce the familiar dwarfing and gnarling of the vegetation. The combined effect of these ecological factors often limits the growth of trees to a sprawling mat only a few centimeters high near the summit, whereas in the protected valleys trees of the same species grow to heights of over 15 m.

In the water medium abrasive action is an even more serious influence with which the organisms must contend. Only strongly attached plants and those animals with streamlined forms and special hooks, sucking discs, or other devices for clinging to the bottom can exist in turbulent mountain streams (Nielsen, 1950; Welch, 1952, Ch. 17). Currents of moderate velocity, such as are encountered in the lower reaches of streams and along the shores of lakes and of the ocean, produce a force that must be resisted or avoided by the animals and plants attempting to maintain a foothold in such habitats. Moving sand and silt continually threaten to abrade or to smother the organisms present. A current with a speed of only 1.4 m per sec (2½ knots), for example, will move stones and gravel up to 2.5 cm in diameter and thus would grind up all unprotected forms.

At the margin of lakes and particularly on the ocean beach the force of breaking waves, and of the sand, gravel, or ice carried by the water, produces an extremely serious abrasive action. Where exposure to such molar action of waves is particularly severe, the shoreline is often barren except for especially adapted species. However, in zones of very considerable wave action, a surprisingly large number of species of plants and animals have developed methods of maintaining themselves.

Devices for withstanding the serious molar action of the water medium are extremely varied. Anyone who has caught and cleaned a bass, a scup, or other fish inhabiting turbulent coastal waters knows how much protection the tough skin and thick scales provide for the surface of the animal. This resistant integument is in sharp contrast to the tissue-thin skin of the deep-sea fish. These latter animals living deep in midocean have no wave action to contend with, nor are they subject to chafing against rocks or gravel by currents. The invertebrates of the shoreline as well as the fish are protected by a resistant outer surface. The shells of mollusks and of crustaceans inhabiting such situations are characteristically thick and hard.

During the course of evolution many species in the littoral zone have developed holdfasts, cementing organs, suckers, etc., which prevent their owners from being washed away. Instead of evolving with more and more rigid outside surfaces, certain inhabitants of the surf zone solved the problem in the opposite direction. The seaweeds, such as the kelp and the rock weeds, are composed of flexible tissue with a leathery exterior. These forms give with the surge of the waves rather than being built to resist their force. The form and structure of these plants present a sharp contrast to the brittle nature of the typical land vegetation. Imagine what would happen if your flower garden were suddenly transplanted into the middle of the breaker zone!

Sessile animals, of which there are many representatives in the tidal zone, sometimes show a difference in growth form according to whether the individuals are living in an exposed or a sheltered location. Sponges and tunicates, for example, grow with long pendulous processes in quiet water, but, if exposed to strong currents and wave action, individuals of the same species grow closely appressed to the rocks (Wilson, 1951).

Certain physiological adaptations also exist for life where currents are strong. Many motile animals exhibit a *rheotaxis,* that is, an orientation of their locomotion with respect to the direction of the current. The rheotactic reactions of most stream fish is such that they swim against the current and thus maintain their position in the stream. Interestingly enough, in some species at least, this reaction is mediated through the eyes. The fish are stimulated to turn and swim until the image of the stream bottom no longer moves across the retina. Other fish are stimulated by differential pressure or touch. Many stream animals react in such a way as to move out of the current and thus reach quiet water or protected eddies.

Other reactions to the current are even more elaborate. Some caddis-fly larvae, for example, alter the shape of their cases and the materials of which they are built according to the strength of the

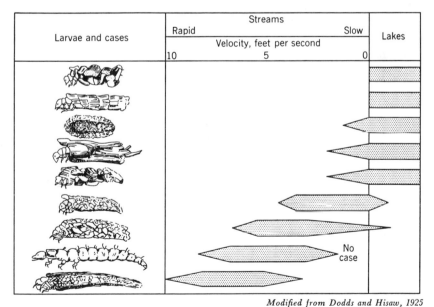

Modified from Dodds and Hisaw, 1925

Fig. 2.15. A series of caddis-fly larvae and their cases from quiet and swift waters.

current. Larvae living in quiet water build their cases of large and irregular material (Fig. 2.15). With increasing strength of current the cases become more and more streamlined and are built of finer material. In the swiftest streams they are either completely stream-lined or else done away with entirely.

The power of *autotomy* exhibited by some crabs may have arisen partly in response to the dangers of life in turbulent areas. When the leg of a crab has been caught or crushed between moving stones it can be cast off, thus setting the animal free. After autotomy has taken place, regeneration commences and a new leg grows from the base of the old leg.

Emphasis has been placed in the preceding paragraphs on the harmful action of fast-running water and breaking waves. There are situations, however, in which extreme turbulence may be beneficial. Some species of coral grow best where the pounding of the surf is the heaviest, because waves remove sediment which in quiet waters would accumulate on the coral polyps and tend to smother them. Thus stimulated, coral colonies of this type rapidly produce "heads" of coral rock at the exposed outer edge of the reef. Coral heads reach such a size that they are eventually broken off by the force of the waves. The form of the reef is the result of a balance between the increased growth due to the turbulence of the surf and the loss due to the breaking off of coral material. Here we have another il-lustration of the dynamic balance represented by natural communities and their environments.

3

The Substratum

As a factor of the environment the substratum is only slightly less elemental than the medium. The substratum is the surface upon which the organism rests or moves, or the solid material within which it lives in whole or in part. Some ecologists have not distinguished between medium and substratum. Another possible source of confusion is the use by bacteriologists of the term "substratum" for the nutrient medium used for growing microorganisms. The important point is to distinguish between the concepts, and it seems most logical to use "medium" exclusively for the material which immediately surrounds the organism, and "substratum" only for the surfaces or solid materials of the environment on which or within which the organism lives.

SIGNIFICANCE OF THE SUBSTRATUM

The substratum is not inevitable as is the case with medium. Every organism has a medium, either air or water, but some organisms can do without a substratum. In the aquatic environment the permanent plankton and many pelagic fish have no substratum at any time, but terrestrial organisms must have a substratum for at least part of their lives since no animal or plant can live permanently suspended in the air. Another general difference between the medium and the substratum is that, whereas the medium is rarely changed from air to water, or vice versa, by the activity of the organism, the substratum can be profoundly modified by many of the animals and plants which live on it or in it.

Needs Provided by the Substratum

Fundamental needs of the organism which may be provided by the substratum are purchase, attachment, shelter, and nourishment.

The limitation of growth or of distribution by the inadequacy of the substratum in respect to these needs will be discussed in subsequent sections of this chapter dealing with the different types of substratum. The substratum may also have importance in various special ways. For example, the hue and pattern of many animals protect them from detection by enemies because they blend with the background (Cott, 1940). The color and texture of the substratum are thus essential considerations in the operation of protective coloration in nature.

The larvae of many sessile organisms will not continue their development unless they find a suitable substratum. This fact has many important practical applications as for instance in oyster culture. For years oystermen have realized that clean, hard surfaces must be available in the spawning areas if the oyster larvae, or "spat," are to make a successful "set" each year. To insure the presence of a suitable substratum the oystermen dump overboard whole boatloads of empty shells or other material at a time when ecological conditions are such that the oysters of the region are about to spawn. This specially provided substratum is known as *cultch,* and its presence in sufficient abundance at the critical moment for the attachment of the larvae is necessary for successful oyster culture.

Attainment of the Substratum

The attainment of a proper substratum is crucially important in the lives of most plants and animals, and special methods meeting this need have developed during the course of evolution. One obvious and common procedure is the broadcasting of such great numbers of seeds, spores, or larvae in the attaching stage that some of them will eventually "fall on fertile soil." The majority of terrestrial plants follow this method, and, although only an extremely small fraction of the seeds are ordinarily carried to a substratum suitable for growth to maturity, enough seedlings usually become established to perpetuate the species.

The tremendous numbers of animal larvae in the attaching stage are often an index of the critical nature of the attaching process. A graphic illustration of the intensity of the reaction for the species to attain a proper substratum was found in the study of the settling of barnacle larvae in experiments conducted in Biscayne Bay, Florida. Glass plates 20 x 25 cm in size were placed in the water each day, and the number of barnacle cyprids which attached to them was determined. On one occasion the count showed that 3860 cyprids had settled on one glass plate during the previous 24 hours! When it is realized that the same intensity of attachment for these fouling organisms extended throughout great areas of Biscayne Bay, the magnitude of the reaction is appreciated.

Reactions to the Substratum

Other animals and plants, rather than relying on chance to reach a suitable substratum, actively seek it. Climbing plants often exhibit a tendency for the growing parts to keep in contact with solid surfaces. This differential growth in response to contact with a surface is termed *stereotropism*. Thus, the tendrils or stems of climbing vines twine around or adhere to objects with which they come into contact. In other species, such as euonymus, the vine simply presses against the solid surface without any special structure for attachment. Root tips, on the other hand, turn away from stones and other solid objects which they may encounter as they grow through the soil. This reaction might be thought of as a negative stereotropism.

Certain animals exhibit a locomotory orientation to surfaces, a response known as *thigmotaxis*, by means of which they keep in contact with, or avoid, solid objects. This reaction can be observed in many insects, and among higher animals it is demonstrated by rats and house mice when they tend to keep in contact with a wall (Fraenkel and Gunn, 1940).

Many worms and insects are stimulated to continue moving about until their bodies are in contact with surfaces of the environment as they would be when in burrows or under stones. In the laboratory insects will come to rest between the surfaces of glass slides, and this fact shows that the reaction is a positive response to touch rather than an avoidance of light. In nature, since there are no transparent, solid objects, the organism would also be hidden from view. If a caterpillar is placed on its back, it will immediately go through righting reactions until its feet are again in contact with the substratum. However, while the caterpillar is still on its back, if a leaf is placed in contact with its feet, the animal makes no further attempt to right itself. It will be perfectly content to remain upside down as long as its feet are firmly attached to a solid surface.

A great many animals obviously exhibit the reverse reaction, avoiding solid objects, and ordinarily do so by the use of sight or touch. A most unusual method of avoiding collision in the dark is now known to be employed by bats (Galambos and Griffin, 1942). At night and in dark caves bats can fly rapidly about without running into each other or into jutting rocks or other objects. The success with which these animals can navigate in darkness was clearly demonstrated on one occasion when a small group undertook the exploration of a cave in Cuba under the guidance of a local plantation supervisor. No sooner had the party passed through the entrance into the inky blackness of the cave than hundreds of bats sprang into the air and flew madly about. The air was thick with bats. At this point the wife of one member of the group demurred. Not wishing to have the lady of the party miss the trip, our guide offered her a dollar for each bat that struck her while passing through the cave. Not a single dollar had to be paid. Bats have been shown to emit supersonic vibrations which are reflected from obstacles and are detectible by the bats' ears. In this unique manner bats can avoid obstructions in their paths during flight through dark forests and tortuous caves.

The Variety of Substrata

Many different substrata exist in the natural community. Almost every object is a potential substratum. One often hears the statement, "Nature is relentless." This saying springs from the fact that, as soon as any manmade object is abandoned, animals or plants attach to it, bore into it, or grow over it. Thus nature is relentless in reducing man's artifacts to natural conditions.

The most common substrata are the many derivatives of rock; these will be considered shortly, but first let us take note of the great variety of substances which can serve as substrata. It is not even necessary for the substratum to be a hard surface. The surface film of water serves as the substratum for a category of organisms called the *neuston*. Many algae, certain higher plants such as the duck weed (*Lemna*) water striders, and "whirligig beetles" which inhabit ponds are supported by the tension of surface film and use it as their regular substratum. Flatworms and pulmonate snails are able to employ the underside of the water surface as a substratum. Under quiet conditions the observer can see these forms progressing steadily along the interface between the air and water. Mosquito larvae similarly can attach to the underside of the surface film (Fig. 3.1). The particular ecological needs of the mosquito in this stage make it possible for man to exterminate the pest, locally at least, by applications of oil or poison to the surface of the water. When undisturbed by public health agents, however, the mosquito larva grows rapidly on food which has accumulated at the water surface. Particles sinking through the air accumulate on the water and other materials floating up from deeper layers come to rest under the surface. Hence the air-water interface presents an excellent feeding ground. By pinching the surface film with its specially adapted mouth parts the larva obtains the food material and causes more distant particles to move nearer the area of its activity. In this way the larva is said to be able to gather food from a circle perhaps 30 cm in radius around its point of attachment.

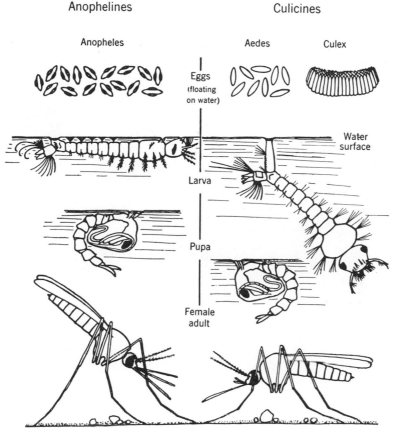

Fig. 3.1. Diagram of life cycle of mosquito, showing the use of the water surface as a substratum in the early stages. The larvae use the surface film not only for support but also for a feeding ground.

Another special substratum of interest is wood. In the air environment "dry rot" fungi, termites, and other organisms find this material a suitable substratum for their activities and for their nourishment. Far from human habitation the destruction of dead timber by these plants and animals merely aids in the reduction of organic materials to simpler substances.   But when these species attack buildings, tele-graph poles, and railroad ties unchecked, they cause tremendous damage, often within a short time.   A knowledge of their ecological relations then becomes a matter of vital economic concern.   Wooden structures under water similarly serve as the substratum for other rotting fungi, for the "shipworm" *Teredo*, and for other forms, which are consequently also of great economic importance.   It is a curious fact that, although the shipworms honeycomb a piece of wood, their tubes rarely run into one another and practically never break through the surface of the wood to the exterior.   In some way the boring shipworm is able to detect when it is nearing the limit of its substratum and stops itself from running out into the open.

Woods Hole Oceanographic Institution

FIG. 3.2.   Mussels and other fouling organisms forming a crust 17 to 30 cm thick and weighing up to 13 kg per 1000 cm² on the bottom of a bell buoy seen as it is being hoisted out of the water off Cape Cod, Massachusetts.

The hulls of ships and the surfaces of underwater structures present specialized substrata in the marine environment that are used as points of attachment for many kinds of fouling organisms including notably algae, barnacles, mussels, and tubeworms.   Even the smooth steel bottoms of modern vessels and navigation buoys are rapidly attacked by such plants and animals (Fig. 3.2).   An understanding of the ecology of fouling is necessary for success in the very practical problem of preventing this attachment. In experiments with different types of materials with which to coat submerged objects including ship bottoms, it was found that no surface could be devised which was so smooth, so slippery, or so soft that a barnacle cyprid could not gain a foothold. Tests showed that fouling could be prevented only by covering the ship's hull with paint that emitted copper or other ions strongly toxic to the attaching stages, as illustrated in Fig. 3.3 (Woods

C. M. Weiss, Woods Hole Oceanographic Institution

FIG. 3.3. Bottom of boat showing reactions of fouling organisms to different antifouling paints. Fouling has been prevented on port side by emission of ions from cuprous oxide paint. On the starboard side fouling organisms have attached because the emission from the metallic copper paint used on that side has been inhibited by the coupling action of the galvanized iron patch seen at right of propeller.

Hole Oceanographic Institution, 1950). Without an effective antifouling paint a battleship is said to require 30 per cent more fuel to maintain cruising speed within 6 months after launching, and its top speed is seriously reduced. The research program on the ecological relations of fouling organisms and on poisoning methods undertaken in American marine laboratories during World War II was reported to have saved the United States Navy 10 per cent of its entire fuel bill.

The substrata used by plants and animals are not restricted to in-

animate objects.   The surfaces of other organisms are also susceptible
to invasion by attaching organisms.   Plants which grow on the external surfaces of other organisms but do not obtain nourishment
from them are called *epiphytes*.   Similarly, animals which gain attachment or shelter without using the tissues of the host organism as a
source of food are termed *epizoans*.   If the attaching forms obtain
nourishment from the host, they are *external parasites*.   The bromeliads and orchids perched on the branches of forest trees in the
tropics are typical epiphytes.   The barnacles on the backs of whales
are examples of epizoans, although they are often erroneously referred
to as parasites.

When the substratum of an organism is another animal or plant,
new relations appear.   The organism may find that its substratum
moves around, grows, or is destroyed.   In such instances the interdependencies between the epiphyte or epizoan and its host become
extremely complex.   For example, the distribution of sessile rotifers
attached to the water plant *Utricularia* depends upon the relative rates
of the migration of the rotifers and the elongation of the stems of the
plant (Edmondson, 1946).   When the growth of the plant is relatively slow, the rotifer population tends to become concentrated.
But, in the reverse situation, the rotifers become spread out with corresponding changes in the age distribution of the population.
Epizoans on the gulf weed *Sargassum* are similarly subject to the
vicissitudes of a living substratum.   The floating gulf weed elongates
at its distal end and dies and breaks off at its basal end.   A slow-
growing hydroid attached to the *Sargassum* might not be able to
maintain itself if its substratum grew out from under it.

ROCK, SAND, AND MUD IN AQUATIC ENVIRONMENT

Influence of the Aquatic Substrata

Although many different materials can serve as substrata in the
water environment, by far the most common are rock and its derivatives.   Whether the substratum consists of smooth rock, loose stones,
sand, or mud has a profound effect on the distribution of aquatic organisms and on the regulation of their growth.   Different textures,
various degrees of stability of the material, and a great variation in
the nutrient content have an important selective action.

In shallow water the difference in fauna and flora on a rocky bottom, on a sandy beach, or in soft mud can easily be studied by anyone
visiting the shore.   On the sea coast, for example, a rock substratum

will characteristically support a rich growth of brown, green, and red algae attached by "holdfasts" and a wide variety of snails, mussels, sea anemones, starfish, and many other invertebrates secured by sucking or cementing devices. Some of these animals indirectly derive nourishment as well as attachment from the rock substratum. The snails, for example, scrape off and eat the slime that forms on all underwater surfaces as well as the bacteria and algae contained in the slime. In shifting sand or gravel few species except rapidly burrowing animals can maintain themselves; but on and in firm sand, especially when mixed with mud, a distinctive and rich population of mollusks, worms, and crustaceans will be found, provided that other environmental factors are favorable. On a mud bottom where the water is quieter, rooted plants like the eel grass often grow in abundance, and sea cucumbers, brittle stars, sea urchins, and a different selection of worms are among the common inhabitants. However, if oxygen has been depleted and hydrogen sulphide is formed in the mud habitat, the benthic population will be greatly reduced. Further

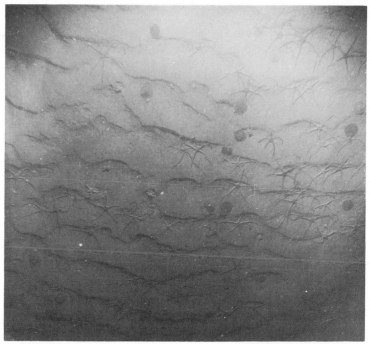

Photo made with Ewing undersea camera by D. M. Owen, Woods Hole Oceanographic Institution
FIG. 3.4. Ripples on the sea floor at a depth of about 100 m on Georges Bank off Massachusetts. The numerous brittle stars and sand dollars visible in the 10 m² area shown are able to maintain themselves on the shifting surface.

examples of the control of bottom fauna and flora by the substratum in coastal water are given by Yonge (1949) and by Pratt (1953), and in fresh water by Krecker and Lancaster (1933) and by Wilson (1939).

Farther offshore conditions cannot be so easily observed, but the modern quantitative dredge and the underwater camera have shown that the same selective action is being exerted by the nature of the bottom material. Samples dredged from mud and from coarse shell-gravel at locations only a few miles apart in the English Channel were shown by Wilson (1951) to contain strikingly different animal types. Such differences influence fish populations feeding upon these benthonic species. Studies made with the underwater camera have the advantage that they reveal the nature of the bottom material and the organisms living on it in their undisturbed condition. The dimensions of bottom features such as ripples, and the spatial distribution of the inhabitants may then be examined quantitatively (Fig. 3.4). In the abyssobenthic zone of the ocean the bottom material usually consists of a soft mud, and here only those animals with long legs, broad bases, or other special adaptation can move about without being smothered. At a depth of 1½ miles the candid underwater camera caught a 60-cm "sea cucumber" as it cruised across the muddy bottom

Photo made with Ewing undersea camera by J. Ewing, Woods Hole Oceanographic Institution
FIG. 3.5. A holothurian ("sea cucumber") moving over the mud at a depth of 2600 m (1½ miles) on the floor of the open ocean off the coast of New York. Note the imprint of the double row of tube feet.

(Fig. 3.5). These holothurians, and other types of bottom animals, pass the mud through their intestines and extract the organic matter from it. For such forms the nutritive value of the substratum may have an even greater ecological importance than its physical nature.

Breakdown of the Substratum

We have seen the various ways in which the nature of the substratum in the aquatic environment limits the growth and distribution of organisms living on it or in it. Turning the ecological picture the other way around, we find that the presence of organisms often has a profound influence on the substratum. Even solid rock can be bored into and broken down by animals living on it. In the intertidal zone of the Oregon coast sea urchins have carved craters for themselves in the sandstone. So abundant are the sea urchins and their craters that in many places the shelving rocks present a honeycombed effect. Even more remarkable is the ability of bivalve molluscs of the family Pholadidae to drill into gneissic rock and into concrete. Some of the pillars of the causeway to Key West have been pockmarked by these animals. Empty shells which form the major portion of the substratum in some regions are broken down by the sponge *Cliona*. The basal part of this sponge produces an acid secretion that hastens the disintegration of the shells. In some situations the complete destruction of an organism's substratum by its own activity has led to its undoing, for without a suitable substratum it is eliminated from the habitat.

Build-Up of the Substratum

In addition to the breaking down of solid materials many aquatic organisms play an important part in building up their substratum. Calcareous algae and many types of coral animals cause calcium carbonate to be deposited in and around their tissues. As a result limestone formations of various sorts are brought into being. Anyone who has visited the tropical ocean is well aware of the vast extent of reef-building activity (Fig. 7.12). In fresh water certain organisms similarly cause the precipitation of calcium carbonate. The marl deposits that are formed in this way often come to be the chief component of the substratum in ponds and lakes.

In some situations the new substratum produced by the activity of living agents consists essentially of the surfaces of the organisms themselves. Occasionally a few mussels become attached to individual stones scattered over a clam flat of fine sand or mud. During the next season young mussels may attach to the shells of the old mussels. Subsequent "sets" gain foothold on the surfaces of the second generation until gradually a mat of mussels spreads across the area that had previously been covered by soft material quite unsuitable for the growth of a mussel population. Mussel mats of this sort have sometimes been a serious economic concern because they have smothered valuable populations of clams beneath.

In other situations the action of the living part of the ecological system is that of binding together loose particles of the bottom material so that a firm substratum is provided in place of the shifting sand or mud previously existing in the area. The eel grass that was formerly prevalent along our Atlantic coast played this important role in many

Murray and Hjort, 1911, copyright Macmillan & Co.

FIG. 3.6.   A washed sample of pteropod ooze from the Indian Ocean showing the conical and angular shells of pteropods, the rounded tests of Foraminifera, and the remains of other types of plankton, enlarged about 10 ×.

bays and estuaries. After the eel grass was killed by a disease in the early 1930's, large amounts of bottom material were washed away from many sections of the shore. As the unprotected sand and mud was scoured out by the tides, a great many other plants and animals that had been living in the area were destroyed. Eventually the complexion of the whole ecological community became altered (Stauffer, 1937).

Another way in which organisms can modify the substratum is through contributing their own remains. The sand on the famous Pink Beach in Bermuda is composed chiefly of coral fragments. In the deep sea some of the bottom oozes consist mainly of the skeletons of planktonic organisms (Sverdrup, Johnson, and Fleming, 1942, Ch. 20). *Globigerina ooze* formed by the accumulation of the shells of a genus of Foraminifera and *pteropod ooze* similarly composed of the shells of gastropods are examples of calcareous oozes (Fig. 3.6). Two important types of siliceous deposits are formed by the accumulation of the hard parts of radiolarians and diatoms, respectively. *Radiolarian ooze* is found in certain tropical waters, and *diatom ooze* is limited to colder seas.

Aquatic organisms also act reciprocally on their own substratum by adding organic material to it. In a peat bog the substratum is practically 100 per cent organic matter resulting from the accumulation of vegetable material (Welch, 1952, Ch. 16). In inland waters and in the sea, fragments of dead organisms reach the bottom as an organic detritus. Seaweeds and shore animals that have died and been broken up by the waves contribute abundantly to this material, but farther from shore the plant and animal plankton are largely responsible for the particulate organic material in the water. This detritus tends to settle out where the current has been sufficiently reduced. The excreta of worms, lamellibranchs, and various Crustacea have been reported to form as much as 40 per cent of the fine material in the mud of the Clyde Estuary. All these organic substances gradually become incorporated into the substratum and serve as sources of nutriment for the mud-eating benthic animals (Twenhofel, 1939).

ROCK, SAND, AND SOIL IN TERRESTRIAL ENVIRONMENT

Influence of the Land Substrata

In the land environment soil is by far the most important substratum, but rock and special materials such as plants and plant products also serve as ecologically significant substrata. As rock breaks down it produces areas of stony ground, gravel, and sand; and with the admixture of organic matter soil is formed from the parent rock substance. Each of these materials has its influence in controlling the growth and distribution of plants and animals. As in the aquatic environment the land substrata provide purchase, shelter, attachment, and nourishment in varying degree according to circumstances.

Land Surfaces and Animals. Physical differences in the land surfaces are correlated with special adaptations of animals inhabiting them. On rocky terrains and in regions with hard, open ground the running speed of animals is improved by the possession of small resistant feet usually with a reduced number of toes, as in the deer, antelope, and ostrich. Animals living in areas of soft sand, marsh, or snow are characterized by spread-out feet, like those of the camel, or of toes that present a large surface, like those of wading birds and the snow-shoe rabbit. Sand-dwelling lizards and insects similarly are enabled to move over loose sand by toes or legs widened by lateral scales or hairs. Other animals have feet especially adapted for climbing trees (squirrels), or for clinging to branches or leaves (tree frogs), or for dealing with other special substrata.

In contrast to the species requiring rapid locomotion over the land surface is a large group of animals that burrow into the substratum. Many rodents, some birds and reptiles, and a great many insects, as well as other types of invertebrates, are built for effective digging in the ground. Certain species such as the mole, the earthworm, and many insects spend most of their lives underground. All these burrowing forms are limited to regions in which suitable soil conditions exist. For example, a tongue of soil running across the Florida panhandle that is too dry for the burrowing of crayfish acts as an ecological barrier separating certain west Florida species of crayfish from species limited to areas farther to the east (Hobbs, 1942).

The chemical composition of the soil substratum affects animals both directly and indirectly through their food. Land snails with calcareous shells are especially abundant on soils rich in lime, but the abundance of the shell-less slugs is not affected in this way. The shell of one species of *Helix* was found to weigh 35 per cent of the total weight of the snail in limestone regions but only about 20 per cent of the total weight in areas with soils poor in lime (Hesse, Allee, and Schmidt, 1951, Ch. 20). The bones of mammals likewise are heavier on limestone soils; this is especially true of deer that annually must grow new antlers sometimes weighing as much as 7 kg. It is no accident that strongly built race horses are raised in the bluegrass pastures on the limestone soils of Kentucky. Many herbivorous mammals require an abundant supply of salt (NaCl) because sufficient sodium must be taken in to maintain a proper ionic balance with the large amount of potassium contained in their plant food. If an adequate amount of salt is not available in the halophytes of salt meadows, ruminants are forced to travel to "salt licks," or are excluded from the region entirely.

The amount of organic matter in the soil is of vital concern to earthworms and other small invertebrates that use this material as a source of food. A great number and variety of small insects and spiders, of still smaller nematodes, and of microscopic Protozoa, which live permanently in the soil, also depend upon this organic matter for their nutrition. Thus the microfauna also is controlled by the chemical qualities of the soil, as well as by its compactness, dryness, and other physical characteristics.

Soil and Its Action on Plants. An adequate discussion of the nature of the soil, its changes in time and space, and its influence on plants, and indirectly on animals through its effect on vegetation, would require a whole book in itself. Nothing more than an introduction to the subject can be given here. For a more extensive treatment of soil itself the reader is referred to Lyon, Buckman, and Brady (1952), Kellogg (1941), and the Yearbooks of Agriculture issued by the U. S. Department of Agriculture. Excellent chapters on the ecological relations of soils in relation to plants are to be found in Oosting (1948) and Daubenmire (1947).

Besides its ecological importance as a substratum, soil has immeasurably great economic importance. Fortunately we are rapidly becoming aware of the critical value of the productive capacity of soil as a support for civilization. Wolfanger (1950) has stated that "the soil of a nation is its most valuable material heritage." The crucial need for immediate soil conservation in almost all countries of the world has been ably pointed out by Osborn (1948), Vogt (1948), and others. A thorough understanding of the ecological relationships involved is essential for the intelligent use of our existing soils, for the prevention of further soil loss and degradation, and for the restoration of the fertility of worn-out soils.

Soil represents an extremely complex matrix consisting of minerals derived from the parent rock of the area, organic matter of local origin, and substances carried in by various agents. The physical nature of a soil depends first of all upon its texture and structure. *Texture* is determined by the size of the constituent particles, and *structure* is dependent upon the aggregation of these particles in the undisturbed soil into grains, clumps, and flakes. Soil particles are classified according to size in the accompanying table.

Sand	1.00–0.05 mm in diameter
Silt	0.05–0.002
Clay	<0.002

In a good loam all three of the categories are well represented. The type of structure into which the particles are arranged affects profoundly the porosity of the soil. It also controls the amount of surface which is presented on the one hand to the air and water moving through the soil, and on the other to the hairs of roots growing in the soil. The relative proportions of the soil constituents and of the air and water present are extremely variable. In an average good soil about half the volume is commonly represented by pore space of which half may be occupied by air and half by water. The solid material of such a soil may consist of 95 per cent mineral particles and 5 per cent organic matter. In tropical soils, however, organic matter may be less than 1 per cent, and in peaty soil it may approach 100 per cent of the dry material. In addition to differences in texture and structure, soils vary physically in the type of layering that they develop as they mature under biological and climatic influences as will be discussed in the next section.

The chemical nature of soils is even more diverse and variable. Upon the disintegration of the parent rocks the whole spectrum of minerals present becomes available for incorporation into the soil. Added to these are a wide variety of organic substances derived from animals and plants and other materials introduced from the air and ground water. Further chemical changes take place within the soil as climatic and biological agents work on it. As a consequence, soils and soil water differ widely in chemical composition, organic content, and total salinity, as well as in degree of acidity, oxidation-reduction potential, and other physicochemical characteristics. Some of these features of the soil are intimately interrelated with the physical characteristics. For example, the smallest particles involved in the texture of a soil are colloids, and their behavior and reactions are also involved in the chemistry and physical chemistry of the soil. The abundance and type of the colloids present affect the amount of water retained by the soil and its availability to plants. At the same time the colloids influence the chemical composition of the soil water.

In the present section we are concerned with soil primarily in its physical nature as a substratum for land organisms. The foregoing brief sketch of soil has indicated the extremely complicated nature of this substratum and the degree to which its physical characteristics are bound up with its chemical and its physicochemical features. Certain of the latter will be further discussed in relation to other ecological factors considered in later chapters.

When gross differences in the land substrata exist, factors limiting plant growth can frequently be distinguished. On a solid rock substratum lichens and certain mosses are characteristically the only plants that can survive. In situations with a coarse, shifting substratum, like a sand dune or a gravel slide, the vegetation is limited to specially adapted forms. Dune grasses with their network of horizontal rhizomes, and certain other plants, such as *Paronychia,* with strong and extensive root systems are among the few plants that can maintain a foothold. When the soil is very hard owing to a high silt and clay content or to the development of a hardpan, the roots of many species cannot penetrate. At the other extreme the presence of very soft soils prevents the establishment of plants that require firm anchorage. Many evidences of this relation were seen in New England after the hurricane of 1938 when whole groves of trees on loose soil were uprooted but neighboring groups of the same species on hard ground remained standing after the storm.

In other situations a gross difference in such factors as the chemical composition, moisture, or temperature of the soil may be distinguishable as the prime influence controlling the vegetation, and examples of these will be considered later in the appropriate chapters. Too often for the peace of mind of the ecologist, however, very complicated or subtle differences occur in the soil, and frequently two or more interdependent factors appear to act mutually in limiting plant growth. More detailed treatments of the ecology of soils, such as those referred to earlier in this section, should be consulted for a further discussion and examples of situations of this type. In some habitats investigators disagree not only as to which of the soil influences is critical in determining the composition of the vegetation but also even as to whether the climatic factors are not more important than the edaphic (soil) factors.

These ecological relations in the soil also frequently illustrate the *principle of partial equivalence:* an increase in one factor may sometimes partially make up for a deficiency in another factor (Allee et al, 1949, Ch. 16). The lack of moisture in a sandy soil may be compensated for to some extent by a greater rainfall in certain localities, or, conversely, plant species for which a given region is generally too humid may find the effective moisture conditions sufficiently reduced in a local area with a sandy substratum.

Action of Organisms on Soil

Having seen the many ways in which the nature of the land substratum may influence the lives of organisms, we now may inquire to what extent the action is reversed. The fact is soon revealed that animals and plants play a very important part in modifying their substratum on land just as they do in water. This activity on the part of terrestrial organisms is particularly striking in relation to the formation and development of soil. It has been truly said that if it were not for organisms there would be no soil—at least none of biological importance. The soil is an outstanding example of the result of the organism and the environment acting as a reciprocating system.

Abundance of Organisms in Soil. The great abundance of organisms which live wholly within the soil and the far-reaching extent of the underground parts of organisms are not always appreciated. Anyone who spades up a garden or transplants a shrub should be impressed with the number of roots and the bulk of the root systems of even small plants. The roots of the typical plant are so finely divided and subdivided into rootlets and root hairs that a tremendous surface is provided for the exchange between the organism and its surroundings (cf Weaver, 1947). Roots are frequently sufficiently abundant to produce a continuous mat or network extending several feet into the soil. The root system of a maize plant may extend over 1 m laterally and $2\frac{1}{2}$ m deep. The roots of 17-year old apple trees were found to have occupied all the soil between rows 10 m apart and to have grown to a depth of $10\frac{1}{2}$ m (Weaver and Clements, 1938).

In the animal kingdom the number of species that burrow through the soil and thus influence it is also very large. Burrowing rodents and moles of one kind or another exist almost everywhere, and they are much more abundant than is generally realized. Although in some instances the actual number of the larger forms may not be impressive, their digging activities may be remarkably extensive. Prairie-dog burrows more than 4 m deep have been reported. In certain parts of California systematic trapping has shown that as many as 50 mice inhabit each hectare ($2\frac{1}{2}$ acres) under normal conditions. Periodically, as we shall see later, the rodent population tends to increase greatly in numbers. Even when the population of mice and other burrowing forms is at low ebb, a considerable influence on the soil may be produced in the course of a year. In addition to a variety of mammals, many kinds of reptiles and amphibians as well as a few species of birds spend at least a part of their lives burrowing in the soil.

Of smaller animal forms, the numbers present in the soil are much greater (Chapman, 1931, Ch. 18). Earthworms have been estimated at hundreds of thousands per hectare, and their burrows may extend to depths greater than 2 m. Insects, especially in the larval stages, are very numerous in the upper centimeters of the soil (Salt et al., 1948). In some regions population densities of several million soil insects per hectare have been found. Spiders, tardigrades, millipedes, and isopods are also abundant inhabitants of the land substratum. An extensive study in Illinois showed that the invertebrates of the soil reached an average summer maximum of 3300 per sq m—or roughly one animal under every 3 sq cm of surface. Since many of these forms are short lived and populations succeed one another in the soil, the study indicated that at least one or two invertebrate animals had existed during the year under every square centimeter of soil surface. In mineral soils of Jutland nematodes have been found to range in number from 175,000 to 20,000,000 per square meter (Nielsen, 1949).

The numbers of microorganisms in the soil are, of course, much greater and produce a profound effect on the substratum. Protozoa may exist in concentrations of hundreds of thousands per gram of soil. The mycelia of fungi penetrate the soil wherever suitable conditions are found, and bacteria are extremely abundant almost everywhere. In raw humus as many as 20,000 bacteria per gram are a common occurrence. In rich loam the bacteria population may rise to 50 or even 100 million cells per gram of soil (Waksman, 1932). All these denizens of the soil from sizable burrowing animals to the smallest microorganisms add their influence to that of the underground parts of plants in modifying the substratum.

Soil Formation. Soil is formed by the combined action of several agents. First may be mentioned the process of *fragmentation,* the mechanical breakdown of rock material into smaller pieces. The process is carried forward partly by geological agents, including especially the freezing and thawing of moisture in the ground. The action of roots in splitting rocks is also important and represents the biological part of the process. No matter how small the rock particles may be, however, plants cannot obtain nutriment from the material until the minerals are rendered soluble. The second step in soil formation, and one that goes on simultaneously, is termed *corrosion* and includes the chemical processes of oxidation, reduction, hydration, hydrolysis, carbonation, and others. These processes go forward and soil materials go into solution under the influence of rain

after it percolates through the ground as soil water.   But the action of
pure rain water would be extremely slow.   Root secretions added to
ground water, including notably carbonic acid, cause the rock materials to go into solution much more rapidly.   If you look closely at a
rock covered by lichens, you can see the results of the combined action
of mechanical breakdown and corrosion due to plant secretions.

The third factor taking part in the process of soil formation is the
addition of *organic matter*.   Plants contribute their deciduous parts
at regular intervals, and when each plant dies it adds its whole
body to the soil.   Since one thinks of plants as growing by withdrawing material from the soil, one might ask how any net gain would
result from the death of the plant and the return of this material to
the substratum.   The answer is that the plant builds additional
materials from the air and the ground water into its tissues.   The
carbohydrate synthesized by the plant is formed from carbon dioxide
and water absorbed from the environment.   Certain bacteria, such
as *Azotobacter* and *Clostridium,* living freely in the soil, are able to
take nitrogen from the air and to use it in their constructive growth.
Other nitrogen-fixing bacteria live in nodules on the roots of leguminous plants to which they pass on the nitrogenous compounds that
they have manufactured.   Thus, more is added to the soil by the
activity of the vegetation than is removed, and, what is more important, the new material is in a very different chemical form.   The
inorganic substances taken up from the soil and from the atmosphere
are converted into complex organic compounds by the growth processes of the plant.   When the plant dies, these organic substances
become incorporated into the soil and many of them decompose only
slowly.

Animals living on and in the soil add their excreta regularly and
contribute their own bodies to the substratum when they die.   Burrowing animals of all sorts mix into the soil the organic remains that
have been added to the top of the ground.   Rodents and many kinds
of insects play an important role in this regard, as well as the pro-
verbial earthworm.   A visit to a deciduous forest where earthworms
are abundant will provide an opportunity for seeing the effectiveness
of this animal in tilling the soil.   If you remove from the surface of
the ground the leaves that accumulated in the last few months, you
find few leaf remnants from previous years.   All the older leaves
have been eaten by the earthworms, and their faeces have largely been
discharged at subsurface levels.   When constructing new burrows,
earthworms deposit their casts of soil from the deeper levels upon the
surface.   This action of the earthworms in mixing the upper layers in

the deciduous forest helps to produce an entirely different soil profile from that found under coniferous trees. Because of the lack of the earthworm population in the typical coniferous forest as well as the slower rate of decay the fallen needles tend to accumulate year after year as successive layers on the surface of the ground.

We have seen that living agents aid in the breakdown of the parent rock material, take part in the vertical mixing and the horizontal distribution of soil substances, and add organic matter to the soil. The by-products of animals and plants, and their own bodies when they die, are the only source of organic compounds for the soil. These organic substances provide necessary soil components, modify the soil into many different types, and make possible the growth of a varied fauna and flora that would not otherwise be able to exist. The organic matter contributed to the soil contains a larger amount of energy than the inorganic substances from which they were formed. Living organisms therefore provide both potential and kinetic energy as well as materials in helping to build the soil.

Humus and the Colloidal Complex. Soils are far more than piles of material derived from rocks and biological sources. Soils have organization. Structure, layering, and other aspects of soil arrangement are influenced by the animals and plants present, and, reciprocally, the activities of the soil organisms are frequently controlled by the organization of the soil material. One way in which animal life and vegetation affect soil organization is through their contribution to the *colloidal complex*. The partially decomposed organic matter added to the soil by living components is known as *humus,* and this material combines with the finest clay particles to form the colloidal complex. Often referred to as the "heart and soul" of the soil, the colloidal complex plays many essential roles in its dynamic activity (Waksman, 1936). In the first place the presence of colloids derived from humus and other sources influences the water-holding capacity of the soil and the rates at which air and ground water can circulate through it. Water tends to move too freely through sandy soil. The addition of humus to such soil tends to bind the grains together, to reduce pore size, and to increase the amount of water held. A contrasting situation is found in soil that is too dense because of an excessive amount of clay. Increasing the amount of humus present has the effect here of separating the soil material into clumps, and thus allowing better aeration, increased percolation, and easier root penetration. In both instances the structure of the soil has been improved.

The colloidal complex also acts as a source of plant nutrients and as a particularly desirable type of storehouse since materials are released from it only gradually. As will be discussed more fully in Chapter 8, the critical plant nutrients of the soil consist of such inorganic materials as nitrate, phosphate, potassium, and calcium, as well as of certain organic substances. These are derived in part from the humus itself and in part from the breakdown of the mineral components of the soil. Many of the nutrient materials are held by the colloidal complex in loose chemical combination or physical adsorption on the surfaces of particles. The reactions involved in the decomposition of soil components and in the association of nutrient materials with colloids are extremely complicated, and the reader should turn to a treatment such as Lyon, Buckman, and Brady (1952) for a further discussion. The general point emphasized here is that the colloidal complex fulfills the important function of providing for the slow release of nutrient materials in such a way that they can be absorbed by plant roots as needed.

The difference between the gradual delivery of nitrogen from the supply in the organic matter and the rapid exhaustion of soluble nitrogen that is freely mobile in the soil has no doubt been observed by the reader for his own lawn or garden. When nitrogen fertilizers are added to the soil, they tend to be rapidly dissolved. In this condition the nutrient salts may be quickly leached away by rain and ground water, or they may produce a "flash" growth of the plants present. More desirable for the growth of cultivated plants, as well as for vegetation in general, is the slow availability of nitrogen from the organic colloidal complex and from the decomposing organic matter, although nitrogen fertilizers are often beneficial if used properly.

The Soil Profile. A broader aspect of the organization of the soil and another on which animals and plants exert a profound influence is the *soil profile*. If you look closely at a fresh vertical section through the soil, as exposed in an excavation or a road cut, you will see a succession of layers, or *horizons* as they are called, that together form the soil profile (Fig. 3.7). This arrangement of the soil material in layers is the result of the action of the living components and the climatic influences of the region on the original parent material. In some regions this master organization of the land substratum has been in the process of formation for thousands of years. The nature of the soil profile is of crucial concern in respect both to the natural vegetation and to commercial crops. We should accordingly think twice before allowing agricultural procedures that may permanently destroy the established layering of the soil.

The depth and composition of each horizon of the soil profile differ

Photo U. S. Soil Conservation Service

Fig. 3.7. Vertical cut through fine sandy loam supporting blue-stem grass at Red Plains Experiment Station, Guthrie, Oklahoma.

A Horizon, 0–1.0 ft (0–30 cm): grayish brown fine sandy loam.
B Horizon, 1.0–2.5 ft (30–75 cm): reddish sandy clay.
C Horizon 2.5–3.2 ft (75–95 cm): weathered parent material.
D Horizon below 3.2 ft: laminated sandstone and shale.

greatly from place to place and change with time in the same region as the soil matures. A varying number of subdivisions of each horizon are recognized in different situations with the result that a complete analysis of the soil profile becomes very complex. In many soils some of the subdivisions are entirely unrepresented, and in other soils strata of considerable thickness may be uniformly mixed. The general nature of the principal horizons and subdivisions are shown diagrammatically in Fig. 3.8.

The process involved in producing and maintaining a typical soil profile are indicated schematically in Fig. 3.9. Here is shown one

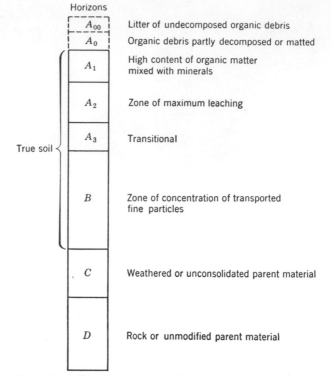

FIG. 3.8. The soil profile with its principal subdivisions shown by a vertical section through the soil.

member of a stand of trees that has grown in the area for a long time and that has produced in the soil the characteristic layering. Perhaps the most important of the climatic agents is the moisture factor, and this involves both rainfall and evaporation. Where the land is sloping a portion of the rain runs off over the surface, sometimes washing away organic materials or even some of the soil itself. The rain that enters the ground percolates through the pore spaces carrying fine particles and dissolved salts with it. In some places the ground water drains completely through the soil into the strata beneath, with the result that the dissolved materials may be lost from the soil. With excessive rainfall valuable constituents may thus be leached from the upper horizons. Other portions of the ground water enter the roots of the vegetation and are carried upward again. Water vapor moves through the pore spaces and evaporates from the sur-

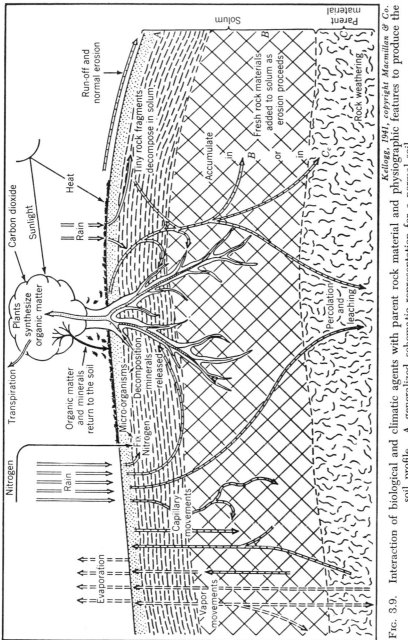

Fig. 3.9. Interaction of biological and climatic agents with parent rock material and physiographic features to produce the soil profile. A generalized schematic representation for a normal soil.

Kellogg, 1941, copyright Macmillan & Co.

83

face. The circulation of soil air provides for the transport of oxygen and carbon dioxide necessary for or resulting from the metabolism of the plant roots, soil animals, and microorganisms.

The diagram also indicates the photosynthesis of the vegetation and the transfer of organic substances formed by the foliage to the roots deep in the soil. Organic compounds in great variety are elaborated by the growth of associated plants and animals. As described earlier, the deciduous parts of plants, the excrement of animals, and finally the bodies of all these organisms, when they die, are added to the soil. These organic remains accumulate on the surface, or are carried to deeper levels by the soil fauna, where they begin the slow process of decomposition.

This interplay of biological and climatic agents working on the parent material results in the production of the soil profile as indicated in the diagram. The *A* horizon is the scene of the major biological activity, and here organic matter chiefly accumulates. Rain entering this layer and percolating through tends to leach out the soluble salts. The *A* horizon is usually darker in color and lighter in texture than the *B* horizon below it, from which it is often sharply distinguished. The *B* horizon is characterized by less intense biological activity. Fine particles tend to accumulate here and mineral salts are often concentrated in this layer. The material of the *B* horizon is usually bright in color and densely compact. The *B* horizon tends to grade rather indistinguishably into the *C* horizon below it where there is little or no biological activity. As the soil matures, the *A* and *B* horizons tend to deepen until equilibrium conditions are reached.

The exact nature of the mature soil profile depends upon the particular balance reached between the climatic factors, the biological agents, the contour of the land, and the type of the parent rock in the given area. The many possible variations and complications should be borne in mind in a consideration of the simplified example outlined above. It should be amply clear, however, that the condition of the soil is a result of the elaborate interaction between organisms and their environment. The dynamic viewpoint of the modern ecologist is, therefore, especially appropriate in the further investigation of the problems of the soil that have been merely touched upon here. As one further illustration let us consider briefly the interaction between the vegetation and the substratum that underlies the differentiation of two great categories of soils.

Soil-Group Divisions. Soils are classified into groups, and in the United States soil groups fall into two great divisions: the pedocals and the pedalfers, in the terminology used by Wolfanger (1950) and shown in Fig. 3.10—or the aridic and the humid soils, in the somewhat different classification used by Lyon, Buckman, and Brady (1952). The *pedocal* division is composed of incompletely leached soils found characteristically in the arid Great Plains of the West. The slight rainfall of these regions does not saturate the soil to a depth sufficient to reach the water table deep in the ground, and lime tends to be deposited in the *B* horizon. When evaporation from the soil begins, the ground water is drawn upward again toward the surface, carrying some of the solubles with it. The water in this kind of soil has been said to be "hung from the top, like Monday's wash!" The roots of the grasses and shrubs that are characteristic of the pedocal soils absorb the water and the contained salts and also carry them toward the surface. Grasses particularly tend to absorb a considerable amount of calcium and to restore this material to the upper layers. This process is aided by the low growth habit of these plants and the great development of rhizomes and other structures near the surface

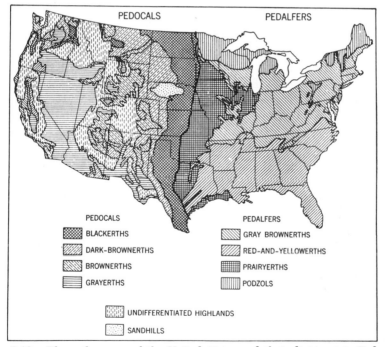

Fig. 3.10. The soil groups of the United States and their division into Pedocals and Pedalfers. (Modified from Wolfanger, 1950, in *Conservation of Natural Resources*, reprinted with permission of John Wiley and Sons.)

of the ground.   For these various reasons calcium tends to accumulate in the upper layers of the soil, and from this fact the name "ped-o-cal" is derived.   The retention of calcium carbonate and magnesium carbonate helps to prevent pedocals from becoming acid.

An outstanding example of the interaction of climatic, edaphic, and biological agents in the development of a pedocal soil is furnished by the *chernozems,* or blackerths, that occur from the Dakotas southward.   The climate is less arid than it is farther west, and a good grass cover is typically present.   The action of the ground water and of the vegetation in retaining salts and other nutrient materials in the upper layers and in maintaining a neutral or slightly alkaline condition is indicated schematically in Fig. 3.11.   Organic matter tends to accumulate in the A horizon, resulting in the development of the rich, dark soil condition familiar in the region.   Chernozems are consequently especially valuable for grazing or for farming because when left undisturbed, or properly managed, the ecological processes present tend to perpetuate soil fertility.

The *pedalfer* division consists of soil groups found principally in the more humid regions of the eastern half of the United States. Here the rainfall is heavier with usually more than 75 cm falling per year.   The solubles of the soil tend to be carried beyond the reach of the roots by the large amount of water percolating through the upper horizons.   Much of this water filtering through the soil reaches the water table and drains off valuable nutrients.   The roots of the typical forest vegetation growing on such soils extract salts but do not remove relatively as much calcium as do the grasses.   The annual leaf-fall is on the surface, and some of the organic matter resulting from decay is carried away by the run-off, particularly in hilly regions.   This loss of nutrient materials is in marked contrast to the situation with the pedocals and the grass vegetation of the prairies.

In the north-central and northeastern parts of the United States the increased rainfall and lower temperatures tend to accentuate the processes just described.   Soils of the *podzol* group, which occur in these regions, represent an extreme development of the conditions found in the pedalfer division (Fig. 3.12).   In the podzols the solubles are rapidly lost by leaching.   The A horizon becomes acid because of the accumulation of leaves, needles, and other organic debris on and in the surface strata.   Calcium is dissolved from the upper layers and is often almost completely extracted from the soil. Aluminum and iron are similarly carried down but tend to be precipitated again as silicates in the less acid B horizon, and may cause the formation of hard-pan at this level.   The tendency toward relative accumulation of aluminum and iron generally in this soil-group division provides the derivation for the term "ped-al-fer."

In the region where the pedalfers exist there is generally sufficient rainfall for agriculture, but the soil tends to lose its nutrients. In the extreme podzol type the interaction of the climate and vegetation is such that solubles are rapidly carried away and the soil becomes progressively poorer and more acid, whereas in the chernozem soil fertility tends to be perpetuated. The contrast between the cherno-

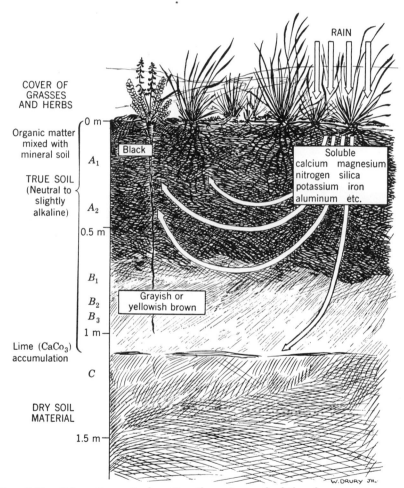

Fig. 3.11. Schematic vertical section through a soil of the chernozem group as representative of the pedocal soil-group division. The subdivisions of the soil profile are indicated in relation to the vegetation and the movement of soil water. The depth scale is representative, but varies greatly.

zem soil as a representative of the pedocal and the podzol as a representative of the pedalfer illustrates the effectiveness with which the activity of organisms coupled with differences in climate can modify the substratum. The soil in its development and its organization is

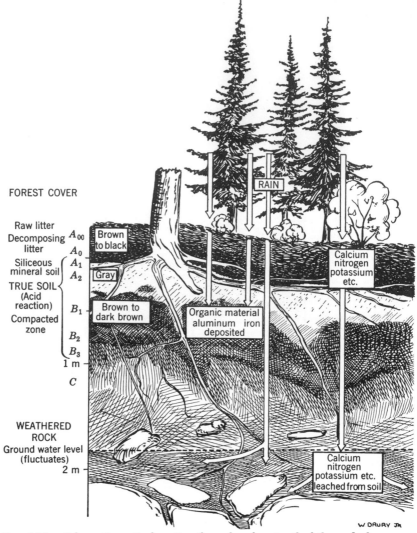

FIG. 3.12. Schematic vertical section through a forest soil of the podzol group as representative of the pedalfer soil-group division. The subdivisions of the soil profile are indicated in relation to the vegetation and the movement of soil water. The depth scale is representative, but varies greatly.

thus seen to be an outstanding example of a system formed by the interaction of organism and environment.

The review of the substratum as an ecological factor given in this chapter has revealed the great variety of surfaces and solid materials on and in which animals and plants live. The manner in which the nature of the substratum controls the distribution and the growth of different species has been indicated. We have also stressed the fact that the activities of living organisms—and the material of their bodies after death—may profoundly alter the substratum in both the aquatic and the terrestrial environments. Sometimes this process itself brings about the further progressive changes in the fauna and flora known as ecological succession, considered in Chapter 12. Most of all, our present discussion focuses attention upon the reciprocally dependent relation existing between the living community and the substratum. The nature of the mud on the bottom of a pond or of the soil on the surface of the land is partly the result of the biological influences and is at the same time partly responsible for their existence.

The physical conditions of the water or the land originally allow certain plants and animals to exist in a given area. These living agents may then modify the substratum, whereupon the substratum may be further affected by the "climatic" factors, perhaps resulting in additional changes in the fauna and flora. When we visit the area after these activities have gone on for a long time, and are still going on, it is not easy to distinguish cause and effect. Nevertheless, with a good grasp of the relations summarized in this chapter we are better equipped to determine the specific action of climatic, physiographic, and biological influences in bringing about the existing conditions.

4

Water

Water plays several different roles in the ecological relations of plants and animals. In Chapter 2 we considered the physical characteristics of water in its mechanical action as a medium. In this chapter we shall discuss water as a substance taking part in the living complex, and in subsequent chapters we shall see how water may modify the action of other factors.

As a material entering the organism water is important as a necessary and abundant constituent of protoplasm, and the plant or animal body as a whole generally contains a large percentage of water—sometimes 90 per cent or more. Water is essential also as one material taking part in the photosynthetic reaction, through which energy becomes available either directly or indirectly to all living beings. Water is necessary as a solvent for food and as an agent for the chemical transformation of the materials within the body. Plants obtain mineral nutrients from the soil after they are in aqueous solution. Although most animals take in their food in solid form, this material must be dissolved before it can be absorbed by the blood and tissues. The intestines could be stuffed full of solid food and yet the animal would starve if no water were available for its digestion. Furthermore, water serves as a vehicle for transport or circulation within the bodies of organisms. Minerals are carried up the stem of the plant by the transpiration stream. Water is the principal constituent of the circulatory, excretory, and reproductive fluids of animals, and it is necessary as a transfer agent at respiratory and olfactory surfaces. Water also acts as a regulator of temperature for plants and animals.

For these essential purposes the proper concentration of water must be maintained inside the organism, and, at the same time, the transfer of water must be suitably regulated. If the organism could live hermetically sealed in a capsule, the retention of the necessary amount of water would be easy, but exchange of this material between the organism and the outside world is necessary. The crucial need for a proper water balance is demonstrated by the consequences of even small water losses in some instances. During starvation, for example, man may lose as much as 40 per cent of his body weight including half of the proteins and nearly all the glycogen and fat without serious danger, but if 10 per cent of the water content of the human body is lost, serious disorders result. If as much as 20 per cent of the water is lost, death follows.

The concentration of water divides the environment into aquatic and terrestrial habitats. At first sight, one might say that more than enough water exists in the aquatic environment and that water is a problem only on land. Closer scrutiny shows, however, that water is tending to enter or to leave the organism too fast in almost every situation. In certain terrestrial habitats the water supply may be excessive for many organisms, as in some tropical rain forests where the air is often 100 per cent saturated and the ground is completely permeated. A visitor to such a habitat sees moisture condensing on every surface and hears the steady dripping of water from the vegetation.

In the ocean in spite of the thousands of cubic miles of sea water a scarcity of water would nevertheless exist for many plants and animals! For these organisms the concentration of water is too low relative to the abundance of salt for proper osmotic equilibrium. Fresh-water environments, viewed similarly in relation to osmotic balance, tend to contain too much water. This contrast between marine and inland aquatic situations is, in a sense, analogous to the difference between dry and humid climates on land. The maintenance of the proper water balance is thus a problem that must be considered in all habitats for all types of organisms.

WATER PROBLEM IN THE AQUATIC ENVIRONMENT

Since the water in natural environments contains a varying amount of dissolved materials and usually a different amount from the fluids of the organism, the resulting differences in osmotic pressure raise a problem in regard to water exchange. In order to determine the tendency of water to enter or to leave the organism we must know something of the composition of the surrounding medium.

Composition of Natural Waters

Representative values for the amounts of the more numerous ions found in sea water and in the water of ponds and lakes are shown in

Water

Table 3. A larger amount of each of the common ions occurs in sea water than in typical fresh water. Hard fresh water contains more dissolved salts than soft fresh water, particularly with respect to the calcium and the carbonate ions. A comparison of the *relative* amounts of each type of ion in each kind of water may be made by recalculations in which sodium is given a value of 100 in each case (Table 4). In sea water chloride and sodium are the first and second most abundant ions, respectively, whereas in typical hard fresh water carbonate is the most abundant with calcium second. In typical soft fresh water the calcium and carbonate ions are relatively less concentrated than sodium and chloride.

TABLE 3

COMPOSITION OF SOME TYPICAL NATURAL WATERS
(After Baldwin, 1948)

	Na	K	Ca	Mg	Cl	SO$_4$	CO$_3$	Total (g/liter)
Soft fresh water	0.016	—	0.010	—	0.019	0.007	0.012	0.065
Hard fresh water	0.021	0.016	0.065	0.014	0.041	0.025	0.119	0.30
Sea water	10.7	0.39	0.42	1.31	19.3	2.69	0.073	34.9

TABLE 4

RELATIVE ABUNDANCE OF IONS (BY WEIGHT) IN NATURAL WATERS

	Na	K	Ca	Mg	Cl	SO$_4$	CO$_3$
Soft fresh water	100	—	62.5	3.3	119.0	43.8	75.0
Hard fresh water	100	76.0	310.0	66.8	195.0	119.0	567.0
Sea water	100	3.6	3.9	12.1	181.0	20.9	0.7

Samples of sea water from different localities are surprisingly constant in respect to the relative abundance of the major constituents. So much is this the case that for many purposes it is not necessary to measure the concentration of more than one ion. The standard procedure for determining the salinity of sea water is to find the amount of chloride ion present by titration and then to calculate the total salinity and the concentration of the other ions from the known ratios. The individual salts occurring in fresh water by contrast, vary widely —often with far-reaching consequences that will be considered later.

At the moment our concern is with the maintenance of the proper osmotic balance between the inside and the outside of the organism.

Since osmotic pressure is determined by the total concentration of molecules and ions in solution, values for the aquatic medium will vary according to the total salt content of the water body (Table 5). Dissolved materials in soft fresh water vary in amount from practically zero to about 65 parts per million. Lakes and ponds with hard water exhibit a variety of higher values for salt content, but the value given in the table, 300 ppm, is representative. Salt lakes may contain exceptionally large amounts of dissolved substances.

In contrast to the extreme variability in the salt content of inland waters, the open ocean tends to remain highly uniform in salinity over huge areas (Fig. 4.1). A fish could swim up the middle of the Atlantic Ocean, for example, from the Cape of Good Hope almost

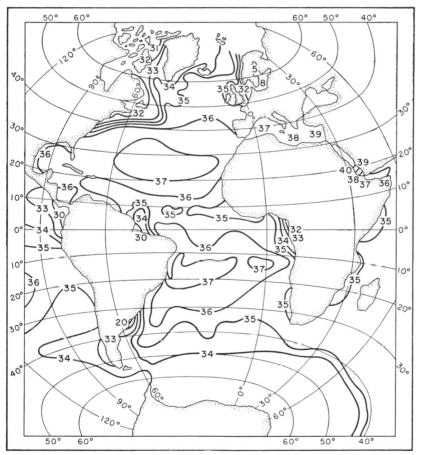

Fig. 4.1.   The surface salinity of the Atlantic Ocean.

to Iceland without encountering a salinity, lower than 35‰ or higher than 37‰ (parts per thousand). Ocean areas with unusually high evaporation, like the Mediterranean Sea and the Red Sea, exhibit salinities that run up to 40‰. On the other hand, the salinity of the Baltic Sea is reduced to 8‰ or less due to the large inflow of fresh water.

In river estuaries and in coastal areas receiving large amounts of run-off, salinity may vary over the whole range from nearly fresh water to full sea water. In smaller habitats, such as rock pools filled by ocean spray, the salinity may be typical of ordinary sea water on one occasion, may be greatly increased by evaporation a few days later, and may be reduced almost to zero by rainfall on another day. However, for the marine environment as a whole, such situations are definitely exceptional. The great length and breadth of the ocean maintains a nearly constant salinity of about 35 to 36‰.

TABLE 5

TOTAL SALT CONTENT OF SOME TYPICAL NATURAL WATERS

Soft fresh water	< 65.0 ppm	0.065‰	0.0065%
Hard fresh water	300.0	0.300	0.03
Devils Lake, N. D.	11,000.0	11.0	1.1
Great Salt Lake	170,000.0	170.0	17.0
Baltic Sea		8.0	0.8
Ocean water		35.0	3.5
Red Sea		40.0	4.0

TABLE 6

TYPICAL VALUES FOR OSMOTIC PRESSURE EXPRESSED AS FREEZING POINT DEPRESSION ($= \Delta$)

	ΔWater	ΔInvertebrates	ΔTeleost Fishes
Mediterranean	2.14	2.2	0.8–1.0
Coastal Atlantic	1.79	1.8	0.7–0.8
Fresh water	0.03	0.1–0.8	0.5–0.6

The osmotic pressure of a molar solution of a non-electrolyte is 22 atmospheres or 1700 cm of mercury. The freezing point of such a solution is depressed to $-1.84°C$, and this fact provides a convenient method for measuring osmotic pressure. In a solution of electrolytes with the same number of molecules the osmotic pressure would be higher because of the dissociation. Sea water is a 0.55 molar solution, and, since the salts are dissociated, sea water has an osmotic pressure almost equal to that of a molar solution of a non-electrolyte.

The salt content of the water in alkali soils may be even greater. Animals and plants living in sea water or in saline soils are therefore surrounded by liquids having a very high osmotic pressure.

Methods of Meeting Osmotic Problem

If the osmotic pressure inside the organism is the same as that outside, relatively little difficulty is experienced in adjusting water equilibrium. If the osmotic pressure of the fluids of an animal or plant departs greatly from that of the outside medium, a problem results in maintaining the proper water balance. If an animal moves into an area of very different salinity, a further adjustment will be required.

Sample values for the depression of the freezing point (Table 6) reveal the fact that because of the higher salinity the osmotic pressure of Mediterranean water is higher than that of Atlantic water. The latter is very much higher than a typical value for fresh water. The osmotic pressure of the internal fluids of plants and of invertebrates is generally equal to, or higher than, the medium in which they are living. Among elasmobranch fishes the osmotic pressure is maintained at different levels but is always higher than the surrounding water due to the retention of urea in the blood.

The osmotic pressure of teleost fishes tends to remain within a relatively narrow range for both fresh-water and marine species. In fresh water the teleost is osmotically superior to its medium, whereas it is osmotically inferior in salt water (Fig. 4.2). In the sea a strong tendency exists for the fish to lose water from its tissues to the surroundings. A brief calculation will indicate the magnitude of the osmotic force with which such an animal must contend in order to maintain its water balance. If the osmotic pressure of the fish is represented by $\Delta = 0.7$ and that of the surrounding medium by $\Delta = 1.8$, the magnitude of the pressure corresponding to this difference of $\Delta = 1.1$ is:

$$\frac{1.1}{1.84} \times 1700 = 1015 \text{ cm Hg}$$

An osmotic pressure of 1015 cm Hg, or 13 atmospheres, is tending to extract water from the fish's tissues! For the teleost, therefore, and for other animals and plants with low internal osmotic pressures sea water has the effect of being physiologically dry. Fresh-water animals and plants that migrate, or are carried, into the sea are indeed entering an arid climate.

The easiest way for an organism to deal with the osmotic pressure of its environment is to establish an internal osmotic concentration of the same magnitude. Even better, if the tissue fluids can be maintained at a slightly higher pressure, then there will be a tendency for the needed water to enter the organism from the surrounding medium. This is the general method followed by plants and by invertebrate animals.

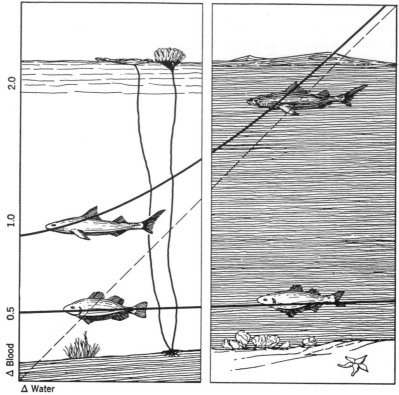

Fig. 4.2. Schematic diagram of osmotic pressure differences between elasmobranch and teleost fishes and their fresh-water (*left*) and marine (*right*) media. The degree of shading indicates the relative values of osmotic pressure. (Modified from H. W. Smith, 1936).

Most fresh-water and terrestrial plants can maintain an internal osmotic pressure ranging up to 2 atmospheres but they find saline habitats with a higher osmotic pressure physiologically too dry and uninhabitable. However, specially adapted plants, the *halophytes,* are able to tolerate higher salinities and to absorb water by virtue of the fact that the osmotic pressure of their tissue fluids is exceptionally high. Halophytes sometimes exhibit internal osmotic pressures as great as 35 or even 40 atmospheres. Such plants inhabit the margins of the ocean and of salt lakes and can grow in saline soils with salt contents considerably greater than sea water. Although the exact relationship is not understood, it is of interest to note that halophytes, living in a *physiologically* dry habitat, exhibit succulence, heavy cutin, and other xeromorphic characteristics familiar in the plants of the *physically* dry desert.

In fresh water the tissue fluids of invertebrate animals have a considerable osmotic superiority because of the typically low salt content of ponds and lakes (Krogh, 1939). The chief problem here is a matter of getting rid of the excess water which enters through the membranes. In marine invertebrates the osmotic pressure of the body fluids is ordinarily only slightly, if any, higher than that of the surrounding sea water. When invertebrates living in estuaries move into fresher water, they must exert more osmotic work to eliminate the larger amount of water that tends to enter (Baldwin, 1948). The teleost fish must actively regulate water transfer both in the sea and in inland waters to prevent excessive loss of water in the former and excessive intake of water in the latter. A few animals can tolerate exceptionally high salinities as is exemplified by a fish that inhabits Japanese rock pools with salinity of 60‰ and insect larvae that live in water of 42 to 62‰ at Dry Tortugas Island (Pearse, 1950).

Limiting Effects of Salinity

The extent to which the various species can endure changes in osmotic pressure influences their activity and range. Organisms with a low tolerance for differences in salinity are known as *stenohaline* forms. Species that are limited exclusively to the open ocean or to fresh water are thus classed as stenohaline. Others may be limited to a narrow range of salinity of an intermediate value, but this is relatively rare. Plants and animals that are able to tolerate a wide range of salinities are termed *euryhaline*. Thus organisms inhabiting an estuary and fish that migrate back and forth from fresh to salt water are euryhaline. Such fish as the salmon and the eel are able to regulate their water balance in either a hypertonic or hypotonic medium.

It should be noted that no sharp line or numerical limit distinguishes stenohaline and euryhaline forms—these terms are entirely relative. The terms also do not bring out the important difference in the effect of time of adaptation. Some species can withstand wide differences in salinity if they become adapted slowly, but are unable to tolerate rapidly changing salinity. Relatively few species can endure both a wide range and a rapid change in salinity. Interestingly enough, some euryhaline organisms may grow best in intermediate salinities, or even require them for a part of their life cycles, although our knowledge is scanty in this area. The division rate of certain species of phytoplankton has been shown in laboratory cultures to be twice as great at a salinity of about 20‰ than at salinities of about 10‰ or 30‰ (Braarud, 1951). We also know that the American oyster can live in full sea water and can tolerate fresh water for short periods, but observations indicate that the larvae of this species will not settle at salinities above 32‰ nor below 5.6‰. The optimum salinity for settlement in this estuarine animal is 16 to 18.6‰. Changing salinities in estuaries may control the growth, reproduction, and distribution of more of the inhabitants than we now realize.

Limits of distribution are sometimes sharply determined by salinity toleration. The vegetation around the margins of salt lakes and in the spray zone near the ocean shore exhibits a characteristic gradation of species from those most tolerant of salt to those least tolerant. In San Francisco Bay the slight difference in tolerance between two species of pile-boring mollusks was of great economic importance. In the upper regions of the Bay wharves and other wooden structures had been built without any special protection against shipworms because the local species of the genus *Bankia* was unable to grow in salinities below 10‰ which frequently occurred in the area. In 1913 another species of wood-boring mollusk, belonging to the genus *Teredo,* was introduced into San Francisco Bay, and this species could tolerate salinities as low as 6‰. Spreading rapidly, *Teredo* attacked the wooden structures of the area and within a few years had caused destruction amounting to more than $25,000,000.

Many interesting problems in relation to salinity tolerance remain unanswered. In most cases we do not know why one species can tolerate a rapid or extensive change in the salt content of its medium and another cannot. Why the euryhaline species have not come to dominate the open ocean as well as the coastal regions is unknown. Another question of interest is how oceanic birds and mammals can balance their water budgets without a supply of fresh water. Many of these forms eat marine invertebrates whose salt content is nearly as great as an equal volume of sea water. It may be that the water contained in the tissues of the food and the metabolic water are sufficient for the needs of marine birds and mammals (Clarke and Bishop, 1948), or these animals may have some special adaptation for excreting excess salts.

AMPHIBIOUS SITUATIONS

It is difficult enough for animals and plants to move from the sea to fresh water or vice versa, but, when aquatic organisms attempt to invade dry land, they are flopping out of the frying pan into the fire as far as the water problem is concerned. Nevertheless life on land does have certain advantages. Plants usually find more light, better anchorage, less abrasive action, and more concentrated nutrients. Animals may make use of the more abundant vegetation for food and shelter, the greater oxygen supply, and the possibility of more rapid movement. Against these advantages there is one signal disadvantage—the scarcity of water. Success in colonizing dry land has been dependent on securing and retaining sufficient water. This could be easily arranged, perhaps, if the organism could seal itself up, but, as already stressed, surfaces must be left open for exchange with the external world. Of immediate importance is the problem of how to feed and to respire in air without drying up. Representatives of relatively few phyla have succeeded in becoming wholly independent of the aquatic habitat. However, some plants and animals have come part way out of the water, or come out for short periods, and we shall consider these first.

Swamps and Temporary Pools

Certain organisms have hit upon methods of using the advantages of both the air and the water environment. The emersed vegetation, for example, which grows in swamps or on the margins of lakes has its roots in the water and its upper portions in the air. In this position the roots find plenty of water available and extract nutrients from the mud, while the leaves are in the best position for receiving light from the sun and carbon dioxide from the atmosphere. However, many plants are not able to survive in a partially submerged condition because of inadequate direct supply of oxygen for the roots. Plants that are adapted to existence entirely under water, or with their roots in water or in saturated soil, are known as *hydrophytes*.

Amphibians are similarly able to utilize both air and water environments. Many species can leave the water to forage on land, and, if their pools dry up, they can migrate to other bodies of water. Such animals are not limited by land barriers as most fish are. Yet amphibians must re-enter the water or visit damp places at intervals to keep their skins moist, and most species need water for reproduction.

Organisms living in swamps and pools must be able to deal with periods of drought when they occur. Physiological adaptations making this possible have been evolved sometimes without any accompanying special morphological structures. Certain species of fish in India can live in wet grass for as long as 60 hours, and other animals burrow in the mud where they remain in a dormant condition during the dry period. Water mites have been shown to be able to live under debris for intervals up to 6 months after their pools have dried. The African lung fish, on the other hand, constructs a special mud cocoon and curls up inside for the duration of the dry spell. The fish secretes about its body an impervious sheath which prevents the loss of water from its tissues, and is thus enabled to survive drought for more than two years. Other specialized structures for tiding over dry periods are the spores and seeds of water plants, and the "resistant" eggs and cysts of various aquatic animals ranging from the Protozoa to the Crustacea.

Another adaptation for meeting the water problem in temporary pools is that of speeding up development and taking quick advantage of water when it is available. In certain animals living in this type of habitat the larval stage is accelerated; in others parthenogenesis has been adopted. If a single female cladoceran such as the water flea, *Daphnia,* finds itself in a temporary pool, it does not have to hunt around for a male. It can go ahead and reproduce rapidly by parthenogenesis. The young animals mature and continue reproducing parthenogenetically until in a relatively short period a large population has built up. Later, however, if the pool tends to dry up, the adverse conditions cause the appearance of males in the population. The females now produce a different type of egg, one which requires fertilization. Only one of these "winter" eggs is formed by each female and the brood pouch is modified into an ephippium (Fig. 2-11). After the death and disintegration of the female, the ephippium remains as a resistant egg case within which the egg can survive prolonged periods of drought and even freezing. In this condition the egg may be blown into another pond or carried in dried mud by animals to another region. When water is again supplied to it, the egg hatches out and is able to start the cycle over again.

Tidal Zone

Another situation that might be classified as amphibious is the *tidal zone*. Plants and animals living on the seashore between tide marks are subject to alternating droughts and floods twice each day. Organisms living in the center of the tidal zone must be able to be aquatic for about 6¼ hours when the tide is in, terrestrial for about 6¼ hours when the tide has ebbed, and so on, day in and day out. The tidal zone is thus a very difficult habitat, and also a very complicated one because of differences in the timing and height of tide. Since low tide and high tide occur about 1 hour later each day, the intertidal area comes to be exposed at all hours of the day and night. During the first and last quarters of the moon *neap tides* occur, i.e., tides of low amplitude, but during periods of new moon and full moon the tides rise higher and fall lower and are known as *spring tides*. In some localities, such as the west coast of the United States, one set of high and low tides each day has a much greater amplitude than the other set. The height of the tide differs greatly from locality to locality, and the duration and depth of inundation varies according to the level within the tidal zone at which a given organism exists. For example, an animal or a plant attached near the upper extreme limit of the tide will be covered by sea water for only a brief period about every two weeks, whereas an individual living near the lower extreme tidal limit will receive only a correspondingly short exposure to the air. The tidal zone comprises the upper portion of the *littoral zone*, as indicated in Fig. 2.4.

Despite these severe conditions a dense population of a very wide variety of plants and animals characteristically inhabits the tidal zone. The fauna and flora consist chiefly of sessile forms, such as the common seaweeds, barnacles, mussels, and clams. Those plants and animals that cannot move out of the tidal area must endure the full effect of the differences in the two media. In addition, certain active forms forage here under favorable conditions and then retreat. At low tide animals come from the land and feed on the material that has been exposed. Shore birds are familiar in this area, but less observed are rats, mice, mink, skunks, and other small mammals that feed chiefly at night. During high tide the reverse situation obtains. Fishes, crabs, and other active animals from deeper water move in for a few hours and then retire. The alternating visitations of these forms remind one of Box and Cox in the famous operetta.

It is of interest to inquire why the tidal zone should be so densely populated since the habitat presents such great difficulties for existence. In the first place all species tend to spread; marine animals and plants are pressing on their boundaries, and terrestrial forms are likewise attempting to invade regions at the margin of their habitats. These species extend their ranges just as far as they can endure the conditions. Furthermore, the tidal zone has certain advantages over conditions in deep water. Shallow water has more light, oxygen, and circulation; and certain predators are excluded. A great amount of organic matter occurs in this zone, and much of this forms a valuable food for the inhabitants. A large part of the organic material exists as detritus resulting from the breakdown of seaweeds and the disintegration products of dead animals. In addition many kinds of smaller planktonic organisms abound in the shallow water and add to the food supply. The adaptations of the intertidal organisms and the control of their activities by the environment will be discussed briefly here; more comprehensive treatment of this special habitat will be found in such books as Yonge (1949) and Wilson (1951).

Practically all the permanent inhabitants of the tidal zone are aquatic organisms, and accordingly their chief problem is dealing with the adverse conditions of the air medium when the tide is out. Many physiological and morphological adaptations are displayed for withstanding the recurring periods of water shortage. Many of the simpler organisms can endure a considerable drying of their tissues without permanent injury. Sea anemones, for example, have been kept out of water 18 days; at the end of this period the animals looked like dried raisins but became active again when replaced in sea water. Attached forms with shells like the barnacles, mussels, and oysters simply close up shop during the period of low tide, and many can remain sealed up in this way for unbelievably long periods without injury. If kept at a low temperature oysters may be stored out of water for 3 months or more and will resume normal activity when replaced in the sea. Snails and starfish move into sheltered crevices when the tide is out; worms, clams, and other burrowing forms dig deeper in the mud and wait for the tide to return.

Certain intertidal forms seem to benefit by periods out of water. A practical application of this fact is made use of by many oyster growers who prefer to raise oysters in situations where they are exposed to the air for at least a portion of each day. The oystermen believe that as a result the muscles which close the shells are strengthened. When the oysters are shipped to market, the shells are held more tightly together thus retaining the fluids within the mantle cavity. These oysters are said to be better able to "hold their liquor!"

Actively swimming or crawling animals may be able to go without food for the period when the tide is out, but they cannot remain active and do without a supply of oxygen for this length of time. There is no lack of oxygen in the air, of course—the problem is to get it without allowing the respiratory membranes to dry out. The gills of many of these animals are placed in partially enclosed cavities of the body where oxygen may reach them but the loss of water from the respiratory surfaces is retarded. A striking gradation in the anatomical adaptations of crabs in the tidal zone has been described by Pearse (1950) for the North Carolina shore. He called attention to the fact that species living higher up on the shoreline show a reduction in the number of their gills and particularly in the ratio of gill surface to the size of the whole animal (Fig. 4.3).

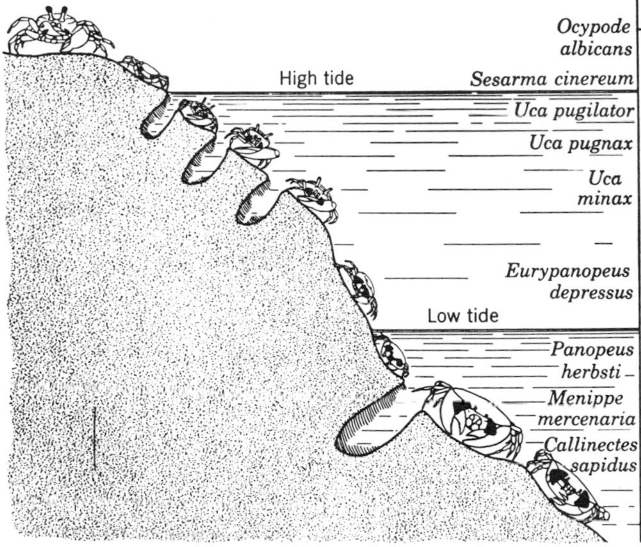

	Number of gills	Body: gill ratio
Ocypode albicans	12	67:1
Sesarma cinereum	16	63:1
Uca pugilator	12	49:1
Uca pugnax	12	46:1
Uca minax	12	40:1
Eurypanopeus depressus	18	36:1
Panopeus herbsti	18	36:1
Menippe mercenaria	18	32:1
Callinectes sapidus	16	23:1

High tide

Low tide

Pearse, 1936

Fɪɢ. 4.3. Reduction in number of gills and increase in ratio of body to gill volume in species of crabs living at progressively higher levels in the littoral zone.

Differences in ability to withstand the progressively more difficult conditions from the low-tide mark to the high-tide mark have resulted in a zonation of the plant and animal species. On rocky shores this zonation is often so pronounced that it can be seen at a distance when

the tide is out.   In the situation shown in Fig. 4.4 the sharp upper
limit for the growth of the rock weeds is easily apparent.   At a higher
level the longer period of air exposure and of lack of sea water imposed a clearly defined upper boundary upon the barnacle population.

Photo by R. W. Miner

Fɪɢ. 4.4.   Rocky shore at low tide showing stratum of barnacles and of sea weeds
(two subdivisions of the Balanoid Zone).

Stephenson and Stephenson (1949) have found that on rocky shores
in many parts of the world three fundamental zones may be recognized: the Littorina Zone, characterized by snails; the Balanoid Zone,
characterized by barnacles; and the Laminarian Zone, characterized
by laminarian seaweeds.   The relation of these zones to the tide marks
is shown in the diagram.

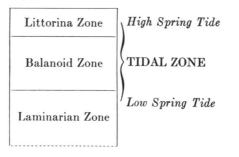

The upper part of the Littorina Zone extends into the spray zone, or *supralittoral zone,* where the salt-resistant outposts of the land fauna and flora are to be found as well as those marine organisms most capable of enduring desiccation (Boyce, 1954). The Laminarian Zone extends for varying distances below low-tide mark.

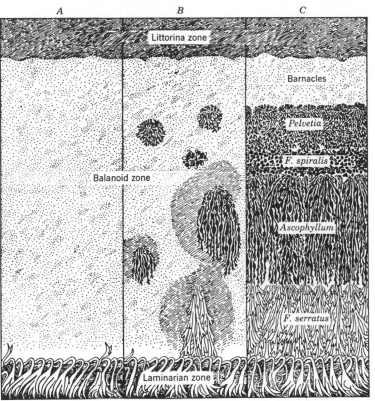

Fig. 4.5. Diagram to illustrate the three fundamental zones of life between tide marks on a rocky shore. Balanoid Zone showing (A) barnacles only, (B) barnacles inhibited by sweep of seaweeds, and (C) algal subdivisions typically encountered on British coasts.

Frequently various subdivisions are superimposed on the main zonation of rocky shores (Fig. 4.5). The vertical limits of the various subzones of fucoid algae and of associated invertebrates are determined not only by relative tolerance in respect to the water factor but also by type of rock, wave action, and relative success in invasion, competition, and resistance to predation.

On muddy and sandy shores zonation of plants and animals between tide marks similarly occurs, but the observer will have to dig
to ascertain the full ramifications of the tidal relationships since many
of the inhabitants are burrowers. In addition, microscopic examination of samples of bottom material reveal a zonation of the microorganisms in the tidal zone. The distribution of copepods dwelling in a
sandy beach of Cape Cod will serve as an illustration (Fig. 4.6). The

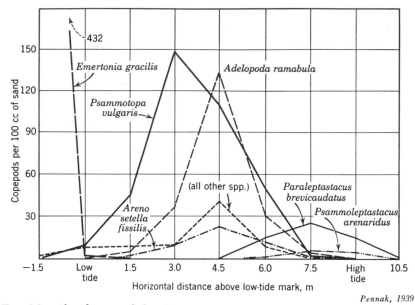

Pennak, 1939

Fɪɢ. 4.6. Abundance and distribution of sand-dwelling copepods across the tidal
zone at Nobska Beach, Woods Hole.

different species present were so nearly alike in general appearance
that they could be distinguished only by careful study. Nevertheless, one species was found to live only below low tide where it is never
subjected to the drying action of air. Another form was most abundant midway between the tide marks. A third species was most
numerous just below the high-tide line. Furthermore, when samples
of sand from different levels beneath the surface were studied, the
numerical abundance of the copepods was found to vary with depth
in the sand as well as with position across the tidal zone. At the low-
tide mark the largest number of animals was found in the upper 4 cm,
whereas at the high-tide mark the largest population occurred at a
depth of 12 to 16 cm. In the tidal zone, as in other amphibious situa-

tions, the water factor thus exerts a major controlling influence on the minute organisms as well as on the more conspicuous species.

WATER PROBLEM IN THE TERRESTRIAL ENVIRONMENT

When we turn to dry land as an environment, the water problem becomes extremely acute. Everyone is familiar with the quick death which awaits aquatic organisms brought out on land. Many terrestrial forms can endure the land environment only if they remain in damp places. This is true for a great many species of plants and also for animals without special protection. A salamander that has escaped from its terrarium and run across the dry floor will soon be dead if it is not rescued and put back in a humid atmosphere. Earthworms frequently crawl out on a concrete sidewalk during a spring rain. If the sun comes out and dries the sidewalk, many of the animals will be killed before they can find their way back to the moist ground.

The successful invasion of the dry land is dependent upon the possession of methods for securing and retaining sufficient water and at the same time allowing adequate exchange with the environment. Terrestrial plants and animals as well as aquatic forms must maintain a proper *water balance* between water income and loss. Great variation exists in the moisture content of land organisms and also in the amount of water intake and output that is necessary to provide for metabolic processes. Insects subsisting on dry food probably hold the record for the minimum water exchange. At the other end of the scale are many types of higher plants that are extravagant water users. Some species of plants absorb and transpire more than 2000 grams of water for every gram of dry matter produced by assimilation. An oak tree may transpire as much as 570 liters of water in a single day.

How many taxonomic groups have succeeded in colonizing dry land? Actually, only a very few of the prominent kinds of plants and animals have accomplished this. In the plant kingdom it is chiefly the vascular forms that are able to live in really dry places, but some low-growing bryophytes, algae, and fungi—particularly the rock lichens—form noteworthy additions to the list. Among the vertebrates, only the reptiles, birds, and mammals can live freely exposed to dry air. Although several phyla of invertebrates are reported in the land fauna, only the insects, spiders, and snails occur in important numbers in dry habitats. By contrast, there are a great many plant and animal groups that are exclusively aquatic.

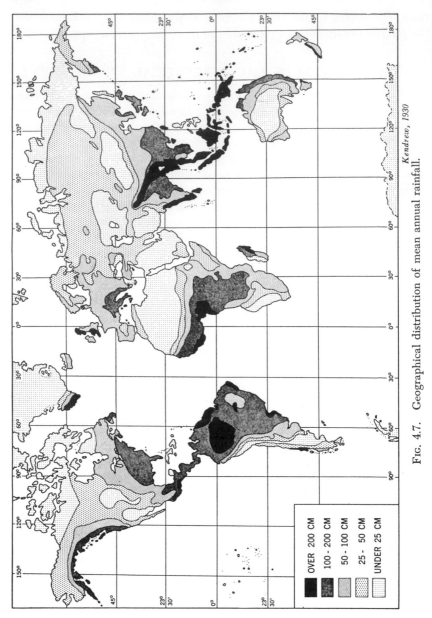

Kendrew, 1930

Fig. 4.7. Geographical distribution of mean annual rainfall.

Occurrence of Water in Land Environment

The only ultimate source of water for the terrestrial environment is condensation—chiefly in the form of rain. If precipitation were evenly distributed, it would cover the earth to a uniform depth of 1 m each year. Quite the contrary is the case. A glance at Fig. 4.7 will reveal the irregularity in the geographical distribution of rainfall. In the desert areas the rainfall is less than 25 cm per year and is inadequate for most organisms. In the black areas of the chart an excessive rainfall of 200 cm or more is reported each year. The mean annual rainfall on the south side of the Himalayas is recorded as 1232 cm. At the other extreme is Iquique, Chile, with an average precipitation of 0.125 cm per year. Among the Olympic Mountains in the state of Washington the annual rainfall totals as much as 380 cm on the windward side of some ridges and as little as 25 cm on the leeward side.

Seasonal variations in the distribution of rain may be of even greater importance than the geographical aspect. In many regions the division of the year into a rainy season and a dry season is of more ecological significance than the change in temperature between summer and winter. In the climatographs shown in Fig. 4.8 two situations are contrasted. In the Chicago region representing a temperate climate, an average of 5 to 9 cm of rain falls in every month of the year, but the average monthly temperature varies from about —4°C in the winter to about 22°C in the summer. In the tropical climate of Barro Colorado Island the average monthly temperature changes by not more than 1 or 2°C throughout the year, whereas the precipitation drops to less than 3 cm per month in the dry season and rises to more than 40 cm per month in the wet season.

Wherever the amount of precipitation varies greatly during the course of the year, the time of occurrence of rain in relation to the temperature cycle has great effect on the vegetation. Only those species will thrive whose varying needs for water in the different life stages are satisfied by the seasonal distribution of available moisture. In many of the grass-covered or forested areas of the temperate zone the major portion of rain occurs in the summer, but in other regions, of which southern California is an example, most of the precipitation occurs in the winter. In the latter situation we find a special type of vegetation with broad evergreen leaves known as the sclerophyllous forest. In the prairie provinces of Canada the average annual precipitation of 50 cm would not be sufficient to support agriculture if the rain were evenly distributed through the year. However, the major portion of the rainfall occurs during the spring growing season, and also at a time before the rate of evaporation has become excessive, with the result that the available precipitation is used to best advantage. The existing combination of ecological conditions thus permits western Canada to be an important wheat-growing region.

The foregoing discussion brings into relief the fact that in considering moisture conditions on land the actual amount of the precipitation is only part of the story. The other part, and often the more

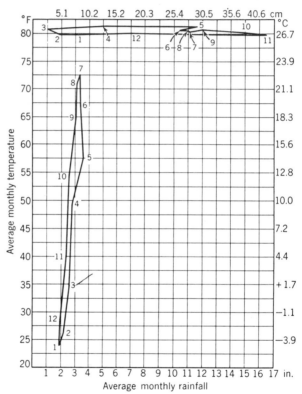

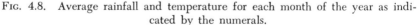

Fɪɢ. 4.8. Average rainfall and temperature for each month of the year as indicated by the numerals.

Lower figure: temperate climate—data for Chicago, Illinois.
Upper figure: tropical climate—data for Barro Colorado Island,
Panama Canal Zone. (Reprinted with permission from Hesse, Allee, and Schmidt, *Ecological Animal Geography*, 1951, John Wiley and Sons, New York.)

important part, is the loss of water. Of the rain that falls upon the surface of the soil, part runs off immediately, part sinks in, and another portion is lost by evaporation. The amount of moisture at any one time and place depends upon the relative rates of the supply of water to the soil and evaporation from it—another example of an ecological factor whose value depends upon an equilibrium. In evaluating the water factor in the terrestrial environment both supply and loss processes must be taken into account.

Moisture in the Soil. Since the terrestrial environment is so varied, it is not surprising that the water factor is very complex, and the moisture in the soil and in the air will first be considered separately. When rain water enters the soil, it fills the spaces between the particles. The volume that can be filled is known as the *pore space* and commonly varies between 60 per cent for heavy soils and 40 per cent for light soils. When the rain ceases, a certain portion of the water in the soil soon drains out, and this is known as the *gravitational water*. The portion of the soil water that is held by capillary forces around and between the particles is the *capillary water*. That part of the pore space which is not filled by gravitational or capillary water may be occupied by water vapor. Another form of soil water, termed the *hygroscopic water*, occurs as an extremely thin film on the soil grains but this cannot move as a liquid. A small portion of the soil water is chemically bound with soil materials and is known as *combined water*. The total amount of capillary, hygroscopic, and combined water plus the water vapor constitutes the *field capacity* and is the maximum amount of water that the soil can hold after the gravitational water has drained away (Fig. 4.9).

The maximum potential supply of water available for the vegetation is represented by the full field capacity of the soil. As plants draw on the soil water, they gradually reduce the amount held in capillary spaces. Below a certain moisture content plants tend to wilt in the hottest part of the day. When the capillary water has been still further depleted, a point is reached at which the plants will not recover from wilting until more water is added to the soil, regardless of other environmental conditions. At this point absorption of water by the plants has become too slow to replace the water lost by transpiration. The moisture then remaining in the soil is designated as the *permanent wilting percentage*, or the *wilting coefficient*. Since little difference has been found in the abundance of soil water when wilting occurs for plants of various species growing in the same soil, the permanent wilting percentage is primarily a characteristic of the soil, and as such has great ecological significance. The amount of water between the full field capacity, as a maximum, and the wilting coefficient, as a minimum, represents the *available water*. As indicated in Fig. 4.9, a considerable amount of water may still remain in the soil after the wilting coefficient has been reached. A fraction of the capillary water, the hygroscopic water, and the combined water, as well as the water vapor, cannot be obtained by the plant, and these constitute the *non-available water*.

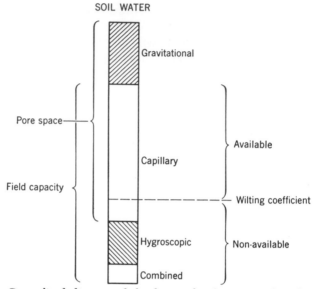

Fig. 4.9. Generalized diagram of the forms of soil water. The relative proportions and the value of the wilting coefficient differ according to the nature of the soil.

Soils vary considerably in the relative proportions of the different categories of soil water. In some instances the amount of non-available water may actually be larger than the available water. The fact that a portion of the water in the soil is unavailable to land organisms and that water in the sea is unavailable to aquatic organisms not adapted to its osmotic pressure contributes further to the general concept of the universality of the water problem. From the ecological point of view the actual amount of water present in any habitat is not as important as its availability.

Moisture in the Air. For many terrestrial organisms the moisture in the soil is chiefly important as constituting the principal source of water, whereas the moisture in the air is mainly significant as controlling the loss of water. For this reason the *absolute humidity*, or

total amount of water in the air, is generally of far less ecological
consequence, than the *relative humidity*. The ecologist therefore
focuses his attention on the relative humidity or the amount of moisture in the air as a percentage of the amount which the air could hold
at saturation at the existing temperature. Since the capacity of air
for water vapor increases with temperature, the relative humidity of
the atmosphere is reduced in any situation in which an increase of
temperature occurs without an accompanying increase in the total
moisture content of the air.

In the terrestrial environment the ecological effect of the water
factor is consequently strongly influenced by the temperature factor.
Of two regions having the same rainfall the warmer is the drier in
the ecological sense (Fig. 4.10). The climate of a locality with a

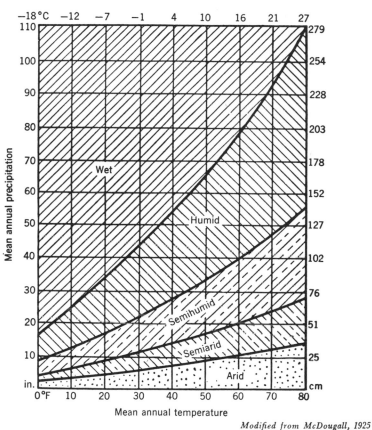

Modified from McDougall, 1925

Fig. 4.10. Schematic representation of the influence of rainfall and temperature
on climate.

mean annual precipitation of 50 cm would be characterized as humid if the mean annual temperature were $-7°C$ or less. On the other hand, another locality with the same rainfall would be regarded as having a semiarid climate if the annual temperature were 21°C or more. The contrast in climate between the Canadian prairie and the Mexican desert, both with about 50 cm of rain but with very different temperature conditions, is an excellent illustration of this principle.

The geographical variation in relative humidity is very great. Relative humidities of 80 to 100 per cent characterize the tropical rain forest. Regions reporting values of less than 50 per cent are regarded as having dry climates, and those with values of less than 20 per cent are extremely arid. It is of interest to note in passing that in cold winter weather the relative humidity inside our houses is rarely higher than 35 per cent.

At any one locality the relative humidity may remain relatively constant for long periods of time or may vary widely. On many oceanic islands the humidity is very nearly the same throughout the year. In other localities, characterized by wet and dry seasons, the humidity fluctuates widely from one part of the year to another. In certain situations as on the plains and in desert regions considerable changes in moisture content may occur during the course of each day. Records made in a short-grass prairie in the United States showed a variation from a relative humidity of less than 30 per cent in the early afternoon to more than 95 per cent in the middle of the night (Fig. 4.11). Obviously animals and plants living in such habitats must be equipped to withstand these rapid and extensive changes in the water factor, and their lives must be attuned to them. In deserts where daytime humidities are extremely low and evaporation is excessive, the greater relative humidity at night helps to relieve the critical moisture condition. Many desert animals take advantage of this situation by going abroad only during hours of darkness; in some desert plants the stomata open only at night when transpiration loss is at a minimum.

The foregoing has been a brief description of the amount of moisture in the air in terms of its relative humidity. As already implied, the chief ecological significance of the relative humidity is its effect on the rate of water loss. Terrestrial animals and plants lose water directly to the air by evaporation and transpiration. The water supply in their substratum is also reduced by direct evaporation from the soil and indirectly by the transpiration of the vegetation. Evaporation takes place very rapidly from soil because of the great surface area presented by the fine particles and causes the drying of the upper layers. Water is lost from the deeper layers chiefly by absorption by roots and attendant transpiration.

The magnitude of water loss by transpiration is often not appreciated. Perhaps some idea can be obtained from the fact that a hectare (2½ acres) of mature oak trees will transpire as much as 25,000 liters of water per day. This volume would be equivalent to a layer of water 0.25 cm deep over the whole area. In other words, if transpiration continued at this rate for 10 days, a rainfall of at least 2.5 cm would be required to restore the water. One might think that the maximum rate of water loss would occur from saturated soil or from a pond. Actually the rate of water loss per unit area from the ground due to the transpiration of the vegetation may be nearly twice as great as that from a free water surface due to evaporation.

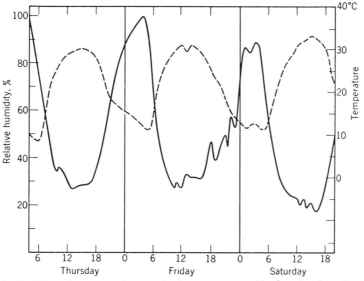

Fig. 4.11. Hygrothermograph record of temperature (*broken line*) and relative humidity (*solid line*) in the short-grass plains of central United States during 3 days in early July. (By permission from *Plant Ecology* by Weaver and Clements, 1938, McGraw-Hill Book Co.)

Three atmospheric conditions that greatly modify the rates of evaporation and transpiration are the saturation deficit, the temperature, and the wind velocity. The *saturation deficit* is the difference between the actual vapor pressure and the maximum possible vapor pressure at the existing temperature. The saturation deficit thus gives more information of ecological significance than the relative humidity alone since the saturation deficit provides a measure of the capacity of the air to take up additional moisture. An increase in the saturation deficit produces a rise in evaporation rate.

An increase in temperature similarly speeds up the evaporation process. A good indication of the magnitude of this influence is obtained from the amounts by which reservoirs are lowered in regions of different temperatures. During one year the water level in a reservoir in Ontario dropped 38 cm, a reservoir in California lost 2.4 m, and one in Egypt was lowered 3.6 m through evaporation alone. The distribution of plants often reveals the influence of temperature on direct and indirect water loss. On mountain slopes vegetation zones are found at different altitudes according to the exposure to the heat of the sun. Moisture-demanding species are restricted to higher levels on the side of the mountain toward the equator than they are on the cooler opposite side. The variation in the amount of rain required for a good growth of short grass furnishes another illustration of the effect of temperature. In Montana a precipitation of about 35 cm is sufficient, but in northwestern Texas a rainfall of 53 cm is needed to produce the same amount of grass. The explanation of this fact is easily apparent when it is realized that evaporation in the 6 summer months in Montana amounts to 84 cm, whereas in Texas it averages 137 cm (Weaver and Clements, 1938).

The wind velocity also exerts a major effect on the loss of water. With a gentle zephyr of only 8 km per hr the transpiration of plants is increased 20 per cent over that which they exhibited in still air. A wind velocity of 16 km per hr increases the transpiration by 35 per cent and one of 24 km per hr increases it by 50 per cent. The desiccating action of warm dry winds sometimes prevents the invasion of windward mountain slopes by vegetation that grows perfectly well on the leeward sides of the same slopes where water loss is much reduced. The harmful effect of excessive evaporation caused by the wind may also be seen in one's own garden. Here winter killing is occasionally due not to very low temperatures, but to a combination of wind and high temperatures! If a warm, dry wind blows for too long a period when the ground is frozen, the plants may lose water faster than their roots can obtain it and they will succumb as a result.

Our discussion of moisture in the soil and in the air has indicated that living organisms—particularly the higher plants—may exert a profound reciprocal influence on the water conditions in the terrestrial environment. Water is a highly modifiable factor in land habitats, and living elements may act either to augment or to diminish the amount of moisture present. Vegetation tends to catch the rain, so that, if the precipitation comes in short showers, the rain may never reach the soil. The plant cover also tends to reduce the water content of the deeper layers of the soil as a consequence of its transpiration, but at the same time it adds moisture to the air. On the other hand, the presence of forest vegetation favors the reduction of evaporation at levels near the ground because it lowers the temperature, slows down the wind, and sometimes causes increased condensation.

The amount of water present at any point in a land habitat and the rates of gain and loss are thus seen to be the result of the equilibrium of processes both climatic and biological. The interrelations of the water factor and the vegetation are frequently very complicated and are the subject of elaborate studies beyond the scope of this book. For further information the reader is referred to such treatments as Daubenmire (1947, Ch. 3). In addition to presenting the general picture, the present discussion reveals the interdependency of vegetation and moisture as another outstanding example of the organism and the environment acting as a reciprocating system.

Microclimates

In the foregoing discussion of the variation in water loss under various conditions of humidity, temperature, and wind the values given were often those characteristic of extensive areas. Very frequently, however, the values of these factors in the immediate surroundings of the organism differ markedly from the regional values. In other words, the immediate climate of the organism is often sharply different from the average climate of the region as reported by standard meteorological records. The realization of this fact has led to the development by ecologists of the concept of the *microclimate*. In considering the effect of climatic influences on plants and animals it is absolutely essential to measure the environmental factors as they actually reach the organism. The effective climate, upon which the life of the organism depends, is its microclimate. The characteristics of the microclimate may, or may not, be similar to the regional climate (Geiger, 1950).

Local variations in climatic factors of concern to many organisms may involve distances of several meters in the surroundings, but the microclimates of forms living in the soil, in rock crevices, under the bark of trees, or in similar confined habitats often have dimensions measured in fractions of a centimeter. The concept of microclimates is particularly important in relation to moisture because relative humidity varies widely within short distances in any irregular habitat.

In swampy woodland, for example, measurements have shown that a high rate of evaporation characteristically exists near the tops of the trees. At half this height the evaporation rate was reduced to 30 per cent in one instance. Lower down, near the damp soil, the animals and plants were subject to an evaporation rate of only 7 per cent of that near the treetops. We are consequently not surprised to find that this vertical change in moisture, as well as vertical gradients in light and in other factors, contributes toward the establishment of a characteristic vertical layering by species of the vegetation and sometimes also of the arboreal animal life in forests. Among animals the difference in evaporation rate with distance above the ground is of particular importance to soft-bodied insects. Many of these are known to move higher in the vegetation at night, but during the day they are forced by excessive evaporation to retreat to lower levels.

Contrasting values for the rate of water loss in two microclimates were reported in an interesting experiment performed in the Middle West. Two sets of green ash seedlings were planted in pots; one set was placed in the midst of a sumac thicket, and the other set was put out on the open prairie only a short distance away. At the end of 8 days the first group of seedlings was found to have lost an average of 0.38 grams of water per sq cm of leaf surface. The seedlings set out in the adjoining prairie had lost 0.88 grams of water per sq cm, or more than twice as much during the same period.

A traditional method of finding the approximate direction of north in the woods is by observing on which side of tree trunks the growth of green "moss" is thickest. In the North Temperate Zone in habitats in which the atmospheric moisture is near the critical point, algae and other non-vascular plants are characteristically more abundant on the north surfaces of tree trunks, because the higher evaporation due to insolation effectively retards growth on the south side. However, in many situations differences in exposure to wind may outweigh the effect of the sun in causing excessive water loss. Thus, although the "north side" rule does not always hold, direct measurements show that the growth of epiphytic moss is a very sensitive indicator of microclimate, and the striking differences in the growth of algae on opposite sides of tree trunks can be seen by anyone who walks through the woods. An average value for the moisture condition of the forest would give no inkling of these small-scale ecological differences of crucial importance to the species concerned.

The burrows of desert animals furnish another example of a microclimate in which the physical conditions are radically different from those of the region as a whole. When the kangaroo rat retreats within its burrow, it breathes air two to five times more humid than that outside. Measurements indicate that, if this animal remained out of its burrow continuously, the rate of evaporation from its lungs would exceed the rate at which it could obtain water, and the resulting water loss would eventually cause death. Temperatures in desert burrows have been found to be as low as 28°C at the same time that values for the surface of the soil surpassed 71°C (cf Table 9). Such critical differences in temperature and in other factors in microclimates will be considered further in subsequent chapters.

Meeting Water Problem on Land

Land plants can live only where sufficient water reaches them either through the air or through the soil. Some species can get along with relatively small amounts of water, and these plants, inhabiting deserts and other arid regions, are termed *xerophytes*. Plants eke out an existence on a reduced water supply in a variety of ways. Certain annual plants are adapted to maintain themselves in desert areas by remaining in the seed stage during the dry season and then passing rapidly through their life cycles when a rainy period occurs. Other desert plants, like the cacti, store water in succulent organs in sufficient quantities to tide them over long intervals of drought. In addition, various species of non-succulent perennials, such as the creosote bush, sage brush, and many grasses are included among the xerophytes because they possess unusual ability to endure long periods of permanent wilting—in some instances running into years. Lichens and some mosses similarly can survive a surprising degree of drying out. Plants with water relations intermediate between those of the xerophytes and the hydrophytes are classified as *mesophytes*.

Since land animals can move about, they can actively seek pools of water from which to drink or can obtain water in the form of snow or dew. Many are able to endure long periods between visits to the water supply. Some terrestrial animals, such as frogs and toads, have the ability to absorb water through their skins from damp surroundings, whereas others find sufficient liquid water in the tissue fluids of their food. Another method of solving the problem of securing water in dry land habitats, and one employed widely by the insects, is the use of *metabolic water*, that is, the water resulting from the chemical breakdown of food materials. The clothes moth and the meal worm have the ability to obtain metabolic water in sufficient quantity to enable them to live their whole lives without any access to free water in the environment. Experiments indicate that the

kangaroo rat of the Arizona desert may similarly secure the whole of
its water supply as a metabolic by-product of its food (Schmidt-
Nielsen, 1950).

Just as important as methods for obtaining water are means for
resisting desiccation. Many of the same general types of adaptations
having this effect have appeared in the course of evolution amongst
both plants and animals. First and most obvious is the possession
of a more or less impervious covering for the body. The cuticle of
plants, the skin of birds and mammals, the exoskeleton of insects, and
the mucous secretion of mollusks are examples. Another means for
avoiding the excessive loss of water is the reduction of body surface.
The leafless plants of the desert are an instance of this plan carried
to an extreme. Other plants fold their leaves or turn them edgewise
to the   scorching heat of the sun. Many terrestrial invertebrates
bury part or all of their bodies to reduce evaporation. It is well
known that the termites which attack our houses are killed by exposure
to dry air, but these pests can cross exposed foundations by constructing runways within which protection from excessive evaporation is af-
forded. In arid regions many of the smaller animals are active only
during the night when drying is less intense.

Water may also be saved by reducing the loss in respiratory and
excretory systems. Respiratory organs are often enclosed within a
cavity as has already been mentioned in relation to the gills of land
crabs. Lungs are commonly located well within the body with only
a small opening to the exterior. The branching tubular tracheal system of the insects is another example, and in many forms the size of
the external openings of the tracheae may be reduced by the spiracles.
In a similar way evaporation from the internal cavities of the plant
leaf is restricted by the guard cells of the stomata.

Reduction in the amount of liquid needed for excretion is a physiological adaptation that also aids the body in conserving water. Many
animals with little available moisture in their habitats and in their
food produce dry faeces. Furthermore, in the interest of saving
water, it is desirable for land dwellers to dispose of their nitrogenous
wastes with the minimum quantity of liquid urine. Mammals accomplish something in this direction by reabsorbing part of the water
in the urine before it is excreted. The ultimate attainment in this
matter is reached by those birds, reptiles, and insects that are able to
excrete nitrogenous wastes as solid uric acid practically without
water loss.

If lack of water becomes still more acute, it may be necessary for
the organism to go into a dormant condition in which its need for

water and its loss of water will be reduced. In the tropics many trees shed their leaves during the dry season. Other plants pass periods of drought as seeds or as spores. Many lower animals form cysts of one sort or another. Terrestrial mollusks close their shells with a thin epiphragm of secreted mucus, and more highly organized animals, such as the ground squirrels, go into a state of torpor in their burrows. Dormancy of this sort occurring under conditions of heat and drought is referred to as *aestivation,* and is found characteristically in desert and tropical communities. Using various combinations of the methods for procuring and conserving water discussed above, plants and animals in arid habitats may live for months or years without rain or access to free water.

Influence of Moisture on Growth and Distribution

The growth of plants is often more directly and obviously affected by the water factor on land than is that of animals. The availability of moisture influences not only the rate of plant growth but also the growth form. Since the roots of most land species will not grow into saturated soil nor into soil devoid of available water, plants will be shallow rooted either if the water table is high or, in the contrasting situation, if the soil water is limited to the uppermost layer. In the latter case growth will be confined to the rainy season. The growth of plants whose roots extend to the permanently moist subsoil are largely independent of rain periodicity.

Competition for water and the horizontal spread of roots often control the spacing of plants in regions where water shortage is critical. The extent of the root system in a typical cactus is shown in Fig. 4.12. The roots are seen to be spread widely just beneath the surface of the soil where they can absorb whatever rain falls before it evaporates. This cactus will capture all the available moisture within the area shown and prevent any other perennial plant from gaining foothold in close proximity. Desert vegetation is often spaced out in a strikingly regular pattern as a result of this intense root warfare for water.

The water factor also controls the geographical distribution of plants on both small and large scales. Such trees as willows and cottonwoods are characteristically limited to the moist banks of water courses because their seeds will not survive more than a few days unless the soil upon which they fall is wet. The seeds of other species can remain dormant in a completely dry condition for months or years but will germinate only when sufficient water is available in the soil immediately surrounding them. In other instances the critical period

for the survival of a plant in relation to its water need may occur
during adult life.   Plants differ greatly in the amounts of water that
they must absorb from the soil and transpire.   Those with a high
water requirement, or *transpiration ratio,* are limited to habitats where
the supply of moisture is adequate.

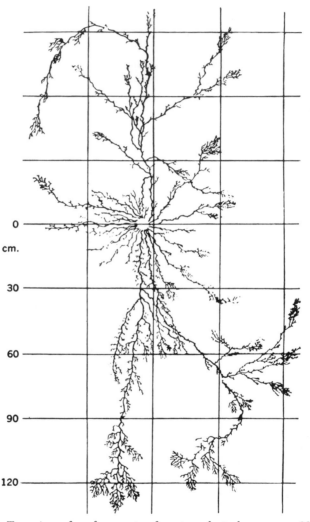

FIG. 4.12.   Top view of surface roots of cactus plant shown on a 30-cm grid.
Almost the entire absorbing system of roots occurred in the upper 2 to 10 cm of
soil.   (By permission from *Plant Ecology* by Weaver and Clements, 1938, Mc-
Graw-Hill Book Co.).

Differential ability to withstand drought will also play its role in controlling geographical distribution. If the soil moisture drops below the permanent wilting coefficient, most annuals and other tender plants will die within a matter of hours or days unless the soil water is renewed. On the other hand, succulents and plants that can aestivate are able to withstand varying periods of drought extending into years with some species. Thus the duration of drought periods is of crucial importance in determining whether a region may be inhabited by different plant types.

Local differences in the moisture factor were clearly shown to influence the species composition of the forest vegetation in a study made in Indiana (Potzger, 1939). A series of observations in a line running from north to south over a ridge revealed the fact that soil moisture was 20 per cent higher on the north side of the ridge than on the south side. Moreover, the rate of evaporation was more than twice as great at stations on the south slope than at those on the north slope. Quadrat counts of the number of trees on the two sides of the ridge gave the tabulated results. Although other ecological factors

Species	North Slope	South Slope
Maple	202	31
Beech	112	0
White oak	0	80
Black oak	0	70
Hickory	4	44

undoubtedly played some part, moisture conditions were chiefly responsible for the very pronounced differences in the occurrence of the various species on the two sides of the ridge.

Another example of the control of distribution by the moisture factor, and one on a much larger scale, is found in the regional occurrence of the natural vegetation in the United States. A glance at Fig. 4.13 will reveal the fact that in the central part of the country, leaving out of account the irregularities due to the mountains, the zones of principal vegetation types tend to run north and south. In the eastern part of the continent the typical natural vegetation is forest (in areas where man has not interfered). West of the forest zone is a belt of tall-grass prairie, and beyond that, running from Montana and North Dakota down to Texas is a zone of short-grass rangeland. Still farther westward lies the desert belt. These fundamental zones are indicated schematically in Figure 4.14.

This zonation is obviously not controlled primarily by temperature since the temperature belts are seen to run generally east and west,

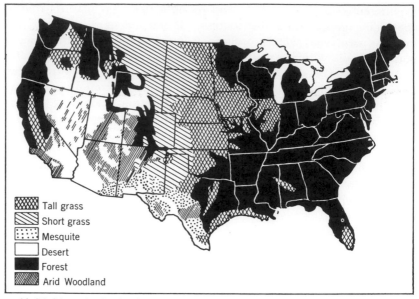

Modified from the Graphic Summary of American Agriculture, U. S. Department of Agriculture

Fig. 4.13.   The distribution of the natural vegetation in the United States.

if we again leave out of account the mountain and coastal regions (Fig. 5.14).   Similarly, no good correlation will be found between the occurrence of these principal zones of vegetation and the annual precipitation taken by itself.   As already explained, regional differences in evaporation must also be considered, and water loss in turn depends in part on temperature.   Both the supply and the loss

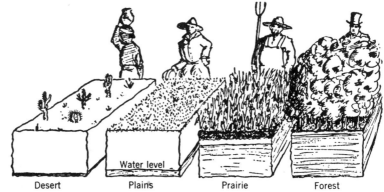

Fig. 4.14.   Schematic representation of the four fundamental vegetational zones in central United States (from *This is Our World* by Sears, 1937, Univ. of Oklahoma Press).

aspects of moisture conditions may be taken into account by calculating precipitation-evaporation ratios for the "frostless season," i.e., the growing season for plants between the last spring frost and the first autumn frost. The pattern of the distribution of these ratios in the United States (Fig. 4.15) shows a general agreement with the occurrence of the major vegetation zones. The natural forest vegetation of the eastern part of the country occurs where the precipitation-evaporation ratios are high. In the Southeast and Northeast, the P-E ratio exceeds 100 per cent; that is, more rain falls during the course of the average frostless season than evaporates. Incidentally, this fact accounts in part for the excessive amount of soil leaching in these regions. In the Middle West precipitation-evaporation ratios between 80 and 100 per cent exist. Values below 100 per cent indicate that the potential rate of water loss is greater than the rate of water supply. The line representing a P-E ratio of 60 per cent runs almost due south from the Dakotas to the southernmost point of Texas. It will be noted that this line agrees closely with the division between the tall-grass prairies and the short-grass rangelands. The 60 per cent line also approximates the position of the division between the pedocals and the pedalfers discussed earlier. P-E ratios of less than 20 per cent are found in the southwestern states, and their occurrence corresponds to the distribution of the desert vegetation.

In view of the modifying influence on plant distribution of such

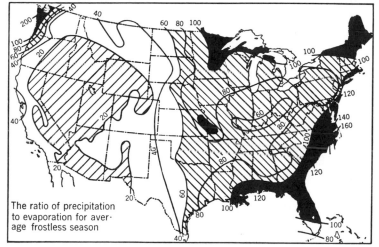

The ratio of precipitation to evaporation for average frostless season

Modified from Livingston and Shreve, 1921

FIG. 4.15. The precipitation-evaporation ratio indicated as a percentage for the average frostless season in the United States.

factors as soil type and temperature and of the interdependence of these factors with moisture it is clear that no simple relation between the type of vegetation and any single physical influence can be expected. However, the broad correspondence between the zones of vegetation and the availability of moisture will suffice to emphasize the major role of the water factor in the region under discussion in controlling both the soil and the plant life that develops with it. The application of the P-E ratios to these distributional problems has again brought into relief the fact that the balance between supply and loss is the most crucial aspect of the moisture factor for the vegetation.

The water factor on land also seriously affects the growth and distribution of animals either directly or indirectly. Since the range of land animals is profoundly influenced by the vegetation, moisture often exerts its greatest effect on animals indirectly through its control of the plants. For the higher vertebrates temperature is generally a more important direct environmental influence than moisture. However, it has long been known that races of birds and mammals in warm humid regions tend to be darker in color than races inhabiting the cooler or drier parts of the geographical range of the species. This generality is known as *Gloger's rule,* but many exceptions exist and the relative effects of heat and moisture are not known. There is evidence that humidity acts more through the color of the soil as a background for the animals than in a direct way. The implications of Gloger's rule will be discussed in more detail below in relation to temperature and light.

For amphibians and for insects and other terrestrial invertebrates moisture is often of great direct importance. Many insects exhibit critical dependence upon humidity conditions with sharp limits of tolerance. For example, the "silverfish" (*Lepisma saccharina*), a common household insect pest, finds optimum conditions for reproduction at relative humidities of 85 to 90 per cent. The newly hatched nymphs die if they are subjected to relative humidities of less than 70 per cent, and they also succumb if their surfaces once become wet. The relationship of insects to moisture is frequently very complex and varies greatly in different species and sometimes even in different parts of the life cycle of the same species (cf. Chapman, 1931, Ch. 4). In the development of the flour beetle *Tribolium* the larval stage is accelerated by an increase in relative humidity, but the duration of the egg and pupa stages is unaffected by wide changes in this factor (Fig. 4.16). Moisture produces entirely different effects upon the survival of this insect. In the larval stage increasing humidities tend to improve survival, but the egg and pupa stages are affected to only a slight extent by relative humidities up to 70 per cent.   However, at humidities above 80 per cent the viability of eggs and pupae drops very sharply.

When the moisture conditions of the environment become adverse, the animals concerned either die or must migrate longer or shorter distances to more favorable locations.   Droughts greatly reduce the occurrence of some species temporarily, or for long periods, by decimating the population.   Locomotor activity, as well as feeding and other reactions, are controlled by humidity in certain animals, especially insects.   It is known that in some instances increased activity without orientation results from a change in moisture conditions; in

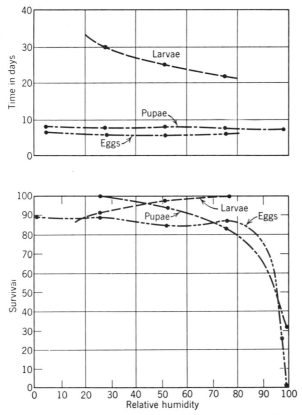

Fig. 4.16.   Duration (*upper*) and survival (*lower*) of the indicated stages of *Tribolium confusum* at different relative humidities under constant temperature of 27°C (by permission from *Animal Ecology* by Chapman, 1931, McGraw-Hill Book Co.).

other instances animals are able to respond directionally to a humidity gradient. However, the whole problem of control of locomotion by moisture in land animals calls for further investigation.

The discussion of water relations in this chapter emphasizes the universality of the water problem. Plants and animals in aquatic, amphibious, and terrestrial situations are faced with the difficulty of providing for water exchange and at the same time maintaining the proper water balance. The amount of water present in the environment and its transfer into and out of the organism are results of an equilibrium of forces. In the terrestrial environment the organisms themselves, especially the plants, can affect the amount of moisture in their surroundings. The total amount of water is not of as great significance as its availability. In some situations the environment tends to extract water from the plant or animal at an alarming rate. If the organisms cannot obtain water fast enough and retain it in sufficient quantity, the lack of this essential material becomes a critical limiting factor.

5

Temperature

Temperature is perhaps the most commonly familiar ecological factor. The great variation in heat conditions and their general influence are evident to everyone. In contrast to many ecological factors temperature may be measured with relative ease. Temperature is a universal influence and is frequently a limiting factor for the growth or distribution of animals and plants. Even when an organism is dormant, the chemical processes going on in its body are controlled by the existing temperature. This factor is also important indirectly as modifying the effects of other ecological agents.

Temperature is the intensity aspect of heat energy. The capacity aspect of this form of energy will also be considered in this chapter. Differences in the heat capacity of the media, of the various types of substrata, and of the bodies of organisms themselves are significant in controlling susceptibility to temperature change. The amount of heat in an ice-covered lake may change considerably without any alteration of temperature, but in most natural situations increase or decrease in heat also affects the temperature. Both aspects of heat energy must be kept in mind, but temperature has the more predominant direct influence on the lives of organisms.

DISTRIBUTION OF TEMPERATURE

Extremes of Temperature and of Tolerance

In considering heat conditions in natural environments the extremes of temperature may first be reviewed. In the open water of the aquatic environment the temperature cannot drop below the freezing point. This means that the temperature of the water in ponds is never lower than 0°C and in the ocean never lower than about

—2.5°C. The maximum temperature in marine environments of any size is probably represented by records of 36°C in the Persian Gulf. In tide pools of the littoral zone and in shallow bodies of fresh water temperatures may go higher.

On land the record for the lowest temperature is held by a locality in the north interior of Siberia where the thermometer was read at —70°C (—93.6°F) in 1947. Temperatures almost as low were reported for a northern outpost in the Yukon territory. At the other end of the scale air temperatures ranging above 60°C (140°F) are recorded in desert areas. Desert soils have been found to rise as high as 84°C when exposed to the noonday sun. The water in hot springs and geysers may approach 100°C, and even higher temperatures occur sporadically in the very special situations presented by volcanic areas.

Are these environmental temperatures beyond the ranges that can be tolerated by animals and plants? Birds and mammals are warm-blooded animals, or *homoiotherms,* that maintain their own constant internal temperature, and their tissues are insulated from the heat or cold of the outside world. All other animals are cold-blooded forms or *poikilotherms.* The tissues of these animals and of all plants, which are also poikilothermous, tend to approach the temperature of their immediate surroundings and to vary with external thermal conditions. No organism can continue to live in an active condition at temperatures below those at which its tissues freeze. As we shall see below, the freezing points of living tissues differ widely, but no poikilothermous animal or plant can actually grow at continuing temperatures lower than a few degrees below 0°C. At the other end of the thermal scale we find certain blue-green algae and thermophilous bacteria growing happily in hot springs, such as those in Yellowstone Park, at 80 to 88°C! However, relatively few poikilotherms can live permanently at temperatures above about 45°C, and Brues (1927, 1939) found no reliable records for poikilothermous animals above 52°C.

It appears from the foregoing that the whole range of temperature in the sea is within the limits of tolerance of many plants and animals. In contrast, land temperatures may be far below or far above the temperatures that can be withstood by organisms in an active condition. Since the range of heat conditions sustained successfully by individual species is very much less, temperature extremes present a problem on both land and sea. The homoiothermous animals form a special case since the thermal range that they can tolerate is generally much greater than that of other animals and of plants, but even this group has definite limits of toleration. We shall be concerned, then, with the limiting action of extreme temperatures, as well as with the controlling action of intermediate temperatures for all kinds of plants and animals.

Changes in Temperature

Changes in Time. Let us consider first the temperature changes to which an animal or plant may be exposed if it remains in the same place. Time changes in temperature are controlled by various astronomical and climatic cycles. Within a few hours the sun may move so as to change the exposure of a sessile form from direct sunlight to shade. On land a very great difference in the heat received may occur within a short period of time. In the water environment the change from sun to shade produces only a minor effect—less than 0.1°C at a depth of 5 m.

Similarly, the diurnal fluctuation in temperature is very much damped in the aquatic environment. In a body of water of any considerable size differences between day and night are commonly less than 1°C. The maximum diurnal change in the ocean is about 4°C, and with increasing depth the amplitude is reduced. Probably no diurnal temperature change is detectable below a depth of 15 m.

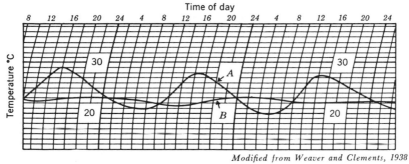

Modified from Weaver and Clements, 1938

Fig. 5.1. Portion of a soil thermogram made in June on the prairie near Lincoln, Nebraska, showing the temperature fluctuations at depths of (A) 7.6 cm and (B) 30 cm.

The temperature of the air near the surface of the land is sometimes 17°C higher in the daytime than at night, and in desert localities this difference may be as much as 40°C. A still greater diurnal range in temperature is reported for the surface of the soil in desert areas. In every situation the amplitude of the change from day to night in the soil is reduced with depth. The soil thermogram shown in Fig. 5.1 illustrates this point and also reveals the lag in the time of occurrence of the maximum and minimum daily temperatures. At a depth of only 30 cm the highest temperature of the day occurred near midnight and the lowest temperature occurred near noon!

In the tidal zone changes in temperature are the result of a combination of the differences in the amount of heat delivered from the sun and of differences in the temperature of the air and of the water. All organisms living between tide marks are subject to rapidly changing temperatures that may test their tolerance to the limit. At one locality on the coast of Maine the temperature of the mud exposed at low tide was observed to rise to 38°C under the midday summer sun. A short time later plants and animals living in this area were flooded by the incoming tide with a temperature of 10°C. In the winter when the tide is out these organisms might be exposed to temperatures as low as −25°C. The occurrence of these extreme and rapid fluctuations in temperature adds to the rigorous conditions of the tidal zone.

Plants and animals are also concerned with seasonal cycles of temperature. In both tropical and polar seas the intensity of heat does not vary by more than about 5°C throughout the year. In the temperate seas, however, changes of 10 to 15°C from summer to winter are common, and sometimes seasonal differences of 23°C or more are observed. At increasing depths in the water these differences become less. Measurements off Portsmouth, New Hampshire, where there was a 15-degree change in the surface temperature showed no measurable variation from summer to winter below a depth of 140 m. Probably more than 95 per cent of the oceanic environment exhibits no seasonal change in temperature that is of significance to living organisms. In lakes and ponds seasonal fluctuations are generally greater than those found in the sea. Springs, however, form a very special fresh-water habitat in which the temperature may vary by only a degree or two the year around. A typical example of the thermal cycle in a lake showing the reduced amplitude in the deeper layers is presented in Fig. 5.2.

On land the seasonal changes in temperature are familiar to everyone and are almost always of ecological significance. The greatest variations are found in continental areas in the temperate zones with lesser seasonal ranges in the tropics and near the coasts. At St. Paul, Minnesota, the average difference between summer and winter is 33.7°C. Possible extremes in range are even greater. From Tibet comes a report of temperatures varying by 77°C from −37°C in the winter to +40°C in the summer. In contrast to the foregoing are certain localities where temperatures vary only slightly throughout

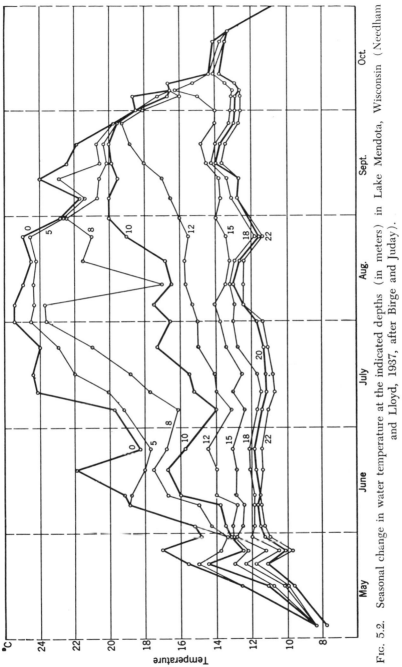

°C

Temperature

FIG. 5.2. Seasonal change in water temperature at the indicated depths (in meters) in Lake Mendota, Wisconsin (Needham and Lloyd, 1937, after Birge and Juday).

the year. At Quito, Ecuador, for example, the average seasonal change is only 0.5°C.

Horizontal Changes. The changes in temperature from place to place over the surface of the globe run the whole gamut of extreme values that have been reviewed. Average temperatures on land are too variable for simple generalization, but a value of 32°C may serve as an approximation for tropical regions and one of −12°C for polar regions. For detailed information a textbook on climatology should be consulted, such as Kendrew (1949). In the sea average temperatures run from about 30°C in the tropics to about −1.5°C in the Arctic and Antarctic Oceans.

Vertical Changes. The temperature of the air varies widely in a vertical direction according to local conditions, but a decrease of about 1°C for every 150 m of altitude is generally found. On Mt. Washington in New Hampshire the tabulated average values were obtained for observations from 1933 to 1940.

	Feb.	July	Year
Pinkham Notch (Altitude 610 m)	− 8.5°C	17.1°C	4.2°C
Summit (Altitude 1915 m)	−14.9	9.9	−2.8
Difference:	6.4°C	7.2°C	7.0°C

The unequal heating of the air horizontally and vertically causes movements of the atmosphere. These are manifested as local winds, trade winds, and storms with consequent further influence on temperature, precipitation, and other ecological factors.

Air is heated at all levels by the solar radiation that it absorbs and similarly may cool at all levels, but the greatest amount of heating and cooling takes place at the bottom. This effect is due to the great transparency of the air and the fact that the surface of the earth is heated faster during the day and cools by radiation more rapidly during the night than the atmosphere. The air in immediate contact with the earth therefore changes temperature more rapidly than strata at greater altitudes. The easy mobility of the atmosphere also contributes to the thermal variations of the air environment. When air overlying heated land masses becomes warm, it tends to rise and to leave the earth's surface, but air chilled by contact with cold earth is heavier and tends to accumulate in hollows of the landscape. In these respects air stands in distinct contrast to the water environment in which heating and cooling take place principally at the upper surface.

The spectral distribution of the energy received from the sun at the earth's surface is shown in Fig. 5.3. It will be seen that about half of the solar radiation is in the infrared region and this represents a direct supply of heat. The visible and ultraviolet portions of the sun's emission will also produce a heating effect after they have become absorbed. The sample calculations in Table 7 illustrate the relative absorption of the various parts of the spectrum by air and water.

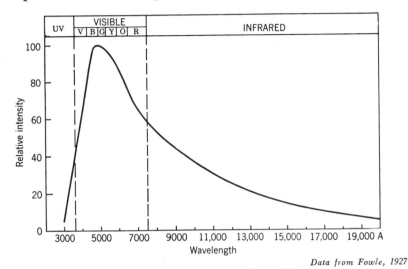

Data from Fowle, 1927

FIG. 5.3. Spectral distribution of solar energy at the earth's surface, showing the ultraviolet (UV), visible (divided into color components), and infrared portions.

TABLE 7

COMPARISON OF RELATIVE ABSORPTION OF SUN'S RADIATION BY AIR AND WATER

	Visible Light at 5500 A		Infrared Radiation at 8000 A	
	Percentage of initial value remaining	Percentage absorbed by each stratum	Percentage of initial value remaining	Percentage absorbed by each stratum
Outside atmosphere	100		100	
		} 7		} 3
Mt. Whitney, California (summit 4420 m)	93		97	
		} 20		} 9
Sea level	75		88	
		} 5		} 98
2 m below surface	71		2	
		} 70		—
30 m below surface (clearest ocean water)	17		—	

The data show that the atmosphere absorbs radiation of short wavelength faster than that of long wavelength, whereas water is most transparent to radiation in the central part of the visible region. In all parts of the spectrum radiation is absorbed by water at far higher rates than by air, and the contrast is particularly great in the infrared. The absorption by a few meters of water is enormously greater than by several thousand meters of air. In general we can say that in comparison with the atmosphere the water medium is almost opaque to the sun's radiation.

Because of the differences in mobility and transparency of the two media we find that the vertical temperature changes in the water environment are controlled differently from those in the air. Radiation from the sun is the only important source of heat for natural bodies of water. Tests have shown that no significant exchange of heat takes place between the water and the mud of the bottom. Since solar radiation is absorbed in the upper strata of water, water bodies receive heat only at their upper surfaces. Cooling of water can take place through radiation, evaporation, or the melting of ice. All of these processes occur at the surface in natural water bodies. Generally speaking, the seas and the inland waters gain and lose their heat primarily at the top.

It is not surprising to find as a consequence of the foregoing that in deep bodies of water the major changes in temperature are limited to the surface strata. In some situations these changes are superimposed on a deeper, permanent temperature structure. In the temperate and tropical regions of the sea a permanent thermal gradient has been produced between the *mixed layer* near the surface and the *deep layer* filling the bottom of ocean basins. The depth and extent of the zone of relatively rapid temperature change, known as the *permanent thermocline layer,* differ in the various parts of the ocean but an illustrative example is given in Fig. 5.4 for water in the great central eddy of the Atlantic Ocean. From roughly 2000 m down to the bottom the water is everywhere just about 3°C. Since the average depth of the ocean is approximately 4000 m, there is obviously a very large amount of space in which the temperature is uniform month in and month out, year in and year out. If you were a fish restricted to 3°C, you could nonetheless travel over more than 60 per cent of the globe without being exposed to a significantly different temperature.

Although essentially all the incident radiation is received at the surface of natural water bodies, we know that some heat is eventually transferred to deeper layers. How does the heat get there? Radiation from one water layer to another is negligible. Conduction through quiet water is similarly very slow. If all the water in Lake Constance with a depth of 100 m were cooled to 0°C and then the uppermost layer heated to 30°C, more than 100 years would be required for a measurable amount of heat to reach the bottom by radiation and conduction alone. It is obvious that heat can be transferred

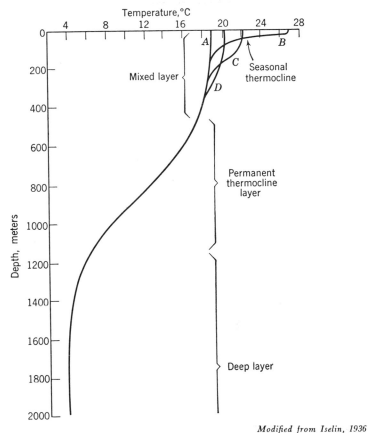

Modified from Iselin, 1936

Fig. 5.4. Permanent vertical temperature structure in the deep water of the central North Atlantic. The seasonal changes in upper layers are indicated: (A) April, (B) August, (C) December, (D) February.

to lower levels only by the actual movement of the water, that is, by vertical circulation.

We are further convinced of this conclusion when we examine situations where vertical circulation has been prevented. When the temperature of the bottom water of a pond has been reduced to 4°C and ice has formed across the surface, no vertical stirring by the wind can take place. Although the air temperature may go far below zero, heat can be lost from the deeper layers of the pond only very slowly because of the insulating action of the ice and the upper strata of water. This is the chief reason why most ponds do not freeze to the bottom during the winter.

Stirring is also inhibited when a sharp density gradient has been developed between the upper strata and the deeper layers. Such a condition arises in situations in which the surface water is warmer or less saline, and hence lighter, than the deeper water. Under these circumstances the vertical stability of the water tends to resist any efforts on the part of the wind and waves to produce stirring, and heat exchanges are consequently limited to the surface. When no important density gradient exists, vertical stirring can become effective and heat will be carried down. This condition commonly occurs during the spring and during the autumn in waters of temperate regions, Under some circumstances the density of the surface stratum may become actually greater than the underlying layers resulting in a gravitational overturn of the water.

Seasonal Changes in Vertical Temperature Structure. The typical temperature cycle in a lake during the course of a year is indicated diagrammatically in Fig. 5.5. Since the maximum density of fresh water occurs at 4°C, any warmer or colder water will float on top of water of this temperature. If the underlying water has a temperature lower than 4°C as it may in the early spring, or higher than 4°C, as it may in the autumn, then a top-heavy condition will develop. Archimedian forces aided by strong winds will then bring about the *spring overturn* and the *fall overturn*. *Winter stagnation* occurs when the lake is ice covered and *summer stratification* is found after a distinct density gradient has been produced by the warming of the surface layers. The layer of rapid vertical temperature change is termed the *thermocline* and in lakes is defined as having a thermal gradient of at least 1°C per m. In lakes the wind-stirred and largely homogenous water layer above the thermocline is known as the *epilimnion* and the relatively stagnant water mass below the thermocline as the *hypolimnion*. The very considerable changes in temperature and the occurrence of stagnation and of circulation which they control exert a profound effect upon the biota of the lake as will be discussed in later sections. For further details on the thermal cycles of lakes the reader should consult a textbook of limnology such as Welch (1952) or Ruttner (1953).

A similar seasonal cycle of temperature occurs in the ocean but the circumstances are somewhat different. For a fuller treatment of the subject reference should be made to a textbook of oceanography such as Sverdrup et al. (1942). In the open ocean the seasonal changes are superimposed upon the permanent thermal structure as relatively minor fluctuations (Fig. 5.4), but in coastal regions the water may be

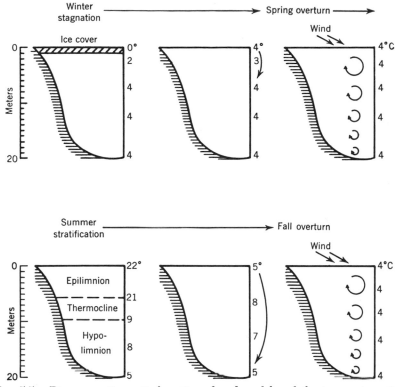

Fig. 5.5. Diagrammatic vertical section of a deep lake of the temperate region, showing the seasonal cycle of temperature (by permission from *Limnology* by Welch, 1952, McGraw-Hill Book Co.)

sufficiently shallow for the seasonal effects to reach the bottom (Fig. 5.6). In this type of situation the thorough stirring of the water during the winter produces a uniform temperature from top to bottom with a minimum value in February for the North Temperate Zone. As spring comes on, the larger supply of solar heat, often combined with lowered salinity due to increased run-off, causes the surface water to become lighter and tends to stabilize the upper layers. This effect is self-accelerating. By August the relatively thin stratum at the top has attained its maximum temperature. Below this layer a sharp thermocline leads to the deeper water which is still quite cold. With the onset of autumn solar radiation has become reduced and the winds have been stronger with the result that the surface waters are stirred downward, and the thermocline is shifted deeper and eventually destroyed. By November the whole water column has become mixed at an intermediate temperature and remains uniform as it cools to its minimum temperature during the winter.

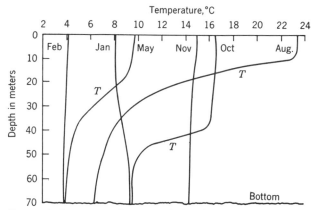

Fig. 5.6. Seasonal changes in the vertical distribution of temperature in coastal water off New York, showing the positions of the thermocline (T) (Modified from Clarke, 1940.)

The radiation received from the sun reaches a maximum in June in the North Temperate Zone, but owing to the lag in the heating effect the highest temperatures on land ordinarily occur in July. At the surface of water the maximum heat of the season is not experienced until August, and in subsurface layers the thermal peak is even more delayed. If you imagine yourself a worm living in the bottom mud in the situation represented by Fig. 5.6, "summer" for you would not begin until November! In similar fashion the seasons are often completely reversed in deep lakes.

This review of the thermal conditions has shown that in the ocean and in lakes there is no temperature too high and no temperature too low for active life of some kind. Temperature changes are much less and much slower than in the terrestrial environment. Furthermore, organisms can usually get out of excessively high or low temperatures by a short journey into deeper water. In these respects life in the water is much easier than life on land. The results of this situation over the ages has been that many oceanic plants and animals have become adapted to a relatively stable temperature.

The disadvantage of this easy life in the water is that when an unusual change in temperature occurs dire results may follow. Many instances are known in which slight temperature changes have caused mass mortality in the aquatic environment. A spectacular example occurred in 1925 off the coast of Peru (Murphy, 1926). In the spring of that year the cool Humboldt Current, which flows northward along the coast, apparently moved slightly offshore, allowing the warm countercurrent, El Niño, to flow farther south than usual, raising the temperature 5 or 6°C above normal. The result was that the plankton and a great many of the local fishes were killed. Larger fishes, dependent upon these smaller forms of life for food, soon afterward succumbed and washed up on the shore in windrows. In addition huge numbers of fish-eating birds died of starvation. Many of these birds inhabited coastal islands where their droppings produced guano deposits of extreme value as fertilizer. Guano production was stopped, and the coast line for miles was strewn with the carcasses of the dead birds. Torrential rains caused by the slight change in ocean temperature washed away tons of guano that had required generations to accumulate. The heavy rainfall also devastated the neighboring ordinarily arid land areas, disrupting the natural fauna and flora, and destroying crops, roads, and buildings. The ecological and economic repercussions of the oceanic change thus extended to the shore and inland. A few months later the ocean currents returned to their normal course, and after a period of years the fauna and flora were gradually restored. This cataclysmic destruction of ocean life off Peru well illustrates the far-reaching consequences of a slight temperature change in a situation where the plants and animals have become adjusted to relatively uniform conditions.

BIOLOGICAL ACTION OF TEMPERATURE

What are the ecological consequences on land and in the water of the thermal conditions that have just been reviewed? Environmental temperature exerts a direct action on the tissues of poikilothermous organisms, that is, of those whose body temperatures vary with the surroundings. The heat exchanges of homoiothermous animals are also affected by external thermal conditions, but the insides of these animals are thermostatically maintained at a nearly constant, and relatively high, temperature.

Extreme Temperatures

Minimum Temperatures. We may consider first the danger to the organism of the freezing, or the actual congealing, of its living tissues. Freezing is likely to produce mechanical harm in the form of the rupture of cell walls and the stoppage of circulation. When ice crystals are formed, they also withdraw water from neighboring areas, producing a condition similar to desiccation in the surrounding cells. No tissue will freeze at 0°C. The concentration of solutes in body fluids and tissue fluids causes a depression of the freezing point with the result that even unprotected protoplasm will not freeze until a temperature a few degrees below zero is reached. For this reason many tissues can be active at 0°C; rye seeds, for example, will germinate on ice.

In situations where the temperature drops considerably below zero the danger of freezing is ever present. Some forms have special adaptations for lowering the freezing point of their tissues still farther so that congealing does not take place until a very low temperature is reached. In addition a few species are able to withstand actual freezing for short periods of time. The green alga, *Chlorella,* while in active vegetative condition, has been frozen at −182°C for 1 hour without harm. At subzero temperatures ice crystals are known to occur in the needles and wood of the Norway spruce, and their presence evidently produces no serious injury to the tree. Among the higher animals the Alaskan blackfish has the ability to recover normal activity after being frozen for periods of 40 minutes at temperatures down to −20°C.

Many plants and animals are killed by temperatures that are too low for them but are nevertheless far above values at which tissues would actually freeze. Similarly, at the other end of the scale we find many instances of death from excessively high temperatures but at values below those producing heat coagulation. Lethal extremes vary greatly from species to species, and the organism as a whole may be killed by a degree of chilling insufficient to cause direct damage to individual protoplasmic structures. Temperatures that are too low for some species may be favorable, or even too high, for others. The English daisy grows and flowers best when subjected to night temperatures below 10°C and dies if kept for long periods above 20°C. In contrast the African violet is killed by long exposure to night temperatures below 10°C and grows best and flowers when the thermometer stands above 20°C (Went, 1950).   Many Arctic fish do not venture south into waters as warm as 10°C, but this same temperature would be far too cold for most tropical fish.

If the tissues do not freeze, why are these animals and plants killed by moderately low temperatures?   Most chemical reactions are slowed down by lowering temperature and eventually stop.   The cessation of any one of the vital processes will cause the death of the organism. However, the various processes going on in the body come to a stop at various points on the temperature scale.   No one biological zero exists for all reactions even within the same individual.   Under some circumstances the organism may die when all the vital processes are still going.   The explanation may be that the different reactions are slowed down by different amounts with the result that mutually dependent processes get out of adjustment and cause the death of the organism.

The minimum temperature for the organism as a whole is thus determined by the most susceptible of the vital processes.   The lowest temperature at which the organism can live indefinitely in an active state is termed the *minimum effective temperature*.   After a further reduction of temperature the organism goes into chill coma.   If too long a period does not elapse before the organism is again warmed, it will become active once more.   The lowest temperature at which survival is possible is called the *minimum survival temperature*.   The actual value of this temperature depends upon the period of exposure. For example, the eggs and larvae of the fruit fly, *Ceratitis capitata*, were killed at 7°C only after an exposure of 7 weeks, but death was caused after 3 weeks at 4°C or after 2 weeks at 1°C.   Accordingly, a statement of the minimum survival temperature for an animal or a plant has no meaning unless the period of exposure is also stated.

Maximum Temperatures.   At the other end of the temperature scale the same sort of situation exists.   The *maximum effective temperature* is the greatest intensity of heat at which the species can live indefinitely in the active state.   The *effective temperature range* within which the organism can carry on its active life and beyond which death eventually results extends between the maximum and minimum effective temperatures.   At higher temperatures the organism goes into heat coma but will recover if restored before too long to cooler conditions.   For the *maximum survival temperature* the period of the exposure of the organism to the specific heat conditions must be given. All these thermal relations are illustrated for the house fly in Table 8.

Methods of Meeting Temperature Extremes

A surprising number of plants and animals can withstand considerable thermal fluctuation but do not possess any special mechanism for meeting the problem of temperature extremes. When the thermometer rises too high or drops too low, these animals and plants must either "take it" or die. This is the situation for most sessile aquatic invertebrates, for many other invertebrates, for many plants, and for some higher animals. As we have seen, getting along without a special temperature adaptation is easily possible for many organisms in the aquatic environment. On land, however, north and south of the killing frost line, and in areas exposed to intense heat, something must be done to survive periods when the temperature exceeds the effective range within which active life can be maintained.

Morphological and Physiological Adaptations. During the course of evolution many specialized structures have been developed that relate to the temperature problem. Certain animals and plants produce spores, cysts, eggs, pupae, or seeds that are capable of resisting thermal extremes. Each of these structures represents a whole organism. In other species special parts of the fully developed organism are resistant to extremes of heat and cold. Such is the situation with the hardy roots and stems of many perennial plants. For example, the tops of grass plants freeze off in winter. Life remains in the stolons and roots of the grass, and from these organs new leaves are produced when warm weather again returns.

TABLE 8

TEMPERATURE RELATIONS OF THE HOUSE FLY, *Musca domestica*

Death	46.5°C	in few minutes	Maximum survival temperature
Heat coma	44.6		
Excessive activity	40.1		
Rapid movement	27.9		⎫ Maximum effective temperature
Normal activity { 23 / 15			⎬ Effective temperature range
Feeble movement	10.8		⎭ Minimum effective temperature
Begins moving	6.7		
Chill coma	6.0		
Death	− 5.0	in 40 minutes	Minimum survival temperature
	− 8.0	in 20 minutes	Minimum survival temperature
	−12.0	in 5 minutes	Minimum survival temperature

In some species physiological changes take place in the tissues that prevent freezing. Osmotic concentration is increased, and water is "bound" in colloid form with the result that the freezing point is depressed below values ordinarily experienced. If you walk through a field of winter rye on a day when the temperature is well below 0°C, you will notice that the leaves and stems are flexible and not brittle as they would be if the tissues were frozen. The completion of these hardening processes takes time, and the actual high or low temperatures that an animal or a plant can withstand often depend upon the interval available for acclimatization. Evergreen trees and many other types of plants similarly become "frost hardy" during the winter. Everyone is familiar with the ability of crocuses, snowdrops, and other spring flowers to withstand frost and even to push up through a layer of snow. On one occasion a fully opened crocus blossom was observed unharmed after a night during which the air temperature had dropped to −16°C. Various species of alpine plants exhibit a sequence in their flowering in or near snowbanks according to their differing tolerance of low temperatures. Many insects are similarly able to form bound water in their tissues and thus avoid the dangers of freezing.

Another method by which extremes of temperature are endured involves the removal of water from the tissues. Dried seeds, spores, and cysts avoid freezing because no liquid remains that can freeze. Dry seeds have germinated successfully even after exposure for 3 weeks to liquid air (about −190°C). In another experiment nematodes and tardigrades are reported to have recovered after chilling for several hours at an even lower temperature. At the other extreme tardigrades in a resistant condition have endured immersion in boiling water for short periods of time, and dried cysts of the ciliate, *Colpoda cucullus,* have survived after exposure to dry heat at 100°C for 3 days. The even greater thermal resistance of some bacterial cysts is well known. Among some plants unusually high temperatures not only are tolerated but also actually accelerate development. Seeds of the wattlebark tree are commonly boiled 1 hour to hasten germination before planting. The seed cones of certain species of pine trees (e.g., *Pinus banksiana*) open promptly only after fire has scorched them. This fact has obvious implications for the ecological effects of forest fires as will be discussed later.

Another special adaptation for dealing with extremes of temperature is dormancy. The term *hibernation* is often used loosely to describe all instances in which metabolism is reduced during winter when the environment becomes too cold. A great many poikilothermous animals go into such a hibernating condition in crevices, under rocks, or in the mud. Plants similarly are sometimes spoken of as hibernating when in the dormant winter condition. Plant dormancy is induced by lowered autumn temperatures often accompanied by desiccation.

Dormancy during the summer, when high temperatures, excessive dryness, and/or shortage of food may occur, is called *aestivation,* and, although less common than hibernation, it is found widely among insects and some other invertebrates, as well as among plants and certain mammals. In many insects dormancy takes the form of a *diapause,* that is, a stage in the development of the animal during which morphological growth and development are suspended or greatly retarded. Species having the capacity for diapause usually display a rhythm in the life cycle that is related to the seasons. During periods of unfavorable climate the greater part of the population is in the resistant, diapause stage. Andrewartha (1952) reports that in the absence of diapause the grasshopper, *Austroicetes cruciata,* which maintains high numbers over a wide area in southern Australia, would almost certainly die out in most of this area, or at best become a very rare species. Since in general dormancy is correlated with severe environmental conditions, insects of the same

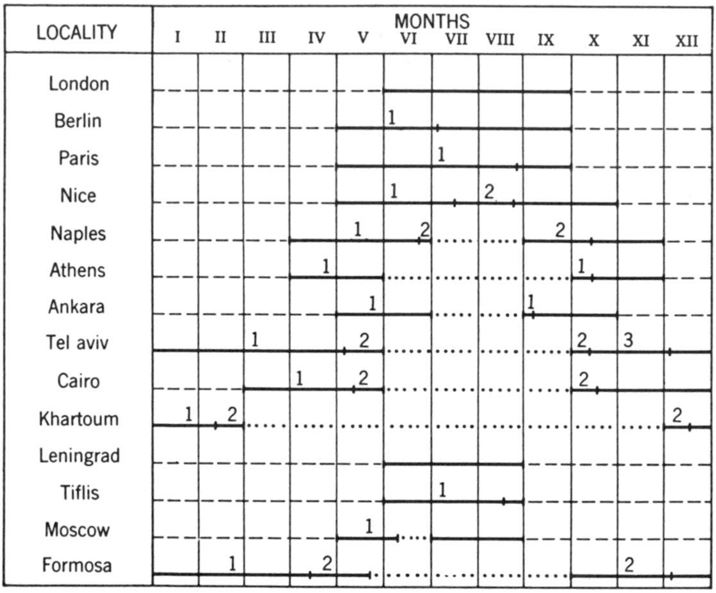

LOCALITY	I	II	III	IV	V	VI	VII	VIII	IX	X	XI	XII
London												
Berlin						1						
Paris							1					
Nice						1		2				
Naples					1	2			2			
Athens				1					1			
Ankara				1				1				
Tel aviv			1		2					2	3	
Cairo				1	2					2		
Khartoum	1	2										2
Leningrad												
Tiflis							1					
Moscow				1								
Formosa			1		2						2	

After Bodenheimer, 1938

FIG. 5.7. Variation in the seasons of dormancy and in the number of complete and partial generations in the ladybird beetle, *Coccinella septempunctata,* in different parts of its range. _____development; . . . . aestivation; _ _ _ _ _ hibernation.

species in different parts of the world may go into hibernation or aestivation at quite different periods of the year (Fig. 5.7).

Certain mammals, and at least one bird (Jaeger, 1949), also become dormant with reduced metabolism under seasonal extremes of climate. Since this type of dormancy involves a physiological change peculiar to warm-blooded animals, a separate term should be employed to describe it, but in the absence of a special word the terms hibernation and aestivation are used for mammals (and birds) as well as for lower animals (Lyman and Chatfield, 1950). In mammalian hibernation the internal temperature drops to about 1 degree above the temperature of the animal's surroundings, provided that the latter does not fall lower than a few degrees above 0°C. This is not likely to happen in the burrows or caves where the animals usually hibernate (Fig. 5.8). In laboratory experiments a reduction of the external

Photo by D. R. Griffin

Fig. 5.8. Hibernating bats, *Myotis l. lucifugus,* hanging in clusters head downward by hind claws hooked to the rough limestone in a Vermont cave.

temperature below 0°C causes the hibernating mammal either to be aroused from its dormant condition or to be killed by freezing. Temperatures well below 0°C for long periods in the winter would prevent any mammal from hibernating in the Arctic unless it could find a sufficiently tempered retreat. Whether for this or other reasons there are few hibernating mammals in the far north. The Arctic ground squirrel hibernates in burrows made in local areas of unfrozen ground under deep snow. Other small mammals remain active in lined nests made in the snow itself. Measurements at Fairbanks, Alaska, showed that at less than 1 m beneath the snow surface a microclimate temperature of —5°C existed at a time when a value of —50°C was recorded in the air just above the snow.

Less is known about the physiological adjustments of aestivation in mammals, but this type of dormancy similarly involves a shift of metabolism into low gear and a complete change in the control of internal temperature (Hamilton, 1939). An example of mammalian aestivation is found in the summer dormancy of the ground squirrels of southern California. By remaining torpid in their burrows for several months these animals not only avoid the high summer temperatures but also tide over periods of water and food shortage.

A special device for dealing with extremes of temperature *while in the active condition* is homoiothermy, or warm-bloodedness. Birds and mammals are able to maintain a remarkably constant internal temperature despite great variations in the outside world. Limits exist, of course, beyond which these animals cannot maintain their temperature control, but by allowing a regulated amount of evaporation to take place from their bodies they can keep their own temperatures down to normal values under the highest environmental temperatures ordinarily encountered. Under extremes of cold weather birds and mammals are able to maintain their relatively high internal temperature through the insulating action of fur, feathers, and fat, as well as by suitable physiological adjustments (Scholander et al., 1953). The remarkable ability of mammals to maintain their normal thermal level under severe winter conditions is exemplified by a varying hare whose internal temperature was found to be at its normal value of 38°C on a day when the thermometer stood at —46°C.

Thermal Migrations. Another method for dealing with excessively high or low temperature conditions is to move out of them. This method is obviously available only for locomotory forms, and it cannot be used by the majority of plants. Journeys taken by animals that enable them to escape from extremely hot or cold situations are referred to as thermal migrations. Some of these migrations are relatively short trips involving movements of only a few meters or even a few centimeters. Thermal migrations are made on a small scale from exposed positions to the shade to avoid the scorching heat of the desert and from shade to sun in cold regions. We commonly think of desert animals as being able to withstand extremely high temperatures. As a matter of fact most desert animals have become nocturnal in their habits and thus avoid the heat of the day. This is true even of characteristic desert reptiles such as the rattlesnake. Ecologists working in the desert areas of southern California have found that rattlesnakes will succumb if forced to remain for more than 15 minutes on the hot desert soil exposed to the midday sun. The red racer is one of the few desert reptiles that venture forth regularly in the daytime. Since this species is one of the fleetest of the snakes, it is able to cross hot areas and get back into the shade before becoming harmfully heated.

In less severe environments we are familiar with the short journeys of terrestrial amphibians into shaded places in hot weather. However, the chief benefit from a movement out of the sun for salamanders and other forms with wet, permeable skins may be conserving water rather than keeping cool. The excessive evaporation experienced by an amphibian in an exposed, windy location would cause a chilling of the body, and, in addition to avoiding water loss, the animal might go into a sheltered place to keep warm.

The short trips into or out of the water made by frogs, turtles, and other amphibious forms are familiar to everyone and serve to provide cooling or warming for the animals concerned. An unusual temperature relation is displayed by the white pelicans that nest on islands of the Salton Sea, California. In this extremely hot location the eggs and young in the nest would be killed if exposed for more than about 20 minutes to the intense radiation from the sun. The brooding of the mother birds acts to keep the eggs and young cool rather than to keep them warm! At intervals the adult pelicans wet their plumage by a trip into the water and take advantage of the cooling produced by evaporation.

Burrowing animals escape excessive heat or cold by short journeys deeper into their substrata. Soil organisms avoid summer heat by moving deeper into the earth. Ground squirrels are included in the desert fauna of southwestern United States but they are rarely exposed to the extremes of heat in that area. In the hot season these rodents retire into their burrows where a microclimate of much more moderate temperatures prevails (Table 9). At a later season the same

TABLE 9

REDUCTION IN TEMPERATURE AT INCREASING DEPTHS BENEATH THE SURFACE OF THE DESERT AT TUCSON, ARIZONA

Air (maximum)	42.5°C
Surface (maximum)	71.5
10 cm below surface	41.1
30 cm below surface	29.8
45 cm below surface	27.9

type of migration serves to avoid the severity of winter. Some animals work their way into rotten logs, others dig deep in the soil, and many species squirm into the mud of swamps or pools. This movement of animals into winter quarters is often loosely referred to as hibernation, and should not be confused with the structural and physiological changes often occurring in winter dormancy and described by the same term.

Somewhat longer journeys that result either primarily or secondarily in the avoidance of extreme temperatures are made by larger land animals. Bear, deer, and other game animals descend from the mountains into the sheltered valleys when the weather gets cold. In the spring they return to higher elevations and to more exposed situations. The same type of thermal migration of moderate length is seen in the aquatic environment. Many fishes and other active aquatic animals leave the shore in the summer when the water has become too warm. Conversely, other species migrate into deeper water during the winter to avoid what are for them excessively low temperatures. Such migrations at contrasting seasons are illustrated very neatly by two species of flounder that inhabit the coastal areas of New England. The so-called summer flounder (*Paralichthys dentatus*) enters the shallow water of the bays in June and departs in October. The winter flounder (*Pseudopleuronectes americanus*), on the other hand, is not able to tolerate the inshore temperatures characteristic of July and August. Fish of the latter species are abundant in the upper reaches of Great South Bay, Long Island, during the winter. As spring comes on the population moves toward the mouth of the bay, and, when the summer sun warms the water beyond about 20°C, the majority of this species migrates to the cooler, deeper water outside the inlet (Fig. 5.9). During the autumn months the winter flounder returns once more into the bay.

Migrations of still greater length are carried out by certain mammals, insects, and birds. Although change of temperature is not the primary cause of some of these mass movements, escape from climatic extremes is certainly an important consequence in many instances. The caribou migrate long distances, and in former times gigantic herds of bison traveled hundreds of miles across the American plains from their winter grounds to their summer feeding areas. The extensive north-south migrations exhibited by some insect species should also be considered as thermal migrations in part at least. Most spectacular of all are the trips made by migrating birds. Considerable evidence has now accumulated to indicate that change in day length is the factor that initiates the southward migration of birds at the end of the breeding season. However, many species of birds inhabiting high latitudes during the summer would succumb from temperature alone if they remained in the far north through the winter. Other species could perhaps withstand the winter cold but would succumb through an indirect action of the heat factor resulting from the disappearance of their food supply or from the inability of the birds to obtain the larger amount of food necessary to maintain their internal temperature in winter. For these reasons it seems probable that the avoid-

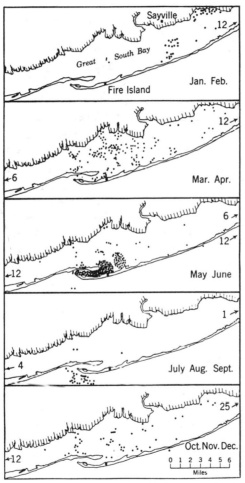

Modified from Neville and Perlmutter, 1941

Fig. 5.9. Thermal migration of the winter flounder as revealed by the recapture, at the points indicated, of fish tagged and released in Great South Bay, Long Island.

ance of temperature extremes played an important role in the evolutionary development of the migration habit of birds and of other animals, even if this factor does not provide the trigger that sets off the seasonal journeys each year.

Action within Effective Range

Although the action of temperature extremes may be drastic at times, the plants and animals of any habitat spend most of their lives at intermediate temperatures. We shall now consider the action of the heat factor in the range between the minimum effective temperature and the maximum effective temperature. Just as with extremes of heat and cold, the influence of a given temperature within the effective range depends upon the thermal conditions to which the species of plant or animal is adapted. Many tropical, temperate, and polar species have become attuned to the temperatures characterizing their respective regions so that many of their life processes go forward at approximately the same rate in spite of considerable temperature differences. For example, the rate of oxygen consumption in certain lamellibranchs is of the same order of magnitude for species living at 0°C in the Arctic, at 8°C in boreal seas, at 12°C in the Mediterranean, and at 27°C in tropical waters (Thorson, 1950). Seasonal adjustment to temperature is exhibited by the sand crab (*Emerita talpoida*) in the Woods Hole area to the extent that its metabolism at 3°C in winter is four times greater than in summer. As a result the animal can be active and can grow during the winter when many other species in the tidal zone become inactive (Edwards and Irving, 1943). The action of specific temperatures on life processes must be considered for each species separately, and also for geographical subspecies, but we can delineate certain generalities in regard to the role of the heat factor within the effective range.

Effect of Temperature on Biological Rates. The influence of temperature on the rates of biological processes is most clearly seen in poikilothermous animals and plants. Although mammals and birds are definitely affected by the heat factor, the action is largely indirect because these warm-blooded forms carry their own temperature around with them. When acting directly, a rise in temperature of 10°C usually causes a doubling or a tripling of the rate of a biological process, and the process is said to have a Q_{10} of 2 or 3 in accordance with Van't Hoff's law.

If you will take the trouble to listen to the cadence of the crickets on several evenings, you will observe that the frequency of their chirping is higher in warm weather and lower in cool weather (Fig. 5.10). This relationship was put to use by a blind astronomer who was able to "read' the temperature by timing the chirps produced by the crickets outside his house and applying a formula that he had worked out (number of chirps in 13 sec + 42 = °F).

Another example of the increase in reaction speed caused by rise in temperature is given in Table 10. The data show that the cod egg will develop at a temperature as low as −1°C. Its speed of development increases regularly to a temperature of 14°C, above which the egg will no longer survive. The relationship with temperature in this

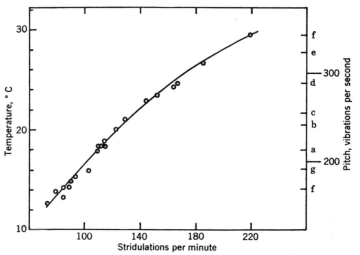

Fig. 5.10. Relation of stridulation rate of tree cricket *Oecanthus* to temperature and also to pitch. The note C is "middle C." (Modified from Matthews, 1942, *Science.*)

TABLE 10

RELATION BETWEEN TEMPERATURE AND RATE OF DEVELOPMENT OF EGGS
OF A COLD-WATER AND A WARM-WATER FISH

	Cod			Mackerel
−2°C	No development	(ecological zero)	+8°C	No development
−1	Hatch in 42 days		10	Hatch in 207 hours
+3	23		12	150
5	18		15	105
8	13		18	70
10	10.5		20	60
12	9.7		21	50
14	8.5		23	No development
16	No development		—	—

and in most other biological processes is not linear, and sometimes varies in a complicated way. For the cod egg a rise of 4° from −1°C to + 3°C produces a doubling in the rate of development, but a similar increase of 4° from 10°C to 14°C results in only a slight acceleration. A temperature of 10°C, which is the minimum at which the mackerel egg will develop, is near the maximum temperature for the cod egg. As the temperature is raised from 10°C to 21°C the rate of development of the mackerel egg is increased until at the upper value it will hatch in just over 2 days.

An increase in temperature beyond a critical point may cause a reduction in the rate of some life processes in certain species. The growth of the hypocotyl of the pea seedling shown in Table 11 illus-

TABLE 11

RELATION BETWEEN TEMPERATURE AND THE GROWTH OF THE PEA SEEDLING
AS INDICATED BY THE ELONGATION OF THE HYPOCOTYL

Temperature °C	Growth Mm per Day
14.1	5
18.0	8
23.5	30
26.6	54
28.5	40
33.5	23
36.5	9

trates this point. As temperature increases from 14.1°C to 26.6°C the amount of growth recorded each day steadily increases, but at higher values the daily elongation of the hypocotyl becomes less. In contrast to the growth in fish eggs, the pea seedling continues to elongate after the temperature has been reached at which growth is the fastest. This fact does not mean that increase in temperature has a negative effect on a reaction. Growth, like most other biological processes, is the result of a number of biochemical reactions going on simultaneously. In the present instance the rate of some inhibiting reaction may have been increased more by a rise in temperature than the reaction for elongation with the result that after a certain point the rate of growth becomes less.

In other instances temperature may have little or no effect on the rate of biological processes. Between certain limits the incubation period for many reptiles is only slightly influenced by thermal changes in the surroundings. The diamond-backed terrapin, for example, undergoes normal hatching between 18°C and 33°C, but within that range no regular correlation exists between temperature and time of development. On the other hand, some life processes go forward only within a very narrow thermal range. Everyone who has raised chickens knows that it is impossible to persuade the eggs to hatch more quickly by increasing the temperature. Although the hen's egg has no temperature control of its own, it will hatch only if maintained between 40°C and 41°C and only after 21 days of incubation.

Optimum Temperature. The foregoing discussion of the influence of temperature on the rates of biological processes leads to a consideration of the optimum temperature. However, the concept of the optimum in ecology is a slippery customer unless the life process concerned is specified. The optimum temperature may be considered that value at which a certain process goes on the fastest. But the temperature for the maximum rate often varies considerably for different processes within the same organism and also for the same process at different stages in the life cycle.

Among plants in the temperate zone the optimum temperature for germination usually differs markedly from the optimum value for the fruiting process, and the optimum heat condition for photosynthesis may occur at a value different from either of the other two. Similar variations in thermal relations are found among animals. The optima for the various developmental stages are frequently found at values widely different from the optimum for the adult. The eggs and larvae of terrestrial species usually require a higher temperature than the adult stage, but notable exceptions are provided by many animals as, for example, by the corn borer, and the eastern brook trout. The trout spawns in October or November, and the eggs can develop at 4°C or less. The optimum temperature for the development of trout eggs is 8°C. The adult trout, on the other hand, do not feed much and therefore do not grow until the water is warmer than 10°C. The optimum for the growth of the adult falls between 13°C and 16°C. These examples are sufficient to indicate that no one point on the thermal scale can be designated as the optimum for the entire growth of an organism, but that optimal values differ according to the life stage of each species.

The most favorable temperature for survival often differs considerably from the optimum value for growth, reproduction, and other life processes. Mackerel eggs develop at the fastest rate at 21°C, but in the same investigation the survival of the eggs was found to be best at 15°C. Other experiments showed that the life span of the common water flea, *Daphnia magna*, is greatest at 8°C (Table 12). In contrast, the shortest time for the production of the first batch of young

Daphnia occurs at 23°C, and the optimum from the point of view of the largest number of young produced is found to be at 18°C (MacArthur and Baillie, 1929). The ecological effect of these divergent optimal values will depend upon whether they are applied to the individual or to the population. The individual Daphnia lives longest at one temperature, but the population as a whole grows the fastest at another temperature. The optimum temperature for a species can therefore be only a general concept. The optimum is best thought of as a range of temperatures, and it is the range within which the organism as a whole functions best.

TABLE 12

TEMPERATURE RELATIONS OF THE CLADOCERAN, *Daphnia magna*

	Average Length of Life (days)	Time for Production of First Young (days)	Average Number of Young Produced
8°C	108	—	—
10	88	—	—
12	—	16	6
18	40	8	24
23	—	6	9
28	26	—	—

Other Effects of Temperature. In our discussion of temperature thus far we have dealt chiefly with growth and survival. Many other influences of this factor are of importance in the ecology of animals and plants. A drop in temperature ordinarily means a decrease in activity, especially among the cold-blooded animals and plants. As winter comes on, insects and other invertebrates ordinarily become dormant. In the spring on land the thermometer usually must climb above 8°C before cold-blooded animals become abundantly active. The snow flea, *Collembola,* forms an interesting exception to the foregoing generality. These small black insects are often found swarming on the surface of the snow among the trees in February or March. Evidently the animals can absorb enough heat from the strengthening spring sun in their protected microclimates at the base of trees to be active. In the aquatic environment many animals are adapted to carrying on a very active life at temperatures only a few degrees above 0°C. No one who has hooked a salmon in a northern stream will claim that a high degree of activity is impossible for cold-blooded animals at these lower temperatures.

Certain behavior patterns are influenced by the heat factor. Some of the more primitive animals exhibit a *thermotaxis,* that is, an orientation toward a source of heat. Ticks are aided in locating their warm-blooded hosts by a turning reaction to the heat of their bodies. Rattlesnakes, copperheads, and other "pit vipers" can detect the presence of mammals or birds that may be only a few degrees warmer than the surroundings. Oriented by the heat radiation, these snakes can strike accurately at their prey even in the dark. Other behavior reactions are influenced by heat conditions. When the temperature drops below 5°C, the leopard frog is stimulated to burrow into the mud bottom of its pond. At the same temperature sunfish crowd together in aggregations but, if the water is warmed to 8°C, the fish tend to swim about separately. Snakes similarly gather in aggregations and form balls in their retreats among the rocks when cold weather arrives in the autumn.

Temperature, as well as moisture, light, and other factors, has long been known to affect the coloration of some animals. In warm, humid climates many mammals, birds, and insects, tend to be more melanic, that is, darker in color than races of the same species living in cool or dry climates. This generality, already referred to as Gloger's rule, is well recognized but many exceptions are encountered, and the relative influences of heat and moisture are not known. In some instances coloration seems more affected by genetic selection than by the direct action of climate. The possibility of hereditary transmission of heat-color relationships is demonstrated by experiments showing that the temperature to which pupae are exposed will affect the wing color of butterflies even to the second generation. This whole subject is controversial since observations on various species in different areas do not agree. Coloration is evidently controlled by interactions between environmental and hereditary factors, but a more exact understanding must await further study.

The temperature factor is also known to affect the absolute size of many animals as well as the relative proportions of certain parts. The general fact that among birds and mammals the same species attains a greater body size in cold regions than in warm regions and that among closely related species the larger ones inhabit the colder climates is known as the *Bergmann principle*. Poikilothermous animals, as exemplified particularly by reptiles and amphibians, exhibit the reverse relationship since they tend to be smaller in colder climates.

The related observation that extremities, such as the tail, ears, and legs, of mammals are shorter in colder climates has been delineated as *Allen's rule*. Since both these generalities apply to warm-blooded forms, they are probably related to the difficulty of retaining heat at low temperatures and the desirability of losing it at excessively high temperatures.   Animals with large bodies have surfaces that are relatively smaller in relation to their masses than small animals.   Smaller extremities expose smaller surfaces (Fig. 5.11).   Since heat is lost through the surface, the smaller the area of an animal's skin, the more easily may the animal maintain its temperature in cold weather. Conversely, the development of extremities with large areas aids heat loss and evaporation in hot climates.   These simple ecological relationships, in addition to underlying Bergmann's principle and Allen's rule, undoubtedly account in part at least for the fact that no extremely small mammals or birds exist, that is, as small as the majority of insects.

Fig. 5.11.   Head of (*left*) arctic fox, *Alopex lagopus,* (*center*) red fox, *Vulpes vulpes,* and (*right*) desert fox, *Megalotis zerda,* showing gradation in size of ears. (Reprinted with permission from Hesse, Allee, and Schmidt, *Ecological Animal Geography,* 1951, John Wiley & Sons, New York.)

A very specialized influence of temperature on morphology is the apparent control it exerts on the number of vertebrae in certain species of fish—a relationship known as *Jordan's rule.*   Cod hatched off Newfoundland where temperature ranges between 4 and 8°C have 56 vertebrae, whereas cod hatched east of Nantucket in temperatures averaging 10 to 11°C possess only 54 vertebrae.   The relationship is brought about through the control by temperature of metameric segmentation at an early stage of development.   Incidentally, the fact is of use to fishery biologists in ascertaining the origin of populations among those species of fish that exhibit this geographical difference in structure.

The temperature of the environment controls egg type and sex ratio in certain animals.   Under moderate heat conditions Cladocera produce parthenogenetic eggs, and these hatch usually into females. Under ordinary circumstances few if any males exist in the population, but their production and the appearance of "winter" eggs is favored by extremes of temperature.   The winter egg of the Cladocera, as described earlier, is able to withstand desiccation and freezing but, since it is a sexual egg, it must be fertilized by a male before it can develop (cf. Fig. 2.11). In *Moina macrocopa*, when the temperature drops below about 14°C, or rises above 30°C, males appear in the population and sexual eggs are produced. This control of egg type and sex ratio is attuned to the fact that in temporary pools the occurrence of very high temperatures often precedes the drying up of the pond in summer. At the other end of the year a drop in temperature will presage the possibility of freezing and the necessity that the animal go into a life structure in which the severity of winter can be endured.

ACTION OF TEMPERATURE ON DISTRIBUTION

Mode of Temperature Limitation

In many early attempts to describe the ecological action of temperature an effort was made to correlate geographical distribution with mean temperatures. Although we see many average temperatures in print, we never encounter one in nature. A distinction must be made between the use of a temperature value as an index and the action of temperature as an agent controlling distribution. The limits to the spread of a population are always set by ecological factors acting on the individuals making up the population. In most situations the individual is not subject to a temperature equal to the average temperature of the region for more than a few hours of the day or a few days of the year.

In eastern Massachusetts the mean annual temperature is about 7°C but on many days in summer the thermometer stands near 24°C and in the winter near −10°C with extreme records far above and below these values. As a consequence the fauna and flora of the region are very different from what they would be if the temperature remained in the neighborhood of 7°C all the year round. In the latter event the local biota would be more like that of the Aleutian Islands or of South Iceland where the mean monthly temperature varies only from about 10 to −1°C with an average of about 4°C. We may conclude that the mean annual temperature is not the chief aspect of this factor which controls distribution, but a more penetrating analysis of the action of temperature must be made.

Careful consideration of the various thermal influences shows that for the permanent life of a species in an area the following temperature requirements must be met:

 a. The temperature must never be so high or so low at any time as to kill the organism.

 b. The temperature must be high enough, or in some instances low enough, for a sufficient period to permit the reproduction and growth of the species.

Limiting minimal temperatures for survival ordinarily occur in winter, and minimal heat required for reproduction and growth will be found in summer. Either or both of these influences determine boundaries of distribution toward the poles or higher altitudes. Limiting maximal temperatures for survival commonly occur in summer and minimal chilling necessary for reproduction and growth will be found in winter. These influences determine boundaries of distribution toward the equator or low altitudes. On the basis of the foregoing generalities Hutchins (1947) has delineated four basic types of zonation in geographical distribution and has discussed them particularly in relation to the ranges of marine animals. As we shall see, in these common types of temperature zonation as well as in more irregular situations, failure to meet the thermal requirements listed above may occur at any stage of the life cycle and at various seasons of the year.

Control by Extremes. The simplest type of control of geographical distribution by temperature extremes is that in which the polar limit of the range of a species is determined by the minimum temperature in winter and the equatorial limit is fixed by the maximum summer value. Many illustrations of this type of control will occur to the reader and can be found in treatments of plant and animal geography. Sometimes the lowest temperatures tolerated by tropical species are encountered far to the south (in the northern hemisphere), and the highest temperatures tolerated by arctic species are found well to the north. There is evidence, for example, that the southward (and eastward) distribution of three flowering alpine perennials in Scandinavia is correlated with the maximum temperatures in summer as indicated in Fig. 5.12. Although the exact causal relationship in such instances is not known, it is possible that the protoplasm of the northern species is adversely affected, that respiration is increased faster than assimilation, or that temperatures are too high for the proper transport of assimilated products (cf. Went, 1950).

Intensive study of certain species has revealed the fact that control by extremes may involve unexpected complications and that other aspects of temperature influence may be in operation simultaneously. A multiphased action of temperature will probably be found in many

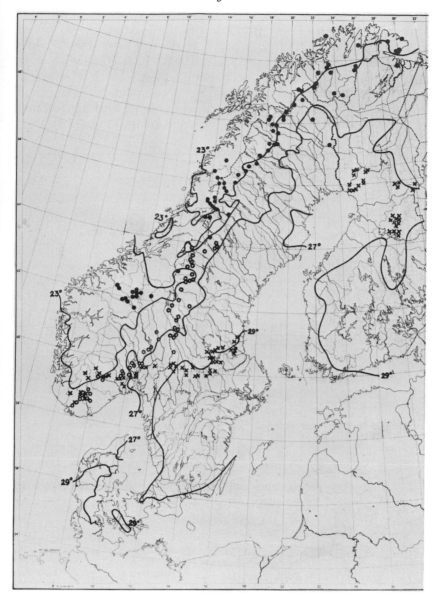

Dahl, 1951

Fig. 5.12. Locations of the most southern and eastern records in Scandinavia of three flowering alpine perennials and the maximum summer temperatures.

    x *Lactura alpina*, correlated with 29°C isotherm.
    o *Ranunculus platanifolius*, correlated with 27°C isotherm.
    • *Saxifraga foliolosa*, correlated with 23°C isotherm.

more species when they have been more closely investigated. According to Iversen (1944), for example, the northern and eastern limit in Europe for the growth and reproduction of the ivy, *Hedera helix arborea*, is determined by the minimum winter temperature in situations where the average temperature for the coldest month is −1.5°C or below, but in areas with less severe winters the northern limit is fixed by the occurrence of sufficient summer heat as indicated by the average temperature for the warmest month (Fig. 5.13).

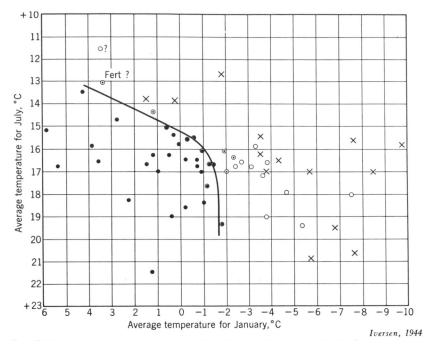

Iversen, 1944

FIG. 5.13. Temperature conditions at localities in Europe in which the occurrence and condition of the ivy, *Hedera helix* f. *arborea*, have been investigated.

- Ivy sets fruit regularly.
- ⊙ Ivy sets fruit occasionally.
- o Ivy occurs but does not set fruit.
- x Ivy does not occur.

The harmful action of high temperature is not necessarily limited to midday hours in summer nor that of low temperature to the coldest night in winter. We have seen in the previous chapter that winter killing of vascular plants is sometimes due to the excessively warm, dry wind during periods when the ground is frozen. For many plants the danger of injurious low temperatures occurs in the spring after germination, and at that time killing will result from temperatures that are not nearly as low as those which the plant successfully withstood during the winter while it was in a dormant condition. An unexpected temperature relationship is exhibited by certain plants in northwest Europe that can extend their range farther poleward in the interior of the continent than they can along the sea coast. The explanation is that the milder winter and earlier rise of temperature near the ocean stimulates the plants here to earlier germination, but since the spring temperatures rise more slowly the seedlings may be killed by late frosts.

Among those species whose geographical range is limited by temperature extremes we find a great variation as to the part of the life cycle that is chiefly concerned. The limitation is brought about by the most susceptible stage; the boundary of distribution is determined by the weakest link in the life cycle in respect to temperature tolerance. Other life stages may extend temporarily beyond the area of permanent existence.

We often think of the youngest organisms as the most sensitive to harmful influences in the environment, and this is indeed sometimes true in respect to temperature. The early stages of development often exhibit a very narrow range of temperature tolerance and may thus represent the "heel of Achilles" for the species as far as damage from excessive heating or chilling is concerned. For example, fish eggs characteristically show a greater susceptibility to harm from temperature than adult fish of the same species. The eggs of birds, although a special case because birds are homoiotherms, will tolerate only an extremely narrow fluctuation in temperature and frequently die as the result of unusually cold or hot weather. In some animals, on the other hand, the egg is far more resistant to temperature extremes than any other stage. In other species the most resistant stage is found later in the life cycle and may be represented by a cyst or pupa. The seed of the higher plants similarly represents a tough, resting stage and one that is characteristically able to withstand a range of temperature far greater than that tolerated by the adult plant. Sprouts can often survive a frost that would critically injure the reproductive tissues of the mature plant.

Very frequently the greatest susceptibility to heat or cold damage lies in the intermediate stages of growth. The period after the egg has hatched or after the seed has germinated is a critical one in some species; it represents the stage at which pioneering individuals at the margins of their range will be killed off by adverse temperatures. The fate of copepod populations carried by currents each year from the Gulf of Maine into the Bay of Fundy serve as an illustration of this situation. Fish and Johnson (1937) report that adult copepods brought into the Bay of Fundy find the temperature tolerable, breed successfully, and produce eggs that are viable under the existing thermal conditions. The temperature remains too low for the ensuing larval stages, however, with the result that the new generation is eventually killed off. The copepod population is consequently reduced until the next year when it is again renewed by currents from the Gulf of Maine. Sometimes the harmful action of temperature is quite indirect. Although the free-swimming life of the oyster, *Crassostrea virginica*, is extended from 7 days at 25°C to 21 days below 20°C, the animal develops perfectly well at the latter temperature. The principal significance of low temperature for the larvae is that it prolongs pelagic life and hence increases the period during which the larvae fall easy prey to enemies (Thorson, 1950).

In some species the adult stage is more sensitive to extremes of temperature than any of the younger stages. Excessive heat or cold may reduce the vitality of the plant or animal as a whole, or it may cause damage to specific tissues or functions. The organs of reproduction are frequently the most susceptible. For example, the northward distribution of peach trees in the United States is limited by damage to fruit buds by late frosts in the spring, although the other parts of the plant remain quite uninjured. The foregoing discussion will suffice to illustrate the fact that extremes of heat or cold may kill off animals or plants at whatever season the most vulnerable stage of development occurs.

Control by Need for Minimum Amount of Heat. In order that a species maintain itself in a given locality, the temperature at some season must rise above the threshold, that is, above the minimum at which the vital processes of the organism can go on, and it must remain above that value for a period sufficient to allow growth and reproduction to be completed. The great variation in the length of the frostless season within the United States is indicated in Fig. 5.14. Many organisms require temperatures considerably above freezing at some season, but occasionally we find instances of plants or animals that can get along with remarkably little heat. Lichens were found growing on Antarctic nunatacs (rocky peaks protruding through the ice) where extreme cold prevails for much of the year and the temperature rises above 0°C on very few days. Similarly, a rich and varied marine invertebrate fauna and associated flora are known to grow and to reproduce along the coast of Greenland where the water temperature never exceeds 0°C.

Above the thermal threshold it is generally true that, the higher the temperature, within limits, the shorter the period needed for the same amount of development. This fact led to the belief that the heat requirements for the growth of an organism from its youngest stage to maturity, or for the completion of any other life process, might be calculated quite mechanically as a "heat sum" (or "thermal constant") expressed as "degree days" or "degree hours." The heat sum was obtained by finding the threshold temperature for the process concerned and summing the differences in degrees between this value and the average temperature on each day until the completion of the process. Thus the heat sum required for the flowering of corn plants in Ohio was found to lie between 660 and 1050 degree days, basing the calculation on the number of centigrade degrees above 6°C recorded for the temperature each day. The lengths of the life histories of many insects have been shown to depend upon a relatively constant temperature sum over a considerable range of temperatures, and hence of velocities of development (Allee et al., 1949, Ch. 6).

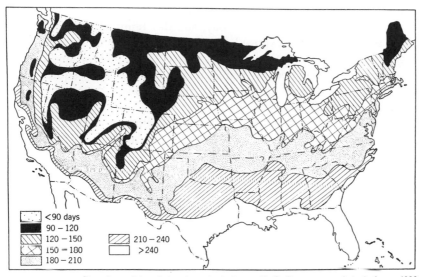

<90 days	
90 – 120	
120 – 150	210 – 240
150 – 180	>240
180 – 210	

Data from Atlas of American Agriculture, U. S. Department of Agriculture, 1936

Fig. 5.14. Average number of days between last killing frost in spring and first killing frost in fall.

Although the results of temperature summation agree generally with the fact that a given type of plant or animal requires longer to mature in a cold than in a warm climate, closer scrutiny shows that, in many species at least, temperature dependencies are far more involved than are indicated by heat sums. In the first place the heat sum for a process is constant only for that range within which there is direct proportionality between growth rate and temperature. Lack of such proportionality is usually found near both the upper and the lower limits of tolerance. Indeed, as mentioned earlier, above certain "optimal" temperatures the rates of many metabolic processes actually decrease. Furthermore, since heat sums are based on average daily temperatures, they do not take into account the possible special effects of the maximum or minimum daily values, night temperatures, or differences between diurnal and nocturnal temperatures.

The critical importance of these more detailed aspects of temperature in controlling life processes is discussed in greater detail by Daubenmire (1947) particularly in relation to land plants. Some plants exhibit normal responses only when grown in temperatures that fluctuate with a regular diurnal rhythm—a phenomenon known as *thermoperiodism*. And to make matters more complicated, the precise action of temperature may be further modified by the intensity of light and the length of day. Went (1950) points out that no heat sum can account for the ripening of the tomato. In addition to proper light intensity, length of day, and day temperature, the tomato plant sets seed only if exposed to a series of five or more nights during which the temperature remains above 15°C. These findings are compatible with the general principle of minimum heat requirements, but they show that in certain land plants at least the matter is far more complicated than first supposed.

Control of the geographical distribution of many animals can similarly be related to the need for a minimum amount of heat. The American oyster as an adult can survive at temperatures from 32°C down to the freezing point of salt water. A temperature above 15°C, or higher in some races, is necessary for spawning to take place in this species, and good development of the larvae requires water above 18 or 20°C. The adult lobster can live at temperatures ranging from about 17°C down to 0°C, but breeding will take place only in water warmer than 11°C. The lower maximum temperature tolerated means that the lobster cannot range to the south as far as the oyster and the lower heat requirement for lobster reproduction produces a marked difference in the breeding range of the two animals. For a complete study of the effects of temperature on distribution the thermal conditions in each bay and inlet should be investigated, but the range of temperature along the coast is sufficient to illustrate the general influence of this factor.

A glance at Fig. 5.15 will show that north of Cape Cod coastal temperatures are generally lower than 18°C until the Gulf of St. Lawrence is reached where surprisingly warm conditions occur in summer in the shallow areas around Prince Edward Island. Temperatures in the central part of the Bay of Fundy are prevented from rising above 11°C by the intense tidal stirring, but the stratified water along the outer coast of Nova Scotia becomes considerably warmer than this. Correlated with these temperature conditions we find that in New England oysters grow naturally in commercial quantities only as far north as Narragansett Bay but "seed" oysters may be transported to Cotuit and elsewhere on Cape Cod, where they are fattened for mar-

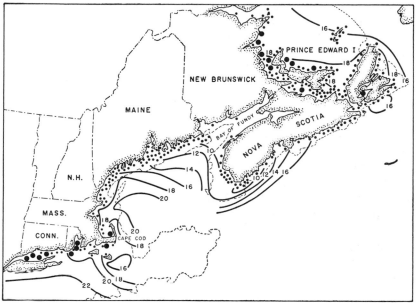

Modified from Ackerman, 1941

FIG. 5.15. Regions of abundant occurrence of lobsters (*small dots*) and oysters (*large dots*) in relation to August surface temperatures as indicated by the location of the commercial catch in 1934.

ket. Oysters again become sufficiently numerous to market in the littoral zone around Prince Edward Island and in certain warm bays of Cape Breton and northeast New Brunswick. Lobsters, on the other hand, breed successfully in abundance all along the coast of Maine, on the outer coast of Nova Scotia, and into the Gulf of St. Lawrence, but these shellfish are not taken in commercial quantities within the Bay of Fundy. Although lobsters wander into the Bay of Fundy and some of them grow to a large size, the lack of water of sufficient warmth prevents the establishment of a native breeding population despite the fact that the animal's range extends much farther north in situations where the heat requirements are met.

The northward distribution of turtles in inland waters is similarly determined not by the extremes of temperature but by the need for the minimum amount of heat for the completion of the life cycle. Since turtles burrow in the mud during the winter, the extreme minimum air temperature at that season is of no consequence. But these reptiles require the heating action of the summer sun to incubate their eggs. The snapping turtle, for example, lays its eggs in the sand during the month of May, and sufficient heat must reach them during the summer in order for the young turtles to hatch out successfully in September. The northerly distribution of turtles is correspondingly limited by this long heat requirement to the upper or central part of the United States, but snakes can extend their range well over the Canadian border because heat for the incubation of their eggs is needed for only a short period.

Differential control of geographical range is also illustrated by the distribution of frogs, whose temperature requirements are widely divergent. Some species of frogs seem to need little more heat than that necessary to thaw out their ponds just long enough for reproduction. The eggs of the wood frog, *Rana sylvatica,* develop at a temperature as low as 2.5°C, and the larval stage requires only 60 days. This species extends northward in Canada to the mouth of the McKenzie River. The pickerel frog, *Rana palustris,* on the other hand, must have a temperature of 7.5°C and a period of at least 90 days for its development. The range of this species is correspondingly limited to the latitude of James Bay. In contrast, a third species, *Rana clamitans,* will not develop until the temperature exceeds 11°C, and its range extends only slightly above the southern boundary of Canada.

Control by Need for Chilling. Some organisms require a certain period of cold weather for their life cycles to be completed. No one would plant tulips or crocuses in June and expect them to bloom in August. These plants come into flower only after the bulbs have passed through a winter period of low temperature. The dormant buds of certain fruit trees and berry plants similarly require a period of chilling before they will flower successfully. Experiments have shown, for example, that some types of blueberries require an exposure of 800 hours to temperature below 7°C before the dormant buds will develop. In other species the initial formation of flower buds will take place only at low temperatures.

The seeds of some plants must be chilled under moist conditions before they will germinate properly. In other species, such as winter wheat, satisfactory development takes place only if a period of chilling occurs during or after germination. It has been discovered that the seeds of certain plants must undergo two successive cold intervals before the seedling will grow (Barton, 1944). This requirement means that under natural conditions development of the plant can go forward only after the second winter.

In nature all species requiring low temperatures are limited in their altitudinal distribution down the sides of mountains and in their latitudinal extension toward the equator. This cold requirement also imposes serious restriction on the successful cultivation of temperate varieties of fruit trees in warm climates. Although little is known of the physiological mechanisms upon which the need for chilling depends, the empirical knowledge is put to practical use through *vernalization*, that is, the artificial exposure of seeds to cold. Such procedure allows certain crop plants to be grown farther north and also farther south than would otherwise be possible.

Another need for low temperatures results from the varying effect of this factor on anabolic and catabolic processes. We have seen that sufficient heat must be available to plants and animals so that the growth and reproductive processes may make up for the destruction of tissue materials and the death of individuals. As temperatures rise, most vital reactions are accelerated, but sometimes at very different rates. If catabolic processes are speeded up disproportionately, the organism will suffer rather than gain from high temperatures. Above certain temperatures the respiration rate of most plants becomes higher than the rate of photosynthesis. Food manufacture is consequently curtailed, and growth, reproduction, and the accumulation of food reserves may be inhibited. The range of plants toward low latitudes and low altitudes and their seasonal activity are limited to areas and periods when temperatures remain low enough to permit a favorable photosynthesis-respiration relationship.

Although the need for low temperatures during part of the life cycle has been extensively studied in relatively few animals, there is little question that failure to meet this thermal requirement limits the distribution of some species. Desert mammals and insects that are forced to aestivate by high temperatures would not be able to continue active life if some portion of the year did not have a cooler climate. The gemmules of sponges hatch at a much lower temperature and in a much shorter time after a period of freezing. The eggs of the white mayfly, *Ephoron album,* must be chilled to within a few degrees of freezing for several weeks (or subjected to a few days of actual freezing) for good hatching to be assured. As a result, this insect cannot extend its range in the eastern part of the United States farther south than 40° N latitude.

The eggs of the Australian grasshopper will not continue growth beyond a certain stage unless they are exposed to low temperatures within the range that will permit diapause development to proceed rapidly (5–13°C), and later, to high temperatures (17–35°C) which permit morphogenesis to go forward (Fig. 5.16). This dependency

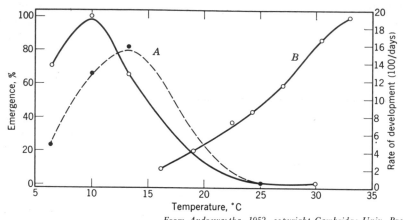

From Andrewartha, 1952, copyright Cambridge Univ. Press

FIG. 5.16. The influence of temperature on (A) diapause development and (B) post-diapause morphogenesis in the embryo of the grasshopper, *Austroicetes cruciata. Solid line:* eggs from South Australia; *broken line:* eggs from West Australia.

on chilling is nicely attuned to the normal life cycle of this grasshopper. Since the insect reaches the diapause stage at the beginning of winter, it is in the condition to endure best the severest cold weather of the year and also to take advantage of low temperatures for the completion of diapause development. Other species in which diapause occurs during later stages of the life history exhibit a different timing in their adjustments to the ecological conditions of their habitat. The eggs of the moth, *Euproctis,* hatch during July, and diapause does not take place until the larvae have reached the second or third instar. By the time the animals enter diapause autumn has arrived and the species overwinters in the larval stage.

In New England the gypsy moth lays eggs in summer, but development will normally start again only after chilling, or not until the following spring. This timing not only fits the life cycle of the moth but also is most fortunate for the survival of the vegetation in areas where this pest is abundant. If reproduction continued throughout the late summer and autumn months, the trees upon which the caterpillars depend for food would have no opportunity to recover from the spring and early summer inroads of feeding. Even in species without a recognized period of dormancy distribution toward warmer regions may be limited by the fact that warm conditions inhibit certain necessary processes long before temperatures are reached that would be immediately lethal. The southern (equatorward) boundary for the barnacle, *Balanus balanoides,* appears to be determined by the isotherm for a minimum surface temperature of 7.2°C (Hutchins, 1947). Evidently this barnacle requires a certain period of low temperature in order to complete its reproduction successfully; this conclusion is supported by the fact that the species breeds during the summer in the northern part of its range, but breeds only during the winter in the southern areas of its distribution.

The foregoing consideration of the limitation of distribution by thermal requirements has called attention to the complexity of the relationships involved. Temperatures that are harmful, or that are necessary, differ widely with species, age, and physiological condition. Resistant stages of a species may be found far beyond the boundaries of the area within which all parts of the life cycle may be carried on. For marine bottom invertebrates, for example, Thorson (1950) has delineated three areas of distribution: (1) an extensive area throughout which the adult animal may live at least vegetatively; (2) a smaller area within the first in which the animal will ripen its sexual products and spawn; and (3) a still smaller area within the second in which the embryos and larvae will develop successfully. Other types of animals and plants have different patterns of temperature sensitivity at different life stages. As we have seen, the effect of temperature may vary for different life processes in the same organism or even for the same process in different parts of the organism. Each species of animal or plant can live only in those regions in which the temperature pattern is tolerable and adequate for the needs of the species. The organism is restricted to habitats in which the annual, seasonal, and diurnal fluctuations in temperature occur at such times and in such magnitudes as to allow all life processes to be completed but do not occur so as to cause serious harm. The intriguing interdependencies outlined here certainly need and invite further investigation by ecologists.

Results of Temperature Limitation

One far-reaching consequence of the action of temperature in the various ways that have been reviewed is to impose a north-south gradation on the distribution of many animals and plants both in water and on land. The ranges of species that are controlled primarily by temperature, rather than by moisture or some other ecological factor, have boundaries tending to run generally east and west. Latitudinal zonation is considerably modified, however, by temperature anomalies due to currents in the ocean, and to differences in altitude, proximity to oceanic areas, and other influences on land. Across the United States, for example, less severe cold is experienced along the Atlantic and Pacific coasts than in the center of the continent, and cold weather occurs farther south in the mountain areas. The ranges of many species correspondingly extend farther north along the coasts but are restricted to more southerly regions in the Rockies and in the Appalachians. On the other hand, in northwestern Europe species for which the northern boundary is determined by summer warmth range farther north toward the interior of the continent because the temperature in summer is higher there than on the coast.

There are no temperature boundaries to which the ranges of *all* plants and animals conform. The complex influence of thermal conditions must be investigated for each species separately before generalities applying to groups of animals and plants can be established. As we go north or south species drop out irregularly and their ranges overlap. The pines of the north, for example, extend into the realm of the palms of the south. The live oaks, typical of southern United States, overlap in their distribution the white oaks, whose center of distribution lies farther north. The quail extends its range northward into New Hampshire, but the grouse, a similar type of bird common in Canada, spreads southward as far as Virginia.

The same sort of overlapping occurs with aquatic organisms. Of 40 species of marine invertebrates common along the eastern coast of the United States, 16 have their northern boundary at Cape Cod, 14 have their southern boundary at the same point, but 10 species occur on both sides of the Cape. In the study of geographical distribution as influenced by temperature, we see again the necessity for the analytical approach—for dealing primarily with the mechanism of control of individual species.

Special Cases of Common Boundaries. Only in special instances do a large number of plant and animal species share a common thermal boundary for their distribution. Under unusual circumstances the horizontal temperature gradient may change abruptly. At the northern edge of the Gulf Stream, for example, the temperature may drop as much as 5°C within a few miles—an extreme thermal change for the oceanic environment. We are not surprised that many species inhabiting Sargasso water have northern boundaries and species inhabiting continental slope water have southern boundaries at the Gulf Stream. Similar sudden changes of climatic conditions occur on land in relation to unusual topographical changes, such as an abrupt change in altitude at the edge of a plateau. In these situations a considerable number of plants and animals share common boundaries based primarily upon the temperature factor.

Frost Line. The *frost line* on land constitutes another special thermal situation but one in which there is no sudden change in temperature geographically. The fact that the tissues of animals and plants in active condition freeze not far below 0°C results in the occurrence of a boundry of general importance at the frost line. All plants and all animals that are not frost hardy and that do not have modes of escape are limited in their poleward and altitudinal distribution by the harmful results of freezing. At the same time any plants or animals dependent upon these frost-sensitive species will drop out. The palm trees are an example of plants that are unable to stand a continued frost. In North America the natural range of the true palms does not extend north of the central part of Florida, the Gulf coast, and the southern part of California. Smaller plants and animals associated with the palms are necessarily limited in their distribution to essentially the same boundaries.

Tree Line. Other abrupt changes in the fauna and flora commonly occur where one major type of vegetation gives place to another, since the dominant vegetation influences the presence of many subordinate species of plants and animals. An outstanding instance of common boundaries due to the dependence of many species on the type of vegetation is seen at *tree line*. Here again there is no sudden change in the distribution of temperature. When thermal and other conditions have been modified to such a point that trees no longer can grow, an important change in the whole ecological situation takes place. In any forested region trees have a profound controlling influence on the subordinate plants and on the associated animal life. Thus the environmental situation that limits the trees indirectly sets boundaries to the distribution of many other species as well. Tree lines dependent in part at least on temperature occur across the continents at the poleward margins of the forests and also on mountain slopes at the upper limits of forest vegetation. We may consider first the northward boundary of timber in Canada as an example of a continental tree line.

A traveler going north in the eastern part of North America passes from the southern region of palm trees into the belt of southern pines and then into the "central hardwoods," dominated by white oaks and hickories. The central hardwoods extend into southern New York, Connecticut, Rhode Island, and maritime Massachusetts. In east central Massachusetts and up the valleys in New York, Vermont, and New Hampshire the vegetation changes to the "transition forest," in which the maple, red oak, ash, and black birch are the most abundant species. In northern New York, central Vermont, and New Hampshire the forest becomes the "northern hardwood" type, with maple, beech, and white and yellow birch predominating. When the traveler reaches northern Maine and the corresponding parts of Ontario, he finds himself in the spruce forest. Here red spruce, firs, and white and yellow birch are the common trees. Still farther north, about at the southern edge of Hudson Bay, the trees have become so small that the Indians referred to the area as the "land of little sticks." Then the forest stops.

Although temperature is believed to play a major role in determining the poleward boundary of forest vegetation, it is difficult to determine just how this factor operates. We know that tree line is not related primarily to the coldness of winter since even in Siberia, where extremely low temperatures are recorded, heavily forested regions are found. Nor is the tree growth determined directly by the occurrence of certain maximum temperatures in summer, since in Labrador and in Alaska, far beyond the tree line, temperatures of 32 to 38°C have been recorded. High daily maxima are beneficial since they hasten the melting of snow. In order to survive trees must have sufficient heat for growth in the interval between the arrival of effective temperatures in the spring and their disappearance in the fall. In Alaska, and also on the San Francisco mountains, the conifers reach but do not pass the July isotherm of 10°C (Griggs, 1946). On the other hand, the position of the tree line in Scandinavia appears to be chiefly influenced by the occurrence of a season with sufficient heat for seed germination, especially of the birch.

In some regions the curtailment of tree growth is brought about by excessive *solifluction*—the heaving of the soil by frost action. Trees are tilted and their roots broken by severe solifluction, and in such situations this indirect action of climate may be more significant than its direct effect. The occurrence of *permafrost* (a stratum of permanently frozen soil) prevents the penetration of tree roots, and, although trees will grow in an unfrozen stratum over permafrost, its presence usually increases the severity of solifluction. Raup (1951) regards timber line in Alaska as occurring at the point where frost action prevents the white spruce from surviving in numbers on the uplands. Isolated stands of spruce trees are found growing hundreds of miles north of the recognized tree line in areas where local drainage conditions result in little or no solifluction.

Fortunately, the student of ecology may observe the profound effects of the tree line without the necessity of visiting Alaska or the vicinity of Hudson Bay. In the United States many of the accessible mountains both in the east and in the west rise to sufficient heights to display altitudinal tree lines. At the upper edges of the coniferous forest, the spruce, fir, and birch become progressively reduced in size until they culminate at tree line in a dense scrub growth or dwarfed individual specimens. The actual altitude at which tree line occurs differs widely according to local circumstances. The harmful effects of strong wind, including especially excessive evaporation, are believed to restrict tree line to lower altitudes on exposed mountain peaks than would be the case if temperature were acting alone (Griggs, 1946). Physical influence of ice formations, avalanches, landslides, and solifluction may exert a further control locally (Fig. 5.17). Thus on different slopes of Mt. Washington, New Hampshire, described as having "the worst weather in the world," trees give way to alpine tundra at altitudes ranging from about 1200 m to 1740 m, whereas in the Rocky Mountains forests may extend to 3300 m (Fig. 5.18). Tree line occurs at sea level in parts of Belle Isle Strait but at an altitude of about 300 m at Bay of Islands, Newfoundland.

Life Zones. The progressive change in temperature and other climatic factors from the equator toward the poles and from the lowlands to the mountain peaks controls the distribution of certain major vegetation types and these in turn are accompanied by characteristic sets of subordinate plants and associated animal species. As a result, we may recognize a series of *life zones* extending across the land from the tropics to the polar regions, and, on a much smaller scale, extending up mountain slopes from the warm lowlands to the alpine conditions of high elevations. Although many irregularities exist and although the special circumstances influencing the distribution of each individual species must be kept in mind, the general sequence of the latitudinal and altitudinal life zones is clear, and the two series have recognizable counterparts (Fig. 5.19). The continental life zones are formed by the roughly latitudinal arrangement of certain of

FIG. 5.17.   Winter view of tree line on Mt. Mansfield, Vermont, with spruce trees in foreground encased in ice.   Severe frost action and other adverse climatic influences reduce the trees to stunted dwarfs.

Photo by D. B. Clarke

FIG. 5.18.   General view in midsummer of tree line on Mt. Rainier, Washington, and of the alpine meadows above it.   Tree line here is believed to be relatively stationary because of the occurrence of both old and young trees among the outposts of the forest.

Fig. 5.19. Approximate correspondence of latitudinal and altitudinal life zones in North America. (By permission from *Animal Biology* by Wolcott, 1946, McGraw-Hill Book Co.)

the principal biotic formations, or biomes, that will be discussed more fully in Chapter 12.

A synoptic view of the life zones of the world could be obtained by chartering a plane at the equator and flying toward the north pole, or toward the south pole. On such a trip, you would observe that the life zone characteristic of the equatorial region is the tropical rain forest. In this zone a wide variety of trees provides continuous shade and humid conditions for the many species of plants and animals that live in and under the forest. North of the tropical rain forest the flying ecologist comes to a life zone in which dry seasons alternate with rainy seasons. Farther to the north the plane passes over a belt of varying width of desert or grassland and thence over deciduous forests of oak, hickory, beech, and maple. The colder region to the north is heavily forested with spruce and other conifers that form a circumpolar life zone. At the limit of the spruce forest the plane crosses the tree line and reaches the tundra where dwarf birches or willows, scattered grasses or other flowering plants, mosses, and lichens struggle to keep alive on ground that is frozen for much of the year. Eventually all land vegetation is lost to view in a landscape of universal snow and ice. If the plane trip had been made from the equator southward, the same general sequence of life zones would have been traversed except for the gap caused by the great expanse of the Antarctic Ocean.

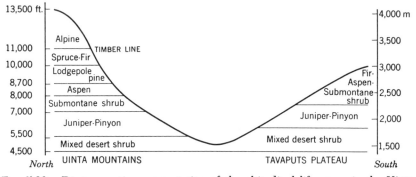

Fig. 5.20.   Diagrammatic representation of the altitudinal life zones in the Uinta Basin.   (Graham, 1937.)

Without an airplane you may observe the same general series of life zones on a much smaller scale by climbing a mountain. If the mountain is a high one and located in the tropics, as is Mt. Popocatepetl in Mexico with an altitude of 5448 m, the basal slopes may be covered by rain forest and the summit by snow. As you climb upward you emerge from the dense vegetation of the tropical forest and pass progressively through life zones of savannah, deciduous forest, and coniferous forest. Higher up you reach a belt of dwarf pine, fir and alder. Above this a life zone of grasses, lichens, and mosses exists, corresponding to the tundra and giving way finally to

TABLE 13

OUTLINE OF PLANT COMMUNITIES IN THE UINTA BASIN AND THEIR RELATION TO ALTITUDINAL LIFE ZONES (Graham, 1937)

Upper altitude	Alpine zone	*Sieversia-Carex* association
	Spruce-fir zone	*Picea-Abies* association Upper-altitude meadow Upper-altitude lake
Mid altitude	Lodgepole pine zone	*Pinus Murrayana* association
	Aspen zone	*Populus aurea* association Mid-altitude valley
	Submontane shrub zone	Mid-altitude *Artemisia* associations
Low altitude	Juniper-pinyon zone	*Juniperus-Pinus* association
	Mixed desert shrub zone	*Eurotia* association Low-altitude *Artemisia* association *Atriplex-Tetradymia* association *Chrysothamnus* association *Kochia-Hilaria* association Mat *Atriplex* association *Sarcobatus* association
		Desert gulch Badlands *Distichlis* meadow *Scirpus-Typha* swamp Cottonwood river flood-plain

bare rocks, snow, and ice. Altitudinal zonation on the slopes of mountains in the temperate region is often equally striking but may not be as extensive. The report by Graham (1937) of the Uinta Basin of Utah and Colorado contains a detailed study of the life zones at different altitudes with many excellent photographs of representative plant communities (Fig. 5.20 and Table 13).

Although temperature relations are sometimes chiefly responsible for the demarcation of certain life zones, it is obvious that moisture is extremely influential in many instances, and other ecological factors such as soil condition and length of day play contributory roles. The positions of life zones cannot be universally correlated with any one influence of the environment but are the result of a complex of interacting factors.

Nevertheless, an attempt was made by Merriam in 1894 to set up zones based exclusively on temperature into which the entire fauna and flora of North America could be divided. These were called *biothermal zones* and, unfortunately, were accepted uncritically by many ecologists. There are certain specific objections to the wide application of Merriam's scheme besides the general warning that the presence of an organism in a certain locality cannot be accounted for by saying that it is a "member" of a certain biothermal zone (Daubenmire, 1938). In the first place the heat requirement calculations for Merriam's zones were based on 6°C as a threshold temperature for the germination of wheat, and therefore obviously should not be directly applied to other species of plants and particularly not to animals. The assignment of birds and mammals to zones based on environmental heat conditions is especially inappropriate since these warm-blooded animals carry their own temperature around with them.

Other objections to the use of Merriam's zones appear from a critical understanding of the varied effects of temperature. For example, the number of the degree days required for development is not constant over a wide temperature range. Fifty days at 2°C above the threshold have a very different influence from that of 5 days at 20°C above the threshold, although the "thermal constant" would be the same in both cases. Furthermore, as explained above, temperatures at seasons of the year other than those used by Merriam may be critical in controlling the distribution of many species. The fact that distribution of a species may agree with certain isotherms of the region does not necessarily prove a direct causal relation. The existence of many minor species of plants is controlled by the presence of dominant or accessory species. The geographical range of the dominant species may in fact be controlled by temperature, or it may be dependent primarily on the moisture factor, which in turn is influenced by temperature.

Animal populations also may exist in characteristic zones for reasons that are only indirectly related, or unrelated, to temperature. Horned larks, for example, are found all the way from Colombia to the Arctic and occur in very divergent climates and hence in various biothermal zones. The primary relationship is with the vegetation: these larks are found wherever broad expanses of shortgrass occur regardless of thermal conditions. Cone-feeding birds are similarly found wherever suitable conifers are growing. The range of this type of bird may include areas in one life zone where a northern conifer is growing and also in another life zone where a southern conifer is growing. It is obviously absurd to think of the range of this bird as primarily determined by biothermal zonation.

Temperature and Moisture Acting Together

A discussion of temperature as an ecological factor should not be concluded without calling attention again to the close interrelationship between temperature and moisture in the terrestrial environment. Emphasis has been placed on the fact that temperature affects relative humidity and the rate of evaporation. The converse is equally true that when evaporation and condensation occur, they tend to modify the temperature. We are accordingly not surprised to find that temperature and moisture often interact in such a way as to make it difficult or impossible to disentangle the individual effects of these two factors. Does the salamander go into a sheltered place to keep cool, to get warm, or to avoid excessive evaporation? Added to the complication is the fact that for many organisms the indirect effects of these factors may be more significant than the direct effects because of their control of the vegetation.

We have evidence that the influence of humidity on insects is often greatly modified by the existing temperature. The dual effect of these factors on the rate of development of the cotton boll weevil provides an admirable illustration (Fig. 5.21). This insect pest cannot develop if the relative humidity is less than 40 per cent or more than 88 per cent, no matter how favorable the temperature may be. On the other hand, the animal remains dormant regardless of humidity if the temperature is lower than 17°C or higher than 39°C. Within these ranges the speed of development depends upon the values of both factors. At a temperature of 28°C, for example, the boll weevil requires 21 days to develop under a relative humidity of 40 per cent, but it develops in only 11 days if the humidity is between 60 and 65 per cent.

In the foregoing example of the combined influence of temperature and humidity on rate of development it is of interest to consider what the limiting factor is. Picking the point on the diagram representing a temperature of 24°C and a relative humidity of 55 per cent, we see that the speed of development will be increased if *either* the temperature or the humidity is raised. In this instance more than one limiting influence is present. In certain situations, two (or more) independent factors may be unfavorable and *both* of these must be improved before the organism can continue its growth or extend its range. In other situations, the limiting effect of one factor depends upon the value of another, as in the development of the boll weevil. The two factors acting together produce the limitation, and may be referred to as a "limiting combination." The ecologist should always be on the lookout for possible multiple adverse or modifying influences in the environment. Limiting combinations are probably in operation under natural conditions more frequently than is now realized (Shelford, 1951).

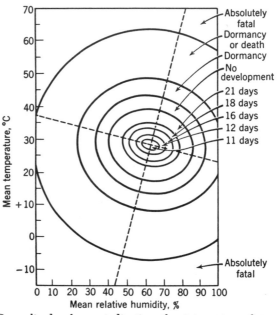

Fig. 5.21. Generalized scheme indicating the interaction of temperature and humidity in controlling dormancy and the number of days required for development in the cotton boll weevil. (By permission from *Animal Ecology* by Chapman, 1931, McGraw-Hill Book Co.)

An illustration of the combined action of temperature and moisture on vegetation is the effect of these factors on the form of growth of plants and on the *life form* of the whole plant. The climate exerts a major control over the type of plant that can exist in each region, and consequently the life form of the vegetation is to a certain extent an expression or an indicator of climate. This idea has been extensively developed by the Danish botanist Raunkiaer (1934), whose work should be consulted for a thorough treatment of the subject. Raunkiaer stresses the significance of the adaptations of buds and shoot tips for withstanding adverse temperatures and surviving drought. On this basis Raunkiaer delineates different groups of plants. Trees and shrubs are placed in one group in which the surviving buds project into the air. The perennial grasses are included in another group in which the buds are situated on or near the soil surface. Plants with bulblike buds that are protected during adverse seasons by being buried in the ground are placed in a third group.

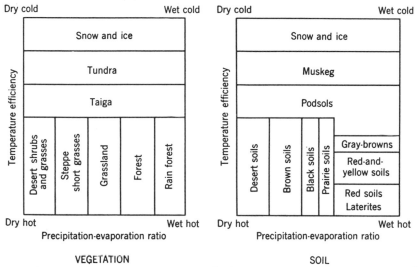

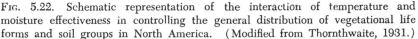

Fig. 5.22. Schematic representation of the interaction of temperature and moisture effectiveness in controlling the general distribution of vegetational life forms and soil groups in North America. (Modified from Thornthwaite, 1931.)

Deciduous trees, conifers, shrubs, succulent xerophytes, mosses, grasses, annual plants, and epiphytes represent contrasting life forms. As we have seen the major life zones are distinguished by the life form of the vegetation. Plants of distinctive life form characterize the major plant communities, and these communities are the dominant feature of the biotic formations, or biomes, of the world, as described in Chapter 12.

Thornthwaite (1931) has worked out indices of the effectiveness of thermal and moisture elements of climate as related to the range of temperature and the rate of evaporation in influencing the distribution over the continent of certain vegetational life forms. The scheme presented in Fig. 5.22 shows in diagrammatic fashion that above a certain value of thermal efficiency, moisture tends to be more responsible than temperature for the control of life form. In colder climates temperature is generally more important. Soil groups are influenced in a similar way by the climate as well as by the vegetation. With low precipitation-evaporation ratios and high temperatures the moisture factor is more significant than the heat factor. In the far north the temperature is by far the more critical, but in intermediate regions moisture and temperature play more nearly equal roles in determining soil groups. Here then we have another illustration of the extremely wide direct and indirect influences of the temperature factor in the ecological adjustments of both plants and animals.

6

Light

The chief natural sources of light are sunlight, moonlight, starlight, and the light from luminescent organisms. In this chapter we shall deal primarily with visible light, but since the sun's emission also includes ultraviolet and infrared radiation these components of sunlight will also be considered. Practically all the energy of importance for organisms under natural conditions is derived directly or indirectly from the sun. It is true that man has learned to obtain energy from other sources such as tides, and more recently from nuclear fission, but man like other organisms depends primarily on the sun for his main supply of energy.

The radiation from the sun produces a direct heating effect, and also produces photochemical transformations. After these transformations have been completed, the energy appears in the form of heat. Accordingly, all the sun's energy eventually ends up as heat, but certain portions of the radiation from the sun take part in vital photochemical processes before becoming heat.

Light as an ecological factor is generally highly directional. It differs in this respect from the temperature factor since heat often reaches the living organism from many different directions at the same time. Light is extremely variable. It changes over a tremendous range, often very rapidly. Many organisms can respond to a value of light that is only one ten-billionth of full sunlight. Although we often think of temperature as varying widely on the earth's surface, the magnitude of its variation is extremely small compared to that of light. Light can change from a value near zero to its maximum within a few hours.

Light is essential for most plants and animals, though some can do without it. For the continued existence of organisms two requirements must be met. First, light must not be so strong as to cause serious harm at any stage in the life history. We shall see that a considerable variation exists in the upper limits of tolerance to the light factor. Second, for those animals and plants that require light it must be sufficient in intensity and in duration. The intensity of the light must be above the threshold for the organism concerned, and the total amount of light received during the period when it is needed must be adequate.

DISTRIBUTION OF LIGHT

In discussing the distribution of light it is convenient to start with sunlight as the chief source and trace the radiation as it passes through the air and water environments. The magnitude of the solar radiation as it reaches the outer atmosphere referred to as the *solar constant* has the value of about 1.9 g-cal/cm²/min. At sea level the intensity of solar radiation averages about 1.5 g-cal/cm²/min. If the radiation received from the sun were evenly distributed over the surface of the globe, it would be sufficient to melt a layer of ice 35 m thick during the course of a year. At a latitude of 44° N the energy received on the earth's surface from the sun is equivalent to the light that would be produced by hanging a 250-watt lamp over each square meter of the ground.

We know very well, however, that the radiation from the sun is not evenly distributed either in time or in space. We wish to inquire what its variations both in quality and in quantity are. Light changes in spectral distribution and in angular distribution. The light factor also varies in intensity and in duration, resulting in differences in the total amount of light falling on each unit of surface for each unit of time, such as a day or a month. The changes in the light factor in these respects will be examined as they affect the terrestrial and the aquatic environments.

Light on Land

Spectral Composition. The spectral distribution of light as it reaches the earth's surface is shown in Fig. 5.3. Authorities differ as to the exact wavelength limits to be assigned to the different portions of the spectrum. Roughly speaking, radiation of wavelength longer than 7600 Angstrom units is considered to be infrared, and that of wavelength shorter than about 3600 A is designated as ultraviolet. Almost one-half of the total emission of the sun is infrared radiation, and almost one-half is visible light. These proportions remain approximately the same at the earth's surface, regardless of the total intensity of sunlight. The ultraviolet component, however, is always only a small percentage of the total radiation, and it may be reduced to immeasurably small quantities under certain circumstances.

Intensity of Light. The intensity of light reaching the earth's surface varies with the angle of incidence and with the amount of absorption by the atmosphere and by obscuring features. The lower the altitude of the sun, the smaller is the angle of incidence and the longer is the path of the light through the atmosphere with corresponding reduction in intensity. Changes in the sun's altitude result from differences in latitude as well as from changes in the season and in the time of day. The greatest intensity of sunlight occurs at positions on the earth's surface and at times at which the sun is most nearly overhead. At higher latitudes, the intensity of light is correspondingly reduced. At 50° N latitude, for example, during the period of the equinox in March and in September when the day is everywhere 12 hours long, the intensity of sunlight is only about one-half of what it is at the equator (Fig. 6.1).

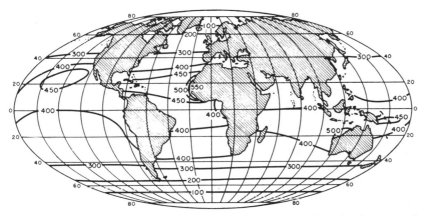

FIG. 6.1. Total solar radiation (g-cal/day/cm² of horizontal surface) on March 21 with average cloudiness. (Modified from Kimball, 1928.)

Latitude thus has a definite effect; but other factors may have much greater influence upon the light factor. Moisture, clouds, and dust in the atmosphere have a profound and irregular effect in reducing illumination. Living organisms may also act to diminish the intensity of daylight, as is clearly shown by the forest vegetation, and this represents a reciprocal action in which the inhabitants modify the light factor in their own environment.

Different forest communities vary widely in the degree to which they diminish the sun's radiation. Cottonwood (poplar) trees tend to grow rather widely spaced, and the relatively sparse foliage allows many patches of sunlight to reach the ground. The canopies of pines and oaks usually have fewer gaps. Measurements made in Illinois revealed that the portion of the forest floor exposed to direct sunlight was 84 per cent for poplar, 77 per cent for pine, and 35 per cent for oak. In elm-maple forests and in tropical rain forests the canopy typically is complete, with the result that none of the direct sunlight reaches the forest floor. Other measurements showed that the light on the forest floor which had passed through the leaves of the canopy was reduced in intensity to 3.5 per cent of its value above the tree tops in the oak forest; corresponding figures for elm-maple and rain forests were 0.4 per cent and 0.2 per cent, respectively. Thus less than 1 per cent of the light outside the forest reaches the ground if the canopy is complete.

Different types of forests exhibit different seasonal influences on the light factor. Underneath a stand of pine trees the light is reduced by about the same amount throughout the year since the trees are evergreen. The illumination on the floor of a pine forest reaches a maximum in the early summer and a minimum in winter corresponding to the seasonal variation in the intensity of the incident sunlight. In a maple forest, however, a very different seasonal picture is presented. During January, February, and March the plants and animals living on the forest floor receive increasing amounts of light, but in April the leaves begin to appear and the intensity of light drops rapidly reaching a minimum in the middle of the summer. Then, as the leaves of the maple trees begin to curl and drop off a larger amount of light is allowed to filter through the forest canopy. The striking seasonal variation in the amount of ultraviolet radiation penetrating different forest types is shown in Fig. 6.2. The changes in the total visible illumination are of a corresponding nature (Park, 1931). Accordingly, if you were a beetle, or, if you prefer, a lily growing in a maple forest, the brightest month of the year for you would be April and the darkest would be July. In this situation living organisms have modified the environment in respect to the light factor so that the seasons have been practically reversed.

Duration and Amount of Light. The total amount of light received by an organism is determined both by the intensity of the light and the duration of the period of irradiation. The situation is similar to the exposure of a photographic plate. The amount of blackening of the plate is determined by the intensity of the light times the period of exposure. In natural habitats, the variation in the length of day

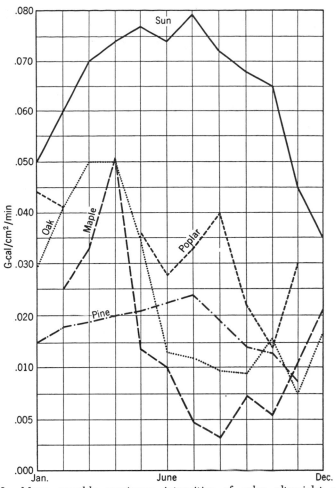

Fig. 6.2. Mean monthly maximum intensities of solar ultraviolet radiation (2900–4000A) in forest communities of northern Indiana. (Strohecker, 1938.)

often has a greater effect on the total amount of light received than do differences in the intensity of the sun at noon.

On the equator the day is always 12 hours long, but in the temperate regions the day grows longer as spring progresses. This effect is accelerated at higher latitudes, and the day becomes 24 hours long during the summer in the polar regions. The day becomes correspondingly shorter after the summer solstice (Fig. 6.3). Up to moderately high latitudes the increase in length of day during summer has more effect on the total amount of light received per day than the

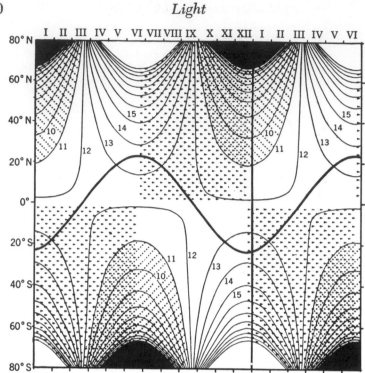

FIG. 6.3. Variation in length of day at the indicated latitudes during the indicated months. Arrowheads indicate periods of decreasing daylength. The heavy line shows the course of zenith sun (Baker, 1938.)

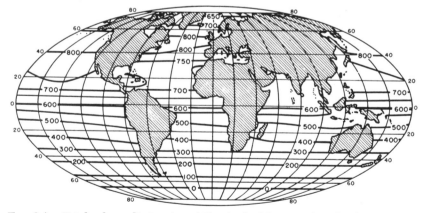

FIG. 6.4. Total solar radiation (g-cal/day/cm² of horizontal surface) on June 21 with cloudless sky. (Modified from Kimball, 1928.)

reductions in solar intensity due to the greater angle of incidence. The greatest northward development of this influence is illustrated in Fig. 6.4 in which the total solar radiation, determined by the combined action of intensity and duration, is plotted for June 21 under conditions of cloudless sky. At that period the amount of solar radiation received each day at 50° N latitude is considerably greater than that received at the equator, and the daily amount of light received in Scandinavia is roughly the same as that falling on tropical Africa. If you are amazed to find potatoes growing in Norway, or wheat being harvested in Alaska, don't forget that once the plants have begun to develop in the late spring, sufficient light exists in these latitudes for the plants to continue growing all day and a good part of the "night."

The foregoing review of the circumstances of light on the earth's surface has shown that light is everywhere sufficient for life of some type at least for part of the year. Plants and animals exist from pole to pole. Mosses and lichens grow in abundance right up to the edge of the ice in the polar regions. On the other hand, light is nowhere too strong for animals and plants of some sort. Thus the whole range of light on the earth's surface is generally compatible with life. Of course, light may sometimes be too strong or too weak for individual species, and in these instances it controls growth and distribution.

Light in Water

The sunlight available for plants and animals in the aquatic environment has entered the water from the air and hence has first been subjected to all the changes imposed upon it by the conditions above the surface. Ten per cent or more of the light is lost by reflection at the surface or in the special conditions just beneath the surface (Clarke, 1939). In addition, in passing downward, the light is further modified by the water medium in respect to intensity, spectral composition, angular distribution, and time distribution.

Extinction and Modification of Light. The light factor in the water environment is subject to a number of variable influences that modify it profoundly. In order to consider the situation first in its simplest terms, imagine a lake from which we have pumped out all the natural water and refilled with distilled water. Our lake then contains water of uniform and maximum transparency from top to bottom. Light is reduced in intensity both by absorption and by scattering, and the rate of reduction is measured as the extinction rate, although the term absorption rate is sometimes used loosely for the combined effect. Pure water causes the extinction of light at different rates in different parts of the spectrum. Measurements of illumination made with a photometer placed in a watertight case and lowered into our imaginary lake would reveal the changes presented in Fig. 6.5 At a depth of 70 m the blue component of sunlight has been reduced to about 70 per cent of its intensity at the surface. At the same depth the yellow component of sunlight has been reduced to 6 per cent of its incident value. The orange and red components have been extinguished very much more rapidly. At a depth of 4 meters, red light has already been diminished to about 1 per cent of its surface intensity.

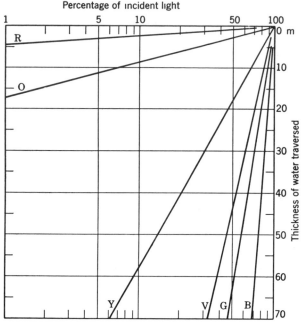

Fig. 6.5. Reduction in intensity (logarithmic scale) of the color components of sunlight (indicated by initial letters) at increasing depths (linear scale) in a lake of optically pure water. (Clarke, 1939, *AAAS Pub. No. 10.*)

Since we know that the daylight incident upon the surface of our lake differs markedly in intensity in different parts of the spectrum, we are dealing with the unequal extinction of an unequal spectrum. As shown in Fig. 6.6, the extinction by pure water of light at the two ends of the spectrum is much more rapid than in the middle of the spectrum. The blue component of light is also the most penetrating in the clearest ocean and lake waters. At depths of 100 m or more the blue light becomes completely predominating; this was observed directly by Beebe in his bathysphere dive off Bermuda. An observer looking straight down into the water from the deck of a ship in the clear tropical parts of the ocean sees the blue color resulting from this selective absorption. Since sunlight has been shorn progressively of its longer and shorter wavelengths, the only component remaining to be scattered upward again to the eye is the blue. Anyone who has seen the intense indigo of the tropical oceans will never forget it.

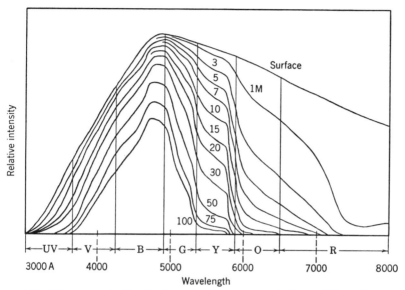

FIG. 6.6. The spectral distribution of solar energy at the earth's surface and after modification by passage through the indicated meters of pure water. Similar light conditions would be found in the clearest ocean and lake waters. (Clarke 1939, *AAAS Publ. No. 10.*)

The foregoing has shown that even pure water absorbs light at a very rapid rate compared to air and causes a profound change in spectral distribution. In the clearest parts of the ocean and in exceptionally clear lakes the optical properties of the water are closely similar to those of pure water. Other natural waters contain suspended particles and dissolved material in sufficient quantities to cause a further reduction in transparency and a further alteration in spectral composition.

Suspended material in the water includes living organisms that increase the extinction of the light and thus modify their own environment in this respect. Illumination is reduced by beds of kelp along the seacoast and by submerged or floating vascular plants along the shores of inland waters in much the same way that light is cut down by the larger vegetation on land. In the free water of ponds, lakes, and the oceans the phytoplankton is sometimes sufficiently abundant to produce a noticeable reduction of light. Plankton populations may cause an additional extinction of light indirectly by adding detritus or stains to the water after the organisms have died and disintegrated. A thick "bloom" of algae in a pond may thus reduce the light supply to such an extent as to curtail its own growth and that of other plants in the water layers beneath.

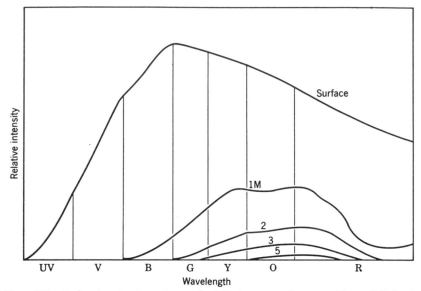

Fig. 6.7. Reduction in intensity and shift in spectral composition of light in heavily stained Rudolph Lake, Wisconsin. (Clarke, 1939, *AAAS Publ. No. 10.*)

In temperate and coastal seas and in the majority of clear inland lakes fine particles or stains are present that tend to absorb or scatter the blue component of light more strongly than occurs in pure water. As a result the green component of sunlight is usually the most penetrating in these situations and gives the water its characteristic emerald color. The organic stains occurring in some ponds and rivers absorb the shorter wavelengths so strongly that the red or orange components of sunlight become the most penetrating. In Rudolph Lake, Wisconsin, for example, the combined absorption of the water and of stains in the water causes not only a very rapid reduction in the light with depth but also a shift in the position of the maximum light to the red region of the spectrum (Fig. 6.7).

Since natural waters differ very greatly in transparency and in selective absorption, a study of the penetration of each part of the spectrum in each body of water would have to be made for a complete description of the light conditions. An approximate comparison of the illumination in various natural waters can be made on the basis of the relative transparency to the central part of the spectrum. Sample values are given in Table 14 for representative bodies of

TABLE 14

TRANSPARENCY OF WATER TO CENTRAL PART OF VISIBLE SPECTRUM
(5000–6000 A)

	Extinction per Meter (%)	$k*$	Depth for 1% of Surface Light	Secchi Disc Depth†
Distilled water	3.8	0.039	118 m	44 m
Caribbean Sea	4.1	0.041	110	41
Continental slope	7.2	0.072	60	24
Gulf of Maine	10.0	0.10	42	17
Woods Hole Harbor	26.0	0.30	16	6
Crater Lake, Oregon	6	0.06	77	28
Crystal Lake, Wis.	15	0.16	28	11
Trout Lake, Wis.	33	0.40	11	4
Midge Lake, Wis.	78	1.5	3	1

* Extinction coefficient, k.

$$\frac{I}{I_0} = e^{-kL}$$

where I_0 = initial intensity.

    I = intensity at depth, L, in meters.

    e = 2.7.

† Depth at which a 20-cm white disc disappears when lowered from the surface.

water. Since the great differences in the extinction of light per meter have a cumulative effect, an even greater contrast is presented in the depths at which a given fraction of the light is found. The depth at which the light intensity is reduced to 1 per cent of its surface value is of particular importance because it represents the approximate lower limit for plants, as will be discussed later. In general the table and the representative curves in Fig. 6.8 show the profound variation in the intensity of light available for organisms at increasing depths in different natural waters.

Another way in which light is changed by water is in its angular distribution. The direct beam of light from the sun is bent by refraction toward the perpendicular at the water surface. Since waves or ripples almost always exist in natural situations, the light from the sun tends to be broken up to a considerable extent in passing through the surface. Within the water itself further diffusion is produced by scattering. When larger amounts of suspended materials are present, scattering proceeds at a very rapid rate, with the result that measur-

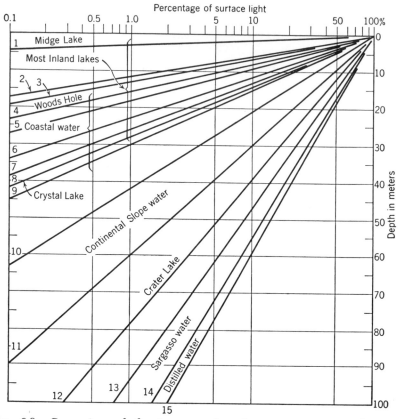

Fig. 6.8. Comparison of the transparencies of representative natural waters. Curves based on the average extinction rate for the yellow-green (5000–6000A) component of daylight. (1) Midge Lake, Wis., (2) Trout Lake, Wis., (3) Gunflint Lake, Minn., (4) Woods Hole Harbor, (5) Thatcher Pass, San Juan Islands, and Buzzards Bay, Mass., (6) Vineyard Sound, (7) Baltic Sea, (8) Crystal Lake, Wis., (9) English Channel, (10) Gulf of Maine, (11) off Vancouver Island, and off Nantucket Shoals, (12) Crater Lake, Ore., (13) Gulf Stream, (14) Caribbean Sea, (15) distilled water. (Clarke, 1939, *AAAS Publ. No. 10.*)

able light is passing in every direction. In the upper strata the light passing in the direction of the refracted rays from the sun is the strongest. With increasing depth the direction of strongest light intensity tends to move toward the vertical, and a limiting pattern of diffusion is established (Jerlov, 1951). Thus, although a variable degree of diffusion occurs, the directional character of the light in the water is never entirely lost.

Changes in Transparency. Parts of the ocean and of lakes that are well stirred exhibit a uniform transparency from the surface downward, but, when strong density gradients exist, considerable changes in transparency may occur with depth. Furthermore, the transparency of coastal marine areas and of inland water bodies often changes profoundly from season to season, owing to differences in amount of stirring, in the discharge of muddy rivers, and in the growth of plankton. Such variations in transparency are added to the seasonal changes in the intensity of the light received at the surface and in the length of the day. The combined effect of these influences results in surprisingly great fluctuations in the light factor at subsurface levels.

Observations made off the coast of Massachusetts illustrate the magnitude of the foregoing seasonal influences (Clarke, 1938). In this region the maximum hourly intensity of light received at the surface during the summer averaged about twice that received during the winter period. The average total solar radiation received per day in summer was about four times as great as that received during the winter. Significant departures from the average for periods up to several weeks occurred, and such variations are undoubtedly important in causing changes in the response to the light factor from year to year. Values for individual days may also depart markedly from the average. During the investigation referred to above the maximum light received on the brightest day of summer was forty times greater than that received during the dullest day in winter. In the course of the same year the extinction coefficient of the water varied fourfold. Since the effect of extinction is cumulative, the illumination in the subsurface layers varies more because of changes in transparency than because of seasonal changes in radiation reaching the surface. By combining the two effects it was found that for an organism living at a depth of only 30 m the maximum hourly light intensity was 7000 times greater and total daily radiation was 10,000 times greater in May, when high incident light was combined with high transparency, than in December, when both incident illumination and transparency were low. The magnitude of seasonal

changes in illumination in the aquatic environment are therefore frequently very much greater than in the terrestrial environment. Any
water body that displays a much higher transparency in winter than
in summer will have less light available during the summer in its
deeper layers and thus suffer a reversal of the usual seasonal change
in the light factor. The foregoing instances are sufficient to show
that in the aquatic environment light becomes profoundly altered
quantitatively and qualitatively and that its changes may go far beyond those experienced by plants and animals on land.

BIOLOGICAL EFFECTS OF LIGHT

Before concerning ourselves with the influence of the light factor
on growth, reproduction, locomotion, and other activities of the organism as a whole, we shall consider certain general effects of radiation as it strikes the surface of the plant or animal. In addition to
heating the tissues, the absorbed radiation affects biological processes
in the exposed tissues, including particularly their pigmentation.

General Effects

Among green plants light is required for the production of chlorophyll in the chloroplasts. Plants germinated under insufficient illumination will not develop their normal green color. Normal plants
become etiolated in the absence of light; that is, they lose their pigment and develop abnormal form. On the other hand, excessive illumination causes the destruction of chlorophyll. In some plants excessive absorption of light by the deeper tissues is prevented by the
screening action of thickened chloroplasts or of increased numbers of
chloroplasts near the surface. In some species when the light becomes too bright, the chloroplasts line up one behind another so that
a larger proportion of the radiation passes through the leaf between
the chloroplasts. When the light becomes weak, the chloroplasts
spread out and absorb a maximum percentage of the incident illumination.

Light may influence the pigmentation of animals in several ways.
Skin color may be indirectly affected by light through the mediation
of the eyes or other receptors. In other instances differences in color
may have arisen as a result of selective survival. The abundance of
pigment exposed in the chromatophores is sometimes directly controlled by the intensity of the light received. The characteristic lack
of pigment in cave animals is associated with darkness, and certain

aquatic forms have been shown to lose their color when removed from light. Blind cave amphibians and fishes with little or no color have been found to develop abundant pigment in the skin after exposure to normal daylight (Rasquin, 1947). Intense radiation may be harmful because of undue heating or evaporation, because of the lethal action of the ultraviolet component, or in other ways.

The excessive absorption of light by animal tissues must also be avoided. Most animals simply move into the shade, burrow into the ground, or descend to deeper levels in the water. The development of a relatively transparent body would appear also to help deal with this problem. Since only the radiation that is actually absorbed can be effective, the highly transparent tissues of many types of plankton can retain but little light energy. This fact may enable some planktonic animals to endure higher light intensities in the surface waters than would otherwise be possible. As we shall see, many species of plankton are extremely sensitive to light. In other kinds of animals evolutionary development has gone in the opposite direction with the production in the skin of abundant pigment which protects the deeper tissues. Anyone who has lain too long on the beach in June has been painfully aware of the harmful effect of excessive radiation on animal tissue and is familiar with the deposition of pigment in the skin of man to produce tan. In addition, transparency or pigment patterns also serve to render animals less conspicuous.

Protective Coloration. The pigmentation of a great many animals forms a coloration that appears to afford protection from enemies. One very common type of protective coloration is a simple matching of the background in respect to color and pattern. A quail squatting in the grass or a bittern standing motionless among the swamp reeds is exceedingly difficult to distinguish from its surroundings, as is a moth on the bark of a tree or a katydid among green leaves. Many other instances of remarkably close resemblance of birds, insects, and other animals to their background will occur to the reader. A second common type of protection, often combined with the first, is obliterative shading in which the bird, mammal, or fish displays darker pigmentation on its back and lighter color underneath. This difference tends to counteract the stronger illumination received from above with the result that the animal blends with its background.

The protective aspect of other color patterns may result chiefly from the confusion of the enemy by the disruption of the animal's usual outline. Birds with necks or heads of contrasting colors or tropical fish with strong transverse stripes are not easily recognized by man under certain conditions of illumination because of the unexpected pattern and presumably are not easily recognized by their natural enemies. Any such visual deception will, of course, not affect predators that locate their prey exclusively by smell, sound, or other methods. Some species when disturbed produce a flash of some brightly colored or contrasting part that is concealed when the animals are quiet, and the startling effect may serve to distract or to frighten off pursuers.

Another type of protective resemblance is mimicry—a phenomenon that is particularly well developed among the insects. Here one species closely resembles in color and form another totally unrelated species sometimes in an entirely different order. The mimic is believed to derive protection from the fact that it is mistaken by predators for the species it resembles. If the model species is distasteful or harmful as a food organism and hence is avoided by the predators, the mimic may also escape unmolested. Extraordinarily close mimicry certainly exists between insect species, but the reality of the benefit of the mimicry, its mode of operation, and its evolutionary origin are controversial subjects which still await conclusive investigation. For a further discussion of the far-reaching problems of protective coloration the reader may consult more extensive treatments of the subject such as that by Cott (1940).

Some animals are able to change their color or pattern sometimes within a matter of minutes or even seconds. Such changes in appearance occur characteristically as adaptations to the background, and are found among reptiles, amphibians, fishes, crustaceans, insects, cephalopods, and other invertebrates. The mechanisms by which color changes are brought about have been summarized by Prosser (1950, Ch. 21). In many instances they involve the nature of the light received from the background through the eyes, but in other instances, they are activated by direct radiation. A flounder changes its general color tone and also the pattern of the black and white patches of its skin as it moves from one type of bottom to another. Such changes in coloration tending to match the background furnish an obvious advantage in concealment (Sumner, 1935). In other instances color changes serve as protection from high illumination, take part in thermoregulation, or are associated with breeding, as in certain lizards, fishes, and squids. The seasonal color changes of the varying hare, weasel, and ptarmigan from brown in summer to white in winter are obviously related to the conspicuousness of such animals against bare ground or snow-covered landscape.

The different, and usually more brilliant, coloration of the males of many birds and of some other animals is familiar to everyone. In attempting to explain the evolutionary origin of this sex difference, Darwin drew attention to the courtship antics of peacocks, pheasants, and other birds, in which the males appear to vie with one another in showing off their plumage. Darwin proposed that the special plumage of the male evolved after many generations in which the females selected and mated with the "most beautiful" birds. Since we have no reason to suppose that birds judge the attractiveness of male suitors on the same basis as we would, this explanation seems unsatisfactory. As yet no convincing demonstration has been made of any basis for selection or of any other method by which the elaborate decoration of the male may have arisen.

The duller coloration characteristic of the female is undoubtedly related to her greater need for concealment while brooding the eggs. The striking coloration of the males of many species can rarely have any protective value for the male himself, although his conspicuousness might draw attention away from the female on the nest. In some birds, such as Wilson's phalarope, the tables are turned, for the females are brightly colored and the drab males do the housework of incubating the eggs. Difference in appearance may play a useful part in aiding sex recognition. The brilliant breeding plumage of the male is often replaced by a duller garb during the winter season. The length of day has been shown to influence breeding, migration, and color change in many birds and mammals. The light factor may thus be involved in coloration through its effect on reproductive activities as well as through its role in protective resemblance, and the two may be interrelated.

Mention was made in earlier chapters that desert animals characteristically display a pale coloration in contrast to the darker hue of the inhabitants of humid regions. Although temperature, moisture, and light may directly affect the general color of terrestrial animals under some circumstances, these factors often act indirectly through their influence on the color of the ground in relation to the concealment of the animals. Evidence indicates that pale or dark coloration has evolved in many species and races as a result of selective survival as influenced by their conspicuousness against the background. Selection would thus account for the occurrence of a white mouse (*Perognathus apache*) inhabiting an area of white gypsum sands in New Mexico and of a black mouse (*P. intermedius*) living on an adjoining area of black lava (Benson, 1933). The possibility that climate sometimes exerts a direct effect, however, is suggested by the fact that nocturnal animals in the desert have the same pale coloration as those which are abroad during the daylight hours when light would appear to be much more important.

It is a mistake to assume that the pigment developed by an organism necessarily plays a critical role in its present relationships. In some instances the pigment may be primarily a by-product of metabolism without any ecological significance. The red color of the deep-sea shrimp is a case in point. Since there is no red light deep in the water, the shrimp must appear as black as the deep-sea fish which share the same habitat. Similarly, it is unnecessary to assume that the coloration of the scarlet tanager, the oriole, and other birds with brilliant plumage provides any protective resemblance. Certain writers have practically turned themselves inside out in attempts to find a protective function for all bright colors. No one in his right mind would try to claim that *Chromodoris,* a bright blue nudibranch with orange and gold spots, was protectively colored as it creeps over the gray rocks and brown seaweeds of the tidal zone of southern California. In such instances either the bright colors do not attract enemies, or the organism survives in spite of being conspicuous because of the possession of other, sufficiently advantageous attributes.

Activity and Vision

Photokinesis. Light controls the locomotory activity of many of the lower organisms by a direct action upon their speed of locomotion—a phenomenon known as *photokinesis.* The magnitude of this reaction among animals without eyes was well illustrated by a laboratory test on the larvae of the mussel crab, *Pinnotheres maculatus* (Welsh, 1932). These animals swam the length of a 29-cm trough toward a light of 0.5 meter-candle in 34 sec. As the light intensity was increased, their swimming rate was accelerated regularly until at 46 meter-candles they made the trip in 17 sec. Many other animals show a similar increased activity under increased illumination whether or not they are oriented to the light. This simple direct relationship is of profound importance in the lives of many of the aquatic invertebrates and of the smaller terrestrial forms including insects.

Vision. When activity is controlled by light among higher forms it is usually through vision. We should inquire as to the circumstances of illumination under which vision is possible. On land daylight is everywhere sufficiently strong at some period for the vision of those animals that possess eyes. In the water because of the rapid rate at which light is reduced in intensity we may suspect that depths would soon be reached at which vision is no longer possible. Let us inquire what is the minimum illumination for aquatic animals to see sufficiently to feed, to find their mates, or to avoid dangers. Interest also centers on the maximum depths in the aquatic environment at which responses to day and night still exist.

A laboratory test can be set up in which the intensity of light is varied over a considerable range with relative ease. But it is not so easy to ask a fish whether or not he can see small objects—at least it is not so easy to get him to reply. An answer was obtained, however, from the fresh-water sunfish, *Lepomis*, by using the response of the fish to background motion. If this type of fish is placed in a glass cylinder with a surrounding screen made of bars and spaces, the fish responds by a turning motion if it sees the screen rotate. It is through this kind of reaction that many fish maintain their position in a stream. Reactions of this sort are involved in rheotaxis, discussed in an earlier chapter. By reducing the light intensity in an experiment of this type until the sunfish no longer responded, the minimum illumination under which the fish could see small objects similar in size to the bars of the screen, was found to be one ten-billionth (or 10^{-10}) of the value of full sunlight (Grundfest, 1932). The threshold sensitivity of the human eye is similar, and the value for other vertebrates is probably generally of the same order of magnitude.

Assuming that the threshold illumination for other species of fish is similar to *Lepomis*, determinations were made from transparency measurements of the approximate depths at which this minimum intensity of light would occur under different circumstances, and hence the maximum depths at which vision would probably be possible, although other optical conditions such as color and contrast with background would have to be taken into account (Clarke, 1936). In most lakes except the most turbid and in typical coastal areas vision would appear to be possible for fish similar to *Lepomis* at all levels right down to the bottom. In the open ocean beyond the margins of the continental shelf the water is far deeper than this maximum depth for vision. If deep-sea fishes can see as well in blue light as the sunfish tested could see in green light, then vision would be possible for them at depths of more than 700 m in the clear tropical ocean.

Many aquatic animals may show some activity response to the increase or decrease of light at still lower intensities. Studies of the diurnal vertical migration of zooplankton indicate that certain species may react to light from the surface at 800 m and possibly at 1000 m, or more than half a mile down. This depth probably represents the biological zero for the response to daylight penetrating from the surface. Below this level day and night no longer exist, and no seasonal change in illumination can be detected. Since the average depth of the ocean is about 4000 m, it is clear that more than three-fourths of the volume of this environment is devoid of any influence of daylight. The whole of the deep sea is by no means completely dark, however. Light of biological origin occurs irregularly through the marine environment, and bioluminescent organisms are sometimes very abundant in the sea.

Bioluminescence. Our discussion up to this point has dealt primarily with light emanating directly or indirectly from the sun, but light of biological origin, known as *bioluminescence,* or popularly as "phosphorescence," has ecological significance under certain circumstances. As mentioned above, bioluminescence is the only source of light in the deep sea. Near the surface of the ocean and on land it is frequently prominent during the night, but it rarely occurs in fresh water. Luminescence is produced by members of various taxonomic groups scattered through the animal kingdom including in the sea certain fishes, crustaceans, coelenterates, and many other invertebrates, and on land particularly the insects. Fungi and such microorganisms as the dinoflagellates and many groups of bacteria also are luminescent. For a complete summary of the occurrence and physiology of bioluminescence the reader should refer to the book on the subject by Harvey (1952).

The very considerable amount of illumination that can be provided by luminescent organisms may be appreciated by anyone who catches some fireflies and brings them into a darkened room. A few fireflies in a bottle will provide sufficient light for reading newsprint. The "phosphorescence" of the sea sometimes is almost dazzlingly brilliant on a dark night, at which time waves and the wake of a boat appear like "burning water." The bodies of fish and other organisms swimming through the water are outlined by millions of tiny lights. This illumination is caused by the luminescent discharge of the plankton organisms. Measurements have shown that the intensity of light emitted by the surface waters of the sea may be one thousand times greater than the threshold intensity for the vision of man.

Bioluminescence is thus sufficiently strong to evoke reactions under a variety of circumstances. Although this living light may serve no useful purpose in some situations, in other instances it probably fulfills one or more of the following functions: (1) illumination, (2) recognition, (3) lure, and (4) warning.

The luminescence of deep sea animals undoubtedly provides a useful amount of illumination for the individuals producing it as well as for other inhabitants in the immediate neighborhood. In shallow water and on land during the night animals may similarly use their photophores as lanterns. The employment of luminescence in recognition of one sex by another is clearly exemplified by the firefly. Among the American *Lampyridae* each species has a characteristic code of flashing by which the females can recognize males of the same species and distinguish them from males of other species. After dark the female climbs up on a blade of grass and when a flying male signals in her vicinity she attracts him to herself by recognizable flashes in response (Harvey, 1952, Ch. 13).

In the abyssal depths of the sea, fish can perhaps locate each other by recognizing the pattern of lights presented by the luminescent organs. It has also been suggested that squid are able to keep together in a school during the dark hours of the night by means of their characteristic flashing.

Animals may lure prey by means of their luminescent organs. Since many small fish and planktonic invertebrates are attracted to light, these animals would be expected to move toward the luminescent organs of predatory fish, many of which are located near the jaws or even on filaments dangled in front of the mouth. On the other hand, the sudden flash of luminescent organs may act as a warning to scare off predators. Certain deep-sea shrimps produce a luminescent secretion that may be discharged into the water. This is an interesting counterpart to the sepia produced by squid and cuttlefish in shallow water. When the latter are attacked, they can discharge the black secretion into the water and escape from their enemies in the "smoke screen" thus produced. In the inky blackness of the deep sea the shrimps that produce a luminous discharge when attacked may be able to escape in a "cloud of light" (Fig. 6.9)—or these sudden emissions may act simply by distracting or frightening the enemy.

The possession of luminescence may be a definite disadvantage for some organisms if it gives away their presence to enemies. For other species the emission of light may be an accidental by-product of metabolism and hold no ecological significance whatsoever. We cannot imagine, for example, any possible benefit for bacteria that could be derived from their production of luminescence.

A correlation has been thought to exist in the marine environment between the occurrence of eyes, the type of coloration, and the presence of daylight or luminescence. Eyes are well developed among animals inhabiting the upper layer of the ocean, and luminescent organs occur in widely different groups. At somewhat deeper levels the eyes of fish tend to be enlarged or "telescopic" and in some species directed upwards. At greater depths eyes are often degenerate or entirely absent. Eyes would perhaps be of little use here since both daylight and animal light produce very meager illumination.

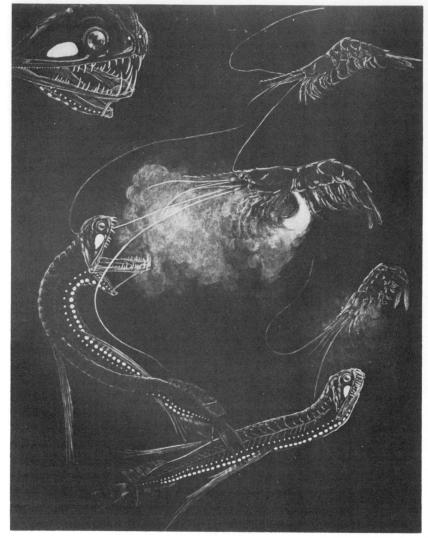

N.G.S. *Copyright, 1934*

FIG. 6.9. Drawing to illustrate the appearance of the photophores of the deep sea fish *Photostomias guernei* and of the luminous discharge of the shrimp *Acanthephyra purpurea* in the inky blackness of the ocean abyss.

In the ocean abyss by contrast, many fish possess well-developed eyes and the bottom-living organisms produce abundant luminescence (Sverdrup et al., 1942).

In caves no luminescence is produced by the aquatic inhabitants and only one terrestrial form—the New Zealand glowworm (*Arachnocampa luminosa*)—is known to be luminescent. The fauna of caves that are completely cut off from daylight consists typically of species that are blind or have degenerate eyes. Cave animals usually have little pigment and contrast strongly with the jet black or dark red deep-sea animals. The heavy pigmentation of the latter may perhaps be explained as a protective adaptation serving to reduce the reflection of luminescent light from their surfaces and hence the chance of detection. Since cave waters are completely dark, the whitish coloration of the inhabitants would be of no disadvantage on this score.

Orientation

Light often plays a significant role in orienting the growth or locomotion of plants and animals. Since orientation to light is often associated with reactions to other factors in the environment, such as gravity, we shall first consider the subject in general terms. Orientation is brought about either by the differential growth or movement of parts of the organism or by a change in the direction of locomotion of the whole organism. The question of why plants and animals grow or move in the directions they do has occupied the attention of investigators for a long time. Many of the theories and terms used have been in conflict, and for a more extended discussion reference should be made to Fraenkel and Gunn (1940) and to Griffin (1953).

The term *tropism* is best used for orientation by growth or turgor movements as exhibited by sessile forms. These forms are usually plants, but essentially the same type of orientation is exhibited by many sessile animals such as the hydroids. If the orientation is to gravity, the term *geotropism* is used. If it is to light, the growth movement is referred to as *phototropism*, and other prefixes are used for other orienting factors. On the other hand, the orientation of the locomotion of motile organisms is best referred to as a *taxis*, although it is sometimes also called a tropism. Here the forms involved are usually animals, although motile plants such as the green flagellates and motile plant gametes or zoospores are included. Applying suitable prefixes, we obtain the terms *geotaxis, phototaxis*, etc., for orientation by the corresponding factors. Orientation in the direction of an orienting force is referred to as a positive tropism or taxis; orientation in the opposition direction is a negative tropism or taxis. Occasionally a transverse tropism or taxis is displayed.

Control of speed of locomotion by the intensity of the factor is termed a *kinesis*. Gravity never changes significantly in intensity, but the speed of swimming, flying, or creeping is influenced by alterations in the strength of other factors; the common occurrence of photokinesis has already been mentioned.

The position of the main axis of the body is the primary orientation of the plant or animal. This is usually determined by gravity, as is seen in the upward growth (negative geotropism) of the shoot and the downward growth (positive geotropism) of the root of a plant seedling (Fig. 6.10). In the aquatic environment the buoyant action

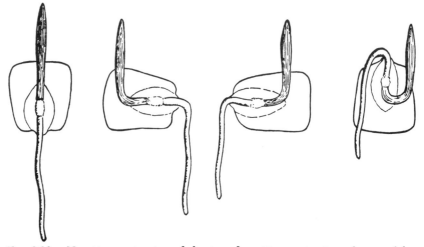

Fɪɢ. 6.10. Negative geotropism of shoots and positive geotropism of roots of four kernels of maize that have germinated in different positions. (By permission from *Botany* by Sinnott, 1929, McGraw-Hill Book Co.)

of water often reduces the effect of gravity so that primary orientation is to light or to current. When the source of illumination is from the side, the primary orientation of a land plant will be a compromise between the influence of gravity and that of light.

The primary orientation of motile organisms is also usually to gravity, and a walking or a flying animal continually adjusts its position to it. However, a fly on the ceiling or on a wall is quite unconcerned as to which side up it is, since it is oriented primarily in relation to the surface upon which its feet rest. Sometimes orientation is brought about passively by the resistance of the appendages as gravity draws the organism through the medium, as is seen in a "floating" butterfly or in slowly sinking plankton.

Superimposed upon the primary orientation, many secondary responses to orienting influences take place. The tips of green plants grow toward the light and hence exhibit positive phototropism. The leaves are oriented generally at right angles to the incident radiation, thus receiving maximum illumination, and they sometimes form a symmetrical pattern (Fig. 6.11) and sometimes a mosaic, as is displayed by ivy leaves on a wall.

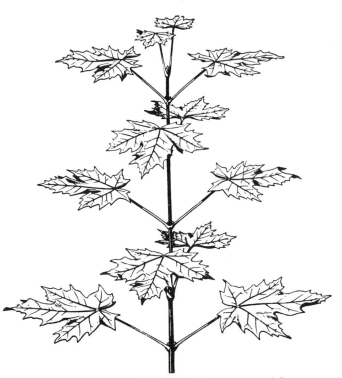

Fig. 6.11. Alternating position and horizontal orientation of leaves on shoot of Norway maple, resulting in maximum exposure to sunlight. (Shipley, 1925, after Kerner, Copyright, Cambridge Univ. Press.)

In such species as the sunflower the top portion of the plant or its leaves are turned by turgor changes during the course of the day, keeping always in the direction of the sun. In regions where light and heat from the sun are excessive, the leaves of some plants, such as the compass plant, *Silphium laciniatum,* are oriented so as to present their edges toward the sun. These examples will suffice to illustrate the turning reaction of phototropism by actual growth or by turgor movements.

Phototaxis, geotaxis, and other tactic reactions involve the orientation of locomotion toward or away from light, gravity, or some other source of stimulation in the environment. In many instances the turning of the moving organism appears to be due to the unequal stimulation of symmetrical sense receptors that control the tonus of the body, leg, or wing musculature. When the animal moves, it is caused to turn by the unequal posture of its locomotory apparatus. For example, in a positively phototactic animal such as the swimming insect *Ranatra*, if the left eye receives more light than the right eye, the legs on the left side of the body will be more strongly flexed, whereas the legs on the right side of the body will be more greatly

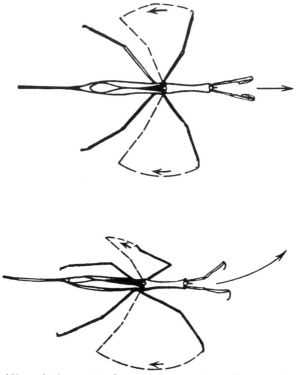

Fig. 6.12. (*Upper*) Symmetrical swimming position of positively phototactic *Ranatra* moving toward a light source in front of it. (*Lower*) Position of normal animal turning toward a light source at its left. This position will be produced permanently if the right eye is removed; if both eyes are removed, the animal's position becomes symmetrical again. (Crozier, 1929, Copyright, Clark Univ. Press.)

extended and will make longer sweeps. As the animal swims in this posture, it will tend to turn toward the source of light. Turning will continue until the amount of light received in the two eyes is equal, whereupon the legs will function symmetrically and the animal will swim straight ahead (Fig. 6.12). In many such instances the turning of the animal appears to be produced quite mechanically, and such reactions were referred to as "forced movements" by Jacques Loeb (1918) who originated the theory of orientation just described. In other instances orientation appears to come about by a trial-and-error procedure in which the animal changes its direction when it encounters unfavorable conditions and tries other directions until it finds a course in which conditions no longer stimulate it adversely.

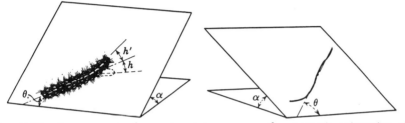

Fig. 6.13. Arrangement of experiment to measure the geotactic orientation at angle θ of caterpillar *Malacosoma* placed on plane inclined at angle a. Lateral movement of head indicated by h and h'. (Crozier, 1929, Copyright, Clark Univ. Press.)

Whether one adopts or rejects a mechanistic viewpoint in interpreting the reactions of organisms, the fact is that tropistic and tactic responses of plants and lower animals play a major role in their lives under natural conditions, and their orientation often appears to be rather rigidly controlled. An example of the mechanical way in which an orienting force may act is provided by an experiment involving the negative geotaxis of the tent caterpillar, *Malacosoma*. If this caterpillar is placed horizontally on a steeply sloping surface, an unequal stimulus of the proprioceptors located within the two sides of the body will result, owing to the animal's weight. A differential response in the tonus of the body muscles will then be produced, with the result that, as the animal creeps, it will turn to move up the slope (Fig. 6.13). As the caterpillar turns from its initial horizontal position toward the vertical, the difference in stimulation of the two sides of the body becomes progressively less, and eventually reaches a threshold beyond which no further turning is elicited. If the plane upon which the caterpillar is creeping is only slightly inclined (angle a), threshold discrimination is reached after a smaller amount of turning, or at a smaller final angle of orientation (θ). When the plane is steeper, the animal continues turning to a greater angle of orientation. The result of a series of trials made with varying angles indicates the mechanical nature of the taxis and the quantitatively exact way in which the response of the animal is controlled by the magnitude of the orienting stimulus (Fig. 6.14).

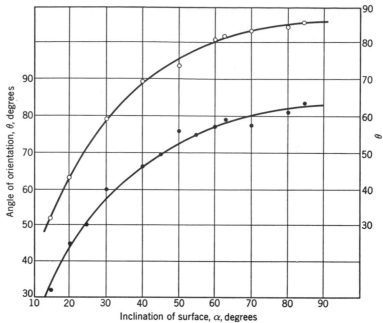

Fig. 6.14. Relation between the angle of inclination of plane (α) and the mean angle of orientation (θ) of caterpillar creeping upon it. Open circles are means for one individual; black circles are means for all individuals tested. The curve is that for $\Delta\theta/\Delta \log \sin \alpha = $ constant. (Crozier, 1929, Copyright, Clark Univ. Press.)

Orientation of growth and locomotion in relation to light and other factors plays a profoundly important role in the lives of plants and lower animals. The responses of all species that survive must obviously generally bring the organism into favorable surroundings, but lack of flexibility in these reactions often produces harmful results under extreme or unusual conditions. The rigidity of the tactic responses of the tent caterpillar is often seen to lead to its destruction. When the animals emerge from their nests in the crotches of trees, they crawl upward in response to their negative geotaxis to the tips of the branches where no doubt the juiciest leaves are found. The caterpillars later may return to the nest by following the silk threads they have left behind them on their upward journey, but they will not ordinarily move further downward over fresh surfaces. The two wild cherry trees shown in Fig. 6.15 have been completely defoliated

FIG. 6.15. Wild cherry trees in southern Rhode Island defoliated by tent caterpillars (*Malacosoma*), whose nests are seen in the forks of the branches. Neighboring oak trees were not attacked.

by tent caterpillars. Following the consumption of all the leaves in their tree, many caterpillars starve, or die of disease (Craighead, 1950) but others crawl or fall to the ground and eventually find their way to another tree. For some reason, as yet unknown, this species does not ordinarily eat oak leaves, and in the area photographed the oak trees only a meter or so away were not attacked. As the time for pupation approaches, negative geotaxis becomes strong and the animals tend to climb up any vertical object encountered. In a neighboring area a series of fence posts was found, on the top of each of which was a seething mass of tent caterpillars that had gathered there as a result of the reactions just described. Since the animals were slaves to their geotaxis, they remained on the fence posts, and, finding nothing else to eat, they proceeded to devour each other.

When an animal moves vertically under normal illumination from above, it is often difficult to ascertain whether the animal is reacting primarily to gravity or to light; that is, if it moves upward, it may be displaying a negative geotaxis, a positive phototaxis, or both. Experiments can be devised that distinguish between the responses of which the animal is capable. An example of such an experiment is given in Fig. 6.16 in which the response of a negatively geotactic and a negatively phototactic *Agriolimax* is shown. When light is allowed to act at right angles to gravity, this lowly garden slug can resolve the forces with more alacrity than is displayed by some college students! The first trial indicated in the diagram was made when the animal was dark-adapted and its reaction to light was stronger than that to gravity. A decrease in the strength of phototaxis as the animal became light-adapted is indicated by the change in the angle of orientation in successive trials.

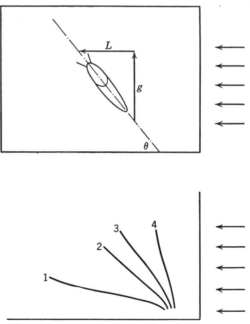

Fɪɢ. 6.16. (*Upper*) Orientation of negatively geotactic and negatively phototactic *Agriolimax* on a vertical plane with light from the right. L = phototactic vector, g = geotactic vector, θ = angle of orientation. (*Lower*) Successive trials at 1-minute intervals made by initially dark-adapted *Agriolimax* on a vertical plane. (Crozier, 1929, Copyright, Clark Univ. Press.)

Other complications occur in the orientation to light. Diffuse light has been shown to exert an effect upon planktonic copepods that is different from that produced by light from a single source. Many plankters are found to be positively phototactic to an electric light, but these animals do not generally swim upwards to the surface of the water toward the sun since the diffuse side illumination in the ocean inhibits the reaction to a single source (Schallek, 1943).

The familiar "bee-line" course which the honeybee takes from its hive to a source of food is determined as a definite angle to the direction of the sun. The bee does not fly directly toward or away from the sun, but orients at an angle to the changing azimuth of the sun. Upon returning to the hive, the bee communicates to its fellow workers by a special "wagging dance" both the approximate distance and the direction relative to the sun of the food that it has discovered. Still more remarkable is the fact that the worker bee is not required to see the sun directly but can be oriented by a small patch of blue sky. The bee's compound eye has been shown to be sensitive to the angle of polarization of sky light, and the bee apparently uses this information in combination with other orienting forces to determine the proper line of flight when the sun is obscured. The bee usually restricts its visits to one species of plant at a time—a fact that is of obvious advantage both to the bee's efficiency and to the plant's successful pollination. Flower species are recognized by shape, scent, and color; the bee's eye can distinguish yellow, blue-green, blue, and ultraviolet, but it is blind to red (von Frisch, 1950).

The ability of homing and migrating birds and fish to find their way over long distances is perhaps even more amazing. The precise method of navigation used by such far-ranging vertebrates has mystified observers for generations. Although birds may use landmarks, persisting cloud formations, prevailing winds, and other ecological cues to some extent, these possibilities do not appear to explain all instances (Griffin, 1952). Evidence has been obtained that certain species of birds may use the direction of sunlight as a means of orientation and that the birds are able to allow for the change in the sun's position during the day (Kramer, 1952).

Under natural conditions the direction of growth or of locomotion of plants or of animals is usually determined by several different influences acting simultaneously. In addition to such common orienting factors as light, gravity, temperature, and moisture, certain species may be guided by sound or other types of vibration, by scent or other chemical sense, or by other special reactions to environmental stimuli. We know that tropistic and tactic responses play a very large role in the lives of most lower organisms in nature. Reactions to the direction and intensity of the orienting influences of the habitat are responsible for getting motile organisms where we find them. In order to understand the mechanism of distribution of these forms, it is necessary to analyze the reactions involved. Many practical applications of such knowledge suggest themselves, such as the control of insect pests.

In attempting to interpret the locomotory reactions of organisms and to apply them to natural situations, the following considerations should be kept in mind: (1) Responses to individual stimuli are usually limited by the influence of other conditions. Thus the positively phototactic moth does not attempt to fly to the sun. (2) The observed distribution may be the result of movement without direct orientation. The reduced locomotory activity of wood lice in situations where moisture is high results in a tendency for these animals to congregate in moist places although they are not specifically oriented to them, just as the traffic on a main highway becomes denser in a bad stretch of road because the speed of the cars is reduced. (3) For an oriented response the orienting factor must provide a stimulus above the threshold of sensitivity, and either the direction of the flux of the orienting force or the direction of a gradient produced by it must be perceptible to the organism. The temperature gradient in the ocean, for example, may be shown to be below the threshold for the response of zooplankton (Clarke, 1934). (4) Factors whose gradients are below the threshold often exert an indirect effect by controlling the sign or the speed of the response to another factor. (5) Responses may similarly be altered under changed internal physiological conditions, as before or after feeding, or breeding. Within the same species the males, females, and various immature stages sometimes orient quite diversely. Thus, in general, we see that the distribution of plankton in the water, of microbes in the soil, or of insects in the vegetation is the result of a complex interplay of the orienting factors of the environment acting directly and indirectly on the changing physiological state of members of the population.

Periodicity

Diurnal Periodicity. A good number of the fundamental rhythms in nature are related to the light factor. Many animals and plants exhibit a 24-hour cycle in their activities; this has long been known as diurnal periodicity. However, the term *diel periodicity* may be substituted if confusion arises from the fact that *diurnal* is also used for daytime activity as opposed to *nocturnal* for nightime activity. The most fundamental diurnal rhythm is that of photosynthesis itself, which necessarily fluctuates because of the daily change of light. Many plants exhibit other more specialized reactions to the alternation of day and night, such as the opening and closing of flowers and the folding of leaves.

Although often not conspicuous, a very large number of the lower animals are controlled in their activities by the change in light from day to night. This is often a matter of simple photokinesis. The animals are more active in the light, less active in darkness or vice versa, but behavior may also be modified by concomitant diurnal changes in other factors such as temperature and humidity. Among the higher animals the reactions are often more elaborate, and sometimes the daily rhythm of activity is only indirectly related to light. Many of the relatively defenseless forms, such as mice, come out to forage chiefly at night when they are less likely to be detected by their enemies. As a further complication many of the predaceous animals are nocturnal as an adaptation to the night activity of their prey or to the fact that they can stalk their prey more successfully under cover of darkness. A patch of woods may be inhabited by two sets of animals which practically never meet because one set is active only during the day and the other active only during the night (Park, 1940).

The fact that a diurnal rhythm in the activity of an organism is sometimes deeply ingrained can often be demonstrated by bringing the organism into the laboratory and observing it under constant or under changed conditions of illumination. In one such experiment the deer mouse, *Peromyscus*, which is normally active at night and quiescent during the day, continued to display a diurnal rhythm in its behavior after seven months in continuous darkness. This and other experiments summarized by Welsh (1938) and by Park (1941) indicate that certain internal physiological processes have become attuned to a 24-hour cycle. In many organisms this rhythmicity persists for long periods and tides over periods when the usual controlling environmental stimulus fails to occur. Under normal conditions the timing of the periodicity is re-enforced by changes in light or other factors each day.

The diurnal shift in the activity of animals frequently results in significant changes in their position in the community. Perhaps no better illustration of this phenomenon could be found than the vertical migration of zooplankton in the sea and in lakes. In general, vast numbers of copepods and other planktonic animals tend to swim toward the surface at night and to move downward to deeper levels during the day. The diurnal changes in vertical distribution of females of the copepod, *Calanus*, in the Clyde Sea area are indicated in Fig. 6.17. The time of ascent in the evening and of descent in the

morning, as well as the depth to which the animals migrate, is correlated with the differences in time of sunset and sunrise and in the intensity of the noon sun during January and July. The complexity of
the response to light is revealed by the fact that in this same area, the
males and the various young stages of the same species exhibit quite
different patterns of behavior.

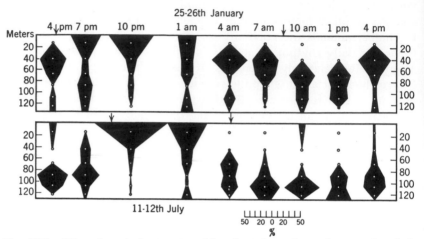

FIG. 6.17. Diurnal vertical migration of female *Calanus finmarchicus* in the Clyde
Sea area during 24-hour periods in January and in July. The abundance of the
population is indicated by the width of the figures. The times of sunset and
sunrise are indicated by arrows. (Nicholls, 1933, Copyright, Council of Marine
Biol. Assoc. of United Kingdom.)

Reactions to gravity and to temperature change often modify the
course or the extent of the vertical migration (Clarke, 1933). The
various theories dealing with the reactions of the zooplankton to the
factors believed to control vertical migration have been summarized
by Cushing (1951). The magnitude of the migration is indicated by
the fact that the copepod population may often move more than 100
m in a vertical direction. This represents a journey of more than
15,000 times the animal's own length twice each day. Even more extensive diurnal vertical migrations are carried out by euphausiids,
fish, and perhaps other large active forms. The widespread occurrence of changes in level of huge populations in the open ocean, during the course of the day, has been revealed by midwater echoes received by the underwater acoustical equipment of ships. A discussion of the kinds of animals probably responsible for this "deep scattering layer" and its vertical oscillation is presented by Moore (1950).
Similar vertical movements occur in terrestrial environments al-

though these are generally less extensive.   Many animals move from the surface to deeper levels in the soil at regular periods each day. Others emerge from under the ground litter at definite times during the diurnal cycle and ascend the vegetation.   Harvestmen, or "daddy-long-legs" (*Leiobunlum rotundum*), in an English oak wood were observed to descend from the tree trunks in the evening to the forest floor where they hunt their prey and to move up onto the trees again in the early morning (Todd, 1949).   Many other insects move regularly from lower levels in the herbs and shrubs to higher positions in the trees at dawn and return at dusk; others migrate in the reverse manner.   These changes in levels of whole populations, both in the water and on land, have profound repercussions on prey-predator relations and other interdependencies among the inhabitants.   For a further discussion of these aspects of stratification and periodicity in the community, the reader should refer to Allee et al. (1949, Ch. 28).

Lunar Periodicity.   Since the days of classical Greece interest has been attracted to the correlation of certain animal activities with periods of the moon.   Oppian in the time of Aristotle wrote:

The shellfish which creep in the sea are reported, all of them when the moon waxes, to fill up their flesh proportionately to her disk, occupying then a bigger space,   On the other hand when she wanes they shrivel and their members grow thinner.

It is true that in the Red Sea the gonads of the sea urchins (the edible portion) do enlarge during the period of the full moon, but the belief was spread fallaciously around the Mediterranean and elsewhere that the lunar cycle controlled many more animal activities than is actually the case.   One even meets the statement occasionally that the 28-day menstrual period in man harks back to our marine ancestors.   Since we know that the menstrual cycle in other mammals has very different periods, the approximate agreement of the human period with the 29.5-day lunar cycle is merely a coincidence.

Modern investigation has shown that the activity of certain widely different types of organisms, usually in relation to the reproductive cycle, shows a correlation with the moon.   The striking nature of these lunar periodicities is well illustrated by the fluctuation in the abundance of conjugants produced by a ciliate living as an ectoparasite on the gills of a fresh-water mussel (Fig. 6.18).   The distinct peaks occurred regularly on the days following the new moon and were not correlated with temperature or other known environmental changes.

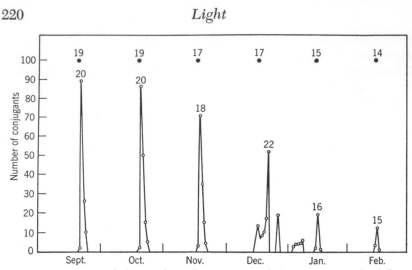

Fɪɢ. 6.18. Average daily number of conjugants of the ciliate *Conchophthirius lamellidens* on the gills of the fresh-water mussel *Lamellidens marginalis*. Dates of new moon (*top*) and of peak numbers are shown. (Ray and Chakraverty, 1934, *Nature.*)

Most of the organisms exhibiting lunar periodicities are marine and hence may be affected by the amplitude of the tide which is greatest at times of new moon and full moon (spring tides) and smallest at the times of the quarter moon (neap tides). For organisms living within the influence of the tides it is obviously difficult to determine how much of the effect may be due to moonlight itself and how much to the action of the tidal cycle. The marine alga, *Dictyota,* for example, produces its gametes at the time of the full-moon spring tide. The spawning of a number of marine polychaete worms shows various time correlations. The palolo worm inhabiting the waters of the South Pacific islands comes to the surface in great numbers on the last quarter of the moon during October and November, producing a luminescence and discharging eggs and sperm into the water. The natives know of the occurrence of this swarming of the palolo worm and take advantage of the opportunity to scoop up large quantities of these animals for food. The worms swim about in small circles in dense masses, giving the sea an appearance of spaghetti soup. The natives gather the worms in crude baskets and celebrate the occasion with religious rites and feasts.

The Bermuda fireworm puts on a similar display of fireworks in the shallow water early in the evening at the time of full moon. The reaction appears to be set off by the drop in light intensity following sunset (Huntsman, 1948). Professor E. L. Mark, who was for years director of the Bermuda Biological Station for Research, took a special interest in studying the swarming of this marine polychaete. He found that swarming and luminescence began at about 55 minutes after sunset and lasted for half an hour. On one occasion when Professor Mark was traveling to Bermuda he realized that he would arrive on a day when the fireworms were due to appear. He interested his fellow passengers in the phenomenon, telling them that the timing was so exact that one could set one's watch by it and invited a large group of people to come to the shore that evening. When the moment arrived for the beginning of the display, not a worm was in sight, nor was there after 5 minutes, 10 minutes, and more. Soon people, feeling that they had been hoodwinked, began moving away, but 20 minutes after the appointed time the worms appeared in great numbers and a spectacular demonstration was given for the visitors who still remained. Not until the next day was Dr. Mark's embarrassment relieved when it was discovered that during the winter Bermuda time had been changed from local sun time to zonal time, resulting in setting the Bermuda clocks ahead 19 minutes.

Perhaps the most fascinating of all the responses of animals to the lunar or tidal cycle is that exhibited by the grunion or California smelt. On the three or four days after the spring tides from April to June the grunion swims in on the beaches of southern California to lay its eggs in the sand. During this period the higher of the daily high tides comes at night. About an hour after the water reaches its highest level on each of these nights the fish allow themselves to be carried up on the beach by the waves. As each wave recedes, an observer can discern hundreds or thousands of fish left behind, wriggling in the wet sand (Fig. 6.19). Within a few seconds the females have burrowed tail first into the sand where they deposit the eggs while the males curl around them discharging the sperm. When the next wave comes in, the fish are washed out to sea once more. Since the eggs have been discharged during the period of descending tides after the highest spring tides and during the hours following high tide each night, the waves do not reach them again during the next two weeks. The eggs are thus left undisturbed to develop in the warm, moist sand. When the next spring tide occurs, the eroding surf of the rising tide uncovers the eggs, now ready to hatch out, and the young larvae swim away. In order for this complicated relationship between the life cycle of the fish and the tides to be carried out, the fish, which ordinarily remain in the waters offshore, must be stimulated in some way to move in to the beach on the proper day and to allow themselves to be stranded on the shore by the waves

FIG. 6.19. Flashlight photograph of grunion (*Leuresthes tenuis*) spawning on Malibu Beach near Los Angeles, California. The females bury themselves tail first in the sand. The males then circle around them and fertilize the eggs. (Photo by Moody Institute of Science.)

only during the proper hour. Just how this timing is controlled has not yet been discovered despite a considerable amount of study. The complexity of the interplay of the tidal and lunar influences and the remarkable precision of the responses of the grunion are indicated in Fig. 6.20.

The foregoing are representative of the varied occurrences of lunar periodicities in nature of which many more instances could be cited (Korringa, 1947). A definite control of the timing of the reproductive cycle is usually indicated, and frequently other special activities such as swarming or luminescent discharge are involved. The mechanism by which the timing is controlled is far from clear, however. For some organisms the changing amount of moonlight may be of chief importance either directly or as a degree of contrast with sunlight or starlight. Since the intensity of full moonlight is more than 10^{-6} of noon sunlight, it is well above the threshold for the response of many organisms. As an alternative the cyclic change in the relation of the moon's gravity has been suggested as possibly controlling the activity of fish and other organisms. Many sportsmen strongly believe that such lunar gravitational fluctuations influence the success of their fishing. At the present time, however, we have no evidence

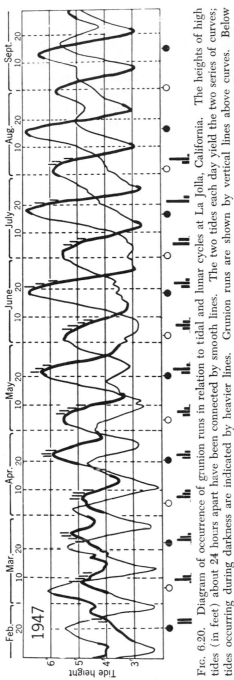

FIG. 6.20. Diagram of occurrence of grunion runs in relation to tidal and lunar cycles at La Jolla, California. The heights of high tides (in feet) about 24 hours apart have been connected by smooth lines. The two tides each day yield the two series of curves; tides occurring during darkness are indicated by heavier lines. Grunion runs are shown by vertical lines above curves. Below graph: open circle is full moon, solid circle is new moon; histograms indicate percentage intensity of runs. (Walker, 1952.)

that the sense organs of any type of animal could respond to the differences in the moon's gravitational effect.

For marine animals of the littoral zone the moon's influence often appears to be mediated at least in part through the change in the tides, but certain lunar periodicities occur in regions where tides are slight or lacking. One great difficulty in studying this problem is that often the behavior pattern persists for a while under changed conditions, as when the moon is obscured, apparently because of a correlation with an internal rhythm. Much more investigation will be required before these intriguing periodicities are completely understood.

Seasonal Periodicity. The seasonal activities of plants and animals are sometimes due to changes in temperature and are sometimes controlled by the cycle of dry and rainy seasons; seasonal periodicity may also be influenced by the light factor. The seasonal effect of light is not so much due to differences in intensity as it is to differences in total amount of light and in the relative lengths of day and night. The response of organisms to daylength is known as *photoperiodism.* The most striking manifestation of photoperiodism is the control of the reproductive cycle in certain plants and animals, although other life processes are involved in some instances. In these organisms the reproductive phase of the life cycle is initiated by days that are shorter or longer than certain critical lengths. Under natural conditions short days are accompanied by long nights and vice versa. Experimental manipulation of the photoperiod has revealed facts indicating that the length of the night may be more influential than the length of the day in controlling the photoperiodic responses of at least some of the plants and animals, but the precise mode of action of the light factor has not yet been determined (Farner et al., 1953).

Photoperiodism was first discovered in relation to plants. Species that flower only when the days are longer than a certain number of hours and the nights are correspondingly short are known as *long-day plants.* *Short-day plants,* on the other hand, flower naturally only under conditions of short days and long nights. However, the reproductive cycle of certain other species is not affected by daylength; these are referred to as *indeterminate* or *indifferent* plants. This aspect of periodicity in the light factor controls the season at which long-day and short-day plants flower in any locality, and it also influences the geographical distribution of the species.

Long-day plants flower naturally only in the middle or high latitudes during the late spring or early summer. Familiar examples are the radish, iris, red clover, evening primrose, spinach, the smaller cereals, and timothy. If such plants are grown under daylengths shorter than the critical photoperiod, stems tend to be shorter and flowering is suppressed (Fig. 6.21). Other effects may also be produced in the plant, as illustrated by long-day potatoes which produce the best tubers when daylength is below the optimum for shoot growth.

FIG. 6.21. Control of flowering and of vegetative growth by daylength in timothy, a typical long-day plant. The daily exposures (in hours) to light are indicated on each container; *C* = natural daylength. Photo taken in July. (Evans and Allard, 1934.)

In the growing season outside the tropical zone short days occur both in the early spring and in the late summer. Certain short-day plants require a long growing period before they are sufficiently mature to react to the flowering stimulus, and such plants can flower only in the shorter days following the summer solstice. Familiar plants that can bloom naturally only late in the year are tobacco, goldenrod, aster, dahlia, ragweed, cosmos, and chrysanthemum. In daylengths above the critical abnormally great vegetative growth takes place and flowering is much delayed or entirely inhibited (Fig. 6.22). Short-day onions and beets develop the largest storage organs under photoperiods that are longer than those best for the growth of the upper part of the plant.

The plants that bloom in the short days of early spring are mostly perennials in which the flower buds were set the previous autumn. The few annuals blooming at this season either germinated during the winter or are so small that they need little time for vegetative

FIG. 6.22.   Control of flowering and of type of vegetative growth by daylength in garden chrysanthemum, a typical short-day plant.   The daily exposures (in hours) to light are indicated on each container; $C =$ natural daylength.   Photo taken in July.   Flowering occurred as follows: 10 hr, July 6; 12 hr, Oct. 14; 13 hr, Oct. 19; 14 hr, Oct. 31; natural day, Oct. 31.   (Allard and Garner, 1940.)

growth before flowering.   Early spring flowers growing on the floor of the deciduous forest are able to take advantage of the great amount of light available before the tree leaves are fully developed.

Since short days occur later in the summer at higher latitudes, the northward distribution of short-day plants may be stopped by the lack of sufficient time for the ripening and hardening of the seed between the occurrene of the critical daylength and the occurrence of a killing frost that terminates the growing season.   Ragweed, for example, which flowers when the days have shortened to $14\frac{1}{2}$ hours, will begin its reproductive phase about the first of July in Virginia, and hay-fever sufferers notice its pollen in the air by the middle of August.   In northern Vermont the summer days are not reduced to $14\frac{1}{2}$ hours until after the first of August, with the result that seed formation is not completed before cold weather, and consequently ragweed is unable to establish itself in abundance at this latitude. The distribution of long-day plants toward the equator is limited by the reverse action of this aspect of the light factor.   Species of *Sedum* that require a daylength of 16 hours or more will flower abundantly in Vermont but will not bloom in Virginia (Naylor, 1952).

Plant species in which flowering is not controlled by daylength also occur at all latitudes, but all plants growing at high latitudes must be able to tolerate long days and short nights since these light conditions exist during the growing season, and tropical plants must be able to complete their development under photoperiods of about 12 hours' duration. Since the vegetation of intermediate latitudes is composed of a mixture of long-day, short-day, and indifferent plants, the seasons of vegetative growth, flowering, and seed dissemination vary among the species of the community, and competition is reduced accordingly. In some instances genetic strains of the same species growing under different climatic conditions respond differently to given photoperiods, apparently, as an adaptation to differences in the time of onset of adverse conditions. The possibility of intraspecific variation of this sort among both plants and animals in their response to all types of environmental factors must constantly be kept in mind.

The control of the reproductive cycle by the length of day is a result of a complicated balance between life processes that go on in the light and in the dark (Leopold, 1951). Since the intensity of light which influences the photoperiodic response is far below that needed for photosynthesis, we know that the reactions responsible are quite different. The delicate nature of the processes involved are indicated by the fact that only a few minutes, or even a few seconds, of light during the middle of a long night may reverse the flowering reaction of the plant. The tasseling of sugar cane can be inhibited by a short light period during the night, and the possibility of retarding the ripening of the crop until the most favorable time for harvesting by sweeping the cane fields with search lights has been investigated by Hawaiian planters. In greenhouse plants and other commercial species the timing of the production of flowers, seeds, fruits, or storage organs is controlled artificially by means of the photoperiodic response.

Photoperiodism similarly plays an important role in the life cycles of many kinds of animals and, interestingly enough, also most frequently controls the reproductive cycle. However, wing production in aphids, metamorphosis in mosquitos, pelage changes in fur bearers (Lyman, 1942), and other life processes are known to be influenced by daylength. The most extensive studies have been carried out on mammals and birds, and these have been reviewed by Bissonette (1936) and Burger (1949). Trout that ordinarily spawn in December can be induced to lay their eggs in August by artificially changing the daylength. The fresh-water pulmonate snail, *Lymnaea palustris,* will not lay eggs on an 11-hour day but lays abundantly when the days are 13½ hours long or longer. The control of reproduction by daylength in this species rather than by temperature was neatly demonstrated under natural conditions by the fact that snails living in a spring with practically no seasonal change in temperature began laying eggs during the same week as did snails inhabiting a shallow ditch that underwent rapid vernal warming (Jenner, 1951). Very little additional investigation of photoperiodism among the invertebrates has been made, but this reaction to light may eventually be found to play an important role in controlling the life cycle of many of the less conspicuous animals. Among mammals certain forms, such as ferrets, are brought into breeding condition by the long days of spring, but others, such as deer, come into heat during the short days of autumn.

Photoperiodism in birds was first discovered as a result of studies of migration. It had long been realized that the arrival of birds in the spring was not closely related to temperature or other common aspects of the weather since birds are often caught by late winter conditions. A similar difficulty arose in explaining the start of the southward migration. Many birds leave the northern regions during July or August when the temperature is high, and when an ample food supply is still available (Fig. 6.23). The length of day was finally

Photo by Allan D. Cruickshank, National Audubon Society

FIG. 6.23.   Tree swallows flocking previous to migration.

recognized as one environmental factor that changed regularly year in and year out and that could account for the exact timing of the migration regardless of the weather conditions. Present evidence indicates that the effect of the daylength is brought about through controlling the amount of light reaching a sensitive tissue in the bird's body (the pituitary gland). Under natural conditions the larger amount of light received during the long days of spring causes an increase in the size of the gonads and also, in some way as yet unknown, sets off the northward migration. Following the breeding season the diminishing daylengths of late summer and autumn cause a decrease in gonad size and provide the stimulus for the southward migration. Evidence on the mode of action of light and other factors on bird migration has been summarized by Farner (1950).

Although photoperiodism thus appears to be basically involved in the annual stimulus for the migration of birds, it does not explain the evolutionary origin of the migratory habit nor, most mysterious of all, how the birds find their way. Once established, however, migration would tend to be perpetuated by its advantages. At higher latitudes the longer days make more time available for nest building and for feeding the young. The young grow more rapidly, and hence the whole process of rearing the family, with its attendant dangers, is completed more quickly than would be the case nearer the equator. By leaving the north during the winter, on the other hand, the birds avoid the hazards of low temperatures and shortage of food.

The migration of birds is evidently a secondary effect of the influence of light. The primary effect is in the control of the breeding cycle since this can be demonstrated in species of birds that do not migrate. The occurrence of breeding in the English sparrow at different latitudes over the face of the earth is indicated in Fig. 6.24. Near the equator some breeding takes place in every month of the year. In areas farther north and farther south reproduction tends to be confined to the months of the year with longer days. North of 50° N latitude breeding is strongly centered in the month of May with no breeding at all during the months of short daylength, and south of 50° S latitude most breeding takes place in December. Outside of the tropics, therefore, the light factor plays an important role in confining the breeding period to the months of the year when reproduction is most successfully carried forward. Since short daylength prevents birds from entering the breeding condition too early and the long days of midspring act to speed up the laggards, the whole population tends to breed within the same favorable period (Bartholomew, 1949).

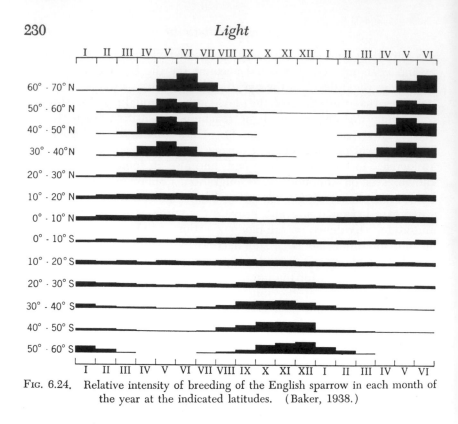

FIG. 6.24. Relative intensity of breeding of the English sparrow in each month of the year at the indicated latitudes. (Baker, 1938.)

Ultraviolet Light

The small fraction of the sun's radiation that reaches the earth as ultraviolet light has certain very special biological effects, and some of these may be of ecological significance. The sensitivity of the bee's eye to this part of the spectrum and its use in orientation has already been mentioned. The population size of certain land animals in north central United States was found by Shelford (1951 and 1951a) to be correlated with the intensity of ultraviolet light, although the reactions that underlie the correlation are not known. The bactericidal action of ultraviolet is familar and causes the destruction of microorganisms that are excessively exposed to the direct rays of the sun. Ultraviolet radiation produces sunburn, or erythema, in man and perhaps causes harmful effects in other animals under natural conditions, although this question has not been investigated from the ecological viewpoint. Ultraviolet also brings about the production of vitamin D with its antirachitic effect. Vitamin D is formed by the irradiation by ultraviolet light of certain sterols, or fatty substances, that occur in both plants and animals. The relative effect of different wavelengths in producing the foregoing influences is shown in Fig. 6.25. Although the curves differ very much from one another throughout most of the range, it is clear that in no instance is ultraviolet radiation effective at wavelengths longer than about 3100 A.

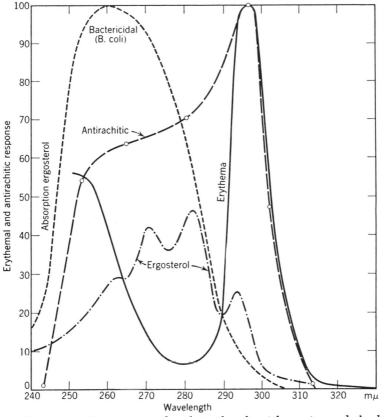

Fig. 6.25. Relation between wavelength in the ultraviolet region and the bactericidal, erythemic, and antirachitic effects of ultraviolet radiation, together with the absorption of ergosterol. (Coblentz, 1939, Copyright, J. Am. Medical Assoc.)

Under ordinary conditions no measurable radiation from the sun reaches the earth's surface at wavelengths shorter than 2950 A. It is clear then that under natural conditions the whole action of ultraviolet must occur between 3100 A and 2950 A. Under the best circumstances solar radiation is extremely weak in this region, and when dust or smoke is abundant the shorter wavelengths are still further reduced. During the winter in the neighborhood of cities no measurable radiation shorter than 3100 A can be found, and hence no appreciable action of ultraviolet can take place at that season. When birds that ordinarily migrate south were retained in Alberta, they died during the winter apparently from lack of vitamin D. Nevertheless, we have little evidence that the lack of ultraviolet in winter is generally of crucial ecological importance, but the matter should be investigated further.

In the aquatic environment ultraviolet is still further reduced by the very rapid rate at which it is absorbed even in the clearest water. Although in some quarters popular imagination has fixed upon the idea that ultraviolet is the most penetrating region of the spectrum, actual measurements have shown that radiation at 3100 A is reduced to 10 per cent of its surface value at a depth of 15 m in the extremely clear water of the Mediterranean and at 1 m in Gullman Fjord on the coast of Sweden. The shorter and biologically more active wavelengths are reduced even more rapidly by absorption and scattering in the water (Jerlov, 1951). In most natural waters the effectiveness of ultraviolet diminishes very rapidly with depth. Carefully controlled experiments have revealed no bactericidal action below 1 m and probably none at depths greater than 20 cm even in clear ocean water. The ecological effect of the lethal action of ultraviolet in very shallow water awaits further study. It is possible that the bacterial population on the bottom mud in the littoral zone is seriously affected when exposed at low water.

How can we account for the formation of vitamin D in fish liver oils? Cod and halibut whose oils are particularly rich in vitamin D live far below the depth at which any measurable ultraviolet could penetrate. It has been suggested that the vitamin D might reach the fish livers through a food chain starting with the phytoplankton and the zooplankton that live near the surface of the sea. Since cod and halibut are bottom feeders, a long food chain must be postulated to extend to the forms on which these fish live. Another suggestion is that the vitamin D formed in the Sargassum weed as it floats near the surface of the tropical oceans finds it way via the food chain into such species as the cod. For the most part we know that the animals associated with the Sargassum weed do not eat the weed directly but live on plankton or materials accumulating on the surfaces of the fronds. In addition we know that a sharp temperature barrier exists between the regions where the Sargassum weed is abundant and areas inhabited by such fish as the cod and halibut. The amount of vitamin D in the liver oils of these species is very great. It seems inconceivable that the supply could have resulted from such tenuous food chains as are described above, even if the fish were able to retain the vitamins in their bodies as mammals are not. Nor has any method been shown by which an animal could manufacture vitamin D without the presence of ultraviolet light. The actual source of the large quantities of vitamin D in the fish liver oils thus remains a mystery. It emphasizes again how little we know about ecological influences of this region of the spectrum, both in the water and on land.

Ecological Aspects of Photosynthesis

Light is fundamentally important as the essential direct source of energy for the growth of all green plants and the purple bacteria. The photosynthetic plants form the first step in the ecological cycle in every natural situation. They are the first link in the food chain and hence are the base of the production pyramid that will be discussed in greater detail later on.

Land Plants. On the surface of the land enough light is received everywhere for the growth of plants of some sort. Within the soil and in the interior of caves light is insufficient to allow photosynthesis. A striking illustration of the limiting action of the light factor is found in caves to the walls of which electric lamps have been secured for the benefit of tourists. Within the cone of light immediately around each lamp mosses have grown from spores brought in by air currents. These "islands" of plant growth present a sharp contrast to the complete lack of vegetation in the remainder of the cave.

Although illumination is generally sufficient for photosynthesis over the entire surface of the globe, the local distribution of individual species of plants is definitely influenced by differences in the availability of light. Species that can grow in shady places are termed *tolerant*, and, although the degree of tolerance is affected by soil moisture, temperature, and other factors, the illumination is the principal controlling influence. Plants that require strong illumination and will not survive or develop in reduced light are referred to as *intolerant* species. Trees such as the spruce, hemlock, beech, and sugar maple, shrubs, such as spicebush, and herbs, such as bloodroot, can grow in deep shade and are examples of tolerant species. The sugar maple can photosynthesize adequately in situations where the illumination is reduced to less than 2 per cent of full sunlight. Birch trees, poplars, willows, and several species of pine, as well as many shrubs and herbs such as sumac, bluestem grasses, and sunflowers are intolerant of shade. The ponderosa pine, for example, requires a light intensity equal to at least 25 per cent of full sunlight.

Intolerant species cannot develop in the shade of a dense stand of their own or other species. Ecological consequences of this fact for the plant community will be discussed further in later chapters. Even among somewhat tolerant species the first plants to become established in an open area will grow to better advantage than individuals subsequently developing around them because of the competition for light and other needs. Differential growth often results in "pyramiding" in the development of such a group of plants (Fig. 6.26). As we have seen in an earlier section, the light on the floor

Fig. 6.26. Pyramiding due to competition exhibited by a group of spruce trees growing in a Michigan bog.

of the temperate deciduous forest becomes seriously reduced when the trees leaf out. Many of the smaller plants are adapted to a period of rapid growth in the early spring while light on the forest floor is sufficiently intense. In the marginal rainforest of Panama a dense undergrowth is possible because during the dry season the leaves fall from the trees and allow light to penetrate. In the equatorial rainforest of Columbia, on the other hand, trees shed their leaves individually and a continuous canopy is maintained, with the result that little vegetation can grow on the forest floor.

In such rainforests many smaller plants have gained access to sufficient illumination by the evolution of the epiphytic habit, that is, by growing in the crotches or on the horizontal branches of the trees. The vertical distribution of the many species of bromeliads in the forest trees of Trinidad reveals their varying degrees of tolerance (Fig. 6.27). One group of species grows only near the tree tops in situations fully exposed to the sun, a second group is found at intermediate levels in partial sunlight, and a shade-tolerant third group inhabits the lower branches of the forest where the illumination is quite inadequate for the other groups.

Aquatic Plants. Reduction of light presents even more serious problems in the aquatic environment. As we have seen illumination diminishes rapidly with depth even in clear water and becomes changed in spectral composition and in other respects. Plants attached to the bottom in the marine environment consist principally of algae with a few species of vascular plants such as the eel grass. In fresh water vascular plants as well as algae are well represented in the submerged vegetation.

Early investigators reported an apparent color zonation in the depth of occurrence of attached plants. In Puget Sound, for example, the green algae are generally the most abundant in shallow water, brown algae dominate the zone from 5 to 20 m, and red algae are usually most numerous in depths of 10 to 30 m. These color types of algae often occur at depths where the complementary color of the penetrating daylight predominates—red algae, for example, tend to be abundant in deep water where the blue or green component of daylight is the strongest. It was formerly believed that the predominating color of the light controlled the depth distribution of the color types of algae because the plants would absorb light of complementary color more efficiently. This generality was referred to as *chromatic adaptation*. Many exceptions occur, however, and we now know that the wavelength of light does not control in any precise way the depth of distribution of algae on the basis of their color (Dutton and Juday, 1944). Furthermore, the pigment of algae living in weak light deep in the water is sufficiently thick to absorb all the light incident upon it, regardless of the part of the spectrum in which it occurs. Evidence exists that some of the light energy absorbed by pigments other than chlorophyll can be transferred to the chlorophyll present and thus enhance the ability of certain algae to live in weak blue-green light (Smith, 1951, Ch. 13).

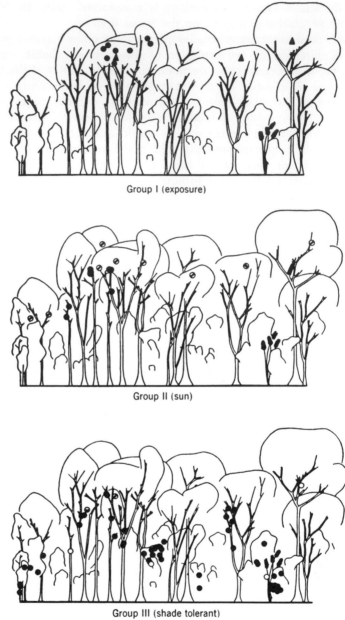

Group I (exposure)

Group II (sun)

Group III (shade tolerant)

FIG. 6.27. Vertical distribution of various species of bromeliads in the forest trees of Trinidad. (Pittendrigh, 1948.)

When algae are grown in the laboratory in light of different colors, they often tend to change color, and this response has also been referred to as chromatic adaptation. Experiments have shown that individual plants photosynthesize most efficiently and grow best in that color and in that intensity in which they have been living. In the course of time fixed algae can adapt themselves to habitats with illumination of widely different conditions of color and intensity. In view of the great range in the transparency of natural waters, it is not surprising that the maximum depth at which attached plants can live varies widely in different situations (Table 15). In general benthic

TABLE 15

MAXIMUM DEPTH IN METERS FOR GROWTH OF ATTACHED PLANTS

Crater Lake, Ore.	120
Crystal Lake, Wis.	20
Trout Lake, Wis.	12
Mediterranean Sea	160
Challenger Bank	100
Off Iceland	50
Puget Sound	30
Baltic Sea	20
Off Cape Cod	10

TABLE 16

COMPENSATION DEPTHS IN METERS FOR PHYTOPLANKTON
(for midday periods)

Sargasso Sea	100
English Channel	35
Gulf of Maine	30
Off British Columbia	19
Trout Lake, Wis.	16
Woods Hole harbor	7

plants will not grow at depths at which the light intensity is less than 0.3 per cent of the surface value.

A glance at a chart of the oceans or of a typical lake reveals that only in a very narrow fringe around the margin is the water sufficiently shallow for enough light to reach the bottom for the growth of plants. We are forced to the realization that in any deep body of water far more organic matter is synthesized by the phytoplankton present everywhere in the surface layers than by the benthic plants limited to the littoral zone. Photosynthesis, the first step in the ecological cycle of the sea upon which all marine life ultimately depends, is carried forward primarily by the minute diatoms and other microscopic planktonic plants. The growth of the phyto-plankton is limited not only by the rapid diminution of light with depth but also by the fact that vertical movements of the water sub-ject the plants to continually changing light conditions.

The greatest depth at which phytoplankton can grow successfully in any body of water may be ascertained by suspending bottles containing samples of the plant population at various levels beneath the surface. Photosynthesis going on within the bottle adds oxygen to the water, and respiration taking place simultaneously removes oxygen from the water. The rate of respiration alone may be meas-ured by placing at each level a blackened bottle from which all light is excluded. The sum of the gain in oxygen in the clear bottles and the loss in the dark bottles gives a measure of total photosynthesis. The increment of oxygen in the clear bottles is the amount produced by photosynthesis minus the amount consumed in respiration and represents the actual increase in energy content or growth of the plants.

With the diminution of light in any environment photosynthesis is reduced but respiration remains approximately the same, pro-vided, of course, that temperature and other factors are essentially unchanged. For each species a point is reached in the reduction of the illumination at which the rate of photosynthesis is just equal to the rate of respiration; this is known as the compensation point or better as the *compensation intensity*. At light intensities below this value photosynthesis may still go on but the plant is fighting a losing battle: it cannot survive indefinitely under these conditions because the loss of energy due to the catabolic processes represented by respiration exceed the gain in energy brought about by the anabolic process of photosynthesis. With further light reduction a minimum intensity is reached below which no photosynthesis at all can take place.

In the aquatic environment the level in the water at which the compensation intensity is found is called the *compensation depth*. Sample values for phytoplankton based on measurements in the middle of the day are presented in Table 16. For phytoplankton in general the compensation intensity has been found to be about 1 per cent of the value of full sunlight at the surface. In Fig. 6.28 the change in the amount of photosynthesis at various depths during the course of the day is plotted for a type of diatom representative of the marine plankton. It will be observed that during the noon hours the illumination close to the surface was excessive and depressed photo-synthesis. The highest rate of oxygen production occurred at 5 m in the middle of the day. No significant amount of photosynthesis occurred at any depth before 0600 in the morning or after 2200 and none below 35 m at 1400.

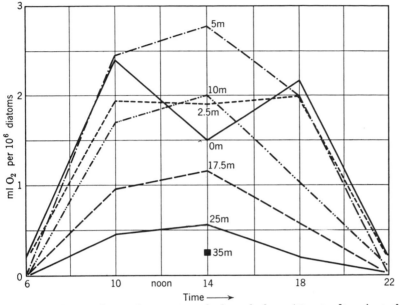

FIG. 6.28. Photosynthesis of a species of phytoplankton (*Coscinodiscus*) at the indicated depths during the course of the day off Stoke Point, England. (Jenkin, 1937, Copyright, Council of Marine Biological Assoc. of United Kingdom.)

If a plant is to grow, its photosynthesis during the day must build up enough organic matter to more than make up for the material lost by respiration not only during the day but also during the night. In other words, the crucial value for the continued existence of the plant is the compensation depth for the 24-hour period. This will obviously occur at a shallower depth than the values reported for experiments limited to the middle of the day. The compensation depth for the complete day ranges between 20 and 30 m during the summer in clear coastal water of the temperate oceans. In the winter and in less transparent water the compensation depth occurs cor-respondingly nearer the surface. No constructive growth is possible for diatoms or other pelagic plants below these levels. When we recall that the average depth of the ocean is more than 4000 m, it is apparent that the zone in which productive growth of the crucially important phytoplankton can take place is a relative skimming of the surface. The photosynthesis in the upper few meters of the ocean and of lakes accounts for the main portion of the initial production of organic matter for the whole breadth, length, and depth of the water.

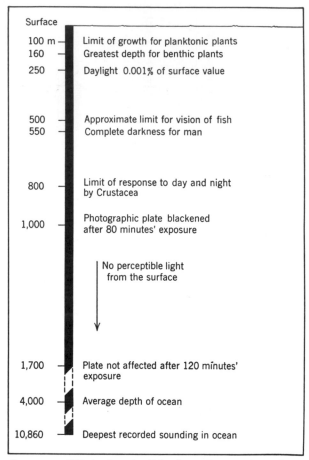

Surface

100 m	Limit of growth for planktonic plants
160	Greatest depth for benthic plants
250	Daylight 0.001% of surface value
500	Approximate limit for vision of fish
550	Complete darkness for man
800	Limit of response to day and night by Crustacea
1,000	Photographic plate blackened after 80 minutes' exposure

No perceptible light from the surface

1,700	Plate not affected after 120 minutes' exposure
4,000	Average depth of ocean
10,860	Deepest recorded sounding in ocean

Fig. 6.29.   Summary of limitations by light factor in aquatic environment. Values are for clearest water.

A summary of the conditions of light in the aquatic environment and its critical limiting effects is given in Fig. 6.29. Here are indicated the maximum depths for the growth of phytoplankton and slightly deeper, of benthic plants. Since the mean illumination necessary for the vision of aquatic animals is so very much smaller, the depth limitation is at a much greater level. Animals can respond to the difference between day and night at somewhat greater depths. Below this level no perceptible light from the surface penetrates and the water is completely dark except for light provided by the luminescent organs of deep-sea animals. Terms used in deep bodies of water for zones based on the light factor are as follows:

Euphotic Zone: Sufficient light for photosynthesis.
Disphotic Zone: Insufficient light for photosynthesis but sufficient light for animal responses.
Aphotic Zone: No light of biological significance from the surface.

The depth limits of these zones differ widely according to transparency.

The discussion in this chapter has revealed the many important roles played by light in the world of life. Although there is generally sufficient light on land for plants and animals, the special circumstances of this factor exert a wide control over the activities of many terrestrial organisms. In the aquatic environment light is even more crucial since, in addition to its various periodicities, its rapid changes with depth impose serious limitations on the lives of both animals and plants.

7

Oxygen and
Carbon Dioxide

With this chapter we turn from the more mechanical or physical features of the environment to a consideration of some of the chemical factors. Two fundamental substances taking part in the chemical exchange between the organism and the environment are oxygen and carbon dioxide. These substances enter into the basic processes of photosynthesis and respiration, as may be indicated by the overall reactions in which $C_6H_{12}O_6$ is taken to represent the carbohydrate of the organism.

$$CO_2 + H_2O \overset{\text{Light}}{\rightleftharpoons} C_6H_{12}O_6 + O_2$$

Photosynthesis

Respiration

Oxygen and carbon dioxide thus stand in a reciprocal relation to each other as regards these fundamental reactions of life, and their abundance in the environment is of direct critical concern to the organisms of every habitat. In addition, these materials take part in subsidiary reactions involved in the ecological relations of plants and animals. Of particular ecological importance in this connection are the decomposition and transformation of organic matter, carried out primarily by microorganisms, since in these processes oxygen is consumed and carbon dioxide is released.

OXYGEN

Oxygen is needed by almost all organisms to make available the energy contained in organic food materials. The great majority of plants and animals use free oxygen from the air or from the water for the oxidation of organic substances; these are *aerobic* organisms.

Anaerobic forms, on the other hand, get their energy by partial decomposition of organic matter without free oxygen. Anaerobic organisms nevertheless depend upon the aerobic forms to produce the organic matter upon which they live. As we shall see, the abundance of oxygen in the environment may become critically low for aerobic organisms but it never becomes harmfully high for these forms. Natural concentrations of oxygen may, however, be seriously detrimental to some anaerobes.

Oxygen is present in the air as one of the gases that are physically mixed together, and it occurs in water in simple solution. Dissolved oxygen does not combine chemically with water itself but it does react with iron and other inorganic materials in the water. Points of contrast in this respect with carbon dioxide will be discussed later in the chapter. Since oxygen is taken up and given off by life processes, its concentration in the environment can sometimes be appreciably, or even seriously, altered by the activities of the plant and animal inhabitants. Under these circumstances oxygen is a modifiable factor of the environment.

Availability of Oxygen

Terrestrial Environment. Oxygen constitutes 21 per cent of the atmosphere, and this value varies by less than 1 per cent the world over. Although plants and animals are continuously drawing upon the oxygen supply in the air, and plants are periodically adding to it, the concentration in the atmosphere is not changed appreciably by these life activities because of the great volume and mobility of the air medium. Most of the terrestrial environment is thus provided with a uniform and adequate supply of oxygen.

In two types of situations of importance in the terrestrial environment a lack of oxygen exists—at high altitudes and in the subsurface layers of the soil. At great elevations the concentration of oxygen is low because all gases have become rarer. The amount of reduction in oxygen with altitude is proportional to the reduction in total atmospheric pressure, discussed in Chapter 2. Thus at an altitude of 5500 m O_2 is only half as abundant as it is at sea level. The oxygen in soils drops from near the atmospheric value of 21 per cent at the surface to about 10 per cent within well-drained loams and to lower values in poorly aerated soils and in layers below the water table. Lack of air circulation results from very fine texture or from the flooding of the pore spaces. Under these circumstances the respiration of roots and of soil organisms, particularly those involved in the decomposition of organic matter, reduces the oxygen supply faster than it can be replenished from the atmosphere.

Aquatic Environment. The total amount of oxygen that water will hold at saturation varies with temperature, salinity, and pressure. Sample oxygen saturation values for fresh water and sea water at temperatures within the range of ecological interest are given in Table 17. When we realize that the 21 per cent of oxygen present

TABLE 17

CONCENTRATIONS OF OXYGEN AT SATURATION

Temp. °C	Fresh Water O_2 ppm. (mg/liter)	O_2 cc/liter	Sea Water (salinity 36‰) O_2 cc/liter
0	14.7	10.3	8.0
15	10.3	7.2	5.8
30	8.3	5.6	4.5

in the atmosphere is equivalent to 210 cc per liter, the contrast between the *amounts* available in air and in water is brought into relief. There may be 25 times as much oxygen in a liter of air as in a liter of water. When the oxygen in the water is in equilibrium with that in the air, however, the *pressure* of the oxygen is the same in both media.

From the foregoing it is clear that the world's main reservoir of free oxygen is in the atmosphere. The chief source of oxygen for the water environment is the oxygen which can be absorbed from the air, but a second source of supply in aquatic habitats is the oxygen released beneath the surface by the photosynthesis of submerged and planktonic plants. Water may lose oxygen by diffusion from its surface out into the atmosphere. Oxygen is also used up by the respiration of aquatic organisms and by the decomposition of organic matter in the water. Living organisms are thus seen to influence both the supply and the depletion of oxygen in natural bodies of water; oxygen is a modifiable factor in the aquatic environment but it is essentially an unmodifiable factor in the air. The actual amount of oxygen present at any one time and place in the water is the result of a balance between the processes of supply and depletion. Here is another situation in which an ecological factor is controlled by a dynamic equilibrium involving both physical and biological processes.

Three general situations may be discerned in regard to the supply of oxygen in the water environment: the surface stratum, the subsurface zone, and the deep layers. The water at the surface tends to be in equilibrium with the air above it so that the oxygen value is at or near the saturation concentration for the existing conditions of temperature and salinity. The thickness of the surface stratum in which saturation equilibrium is found varies greatly according to the amount of turbulent mixing of the water in contact with the air.

In the subsurface zone great variation in oxygen concentration may occur because the water does not have easy exchange with the atmosphere and factors causing both decrease and increase in oxygen are present. Respiration and decomposition, tending to deplete the oxygen supply, occur at all levels, and photosynthesis, tending to increase the abundance of oxygen, takes place down to the compensation depth, that is, to the lower limit of the euphotic zone, as described in the previous chapter. When large populations are respiring or large quantities of dead material are decomposing, the oxygen concentration is reduced to a low level. In stagnant ponds and swamps choked with organic matter, and in rivers or other bodies of water receiving excessive amounts of sewage or other pollutants, the available free oxygen often becomes completely exhausted. Under other circumstances supersaturation may occur in subsurface water layers. If water which was saturated during the winter becomes warmed as the season advances, more oxygen will be present than can be held in true solution at the higher temperatures. Similarly, when photosynthesis exceeds respiration at intermediate levels in the euphotic zone, oxygen may be released into the water faster than it can be carried away. As a result of these physical and biological influences, supersaturated values as high as 180 per cent in the sea and 300 per cent in inland lakes have been reported.

Often cyclic fluctuations in oxygen content are observed in natural bodies of water. Seasonal changes in temperature and circulation coupled with differences in rates of photosynthesis, respiration, and decomposition result in changes both in the absolute amount of oxygen present in the water and in the degree of saturation. Under certain circumstances a pronounced diurnal fluctuation in oxygen concentration is found; this is known as an *oxygen pulse*. During the daylight hours photosynthesis tends to cause an increase in the amount of oxygen present, but, after the sun has set, the respiration of the aquatic organisms and the decomposition processes going on draw on the free oxygen in the water. The amplitude of the oxygen pulse may reach considerable proportions in quiet waters in which green plants are growing in abundance. Measurements in an Ohio lake, for example, revealed a diurnal fluctuation in oxygen concentration extending from 6.7 ppm at 8:00 A.M. to 13.0 ppm at 5:00 P.M. (Fig. 7.1).

How does oxygen get to the bottom of the ocean? We have seen that the sources of oxygen are at or near the surface, but we know that many kinds of aerobic animals live at the bottom of some lakes and in the ocean abyss at depths of several miles beneath the surface. Although oxygen moves slowly through the water by direct diffusion, it can reach the deeper levels at an adequate rate only by the circulation of the water itself.

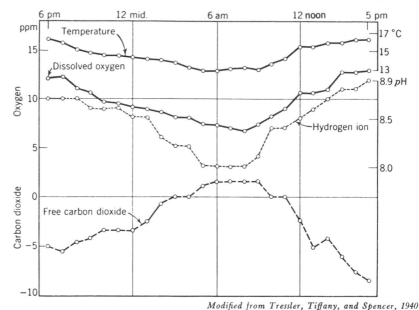

Modified from Tressler, Tiffany, and Spencer, 1940

FIG. 7.1.   Diurnal cycle of temperature, oxygen, hydrogen ion (as *p*H), and carbon dioxide in the surface waters of Buckeye Lake, Ohio, during August 12–13, 1930.   Negative values for CO_2 represent amount of CO_2 required to make water neutral to phenolphthalein.

Oxygen-rich surface water is carried downward by wind stirring, eddy conduction, and mass sinking. *Wind stirring* is very effective in aerating the upper layers of lakes and of the ocean at times when the water circulates freely. Whenever a water body is covered by ice, no turbulence caused by wind or waves is possible. At other seasons stirring is greatly curtailed whenever the water is stratified in respect to density—as a result of salinity differences occurring at any time of year, or as a result of a thermal gradient arising primarily in summer. During periods of pronounced stratification the circulation produced by wind and waves is limited to the layers above the density discontinuity (Fig. 7.2). When stratification has been de-

stroyed, wind stirring may extend sufficiently deep to reach the bottom
of shallow lakes and coastal waters, and thus to replenish the oxygen
supply. There is a limit, however, to the depth to which turbulence
caused by wind is effective. In the open ocean, where the highest
winds and largest waves occur, little influence of wave action is felt
below 100 m.

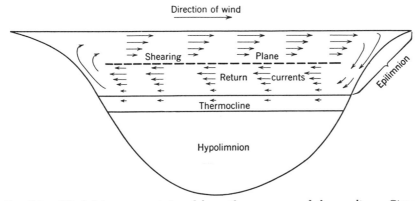

FIG. 7.2. Wind-driven currents in a lake with a pronounced thermocline. Circulation is limited to the epilimnion. (By permission from *Limnology* by Welch, Copyright 1952, McGraw-Hill Book Co.)

Oxygen may be carried to depths beyond the limit of effective wave
action by *eddy conduction*. Wherever differential movement of currents occurs, eddies are generated along the current margins, and
these cause units of water to be exchanged (Fig. 7.3). The exchange
will bring about a transfer of any characteristics of the water that
differ in the adjacent water masses. The rate of transfer depends upon

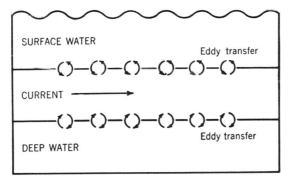

FIG. 7.3. Diagrammatic vertical section of a body of water, indicating vertical
transfer by eddies across the current boundaries. Horizontal eddy conduction
similarly takes place at the lateral margins of the current.

(*a*) the rate of mixing of water units and (*b*) the difference in concentration of each characteristic. The rate of mixing, or *austausch coefficient*, is a property of the water under the existing conditions of turbulence, and it affects all characteristics that are being exchanged between water masses. At the same time that oxygen is being transferred, heat may also be moved downward, phosphate moved upward, and other exchanges carried out by the same eddy action between the water masses. This is an illustration of the *principle of common transport:* a current that transfers one property of the medium also transfers other properties at the same time (Redfield, 1941).

Eddy conduction is a process by which materials are transferred at right angles to the direction of current. The transfer may take place vertically, as in the situation just described, horizontally, or in some other direction. The downward transfer of oxygen by eddy conduction is slow but it is commonly a thousand times greater than the diffusion rate. Although eddy conduction helps furnish oxygen to water layers at middepths wherever currents of different speeds or directions are flowing, it cannot supply an adequate amount of this essential material to the deepest parts of lakes or of the ocean.

Fortunately for the abyssal animals oxygen can reach them by another method, namely, the *mass sinking* or deep circulation of the water. In the typical deep lake of the temperate region water masses charged with oxygen at the surface sink to the bottom during the spring and fall overturns, as described in relation to the temperature cycle. As a result of the extensive circulation of the lake at these periods the water may become turbid and formerly this was often noticeable in poorly filtered water supply systems. When muddy water issued from the taps, the residents would nod knowingly and say, "The pond is working." The limnologist, however, refers to the periods of overturn that bring a fresh supply of oxygen to the deeper layers after winter and summer stagnation as occasions when "the pond takes a breath."

An example of the seasonal changes in oxygen at various depths in a temperate lake is taken from the classic work of Birge and Juday (1914) (Fig. 7.4). During the period of this representative study oxygen was abundant at all depths after the spring overturn, but a rapid depletion began in May following thermal stratification. Oxygen was almost completely absent at depths greater than 15 m during July, August, and September. The fall overturn in mid-October caused a sudden mixing and equalization of oxygen at all levels; in succeeding weeks increasing amounts of oxygen were supplied throughout the lake by deep circulation. In certain very deep lakes the seasonal circulation does not reach the bottom, with the result that the deepest layers may be completely devoid of oxygen throughout the year.

In the temperate regions of the ocean the thermal stability built up during the summer is similarly broken down in the autumn. Turbulence produced by wind and waves then carries oxygen-rich water downward, and this deep stirring continues all winter. The downward extent of the winter mixing is sufficient to reach the bottom in coastal areas but its effect does not go below the permanent thermocline of the open sea (Fig. 5.4). Seasonal changes in temperature and wind action thus do not provide for the delivery of oxygenated water to the great depths of the ocean.

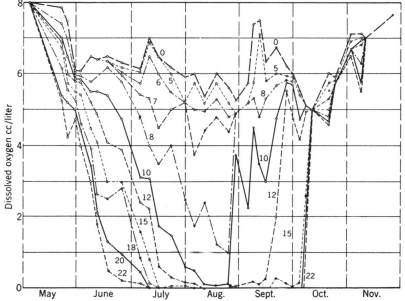

Fig. 7.4. Changes in oxygen during the warm part of the year at the indicated depths in Lake Mendota, Wisconsin. (Needham and Lloyd, 1937, after Birge and Juday.)

Oxygen is supplied to the ocean abyss by deep permanent currents that originate near the surface in high latitudes, sink to intermediate levels or to the bottom, and flow for thousands of miles toward and beyond the equator (Fig. 7.5). This deep flow of water is dynamically integrated with the horizontal current systems with the result that the vertical movements of water follow a complicated pattern (Sverdrup et al., 1942). As a simplified generality, however, the

cold water that sinks to great depths may be understood eventually
to find its way to the surface again in the central part of the ocean,
and a return flow of water from the equatorial regions toward the
poles is brought about as a part of the horizontal circulation of the
upper water masses.

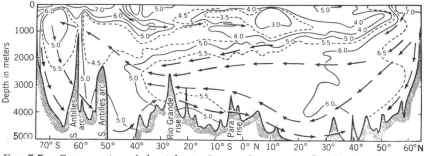

FIG. 7.5. Cross section of the Atlantic Ocean, showing the distribution of oxygen
in cubic centimeters per liter. The north-south and vertical components of the
oceanic currents are indicated by the arrows. (Modified from Sverdrup et al.,
1942, after Wüst.)

Sea water near the surface in tropical regions contains about 4 cc
of oxygen per liter, but as it becomes colder at higher latitudes,
oxygen is absorbed from the atmosphere and produced by photosynthesis until a concentration of about 8 cc per liter is attained.
When the water masses leave the surface and sink toward the bottom,
depletion of oxygen begins as a result of respiration and decomposition, but as much as 5 cc O_2 per liter remains when the water reaches
the ocean abyss. Animals living at the bottom of the sea thus
receive oxygen via a direct flow of water from the enriched polar
seas, but this is perhaps the slowest delivery service in the world.
Calculations based on the rate of consumption of oxygen and also on
the relative proportion of C_{14} in deep water indicate that movement
of Arctic surface water to deep layers at midlatitudes may require a
thousand years or more.

The concentration of oxygen at any point in deep water depends
upon (1) the amount that the water contained when it left the
surface, (2) the rate at which oxygen is used up en route by respiration and decomposition, and (3) the time that has elapsed. Minimum values occur at positions in the ocean at which the combined
effect of the foregoing factors has reduced the oxygen to the greatest
extent. The lowest oxygen values are not found at the bottom but
at certain intermediate regions, as indicated in Fig. 7.5. In no part

of the open Atlantic Ocean is the oxygen completely used up, and minimum values are generally above 3 cc per liter. In the Pacific Ocean, however, oxygen is reduced to zero in certain oxygen minimum layers, as for example, at depths between 300 and 1300 m off the coast of lower California.

Other instances in the marine environment of the complete lack of oxygen, or of very low concentrations, are found only in special situations in which circulation is largely or entirely cut off and decomposing organic matter has accumulated. The classic example of this condition is in the free water of the Black Sea, in which no measurable oxygen is found from a depth of about 150 m to the bottom at 2200 m. Vertical stirring is prevented by a layer of fresh water at the surface supplied by the discharge of the Danube and other large rivers entering the Sea, and deep exchange with outside water is stopped by the shallow entrance at the Bosporus. Organic particles carried in with the river water use up the oxygen as they sink to deeper layers, and anaerobic decomposition produces great quantities of hydrogen sulphide. Similiar conditions on a smaller scale are found within deep fjords with shallow sills and within other estuaries in which the circulation does not supply the oxygen as fast as it is used up (Fig. 7.6). The bottom material of the marine environment is also likely to develop a shortage of oxygen unless it is sufficiently coarse to allow good movement of water through it. Fine muds containing decomposing matter contain little or no oxygen at depths of more than a few centimeters from their surfaces.

Oxidation-Reduction Potential. Another aspect of oxygen availability in the aquatic environment, but less well known, is the oxidation-reduction potential, or *redox potential*. The redox potential (Eh), measured in volts, is an expression of the electropositivity or negativity of a substance in solution as referred to a hydrogen standard. A positive redox potential indicates a condition tending to cause oxidation, and a negative potential indicates the reverse condition, tending to bring about reduction. As used to describe an aquatic habitat, redox is the overall summation of the redoxes of all the solutes present in the water. Redox potentials have two general properties that must be considered: intensity or Eh as defined above; and capacity or poising, which is analogous to the buffering of a pH system. A high capacity reflects the tendency of the system to retain its intensity despite minor changes in its constituents.

In well-aerated natural waters oxygen concentration usually governs the redox potential and produces positive values. However, ferrous complexes or oxygen shortage may allow various inorganic and organic ions and molecules to set more negative values. Such low redox systems represent reducing agents that would tend to combine with any introduced oxygen. An aerobic organism, needing oxygen for its respiration, would find such competition exceedingly difficult, if not insuperable, if the redox system were well poised. Facultative and obligative anaerobes, however, have no such difficulty and are able to tolerate low redox values.

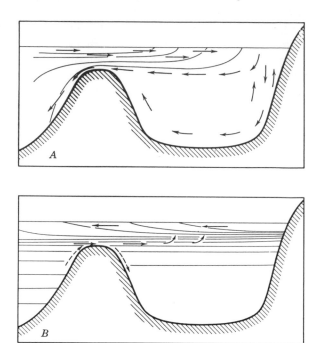

FIG. 7.6. (*A*) Basin with local formation of heavier water and deep outflow across the sill, as in the Mediterranean Sea, the Red Sea, and the Inner Gulf of California. (*B*) Basin with surface outflow of lighter water and occasional inflow of denser water across the sill, as in the Black Sea, Baltic Sea, and many fjords.
(From *The Oceans* by Svedrup et al., 1942, Copyright Prentice-Hall, N. Y.)

Zonation of organisms according to redox potentials has been shown, especially in sediments, but whether the oxygen concentration or the redox potential is the determining factor is hard to ascertain since the latter generally depends chiefly upon the former. In marine muds the redox potential decreases with depth in the sediment with the most rapid change occurring in the few uppermost centimeters. The abundance of aerobic organisms correspondingly drops off sharply, and at increasing depths the anaerobes become relatively more abundant. The type of bottom fauna in certain lakes has also been found to be related to the redox potential. In lakes in which the water above the deepest mud had an *Eh* above 0.4 volt, the mud itself supported a pure or mixed fauna characterized by midge larvae of the genus *Tanytarsus*, whereas in lakes with an *Eh* below 0.3 volt a true *Chironomus* fauna occurred (Hutchinson et al., 1939). For a further discussion of the ecological effects of redox potentials the reader is referred to ZoBell (1946); it is obvious that the influence of this aspect of the oxygen factor is due for closer scrutiny in the future.

Effects of Oxygen Availability

Terrestrial Environment. We may now examine the ecological effects of the varying amounts of oxygen present in different habitats. Since oxygen is amply abundant in the lower portions of the earth's atmosphere, this factor has no important limiting action in most terrestrial situations. The reduction in the partial pressure of oxygen at high elevations imposes a restriction on the altitudinal distribution of organisms having a high oxygen requirement. No mammals can live permanently at altitudes at which the partial pressure of oxygen is less than about 45 per cent of its value at sea level. Oxygen shortage as well as the thinness of air imposes a similar ultimate limit on the altitude at which birds can live. The altitudinal range for most types of lower animals and for plants is limited by low temperatures or by other ecological factors long before the diminished oxygen concentration becomes a serious handicap.

Organisms requiring free oxygen are excluded from soils and ground debris within which the circulation of air is inadequate. The lack of oxygen in poorly aerated soils becomes seriously harmful to the roots of most plants at concentrations below about 10 per cent. Root penetration for most of the vegetation is stopped by soil layers containing less than 3 per cent oxygen and also by the water table since even less oxygen is available in the ground water. If areas with established vegetation are subjected to prolonged flooding, caused for example by the construction of beaver dams, most of the plants will be "drowned"—or killed by the cutting off of root aeration.

The roots of some plants, however, possess special adaptations enabling them to grow in soil layers devoid of oxygen. In some types, including particularly the herbaceous hydrophytes, air passages within the stem and major roots allow oxygen to be brought from the atmosphere, or possibly from internal sources in the upper part of the plant, and delivered to the lower extensions of the root system. In the black mangrove, common along the margins of Florida lagoons, root branches, known as pneumatophores, grow vertically upward through the mud and water until they project into the air, where they have ready access to oxygen.   Other special features of plant growth found in permanent swamps are the "knees" and enlarged trunk bases displayed by such trees as the bald cypress (Fig. 7.7).   The knees

Photo U. S. Forest Service

Fig. 7.7.   Enlarged trunks and "knees" of cypress trees growing in permanent swamp conditions in the Francis Marion National Forest, South Carolina.

were formerly believed to provide aeration for the roots, but evidence now indicates that these root excrescences and the enlarged trunks represent excessive cambial growth resulting from the combination of abundant water and oxygen supply for the tissue at the water line.   The roots of a few vascular plants without observable adaptation for securing outside oxygen, such as the willow, are able to remain active during prolonged flooding; the root tissues in these exceptional instances are presumed to be capable of anaerobic existence.

Most cryptogamic plants and soil animals depend upon aerobic respiration and hence are excluded from soil layers devoid of oxygen. A few of the higher forms, such as the earthworm, may be able to do without oxygen for short periods, as when the soil is rain soaked, but for the most part earthworms migrate to the surface when oxygen becomes depleted. Many organisms encyst, or go into a dormant condition, when oxygen becomes too scarce for the species concerned. However, some of the microorganisms inhabiting the soil can follow an anaerobic existence (Waksman, 1932). Included are members of the genera *Clostridium* and *Rhizobium* that are important as nitrogen-fixing bacteria; *Clostridium tetani* is of particular concern to man as the microbe that causes lockjaw. We realize then that the highly variable conditions of oxygen availability often exert a critical control over the distribution and activity of both aerobic and anaerobic organisms involved in the ecology of the soil.

Aquatic Environment. We have seen that the supply of oxygen in the aquatic environment varies over the complete range from super-saturation to total exhaustion, but that, even when saturated, water contains a much lower concentration of oxygen than the atmosphere. Some fresh-water organisms have hit upon certain dodges by which they can live in the aquatic medium and still breathe air. Many water bugs, such as *Notonecta*, and certain beetles come to the surface, entrap bubbles of air beneath their wing cases, and swim down with a supply of oxygen that will last for a period of time. Other animals, like the water scorpion *Ranatra* (Fig. 6.12), the mosquito larva, and the rat-tailed maggot, possess breathing tubes that extend to the surface. Some kinds of snails periodically refill their lungs with air at the surface, whereas other water animals are able to bore into the stems or roots of emergent hydrophytes and obtain oxygen from the internal air spaces of the plants.

Most aquatic organisms, however, must get along with the relatively meager supply of oxygen dissolved in the water. Let us consider the ecological conditions in well-aerated water before taking up the effects of severe oxygen depletion. Although saturated water contains only a small fraction of the amount of oxygen in an equal volume of the atmosphere, the *partial pressure* of oxygen in the water is equal to that in the air with which it is in equilibrium. Accordingly, the tendency of the oxygen in water to cross the respiratory membranes of organisms is just as great as it is in air. The lower concentration of oxygen in water simply means that less is in reserve. The relatively small amount of oxygen in the water is adequate for aquatic organisms if the medium in contact with the absorbing membranes is rapidly replenished.

Inhabitants of the water environment display a wide variety of adaptations that serve to obtain a sufficient supply of oxygen from the medium. Sessile animals cause water to flow through their respiratory chambers or wave their respiratory organs about in the surrounding water. The echiuroid worms keep a current of water flowing through their burrows in the sand when the tide is in by rhythmic contraction of their bodies, but reduced metabolism allows them to withstand periods of 18 hours when their tide flats are out of water. More active animals, such as most fish and higher crustaceans, possess special mechanisms for pumping water continuously over their gills. Certain fish, however, reverse the process and produce a flow over the gills by swimming rapidly through the water with their mouths open. Some species, as, for example, the mackerel, have come to rely entirely on this latter method, and in the course of evolution the gills and opercular muscles have become reduced, with the result that these fish cannot obtain sufficient oxygen while remaining stationary. If a mackerel is confined in a small space, or prevented from swimming rapidly, it will die of asphixiation even though the surrounding water is saturated with oxygen (Hall, 1930).

In view of the foregoing one might expect that in those aquatic habitats in which the water is not saturated with oxygen, the lack of this vital substance would immediately have serious consequences. However, many aerobic aquatic organisms are quite able to survive with concentrations of oxygen much below normal pressures. The metabolism of some species is so low that a small oxygen supply is sufficient. Certain species possess special respiratory pigments or other physiological adaptations that aid in the absorption of oxygen at very low partial pressures. Chironomid larvae, inhabiting the muddy bottoms of ponds, are furnished with a type of hemoglobin that becomes 95 per cent saturated under a partial pressure of oxygen of only 10 mm Hg, whereas mammalian hemoglobin is less than 1 per cent saturated at this pressure. These insects are also capable of a remarkably simple anaerobic metabolism in which the lactic acid formed from glycogen breakdown is excreted, thus eliminating this toxic compound rather than oxidizing it as most animals do.

The relation of oxygen consumption by animals to the tension of oxygen in the environment follows two general patterns: (1) the non-regulatory type in which consumption is highly dependent upon tension, as seen in certain annelids and arthropods (e.g., *Nereis*, *Homarus*, *Limulus*, and *Callinectes*), and (2) the regulatory type in which consumption is independent of oxygen pressure over a wide range, as seen in certain crustaceans and mollusks (e.g., *Astacus*, *Carcinus*, *Aplysia*, and *Eledone*). In the latter type the harmful effects of insufficient oxygen supply appear rather suddenly when the oxygen drops below the critical tension for the species concerned. The critical oxygen tensions for a large number of animals, a further discussion of adaptations to low oxygen supply, and a consideration of physiological relations to the oxygen factor in general are to be found in Prosser (1950, Ch. 8).

It is difficult to determine the minimum concentrations of oxygen required by various aquatic animals. The value is influenced by temperature, pH, and other modifying factors, as well as by the degree and rate of acclimatization to low oxygen tensions. In the hypolimnion of lakes, where oxygen is likely to be depleted, the temperature is low, with consequent reduction in the animal's metabolism and in its need for oxygen. Organisms require more oxygen when in an active condition than when quiescent; some species enter a dormant condition in which they can withstand varying degrees of oxygen deprivation for varying lengths of time. The ecologist thus recognizes that the animals caught in a water layer containing little or no oxygen are not necessarily able to live permanently under the observed conditions: they may be in a dormant condition for a limited period, or they may have made a temporary excursion into the poorly aerated zone. Nevertheless we have obtained a knowledge of the approximate oxygen requirements of many common aquatic animals, and even among completely aerobic forms great differences in the minimum values tolerated have been revealed. At one extreme are those like the toadfish that seems to be able to survive if any detectible amount of oxygen exists in the water. Carp and other fish adapted to live in muddy ponds often show no harmful effects until oxygen has been reduced to 0.3 cc per liter or even to 0.1 cc per liter. At the other extreme are active fish like the mackerel that requires 3.6 cc per liter (70 mm IIg) at 24°C (Hall, 1930).

In those ponds, lakes, and fjords, in which the oxygen concentration of the lower levels is reduced to zero during the summer (and in some instances also during the winter) the inhabitants must either migrate out of the oxygenless zones or enter upon some sort of anaerobic existence, if they are to survive. Copepods and other types of zooplankton are known to leave the hypolimnion of lakes as summer stagnation begins. Fish and the motile bottom fauna undertake similar seasonal vertical migrations. Many animals and plants with no means of escape die off in large numbers after the exhaustion of the oxygen supply. However, certain species of worms, crustaceans, insect larvae, mollusks, and other invertebrates are known to remain in the bottoms of lakes and to survive for periods of many weeks each year with no detectible oxygen present in the bottom water. A

further discussion of the types of metabolism displayed by invertebrate animals capable of anaerobiosis is given by von Brand (1946).

When the supply of oxygen in a confined aquatic habitat becomes
reduced below the level of toleration, the lethal effects sometimes
appear quite suddenly. We occasionally see reports that all the fish
in a pond have been found dead on one morning whereas the day before they had appeared to be in a perfectly healthy condition. Such a
situation occurs most frequently after a hot calm spell in summer.
Because of the high temperature the amount of oxygen that the water
can hold is low and the rates of respiration by the pond organisms and
of the decomposition of organic materials in the water are high. In
calm weather no effective stirring takes place to replenish the subsurface water levels. As a result of this combination of circumstances
the oxygen minimum reached by the diurnal pulse at the end of each
night becomes progressively lower. Early one morning the oxygen
concentration drops below the toleration point, and the whole population of fish in the pond is suffocated.

In aquatic habitats permanently and completely devoid of oxygen
no aerobic organisms can live. Included in this category are: the
deep waters of certain lakes, the Black Sea, and certain arms of the
ocean with insufficient circulation; the subsurface layers of mud
bottoms; and many heavily polluted waters. Such places can be permanently inhabited only by forms that are able to function indefinitely
on an anaerobic basis. The population of these habitats consists
chiefly of anaerobic Protozoa and bacteria. Many of these obligate
anaerobes are killed by the presence of oxygen. This fact is put to
practical use in the employment of thorough aeration as one step in
the purification of water supplies. Certain higher animals, such as
slime worms (*Tubificidae*), pea clams (*Pisidium*), and insect larvae
(*Corethra* and *Chironomus*), are found in the bottoms of very deep
lakes where oxygen is very low or absent.

The organisms that inhabit the oxygenless water layers carry out a
partial decomposition of the organic matter filtering down from above,
and frequently release large quantities of hydrogen sulphide in the
process. In the Black Sea the permanent absence of oxygen in the
deeper water layer brings the vertical distribution of aerobic benthic
animals to an end at depths varying between 115 m and 165 m according to the locality. The plankton is similarly limited to the upper 125
m in the central part of the sea but may extend to 175 m in marginal
areas where the surface water is stirred more deeply. Lack of oxygen
and abundance of poisonous hydrogen sulphide exclude all life except
anaerobic microorganisms from the lower 2000 m of the Black Sea.

In the foregoing review of oxygen we have seen that this life-giving material is sufficiently abundant in most major habitats, but that it becomes critically scarce in certain special situations. Most land organisms find enough oxygen in their habitats, and the great majority of marine animals are so adapted that the amount of oxygen in sea water ordinarily meets their requirements, although its concentration is far less than in the atmosphere. As green plants photosynthesize and grow, they produce more oxygen than they consume, and hence run short of oxygen only in rare instances. But we have seen that in fresh water and under certain conditions on land and in the sea, available oxygen may become seriously reduced, with the result that whole populations may be killed unless they have means of escape, or are capable of anaerobic existence. The distribution of aerobic plants and animals is sharply curtailed at the margins of habitats permanently devoid of oxygen, and within these areas the relatively few groups of completely anaerobic organisms hold undisputed domain.

CARBON DIOXIDE

A consideration of carbon dioxide as an ecological factor is of vital concern first of all because it is one of the essential ingredients of the photosynthetic reaction. This material thus provides the carbon source necessary for the growth of all green plants and indirectly for all other organisms. Carbon dioxide also influences other features of the environment. Quite in contrast with oxygen, carbon dioxide combines chemically with the water medium itself, and forms carbonic acid. Through this reaction it influences the hydrogen ion concentration (measured as pH), and it forms compounds with calcium and other elements of ecological importance. Carbon dioxide affects the respiration of animals and, in combination with calcium, takes part in the formation of their bones and shells.

When animals and plants respire, organic matter is oxidized and carbon dioxide is produced. This process is the reverse of photosynthesis as indicated in the equations at the beginning of the chapter. Carbon dioxide is also released when dead organic matter is decomposed by the oxidizing or fermenting activities of microorganisms. On the other hand, carbon dioxide is withdrawn from the environment by the growth of green plants and by lime secretion. Thus, carbon dioxide, like oxygen, enters the living complex in an absolutely vital way. Since the abundance of carbon dioxide in many situations is strongly affected by living organisms, we may definitely list this material as a modifiable property of the environment. Because of the reciprocal relation between carbon dioxide and oxygen in the fundamental reactions of nature mentioned above, we generally find that wherever the supply of one of these materials has been depleted the concentration of the other has been increased.

Carbon Dioxide in the Terrestrial Environment

It is a striking fact that carbon dioxide—a material so essential in the ecological relations of organisms—is present in the earth's atmosphere in an extremely small amount; it constitutes only 0.03 per cent of the air medium. Carbon dioxide is thus only about $\frac{1}{700}$ as abundant in the air as oxygen. Because of the great mobility of the atmosphere, however, carbon dioxide is well distributed, and its low concentration is generally sufficient for at least a moderate amount of photosynthesis the earth over. Possibly the reduction in carbon dioxide at great altitudes would seriously curtail the photosynthetic rate of plants, but low temperature or poor soil conditions are usually far more important in limiting plant growth in the mountains.

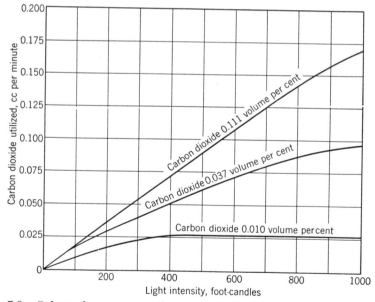

FIG. 7.8. Relation between rate of photosynthesis of wheat plants and light intensity at normal atmospheric, at decreased and at increased concentrations of carbon dioxide. (From Meyer and Anderson, 1939, after Hoover et al., *Smithsonian Misc. Coll.*, 1933.)

The normal amount of carbon dioxide available in the atmosphere, although allowing adequate plant growth under usual circumstances at ordinary altitudes, is insufficient for photosynthesis to attain rates that would be possible under favorable natural conditions if the concentration of carbon dioxide were higher. During conditions of low illumination the light factor ordinarily controls the rate of photosynthesis, but under high illumination the small amount of carbon dioxide in the air acts as the limiting factor. This situation is illustrated in Fig. 7.8 in which rate of photosynthesis of wheat plants in relation to illumination is plotted under conditions of normal, increased, and decreased tensions of carbon dioxide. In this experiment under a normal carbon dioxide tension of 0.037 per cent the rate of photosynthesis (as measured by utilization of carbon dioxide) increases with increasing illumination up to 1000 ft-c. At higher illuminations, beyond the limits of the graph, little further increase in photosynthetic rate took place, as the availability of carbon dioxide became limiting. With carbon dioxide at 0.010 per cent the limiting action of carbon dioxide availability became complete at 400 ft-c, whereas an increase of the carbon dioxide concentration to 0.111 per cent resulted in an augmentation of photosynthesis at all illuminations, with the curve still steeply rising at 1000 ft-c. Practical advantage of this situation can sometimes be taken by artifically increasing the carbon dioxide in sealed greenhouses. Improved growth of certain plants is found for tensions of carbon dioxide of three to twenty times the normal amount, but higher concentrations are harmful.

In nature some instances of local significant increases in atmospheric carbon dioxide have been reported. In certain volcanic areas carbon dioxide escapes from fissures in the rocks and, being heavier than air, forms a layer near the ground. From these "death valleys," such as the one in Java mentioned earlier, all animal life is excluded. The carbon dioxide in soil air generally is increased as a result of decomposition and respiration beneath the ground surface under conditions of poor aeration. The air under dense vegetation may exhibit values considerably above normal, and the air just above the soil of certain cultivated fields has been found to show a tenfold increase in carbon dioxide content, but no evidence is available as to any ecological effects that may have been produced. In an experiment conducted in Georgia, however, the carbon dioxide in the atmosphere was found to be 25 per cent higher on certain foggy days, and during these periods the photosynthesis of plants under observation was increased to as much as seven times the normal value (Wilson, 1948).

Our atmosphere receives carbon dioxide from geological and industrial sources. The supply is increased by carbon dioxide released from the ocean and from respiration and decay. Carbon dioxide is withdrawn from the atmosphere by the photosynthesis of the vegetation. The existing balance between supply and consumption provides a very low concentration of carbon dioxide in the air, but, if the minute amount of this essential gas were not present, all life on land would come to a stop. The lives of terrestrial organisms thus depend upon a very slender thread. In former geologic epochs the abundance of atmospheric carbon dioxide may have been considerably greater or smaller with the consequent possibility of significantly increased or decreased photosynthesis. At present we realize that carbon dioxide is a general limiting factor in the sense that plant growth might go on at a higher pace in the world as a whole if our atmosphere contained more of this gas. However, since carbon dioxide is essentially uniform over the earth's surface, it does not cause significant differences in the distribution and growth of the terrestrial vegetation.

Carbon Dioxide in the Aquatic Environment

The amount of carbon dioxide present in the medium is crucially important for aquatic organisms just as it is for terrestrial forms, but the circumstances of the occurrence of carbon dioxide in the water are much more complex. Carbon dioxide is readily soluble in water, but since the concentration of carbon dioxide in the atmosphere is so low (0.3 cc per liter), water in equilibrium with it will hold only about 0.5 cc per liter free CO_2 at 0°C, or 0.2 cc per liter at 24°C, in simple solution. Actually, the total CO_2 in most natural waters is considerably larger because additional amounts are present in the form of carbonate and bicarbonate ions. Sea water at a salinity of 35‰ normally contains a total of about 47 cc CO_2 per liter, or roughly 150 times the concentration in the air. Taking into account the relative volumes of the ocean and of the atmosphere, it has been estimated that more than 50 times as much CO_2 exists in the seas as in the air (Rubey, 1951). The ocean is thus the great reservoir for the world's supply of available CO_2 and this marine source tends to regulate the amount in the air—just the reverse of the situation with oxygen.

Reactions of Carbon Dioxide in Water. Dissolved CO_2 combines with H_2O to form carbonic acid, and this dissociates as follows:

$$CO_2 + H_2O \rightleftharpoons H_2CO_3 \rightleftharpoons H^+ + HCO_3^- \rightleftharpoons H^+ + CO_3^=$$

The amount of CO_2 in simple solution plus that in the form of H_2CO_3 is called the free CO_2. The amount of the CO_2 in the bicarbonate

ions (HCO_3^-) and in the carbonate ions ($CO_3^=$) is called the combined CO_2. If strong acid is added, the combined CO_2 will be converted to the free form. The amount of acid required to accomplish
this is a measure of the *alkalinity,* that is, of the amount of anions of
weak acids (chiefly HCO_3^- and $CO_3^=$) in the water, and also of the
cations balanced against them. The alkalinity of sea water bears a
fairly constant relation to the chlorinity and hence to the salinity.
The relation of the equilibria of CO_2 to the alkalinity of sea water is
discussed in further detail by Rakestraw (1950); general accounts of
the reactions of CO_2 are given by Harvey (1945) for sea water and
by Ruttner (1953) for fresh water.

When H_2CO_3 dissociates, it releases hydrogen ions (or more properly, hydronium ions, H_3O^+). These affect the *pH*, which is the
negative logarithm of the hydronium ion activity. The *pH* is a measure of the degree to which the water is acid (*pH* below 7) or alkaline
(*pH* above 7). If the equilibrium which is established in the water
is near neutrality (*pH* $= 7$), most of the CO_2 will be present as
HCO_3^- ion. At high *pH* values more CO_2 is present as $CO_3^=$ ion,
and at low *pH* values more is present in the free condition. Thus
pH and the relative distribution of CO_2 in its three components are
mutually interdependent, as indicated in Fig. 7.9. Addition or re-

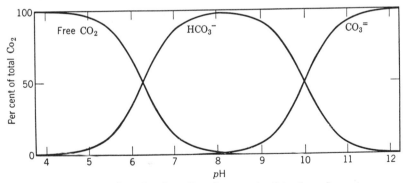

Fig. 7.9. Percentage of total carbon dioxide in each of its three forms in water as
a function of hydrogen ion concentration. (Emerson and Green, 1938.)

moval of CO_2 will affect *pH*; conversely, any other factor changing
the *pH* will affect the CO_2 equilibrium (Dye, 1952).

The bicarbonate and carbonate ions and other anions of weak acids
form a *buffer system* which tends to resist changes in *pH*. The *buffer
capacity* of the water is determined by the abundance of these anions,
and it is therefore also directly related to the alkalinity. Sea water
and hard fresh water are relatively highly buffered natural media.

As a result of buffering, the surface waters of the open ocean rarely depart from a pH of 8.0 to 8.4, the deeper waters being generally confined to a pH of 7.4 to 7.9. In the littoral zone, and particularly in salt ponds and tide pools, the range is greater. The pH in marine muds may drop below 7.0 or rise above 8.5, and in dense growths of sea weeds the pH may reach 9.0. Sea water and hard fresh water are always on the basic side of neutrality. The pH of different fresh waters varies from values below 3 to values higher than 10, although the range of most streams and lakes is confined between pH 6.5 and 8.5. In soft waters with small amounts of combined carbon dioxide and little buffering, the pH value may fluctuate widely within short periods.

The respiration of free-living aquatic plants and animals and the decomposition of organic matter by microorganisms in the water add to the carbon dioxide supply of the water medium. The photosynthesis of the plants, on the other hand, tends to reduce the amount of available carbon dioxide present. In poorly buffered ponds and lakes variation in the relative rates of carbon dioxide production and consumption produces significant changes in the abundance of free carbon dioxide and in the pH of the water. If these water bodies contain a good growth of green plants, the fluctuation in carbon dioxide and in pH displays a diurnal cycle as a result of the fact that photosynthesis regularly exceeds respiration during daylight hours. This carbon dioxide and pH pulse is generally coordinated with, but reciprocal to, the oxygen pulse described above. In the Ohio lake observation illustrated in Fig. 7.1 the pH rose from 8 to 9 between sunrise and sunset and dropped again during the night.

A similar tendency for biological agents to change the pH takes place in the ocean, but often the actual effect on pH is too small to be measured because of the high buffering capacity of sea water. In a study of the English Channel throughout a yearly period, during which photosynthesis varied from its maximum in the spring and summer to its minimum in the winter months, the pH of the upper water layer varied only from 8.16 to 8.25.

The relative constancy of pH values in the sea is one more instance of the stability that characterizes the oceanic environment, and we may pause for a moment to throw a backward glance over the topic. We have noted the high degree of constancy in the open sea in regard to salinity, temperature, and oxygen supply, and now in relation to carbon dioxide, alkalinity, and pH. The ocean thus represents the largest natural environment in which highly stable conditions exist in respect to many ecological factors for weeks, months, or even years together. R. E. Coker (1938) on the occasion of his retirement as president of the Ecological Society of America expressed this thought in the following way:

It seems to have been the work of a Divine Providence to cover the greater part of the earth with the seas and at the same time to endow mankind with no means of making any great change in them. "I will give you" he might have said, "dominion over the lands, over the beasts of the field and the birds of the air, and over the shrubs, trees and grasses, but over the oceans you shall have no control. I trust you with small things, but the greater part of the surface of my beloved mundane sphere I shall keep under my own lock and key. By means of the seas, which you can not measurably modify, I shall protect you against your own follies." So the undisturbed high seas remain the great balance wheel of the terrestrial machine, the chief source of the rainfall necessary for the continuance of organic life on land, the real fountain head of the water whose return journey to the ocean carries the power required for our industries, the mainstay in regulation of temperature, the molder of climates. Concerning the significance of the seas to organic life anywhere, I do not need to say more to climatologists, geologists, or biologists. Suppose that man could have put his plow and machinery and his chemical reagents to work on the whole surface of the earth. Might he not long ago have decided that such a great expanse of brine was an error in Creation, as he has in effect concluded, and perhaps properly, with reference to the great areas of forests and grasslands? Might he not have converted the saline waters into some other chemical form? Think how much more tasty or more useful the sea waters might be were they turned into 20 per cent alcohol, for example, or into gasoline; and we might have had now to form a committee for the preservation of some small marine areas to be kept always as scientific "controls" and as refuges for the native population of non-alcohol addicted and non-gasoline tolerant diatoms, coccolithophores, Salpas, etc.—very useless things in the eye of the practical man, but none the less interesting to the field biologist.

But the designer of nature gave us no opportunity to bring such things to pass. "No," he might have said, "you may change the virgin grasslands into desert, you may pollute the waters and dam the streams as much as you please. You may accomplish much that is good by doing these things wisely. You mean well, but all the same, and for reasons that are quite satisfactory to myself, I put quite out of your reach the seas as the mainstay of organic life on your planet." And this is not as facetious as it may sound.

Ecological Effects of Carbon Dioxide. The most fundamental effect of carbon dioxide in the aquatic environment is the part that it plays in the photosynthesis of green plants, just as is the case on land. We have seen that in most natural waters as in the atmosphere the amount of free carbon dioxide is very small. In sea water with a pH of 8.3, for example, less than 1 per cent of the total carbon dioxide is present in the free form (Fig. 7.9). However, both sea water and hard fresh water contain a large reserve supply of carbon dioxide as bicarbonates and carbonates. Plants living in water of high pH must be able to get along by absorbing the tiny amount of free carbon dioxide present (which is then immediately replaced by dissociation) or else they must be able to use the carbon dioxide existing in combined form. Many pond plants have been shown to absorb the HCO_3^- ion and to use it in their photosynthesis (Steemann Nielsen, 1952). Although we do not know whether most marine plants rely primarily on free or on combined carbon dioxide we find no evidence that the lack of carbon dioxide ever acts as a limiting factor for plant growth in the sea.

In soft-water lakes, in which the total supply of carbon dioxide is small, extensive photosynthesis may reduce the concentration of this material to such an extent that further growth of the plants is prevented. Water is able to absorb carbon dioxide from the atmosphere only at a slow rate; the supply from ground water and from respiration and decomposition may be inadequate to meet the demand of the green plants. The withdrawal of carbon dioxide from the water also causes a concomitant rise in pH. If the change in hydrogen ion concentration is considerable, difficulty is frequently encountered in ascertaining to what extent the limitation of photosynthesis is due to lack of carbon dioxide and to what extent to unfavorable pH values. The growth of populations of planktonic algae in chemically fertilized fish ponds is believed sometimes to be curtailed by the exhaustion of the available carbon dioxide. Lime is commonly added to correct this situation. Improved growth of rooted vegetation in other soft-water ponds has been produced as a result of liming.

The abundance of carbon dioxide also exerts certain specific effects upon the animals of the aquatic environment. The rates of some developmental and metabolic processes are increased at higher concentrations of carbon dioxide and are decreased at lower values, but other animal reactions are inhibited by high carbon dioxide concentrations, so that no general statement of its effect can be made. In vertebrates, and in some arthropods and mollusks the rate of respiratory movements is definitely raised by increase in carbon dioxide tension, but in others this factor has little or no effect (Sheer, 1948).

The concentration of carbon dioxide in the water influences its equilibrium in the blood of aquatic animals. An increase of the carbon dioxide in the blood causes a decrease in the oxygen affinity of vertebrate hemoglobins and of some invertebrate pigments (e.g., hemocyanin). In aquatic habitats with high carbon dioxide tensions animals with the type of blood strongly affected by carbon dioxide in this manner would accordingly experience difficulty in obtaining oxygen. Fish inhabiting tropical swamps with water heavily charged with carbon dioxide have been found to possess a specially adapted type of blood that is little affected by the environmental carbon dioxide. Species of fish dwelling in littoral areas where concentrations of carbon dioxide are above normal have similar adaptations enabling them to extract oxygen from water of wider carbon dioxide range than is possible for pelagic fish.

Changes in carbon dioxide also tend to modify the *p*H and the alkalinity of the blood. Alterations of these characteristics can be compensated for by changes in the abundance of hemoglobin and of cations such as Na and Ca. But these modifications of the blood equilibria require time. Fish that can tolerate but little variation in *p*H and alkalinity of the blood might well be seriously harmed by swimming rapidly across a sharp gradient, as at the thermocline, from water of low carbon dioxide to water of high carbon dioxide or vice versa.

Another influence of carbon dioxide as an environmental factor is in relation to orientation. The movement of certain aquatic animals is affected by differences in concentrations of this gas. Reactions to increased carbon dioxide may have arisen in relation to the harmful effects of an excessive concentration of this gas mentioned above or in relation to the low oxygen tension commonly associated with it. A search has long been made for the factor or factors that guide anadromous fish migrating upstream to a specific tributary within which their spawning beds are located, and differences in carbon dioxide tension have been suggested as a possible orienting feature for salmon. Experiments were conducted by Collins (1952) on the alewife (*Pomolobus*), another anadromous fish, by dividing the stream, in which the fish were migrating, into two channels and adding carbon dioxide gas to the water of one channel. These tests demonstrated that the alewife can distinguish between small differences in free carbon dioxide content (down to 0.3 ppm) and that the majority (72 per cent) "chose" the stream with the lower amount of carbon dioxide. Supplementary tests showed that the fish were oriented primarily by the difference in carbon dioxide itself rather than by the concomitant change in *p*H. Whether a reaction of this sort to naturally occurring differences in carbon dioxide is a chief factor in directing migrating fish into one branch of a stream rather than into another remains to be investigated. Differences in temperature and other factors have been shown to be influential in the foregoing and in other observations, and evidence has been presented by Hasler and Wisby (1951) and Hasler (1954) that olfactory responses involving odor memory may play a part in the orientation of fish.

Hydrogen Ion Concentration

To turn to a more specific consideration of the ecological influence of pH in the free natural waters and in the interstitial water of muds and soils, the hydrogen ion concentration is affected not only by the reactions of carbon dioxide discussed above but also by other solutes present, both organic and inorganic. Since any alteration of the pH of natural waters is accompanied by changes in other physicochemical aspects of the medium, the ecologist must constantly be on guard against assuming that the easily measured pH exerts the controlling influence before determining what effect related changes in the equilibria of the water may have. Edmondson (1945), for example, showed that certain sessile Rotatoria are very likely excluded from lakes by high bicarbonate concentrations, but not necessarily by high pH.

Many early investigators believed that pH would prove to be an ecological factor of major importance in controlling the activities and distribution of aquatic plants and animals. Some later workers, going to the opposite extreme, suggested that the pH of the environment has little or no importance. Present information indicates that the effect of pH as a factor is real, but limited and highly variable in its influence from group to group. As would be expected, pH is generally of minor significance in the ocean because of its relatively constant value in the highly buffered sea water.

In bodies of fresh water the usual hydrogen ion concentrations encountered toward the middle of the pH scale seem to have little differential effect on the majority of the inhabitants. The distribution of many aquatic organisms is unrelated to pH over a wide range, and, when tested in the laboratory, these species often exhibit a tolerance to pH values well above and below those occurring in their natural habitats. Speckled trout (*Salvelinus fontinalis*) are found naturally in waters ranging from pH 4.1 to 8.5 and were subjected to values as low as pH 3.3 and as high as 10.7 without apparent harm. The rotifer, *Monostyla bulla*, is reported to tolerate a range from pH 3.7 to 9.1; the water moss *Fontinalis dalecarlica* can withstand pH values from 3.0 to 10.5. On the other hand, some plants and animals thrive best under acid, others only under alkaline conditions, and others seem to require a nearly neutral medium. A species of *Euglena* is found in water of pH 1.8 draining from mines, and certain bacteria and fungi tolerate values as low as pH 1.4. Other species of animals and plants live in highly alkaline waters: Lake Elmenteita in the African Rift with a pH of 10.7 to 11.2 supports a considerable fauna and flora (Jenkin, 1936), and Soap Lake, Washington, with a pH running up to 10 is found to contain a tremendous population of rotifers and cladocerans during the summer. In contrast to these examples of wide toleration, are instances of organisms that will live only within a very narrow range of hydrogen ion concentration, sometimes extending over less than a pH unit. The ciliated protozoan *Stentor coeruleus* is reported limited to pH 7.7 to 8.0. These aspects of pH and other physicochemical factors of the aquatic environment are reviewed more extensively by Allee et al. (1949, Ch. 11), and by Welch (1952, Ch. 7).

The pH of mud and of soils is frequently one of the most important characteristics of these substrata. A good general account of the ecological aspects of this highly complex subject will be found in Daubenmire (1947, Ch. 2), and more detailed treatments are available in ZoBell (1946) and Waksman (1932). As we have seen, the pH of these aquatic and terrestrial substrata varies widely, depending on the nature of the parent material, the degree of weathering, and the extent of biological activity, including decomposition. Organisms inhabiting mud must be capable of withstanding pH values that may be considerably different from those of the overlying water. The floras of strongly acid soils, such as those developed from granitic rocks in the cold temperate regions, are characteristically different from the floras of alkaline limestone soils. Fungi are the chief organisms of decay in acid forest soils, whereas acid-sensitive bacteria and earthworms are abundant only in soils with a more nearly neutral reaction. The striking difference even in the optimum pH range of plants is illustrated by the accompanying examples (Spurway, 1941).

	pH
Bog rosemary (*Andromeda glaucophylla*)	3.0–5.0
Blueberry (*Vaccinium corymbosum*)	4.0–5.0
Wake robin (*Trillium erectum*)	7.0–7.5
Spleenwort (*Asplenium parvulum*)	7.0–8.5
Stinking chara (*Chara vulgaris*)	7.5–8.5

Plants frequently modify the pH of their substratum by the action of their root secretions and their decomposition products. This activity accounts for the occasional occurrence in limestone regions of species characteristic of acid soils. In such instances the pioneer plants have probably established themselves in microhabitats of lower pH, and subsequent generations have gradually reduced the pH in the adjacent area. Thus we see that in mud and soils, as well as in the free water of the aquatic environment, the pH may act as a specific limiting factor for some species, but that it is most generally useful as an index of the overall conditions.

Calcium Carbonate

Another way in which carbon dioxide exerts an effect upon environmental conditions is through its influence on the formation and dissolution of calcium carbonate (lime). Carbon dioxide in water forms carbonic acid which dissociates to form bicarbonate and carbonate ions, and the latter reacts with calcium ions to form $CaCO_3$:

$$CO_2 + H_2O \rightleftharpoons H_2CO_3 \rightleftharpoons H^+ + HCO_3^- \rightleftharpoons H^+ + CO_3^=$$
$$CO_3^= + Ca^{++} \rightleftharpoons CaCO_3 \text{ (ppt)}$$

The amount of these ions that will remain in solution is greater at higher hydrogen ion concentrations (lower pH) and, unlike most salts, at lower temperatures. Since a change in amount of carbon dioxide affects the equilibrium between the carbonate and bicarbonate ions, it also influences the equilibrium between the precipitated $CaCO_3$ and the Ca^{++} and $CO_3^=$ ions in solution. If CO_2 is added (as by respiration), more H_2CO_3 is produced, and this will dissociate to form hydrogen ions, lowering the pH and reacting with the $CO_3^=$ ions to form more HCO_3^- ions. In nearly neutral solutions the equilibrium is favorable to this reaction (Fig. 7.9). The reverse situation occurs when CO_2 is withdrawn (as by photosynthesis), with the result that more $CaCO_3$ is formed. In this way lime is often caused to deposit on or in the tissues of aquatic plants.

As mentioned in Chapter 3, fundamental differences in the nature of soils depend in part upon the abundance of $CaCO_3$. The amount of lime present is a result of the nature of the parent rock material as modified by the combined action of climatic and biological agents. In the pedocal soil-group division the ecological conditions are such that $CaCO_3$ tends to be retained in the upper soil horizons but in the pedalfer soil-group division carbonic acid and other acids, produced by the metabolism of roots and of soil microorganisms and as by-products of decomposition, tend to bring about the dissolution of any $CaCO_3$ present and thus to allow it to be leached away. Ca^{++} and other cations in the soil tend to be replaced by hydrogen ions, and this causes the soil to become progressively more acid. As soil acidity increases, ion replacement is accelerated and often results in a serious loss of cations needed as plant nutrients, as will be considered further in the next chapter. Carbon dioxide is thus a vital part of a complex web of physicochemical interdependencies in the soil involving carbonic acid, pH, Ca^{++} ions, and $CaCO_3$, each of which has significant ecological relations with the plants and animals living in the soil.

Deposits of $CaCO_3$ in fresh water are referred to as *marl*, although the term is also sometimes used for lime deposits in other situations. Marl in fresh water is sometimes the result of the accumulation of shells, but more often it is produced by the activity of plants. In hard-water lakes which contain large amounts of Ca^{++} ion, the removal of carbon dioxide by photosynthesis readily causes the precipitation of $CaCO_3$—usually deposited on or in the tissues of the plants themselves. The pond weed *Potamogeton* often feels gritty because of the lime present, and *Chara* was named "stonewort" for the same reason. As much as 30 per cent of the dry weight of the latter plant is accounted for by $CaCO_3$ in its tissues. Certain bacteria and various types of algae, especially the Myxophyceae, also cause the formation of marl on the bottom of lakes and ponds. The alga *Cladophora* forms a biscuit-shaped deposit of lime about its tissues, and these "*Cladophora* balls," commonly attaining diameters of more than 8 cm, may accumulate like paving stones over the bottom or along the shore.

In soft-water lakes and particularly those with an acid reaction, we find the reverse situation. Ca^{++} and $CO_3^=$ ions are not only less abundant but they also tend to stay in solution, with the result in extreme instances that the deposition of $CaCO_3$ by the activity of organisms is difficult or impossible. The Ca^{++} ion plays an essential role in membrane permeability and other physiological processes of plants and animals. $CaCO_3$ is a principal component of the shells of mollusks and worms, and is incorporated in the exoskeletons of arthropods where it serves to add stiffness. The skeletons of vertebrates are composed of about 80 per cent calcium phosphate and a considerable portion of calcium carbonate and other calcium compounds. It is not surprising, then, to find that some animals are limited by subminimal supplies of Ca^{++} and $CO_3^=$ ions in the water. Robertson (1941) reports that *Gammarus pulex* requires at least 5 mg Ca per liter before it can harden its exoskeleton. As a general rule few mollusks are found in acid lakes; those occurring are specially adapted to withstand the unfavorable conditions and characteristically display thin shells, often protected by a covering of chitin. However, the bivalves *Pisidium* and *Campeloma* were recorded by Morrison (1932) in water of pH 5.1 to 6.1 containing 3 to 5 mg Ca per liter with shells nearly as heavy as in most alkaline waters. These animals were also found in water of pH 5.1 with as little as 1 mg Ca per liter, but the shells were poorly calcified.

Since the ocean tends to be relatively constant in regard to many of its ecological factors, we might expect to find little variation in the conditions of lime formation in the marine environment. Actually, however, sea water is so nearly saturated with Ca^{++} and $CO_3^=$ ions that slight changes in temperature, pH, and carbon dioxide are sufficient to throw the equilibrium just above or just below the saturation point. The colder and less alkaline parts of the sea are undersaturated in respect to Ca^{++} and $CO_3^=$, and the water can take up additional amounts; the warmer regions of the ocean are supersaturated and $CaCO_3$ is readily formed, chiefly through the activity of various biological agents. The circulation of water in the great ocean basins is thus accompanied by a cycle in which Ca^{++} and $CO_3^=$ ions tend to be taken up in polar or deep water, and lime deposits tend to accumulate in shallow areas of the tropical seas (Fig. 7.10). As surface

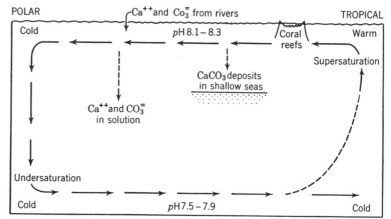

Fig. 7.10. Schematic longitudinal section of northern half of Atlantic Ocean, indicating the cycle of $CaCO_3$. The arrows indicate the north-south and vertical components of the oceanic circulation.

water moves toward the poles it becomes undersaturated in spite of the new quantities of Ca^{++} and $CO_3^=$ added by run-off and river discharge, and the deep return flow remains undersaturated because of the prevailing low temperatures and low pH values. But, as the water rises toward the surface in the tropics, the increase in both temperature and pH bring about saturation and then supersaturation.

These conditions favor the secretion of lime and the building of coral formations in the tropical oceans.

Floating in the open water of the warmer seas are countless trillions of planktonic organisms that use the easily accessible Ca^{++} and $CO_3^=$ ions to build their shells. Prominent among these are biflagellated coccolithophorids, foraminiferans, and pteropods. When these organisms die, their calcareous skeletons rain down upon the bottom, and, if the water is not too deep, their remains accumulate to take part in the formation of globigerina ooze and pteropod ooze. Globigerina ooze is particularly extensive in the Atlantic and Indian Oceans, and this type of bottom deposit sometimes contains as much as 86 per cent $CaCO_3$. In deeper regions of the ocean with lower temperatures and pH values the bottom deposits contain much less calcareous material. These areas of the sea bottom are covered with red clay, or have deposits of diatom ooze or radiolarian ooze formed from the remains of plankton with siliceous skeletons that strongly resist solution (Kuenen, 1950, Ch. 5).

Calcareous formations around shores and on shoals in the marine environment are the result chiefly of the activity of bottom-living organisms. Calcareous sediment resulting from wave action is deposited on the bottom and may possibly be supplemented in some instances by direct precipitation from supersaturated water. The plants and animals taking part in lime production range from microscopic forms to large solitary species and those that form huge colonial aggregations. Particularly notable are certain bacteria, specialized representatives of the Protozoa, Coelenterata, Annelida, and Crustacea, as well as the calcareous algae and a great many kinds of mollusks (Sverdrup et al., 1942, Ch. 20).

Lime-forming organisms are present in all seas, but they are much more prominent in warm waters. Although the physiological processes involved in shell secretion are highly complex (Bevelander, 1952; Wilbur and Jodrey, 1952) and not thoroughly understood, we do know that shell formation is greatly accelerated at high temperatures. In really cold water shell development tends to be suppressed, and exoskeletons of many invertebrates are thin or even absent, as in the naked species of the pteropod *Clione*. Shells in tropical regions are typically larger and thicker than those of related species in temperate regions and often display extra spines, ridges, or other protuberances. The grandfather of them all is *Tridacna*, a bivalve mollusk with a shell that may approach 2 m in length and weigh 250 kg (Fig. 7.11). These animals, hidden among the coral formations, are large enough to be a danger as a man trap since they may close on the foot of a person walking on the reef or on the hand of a pearl diver in deeper water.

Since higher temperatures facilitate the secretion of $CaCO_3$ and accelerate the growth of organisms producing calcareous structures, we are not surprised to find that coral reefs are most abundant in the western portions of the tropical oceans where extensive areas of warm water are found (Fig. 7.12). Coral animals themselves require a temperature above 20°C for good growth, and many other organisms taking part in reef formation flourish only in tropical seas. Foraminiferans, millepores, alcyonarians, barnacles, serpulid worms, and mol-

Photo J. I. Tracey, Jr., U. S. Geological Survey

Fig. 7.11.   Underwater photograph of the giant clam *Tridacna* on the reef flat at Bikini.   The specimen is about 45 cm long.

lusks growing in unbelievable profusion among the corals add their calcareous parts to the formation.   Certain green algae, such as *Halimeda*, often contribute large amounts of lime to the floor of the lagoon.   The reef would not grow as an enduring structure, however, if it were not for the cementing action of lime-secreting Bryozoa and particularly of certain red algae, such as *Lithothamnion*.   These plants, known as encrusting corallines, or nullipores, often produce a sort of pavement protecting the new reef growth from destruction by the surf and thus contribute enormously to reef formation although they are not as conspicuous as the coral animals (Gardiner, 1931; Ladd and Tracey, 1949; Kuenen, 1950, Ch. 6).   The lavish development of calcareous structures (Fig.

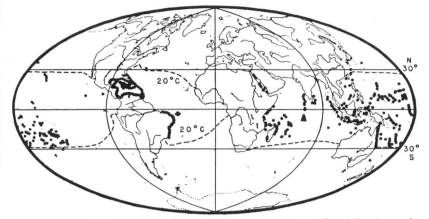

FIG. 7.12. World distribution of coral reefs (Ekman, 1953, after Schott) in relation to the 20° C isotherm for the coldest month in the year. (Hutchins and Scharff, 1947, in the *J. of Marine Research*.)

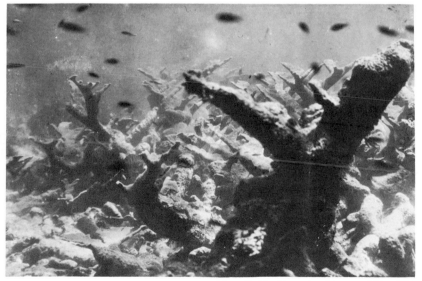

Photo R. W. Miner, Am. Museum of Nat. Hist.

FIG. 7.13. View of coral structures at depth of 8 m on Andros Reef, Bahamas.

7.13) and the extraordinary variety and beauty of the reef community will never be forgotten by anyone who has walked on a reef at low tide, or, better, has explored one with a diving helmet.

These spectacular coral formations are the result of equilibria in the circulation of Ca^{++} and $CO_3^=$ ions that are dependent upon physical chemical, and biological agents. In the words of Redfield (1941): "The calcium cycle involves not only exchanges between land, sea, and the bottom. It includes the consideration of the metabolic cycle, the CO_2 cycle, the temperature cycle, and the cycle of movement of water between the surface and the depths. One could not find a better example of the necessity of considering the environment as a whole as a unified system."

In the foregoing discussion of the ecological influences of oxygen and carbon dioxide we have observed that these "sister" materials, reciprocally involved in photosynthesis and respiration, exhibit a great contrast in the circumstances of their occurrence and in their variability. Oxygen is generously abundant in the atmosphere, whereas the chief reservoir of available carbon dioxide is in the ocean. We have found that in certain habitats either of these substances may be so reduced in amount by the physiological processes of the inhabitants as to curtail the life activities of the organisms themselves. We have also reviewed the particularly intriguing further complications brought about by the fact that carbon dioxide reacts with other materials in the environment to influence the equilibria involving pH and $CaCO_3$. All of these relations with oxygen and carbon dioxide are thus further striking demonstrations of the mutual interdependence of the organism and its environment.

8

Nutrients

NUTRIENTS AND THE ENVIRONMENT

A student once wrote in an ecology paper: "For all organisms nutrition is *par excellence*"—his way of stating that nutrients are a crucially important ecological influence! Indeed, all living things are dependent upon the environment for the supply of energy and of the materials necessary for their nutrition. Green plants use sunlight as a source of energy and synthesize carbohydrates from water and carbon dioxide, obtained as discussed in earlier chapters. To produce living tissue other materials must also be present—particularly protein. Plants build their own proteins from carbohydrates, nitrogen compounds, and other inorganic substances. These simple inorganic building materials constitute the nutrients of the green plant.

Colorless plants and animals must have ready-made organic compounds for their nutrition, and they feed upon material which is, or recently has been, part of another living organism. Energy is obtained by the oxidation of this organic food. Nutrients for green plants are thus obtained from the supply of inorganic substances in the environment, whereas nutrients for animals and colorless plants are represented by the organic matter derived from other organisms.

Nutrition is obviously and necessarily a reciprocal process. The availability of nutrients in the environment influences the growth and distribution of animals and plants, and the activities of living organisms profoundly change the abundance of nutrient materials. The oxidative metabolism of the living organism and the oxidative decomposition of all plant and animal tissues after death result in the return to the environment not only of water and carbon dioxide but also of inorganic materials that can serve again as nutrients for green plants. These relationships are indicated in the following scheme which might be thought of as the "equation of all outdoors":

$$\text{H}_2\text{O} + \text{CO}_2 + \text{Nutrients} + \text{Energy} \nearrow \begin{array}{l} \text{Green Plants} + \text{O}_2 \\ \searrow \text{Animals} \\ \quad\text{Colorless plants} \end{array}$$

Modes of Nutrition

The various modes of nutrition in the living world may be classified according to the accompanying scheme.

> Autotrophic
>   Holophytic (Phototrophic)
>   Chemotrophic
> Heterotrophic
>   Holozoic
>   Saprophytic
>   Parasitic
> Mixotrophic

Autotrophic, or "self-nourishing," organisms can synthesize all essential organic components entirely from inorganic substances; they are therefore not directly dependent upon other organisms for food. This group composed principally of *holophytic* forms which use light as a primary source of energy through photosynthesis is represented most prominently by the green plants, although the purple bacteria are also included. The *chemotrophic* organisms, lacking chlorophyll, are not able to make direct use of solar energy but instead derive their energy from the oxidation of certain inorganic substances. This specialized mode of nutrition is limited to relatively few kinds of organisms. Among those encountered frequently in natural environments are the sulphur bacteria, which oxidize hydrogen sulphide first into free sulphur and then into sulphate compounds, and the iron bacteria, which oxidize ferrous salts to ferric salts.

Heterotrophic organisms require already formed organic compounds as a basis for their nutrition and hence are dependent upon autotrophic organisms for food directly or indirectly. The most prominent subdivision of this group is composed of animals that display the *holozoic* mode of nutrition. These free-living animals characteristically ingest solid food and digest it internally. *Saprophytic* organisms commonly lack a digestive cavity and absorb organic food directly from the environment, usually employing external digestion. Included in this category are most bacteria, many fungi, some flagellates, and a very few higher plants. The *parasitic* mode of nutrition is utilized by some species in almost every taxonomic group of plants and animals. Parasites live on or in other living organisms and obtain organic food directly from the bodies of their hosts.

Mixotrophic organisms are capable of both autotrophic and heterotrophic modes of nutrition of one sort or another. Insectivorous plants possess special anatomical adaptations for entrapping insects and digesting them (holozoic nutrition) and at the same time carry on photosynthesis (holophytic nutrition). Many green flagellates similarly display the capability of utilizing either of these types of nutrition, and, since they are also motile, it is thus a constant source of discussion whether to classify these forms as plants or as animals. When light is available these flagellates can photosynthesize like typical green plants, but at other times they live saprophytically. *Euglena*, for example, is found living in this manner in the decomposing organic matter on the bottom of a pond. Other green flagellates, are provided with a functional mouth and are capable of the ingestion of solid food particles like a typical animal. The green alga *Chlorella* is another Dr. Jekyll and Mr. Hyde, since it is capable of either phototrophic or saprophytic nutrition, and other members of the phytoplankton may be found to lead this double life.

The fact that most animals and colorless plants require for their nutrition the organic matter of other organisms means that the food of these heterotrophic forms has an ecology of its own. The food organisms themselves grow, change, move around, and die. Furthermore, many of these prey species not only serve as a source of nutriment for the predators but may also influence them in other ways as part of their environment. For animals, then, our consideration of nutrients as an ecological factor overlaps the general consideration of the presence of other organisms as environmental influences which will be taken up in subsequent chapters.

But with green plants the situation is quite different. Here the nutritional needs are substances that are relatively simple in the chemical sense. The absorption of nutrients from the environment by plants is a relatively direct and much less complicated process than the food getting of animals. This fact is no doubt one reason why certain aspects of ecology were first developed by botanists. With the holophytic organisms we can often see more clearly the limitation of growth and distribution by the influence of nutrients. We shall accordingly consider first the ecological aspects of the nutritional requirements of green plants since these are by far the most important of the autotrophic forms. Then we shall discuss the significance of the nutrient factor for animals and other heterotrophic forms, including the saprophytes involved in the "return" processes of decomposition and regeneration.

Influence of Nutrients on Green Plants

Nutrients Required. The nutritional requirements of green plants embrace several major materials and a longer list of minor substances. The principal elements that go into the construction of plant tissues are: carbon, oxygen, hydrogen, and nitrogen. We have already discussed the sources of carbon from CO_2, of hydrogen from H_2O, and of oxygen from O_2, CO_2, and H_2O. An enormous supply of nitrogen exists in the air but atmospheric nitrogen is unavailable to most plants. In this respect nitrogen presents a complete contrast to CO_2. We have seen that the quantity of CO_2 in the atmosphere is extremely small but that it is directly and readily available to plants. Since nitrogen makes up 79 per cent of the atmosphere, terrestrial plants would seem to be practically surrounded by this gas—yet only a few special types of bacteria can use free nitrogen. Aquatic plants are similarly unable to utilize directly the large amount of nitrogen gas dissolved in natural waters. Green plants must obtain their nitrogen from nitrogen compounds; these are not generally plentiful and are derived primarily from organic decomposition. Most plants grow best when supplied with nitrate—many can obtain their nitrogen only in that form—but others such as some green algae can assimilate nitrite, ammonia, and amino acids (Algeus, 1951).

Two other elements necessary in moderate amounts for the growth of holophytic plants are sulphur, which is abundant in the soil and in the sea as sulphate, and phosphorus, which occurs as phosphate but is not at all plentiful. Although some phosphate is derived from the disintegration of parent rock, the decomposition of organic matter is the immediate source of this material for most green plants. Essential in smaller quantities are potassium, calcium, and magnesium. Potassium originates from potassiferous silicates found in almost all rocks; the occurrence of calcium has been discussed in the previous chapter. Magnesium, the keystone in the structure of chlorophyll, is usually sufficiently available in the soil and in natural waters.

Other elements known to be necessary for the growth of plants at least in trace quantities include: iron, manganese, copper, zinc, molybdenum, and boron (Stiles, 1946). The fact that plant growth can be affected by zinc in the amount of one part in 200,000,000 illustrates the minuteness of the quantities of these elements that may be effective. Silicon is used by diatoms in the construction of their shells; other elements such as aluminum, fluorine, and bromine are taken up by certain plants but seem to have no nutritional significance. Although sodium and chlorine are commonly present in plant tissues, these substances are probably not necessary for most species. Certain elements found in plants and also in animals have been concentrated hundreds or even thousands of times more than they are in the environment. This condition is strikingly true of trace elements and is easily apparent in the sea where the chemical composition of the surrounding water is highly uniform. Silicon and iron are greatly concentrated in the bodies of diatoms, and titanium, known to occur in certain marine organisms, has not yet been detected in free sea water (Sverdrup et al., 1942, Ch. 7). Vanadium may constitute almost 0.2 per cent of the dry weight of *Ascidia mentula*. Since vanadium is present in sea water in a concentration of only 0.3 to 0.6 mg per cu m, the element has been concentrated roughly four million times in the body of this animal.

Several other elements, that may or may not be essential to the plants, are nevertheless significant for the animals feeding upon the plant material as being either beneficial, e.g., cobalt, iodine, and nickel, or harmful, e.g., selenium and molybdenum. Few if any of these minor nutrients exist as elements in soil or in the water; they mostly occur and must be absorbed as salts or ions in chemical combination with other elements. Above-normal amounts of some of the trace elements are definitely injurious to plants—often with only a narrow range between minimal, optimal, and harmful concentrations. For example, an increase of the boron concentration in the soil to 1 ppm will kill some plants, whereas for other species 1 ppm is optimal and 5 ppm are toxic.

Law of the Minimum. If any necessary nutritive element is completely lacking, the growth and eventually the maintenance of a plant will obviously be prevented. In some habitats all the essential substances may be present, but one or more of them may exist in concentrations so low that certain species cannot absorb them rapidly enough to satisfy their nutritional needs. Under these conditions the growth of the plants will be limited in conformity to Liebig's *law of the minimum.* This law states that growth is limited by the substance that is present in minimal quantity in respect to the needs of the organism. Liebig's law was originally delineated, and is best applied, in relation to limitation by nutrients, but it is sometimes used in a broader sense to include limitation by other factors of the environment.

The reader should understand that the limiting substance is the nutrient that is minimal *relative to requirements* and not necessarily the one that occurs in the smallest absolute amount. In this sense the law of the minimum in ecology is analogous to the law of combining weights in chemistry. The following equation gives the precise amounts of Na and Cl that will combine to form NaCl:

$$23g\ Na + 35g\ Cl \rightarrow 58g\ NaCl$$

If 1000g of Na were added to 35g of Cl, no more than 58g of NaCl would be formed. Under these circumstances the 35g of Cl limits the total amount of NaCl produced. If, however, 23g of Na were allowed to combine with 34g of Cl, somewhat less than 58g of NaCl would be obtained. The 34g of Cl is now the limiting substance, although, in this instance, it is not the smaller quantity of the two components.

The same sort of limitations occur in the growth of plants, but the amounts of nutrients absorbed are not nearly as rigidly fixed as the combining weights in simple inorganic reactions. Much has been learned from water culture methods regarding the variations in the quantities of nutrients used by higher plants in normal growth and also regarding minimal requirements (Hewitt, 1952). Sometimes the amounts or the ratios of nutrient materials used are completely altered at different seasons. For example, a certain group of roses tested in July, took up 450 ppm N and 250 ppm K, whereas in December they absorbed 150 ppm N and 750 ppm K (Turner and Henry, 1948). It has also been learned that a surplus of some nutrients can in certain instances make up for the lack of others—another illustration of the principle of partial equivalence. Experiments have shown that Na is necessary for the growth of the sugar beet, regardless of the amount of K that may be present, although Na is not essential for most plants. Furthermore, if sugar beets are grown with insufficient K, the symptoms of K deficiency are practically eliminated by supplying extra Na (Lehr, 1942).

Similar information on the variation in nutrient requirements has been obtained from cultures of algae. The amount of one nutrient taken in is sometimes found to depend upon the amounts of other nutrients present, and the ratio may change radically according to circumstances. Ketchum (1947) found that the rate of assimilation of phosphorus by the diatom *Nitzschia closterium* was related to the concentration of both phosphate and nitrate in the medium, whereas the uptake of nitrate was independent of the concentration of phosphate and related only to the concentration of nitrate. Various individual cultures grown in the same medium varied by as much as 50 per cent in their phosphorus content (Ketchum and Redfield, 1949). Some cultures multiplied threefold in deficient media and contained only ⅕ the normal amount of phosphorus. These algae not only could make up their deficiency in one day when again supplied with phosphate, but also would absorb more of this material than necessary if excess phosphate were available.

Although a certain degree of flexibility exists in the use of nutrients by plants, in their ability to produce some growth under deficiencies, and in the possible partial substitution of one nutrient for another, an ultimate minimum is eventually reached for the availability of the required elements. If the plants or the nutrients are mobile, the lack of nutriment will affect the whole population at about the same time.

Urban sewage and certain other pollutants discharged into rivers and lakes provide extra nutrients that frequently cause the growth of excessive quantities of algae that are unsightly and odoriferous. Practical application of the law of the minimum has been suggested in controlling this objectionable growth. Since the treatment of all the sewage effluents is costly, consideration has been given to the removal of one essential nutrient only. After the elimination of phosphate from the sewage in pilot tests in Wisconsin the growth of algae was greatly curtailed, although all other nutrients were present in great abundance. The feasibility of using this procedure on a large scale is being investigated.

Pollution from duck farms bordering Great South Bay, New York, cause the water of the bay to be rich in reduced nitrogen compounds and to furnish a low ratio of nitrogen to phosphorus. This unusual situation in regard to the nutrient factor, in combination with other special environmental conditions, has resulted in the suppression of the usual type of phytoplankton in Great South Bay and the production of tremendous quantities of small green algae (Ryther, 1954a). This alteration in the phytoplankton population appears to have prevented the oysters in the bay from feeding and growing normally, with consequent serious reduction in the oyster fishery.

Limitation by Nutrients in Nature. In the terrestrial environment nutrients exert a control over the growth and distribution of plants primarily as a result of deficiencies, although excessive quantities of harmful substances occasionally exclude plants from particular areas. Availability of suitable nutrients is, of course, only one aspect of the soil that determines whether a given species can grow successfully; physical texture, moisture, pH, and other chemical aspects of the environment, as well as the climate, must also be suitable. Emphasis should again be placed on the fact that these factors are often related and their effects mutually interdependent to a considerable extent.

The most commonly deficient nutrients in the soil are phosphate, nitrate, and potassium. A general discussion of the factors tending to conserve or to deplete these materials in the terrestrial substratum was presented in Chapter 3. The existing concentration of these nutrients depends upon the composition of the parent rock material and the extent of the modification of it by leaching and upon the decomposition of biological products. Our information on the limitation of plant growth by lack of phosphate, nitrate, or potassium in the soil is derived chiefly from agricultural research. A consideration of this vast body of knowledge is obviously beyond our present scope, but the reader will find further discussions in the *Year Books* of the U.S. Dept. of Agriculture, in Meyer and Anderson (1952), and in Lyon, Buckman, and Brady (1952).

Under natural conditions the phosphate removed from the soil by plant growth is in part replaced by the breakdown of the parent rock, although this process is extremely slow and some rocks contain little or no phosphorus. Of much greater significance in the restoration of phosphate to most soils is the decomposition of organic matter. Since this material is derived from the bodies of dead organisms and from animal excreta (Hutchinson, 1950), the process represents a critical instance of the reciprocal action of organisms on their environment.

Replenishment of nitrate and of potassium in the soil is similarly dependent primarily on the decomposition of organic material, but the latter element is also derived from potassiferous silicates found in most rocks. Supplementary supplies of nitrate are derived from ammonia formed in rain water by electric discharges in the upper air (Hutchinson, 1944) and from the fixation of free nitrogen by certain soil bacteria.

Not only must the essential nutrients occur in the soil in sufficient quantity, but, even more important, they must be present in *available form*. Iron, manganese, magnesium, zinc, and sometimes phosphorus remain in essentially unavailable states in soils that are too alkaline. On the other hand, under strongly acid conditions phosphorus forms insoluble phosphates with iron and aluminum, nitrates cannot be readily formed from ammonia, and certain elements may become so soluble as to attain toxic concentrations. One of the chief reasons for adding lime to agricultural soils is to correct unfavorable acidity and thus to render nutrients available for absorption by the plants.

Calcium has important effects as a nutrient in addition to the part it plays in influencing pH and other aspects of the environment. Although some plants do not germinate if more than a trace of calcium is present, many more species are dependent upon a generous supply of this element. Plants such as *Aster amellus* and *Libanotis montana* that require a high percentage of calcium in the soil are referred to as obligate *calciphytes* or calciphiles, and their occurrence is limited to limestone or dolomitic regions. Many species are facultative calciphytes. Other plants such as *Calluna* (heather) and *Vaccinium* (blueberry) that occur where the soil contains less than 3 or 4 per cent calcium, are known as calciphobes. Investigation shows that these correlations may be primarily due to the physical structure of the soil, its general richness, or its pH as indirectly influenced by the presence of lime, rather than to a direct nutritive dependence upon calcium. The occurrence of *Sphagnum*, formerly always mentioned as a strong calciphobe, is now believed to be adversely affected by high concentration of hydroxyl ions rather than of calcium. This complicated subject is discussed more fully by Lundegårdh (1931, Ch. 7).

Soils containing large amounts of gypsum (hydrated calcium sulphate) or of serpentine (hydrated magnesium silicate) support peculiar or impoverished floras. Some kinds of plants require gypsum but others are intolerant of it. Johnston (1941) reported that in the deserts of northern Mexico the complex pattern of distribution in certain plants was controlled with remarkable rigidity by their dependence on gypsum coupled with very successful powers of dissemination. *Haploesthes Gregii* (a grass) and *Nama Stewartii*, for example, were often found in widely separated patches of gypsum soils no more than 2 or 3 sq m in extent. Within the same genus one species, *Fouquieria shrevei*, was confined to gypsum areas whereas another species, *F. splendens,* occurred only on non-gypsum soils.

Serpentine can be tolerated by only a restricted group of plant species, and the areas of sparse vegetation growing on soils rich in this material are known as "serpentine barrens." South of Philadelphia barrens of this type may be seen as areas about half a mile wide and several miles long in which pitch pine, black-jack oak, scrub oak, and cat briars are the most prominent species, whereas surrounding regions support good stands of large red and white oaks and gums with few if any pines (Wherry, 1932). A Venezuelan orchid, *Epidendrum O'Brienanum*, exhibits a similarly interesting association with iron ore deposits; the plant grows within areas containing this ore but is not found beyond their peripheries (Buck, 1949).

In other localities deficiencies in trace elements control plant growth. In certain parts of Australia hardly any production of clover could be obtained although general growth conditions and the supply of common nutrients in the soil seemed to be adequate. After a long study it was discovered that required trace amounts of molybdenum were lacking in these areas. When the astonishingly small quantity of 5g of molybdenum per hectare ($\frac{1}{16}$ oz per acre) was added to the soil, a thick growth of clover more than 30 cm high was obtained.

As a result of generations of study of the nutrient needs of agricultural plants we have accumulated a considerable knowledge regarding the use of commercial fertilizers for our common annual crop plants. Bags of chemical fertilizers that we see being applied to farms bear designations such as 6-8-4 or 5-10-5. These numbers refer to the percentages of total nitrogen, available phosphoric acid (P_2O_5), and water-soluble potash (K_2O) that are contained in the fertilizer. Great success has been attained in supplying these commonly deficient materials to agricultural lands by means of such chemical fertilizers. However, we still know extremely little about deficiencies in trace elements and in the more complicated organic compounds. These materials also are leached from the soil by rain, and removed from the area when crops are harvested. In the movement known as "organic farming" the plowing-in of green manure and other types of organic materials is especially recommended with the hope of replenishing as many as possible of the trace elements and organic constituents that are removed from the soil as the result of farming. Crops grown with a full supply of all nutrients, minor and major, will be more vigorous, more resistant to disease and provide more complete nourishment for man and the domestic animals using them as a source of food.

We have much less information about the needs and deficiencies of nutrients for natural vegetation in uncultivated areas. For forest land the time scale is entirely different, and the critical nutrients may also be different. When a crop of trees is harvested after 40 years' growth, we do not know what loss of nutrients the soil has sustained during this long period, nor do we know how to treat forest land to maintain its productive capacity.

Aquatic plants have the same general nutrient requirements as terrestrial plants, and, interestingly enough, two of the elements that are critical on land, nitrogen and phosphorus, are also likely to be seriously scarce in the water environment. Potassium is ordinarily sufficiently abundant in fresh water, and reference to Table 3 will indicate that it is one of the six most abundant ions in sea water. Other materials occurring in small or trace quantities may sometimes act as limiting factors for the growth of aquatic plants. The availability of nutrients in fresh water and in the sea is complicated by the following facts: (1) the supply and the availability of these materials are involved with circulation and various chemical equilibria in the water, (2) the amounts of the nutrients needed by the plants vary according to their physiological condition, and (3) the growth of the plants significantly depletes the supply. For a more detailed discussion of these complicated interrelations than is possible here the reader should refer to such treatments as those of Ruttner (1953) or Sverdrup et al. (1942, Ch. 16).

As would be expected, the amounts of nutrient salts in fresh water vary widely from lake to lake and also may change greatly within the same body of water from season to season, as rates of plant growth and organic decomposition wax and wane. Differences in availability of plant nutrients in the water is the principal criterion upon which European limnologists have divided lakes into three major types: oligotrophic, eutrophic, and dystrophic. Although difficulty exists in applying this classification universally (Welch, 1952), the following general distinctions can be made. *Oligotrophic lakes,* typically very deep, are poor in phosphorus, nitrogen, and calcium; electrolytes and organic materials are low, but oxygen is abundant at all depths and in all seasons. *Eutrophic lakes* are relatively shallow, and are typically rich in plant nutrients and in organic materials; electrolytes are variable in abundance; oxygen is depleted seasonally and may be entirely absent in the hypolimnion. *Dystrophic lakes,* occurring principally in bog surroundings or old mountains, are abundantly supplied with phosphorus, nitrogen, calcium, and organic materials, but the growth of most lake organisms is limited by the occurrence of high concentrations of humic substances. Electrolytes are low, and oxygen is almost or entirely absent in deeper water.

In view of the stress laid upon the constancy of the ocean as an environment in many respects including its salinity, it might be supposed that all nutrient salts in sea water are uniformly abundant. Such is far from the truth, however. The salinity of the ocean is determined almost entirely by the abundance of the salts listed in Table 3, and these are measured in parts per thousand. Phosphate and nitrate are not found in this table at all—they occur in quantities of the order of parts per billion. The paucity of these nutrients is known to be frequently responsible for the curtailment of plant growth in the sea.

Other materials occurring in small or trace quantities may act as limiting factors in the sea. Silicate has been reported upon occasion as insufficient for the production of the siliceous shells of diatoms. The importance of manganese for the growth of phytoplankton is discussed by Harvey (1949). In general, however, we know altogether too little about the occurrence of trace elements in natural waters in relation to the amounts needed for the healthy growth of aquatic organisms. Since artificial sea water prepared from the list of common constituents will not support life indefinitely, we realize that other materials in minor quantities are essential for continued growth.

In both the fresh-water and marine environments particular interest has centered on the availability of phosphate and nitrate not only because these nutrients commonly become critically scarce but also because their depletion is often brought about by the growth of the plant population itself. We have little precise information on the rate of use of nutrients by phytoplankton under natural conditions or their minimum requirements, but a certain amount of data is available from laboratory experiments. In one carefully controlled set of tests a population of *Chlorella vulgaris* of 70 million cells per liter reduced the phosphorus content of its culture medium from 1.6 microgram-atoms (μg-atoms) per liter to 0.4 μg-atom per liter and in another test from 0.8 μg-atom per liter to zero in 24 hours. The diatom *Nitzschia frustrulum* in a population of 40 million cells per liter reduced its supply of phosphorus from 1.6 μg-atoms per liter to zero in a similar length of time (Rice, 1949). The growth rate of these fresh-water species was sharply reduced at the lower concentrations of phosphorus. The multiplication of the marine diatom *Nitzschia closterium* was found to be independent of phosphorus concentration at values above 0.5 μg-atom per liter, but below 0.3 and especially below 0.15 μg-atom per liter division rate was drastically curtailed. By summer the concentration of phosphorus in many natural waters has been reduced to critically low values—for example to less than 0.1 in the English Channel and to less than 0.25 μg-atom per liter in western Lake Erie.

A classical illustration of the seasonal exhaustion of nutrients by the marine phytoplankton is shown in Fig. 8.1 that represents the seasonal changes in phosphate and nitrate in the English Channel. The considerable supply of these nutrients present during the winter is rapidly reduced each spring by the growth of the phytoplankton— sometimes to indeterminably small quantities. The concentration of nitrate and phosphate commonly remains very low during the summer when no effective stirring of the water takes place. Meanwhile the growth of the diatoms is curtailed by the very depletion the diatoms have caused. Further growth cannot take place until the autumnal breakdown of thermal stratification allows a new supply of nutrients to be brought up from the deeper water layers by vertical turbulence. Sometimes a second period of diatom growth occurs during the autumn, temporarily reducing the concentration of nutrients again. Eventually reduced light and the more effective stirring caused by lower temperatures and stronger winds bring this autumnal growth to an end, and allow the surface layers to regain the higher concentration of nutrients characteristic of the winter period.

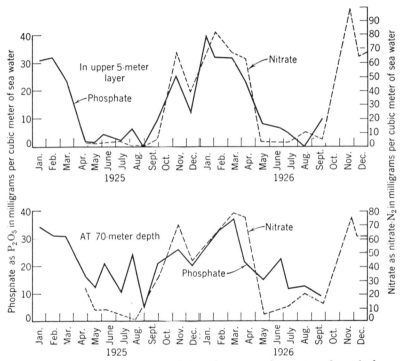

Fig. 8.1. Seasonal changes in availability of nutrients for marine phytoplankton as represented by annual cycle of phosphate and nitrate in the English Channel. (Harvey, 1928, Copyright, Cambridge Univ. Press.)

In bodies of water that are suitable in regard to size and drainage, such as many inland ponds, the seasonal depletion of nutrients may be prevented artificially by adding fertilizer to the water and thus removing this limiting factor for the growth of the plants. Organic manures have been supplied to fish ponds in the Old World for centuries, but in the 1930s the use of chemical fertilizers was begun on an expanding scale in the United States. By broadcasting fertilizer, such as "6-9-2" to "12-9-2," over the pond from the shore (Fig. 8.2), or from a boat, the concentration of nutrients is maintained continuously at such a level that phytoplankton can flourish through the warm

Fig. 8.2. Broadcasting commercial chemical fertilizer over a pond in Belmont, Mass., to supply nutrients to the phytoplankton at the beginning of the food chain.

season of the year. The thick growth of planktonic plants provides abundant food for copepods, cladocerans, and other types of zooplankton and for the bottom fauna, among which chironomids are particularly prominent. The resulting increase in the abundance of these invertebrates stimulates the growth of fish such as the bluegill sunfish that feed upon them, and the enlarged population of these "forage" fish furnishes a rich food supply for predatory species such as the bass. In this way the production of pan fish or sport fish in the pond is significantly improved (Edminster, 1947; Meehean, 1952 and succeeding articles in the *Symposium on Farm Fish Ponds and Management*). Similar augmentation in the growth of marine fish by the use of commercial fertilizer to stimulate the development of phytoplankton and subsequent links in the food chain has been demonstrated in Scottish sea-lochs (Gross, 1947; Raymont, 1950).

In fertilized Loch Craiglin plaice accomplished 2 years' normal growth in 1 year (Fig. 8.3), and flounders accomplished 5 to 6 years' growth in less than 2 years.

Growth of phytoplankton resulting from the fertilization of ponds may produce further effects of ecological importance. Dense "blooms" automatically cause the disappearance of benthic plants by

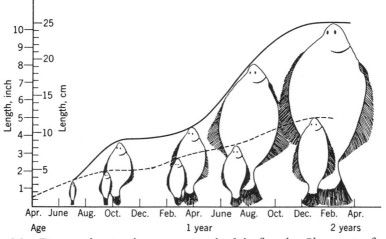

FIG. 8.3. Diagram showing the greater growth of the flounder, *Pleuronectes flesus*, in Loch Craiglin (*upper curve*) after fertilizer was added compared with normal growth in an unfertilized loch (*lower curve*). (Data from Gross, 1947.)

cutting off the light from the bottom. Bottom vegetation is generally undesirable in farm ponds that contain both prey and predator species of fish because its presence allows too many small fish to escape capture by the large fish. On the other hand, the growth of the planktonic algae must not be allowed to proceed to such a point during the summer that the decomposition of the algal material after the growing season will exhaust the oxygen supply and kill the fish during the winter. For this reason the addition of fertilizers must be curtailed in northern regions where the winter is long. Carefully controlled experiments carried out in relation to practical fish farming have provided valuable quantitative data on nutritional and other ecological relationships involved in the aquatic environment. At the same time the failure of hasty or ill-conceived fish farm practices form an admirable illustration of the necessity for a thorough understanding of ecological principles as a background for successful conservation or cultivation of biological resources.

Influence of Nutrients on Animals

As the great majority of animals display the holozoic mode of nutrition, this type of heterotrophism will be considered first, together with certain nutritional aspects of parasitism. The nutritional relations of saprophytes—particularly the fungi and bacteria—will be included in the discussion of decomposition in the succeeding section.

The nutrients required by animals are proteins, carbohydrates, fats, salts, and accessory substances such as vitamins. Limitation by the nutrient factor may result from the shortage of necessary foods in the environment or from the inability of the animal to obtain and digest them. The deficiency of the food itself may occur in relation to its abundance or its composition. In some situations the total amount of nutriment is sufficient but the particles of food are so scattered that they cannot be gathered fast enough to satisfy daily nutritional needs.

The main bulk of the animal diet consists of carbohydrates, fats, and proteins. Considerable flexibility exists in respect to the use of these materials as sources of energy, but at least some protein food is required in the growth and repair of animal tissue. Insufficient supply of food to meet energy requirements or deficiency in amount of protein, minor mineral nutrients, or necessary trace elements may act as a limitation on the growth, reproduction, or distribution of an animal.

Free-living animals and parasites obtain these nutrient materials by feeding on the tissues of other organisms in their environment. The bodies of the organisms preyed upon as a source of food all contain carbohydrates, fats, and proteins, but in widely varying proportions, and they may or may not furnish all the minor and trace materials that are needed. Furthermore, the possible food organisms must be caught, killed, and dealt with mechanically, in the process of ingestion, and chemically, in the process of digestion.

Herbivorous animals may be either larger or smaller than the plant food on which they feed, but carnivores must always be larger, quicker, or stronger than their prey, or be able to overcome them by the use of poison glands or some other adaptation. Parasites are smaller than their hosts. Predators must also be equipped with appendages and mouthparts that are capable of breaking through the bark of trees, the shells of invertebrates, the tough skin of vertebrates, or other types of protective outer covering, and capable of chewing up the food sufficiently for swallowing. Apparently soft grass, for example, contains spicules of silica so hard that only ruminant animals with specially adapted teeth can feed on it as a regular diet.

The necessity for alacrity and for the possession of suitable anatomical adaptation for dealing mechanically with the prey is sufficiently evident, but not so immediately apparent is the necessity for the animal to possess the digestive equipment required to deal chemically with the food once it is inside.   Carnivores do not live on hay —nor do ruminants live on meat.   In studying the food sources of animals the possible lack of enzymes for digesting materials that appear to be abundant and available in the environment is a difficulty sometimes overlooked, especially in relation to lower animals.   For a long time it was supposed that clams, oysters, and other common bivalves obtained their nourishment chiefly from the larger, more conspicuous species of diatoms filtered from the plankton.   Most of these larger types of phytoplankton are now known to pass through the intestines of the shellfish quite undigested.   Physiological investigation has revealed the fact that these mollusks have no extracellular cellulase or protease.   Hence, they are quite incapable of digesting relatively large food particles that are enclosed in an intact cellulose or protein cell wall (Coe, 1948).   The nutritional needs of filter feeders like clams and mussels appear to be satisfied by the ingestion of organic detritus or of a type of nannoplankton small enough to be engulfed by digestive phagocytes.

Many specializations have arisen in relation to the mechanical and chemical requirements of food getting in natural habitats (Allee et al., 1949, Ch. 17).   Although most animals are clearly either herbivorous or carnivorous, these categories are not absolute and some species like the opossum are omnivorous in their diet.   Some carnivores eat considerable plant material. Herbivores occasionally consume animal food, as is exemplified by the fact that reindeer have been known to eat fish when no other food was available.   The diet of the black bear ranges all the way from sizable mammals to tiny ants, and from blueberries and honey to salmon.

Many species of animals are highly modified for feeding on special parts of plants.   The aphids and scale insects have sucking mouthparts enabling them to obtain the sap of their hosts.   Some insects are adapted for boring into and digesting, the wood, the bark, or the cambium of trees.   Not only do certain insects feed exclusively on the leaves of plants, as do many mammals and a few reptiles, but in addition the "leaf miners," which live between the leaf surfaces, are further specialized to feed exclusively on the softer interior tissue.

Many animals, among which birds are prominent, show a predilection for the seeds or fruits of plants, whereas other types eat the flowers, or more frequently, only certain parts or secretions of the flowers, such as the pollen or the nectar. Hummingbirds, butterflies, and bees are well known in the latter category. Finally, the roots of plants form the chief or the exclusive food of some burrowing animals. As a further development of specialization, certain herbivores are restricted to a food from plants belonging to a particular taxonomic group, that is, to one family, one genus, or even one species. An example of selective feeding is shown in Fig. 6.15.

Carnivores also may sometimes display an epicurean fastidiousness in their diets, but specialization on single animal foods is not as elaborately developed as it is among herbivores. Certain species of bats, leeches, insects, mites, and ticks, to be sure, are specifically adapted for bloodsucking, and other instances of preference for certain animal tissues exist. Animals specially adapted for subsisting on dead organic matter include the dung beetles and the carrion feeders such as vultures, flesh flies, and sylphid beetles. Various species of scavengers are restricted to the lipoids, proteins, keratinoids, or tendinous tissues of the dead animal. For the most part, however, carnivores eat all parts of their prey and are guided largely by availability in their selection of food species.

The distribution of free-living animals, parasites, and other heterotrophic forms is obviously closely related to the occurrence of the organisms upon which they depend for food. The nutrient factor limits geographical range in a general way or in a narrowly specific manner, according to the degree to which each species is omnivorous or restricted in its food habits. Grazing animals like the antelope are found in grasslands; browsing animals like the deer live in forested regions. Similar broad control of distribution occurs in the aquatic environment. Off the New England coast cod are caught chiefly on the banks, such as Georges Bank, where mollusks, crabs, and other organisms upon which the cod feeds grow abundantly on the firm bottom. In contrast, the redfish is found chiefly in the deeper water off the banks where the soft muddy bottom supports populations of shrimp which form the principal food of this fish (Fig. 8.4).

Control of distribution on a smaller scale is seen in those heterotrophic organisms that are limited to one type of food. *Monophagous* animals are those that eat only one species of food organism. Parasites generally attack only a limited group of species—sometimes no more than one species. Saprophytes are often capable of deriving nourishment from only one type of organic material, and, if this "sub-

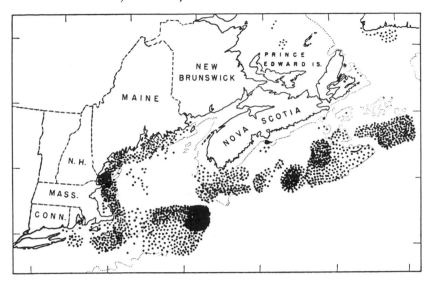

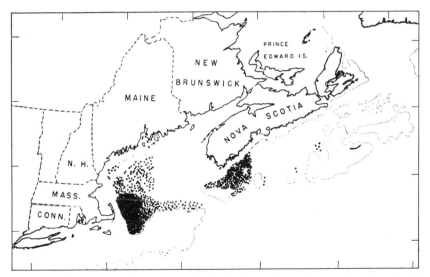

FIG. 8.4.   Contrasting distribuiton of cod, *Gadus callarias* (*upper figure*) and red-fish, *Sebastes marinus* (*lower figure*) as indicated by the catch of the New England commercial fishery in 1936.   Each dot indicates a catch of 25,000 kg; broken line indicates 90 m contour. (Ackerman, 1941, Copyright, Univ. of Chicago Press.)

strate" is highly restricted in its occurrence, the distribution of the saprophyte will be correspondingly curtailed.

Many illustrations of the control of distribution by the nutrient factor for these various types of organisms will occur to the reader, but perhaps the richest source of examples is found in the insect world, as fully discussed by Brues (1946). Our common North American walking stick, *Diapheromera femorata,* feeds generally on the leaves of oaks, whereas a giant East Indian member of this insect group eats the leaves of only a single species of *Eugenia* found in Sumatra.

The degree to which insect pests on crop plants are monophagous is an important consideration in the introduction of new crop species and in the procedures to be adopted in pest control. The Colorado potato beetle, which spread northward from its native home in Mexico, feeds almost entirely on the foliage of the potato plant, and it sooner or later moves into every new area in which potato farming is begun. The cotton boll weevil crossed the Rio Grande from Mexico about 1892, and by 1894 it had spread to six counties in southern Texas. Advancing 40 to 160 miles a year, the weevil had infested more than 85 per cent of the Cotton Belt of the United States by 1922. In view of the terrific destruction caused by this pest to the cotton crop, it is fortunate that the insect is prevented by its monophagous feeding habit from spreading to other crops or to native vegetation.

Insects also provide examples of the high degree of specificity of many parasite-host relationships—a matter in which nutrition is prominently involved. The Mallophaga (biting or bird lice) generally restrict themselves to hosts of one, or of closely related, species. The physiological basis for this specificity is strikingly illustrated by the taxonomic relations of the lice that feed upon the bodies of the cowbird. This bird lays its eggs in the nests of other birds belonging to no less than 158 species, where the young cowbirds would have every opportunity to acquire the lice of the foster species if the infestation depended primarily upon chance contact. Actually, however, the lice of the cowbird are not those of the foster species but belong to genera found on other blackbirds taxonomically related to the cowbird.

The absence of certain minor constituents from the diet may have far-reaching ecological consequences. Lack of sodium chloride in the food causes deer, elk, and other ruminants to travel long distances to salt licks. Big Horn sheep, driven by the advance of civilization into parts of the Rocky Mountains where water is soft, must be provided with extra salt. A rich supply of lime in the food is required by snails, mammals, and certain other land animals. As mentioned in Chapter 3, especially fine race horses are raised in the bluegrass region of Kentucky. Here the abundance of calcium and phosphorus in the grass makes possible the healthy bone growth of the young horses. The fire salamander is an example of an animal that avoids calcium soils. The special need of aquatic organisms for lime has been discussed in the previous chapter.

Certain elements and vitamins are required by animals in only trace quantities, but, if these minute amounts are not present in the diet, serious deficiency diseases and eventually death result. In regions such as the belt from Washington east to Montana and south to Colorado, in which iodine is deficient in the soil, the plants, although themselves healthy, do not contain the amount of iodine needed by animals feeding upon them. As a result goiter develops in live stock, and also in human consumers, unless extra iodine in the form of iodized salt is added to the diet.

Zinc, iron, copper, and cobalt are other elements needed in trace amounts by animals. Zinc is essential in one of the enzymes involved in respiration, and the other three elements mentioned are concerned with formation of hemoglobin, the deficiency of which produces anemia. In certain parts of Scotland and of Australia all attempts at sheep raising were unsuccessful until the difficulty was finally traced to the lack of cobalt in the soil. Only very small amounts of cobalt given the sheep directly, or applied to the grazing areas as fertilizer, were needed to bring about a remarkable improvement in the growth of the animals.

The similar need of animals for vitamins obtained from the food is too well known to require extended comment here. Only minute quantities of vitamins are consumed, but these are absolutely necessary and must be obtained directly from the plants that manufacture them or in some other way, if the animals are to survive. Control of the lives of animals and of other heterotrophic forms by the nutrient factor may thus involve the sufficiency in amount of the common food stuffs, the availability of essential accessory substances in extremely small quantities, or some other necessary aspect of nutrition.

DECOMPOSITION AND REGENERATION

Since the food of animals and of other heterotrophic forms is derived from green plants or from the bodies of organisms that are directly or indirectly dependent upon green plants, the nutrition of these phototrophic forms is clearly of basic importance in the natural community. We have seen earlier in this chapter that for both terrestrial and aquatic plants the nutrients that are likely to run short —particularly phosphate and nitrate—are derived in large measure from the decomposition of dead organisms. The destructive part of the biological cycle is thus revealed to be just as critical as the constructive part in keeping the wheel of life turning. This idea can perhaps be expressed no more graphically than in the words of a student who wrote on an examination: "If it were not for the decomposition process, the whole world would become choked with the dead bodies of plants and animals, and this shocking situation would bring all life to an end."

Processes of Decomposition and Transformation

The release of the nutrients that have been built into the bodies of plants and animals involves two steps: first, the organic matter must be *decomposed* into soluble form and subsequently into inorganic form, and second, the resulting inorganic material must be *transformed* into compounds that can be absorbed by phototrophic plants. Carbohydrates decompose into carbon dioxide and water; fats break down into these materials and also release phosphate. The decomposition of protein is more elaborate, involving hydrolysis into proteoses, peptones, and polypeptides, and then break down into amino acids, ammonia, carbon dioxide, and water in addition to minor constituents. Special complexes present in living organisms, such as cellulose, hemicellulose, chitin, agar, and bone, decompose much more slowly but eventually to the same products.

Living organisms are required to carry out practically every one of these steps in decomposition. Fungi are especially active in decomposing organic matter on land; bacteria are prominent in damp soil and in the water environment. These microorganisms not only work on the surfaces of solid material but also attack dissolved organic matter.

The necessity for the transformation of the products of decomposition from one inorganic form to another is especially apparent in nitrogen compounds. Since most plants can obtain their nitrogen only in the form of nitrate, the ammonia or ammonium salts resulting from the decomposition of protein must be oxidized first to nitrite and then to nitrate. These transformations, comprising the process of *nitrification,* are brought about in both the land and the water environments by the activities of autotrophic (chemotrophic) bacteria: the oxidation of ammonia to nitrite is accomplished by bacteria of the

genera *Nitrosomonas* and *Nitrosococcus,* and the oxidation of nitrite
to nitrate is carried out by bacteria of the genus *Nitrobacter.*

The supply of available nitrogen in the soil and in the water may
be further augmented as the result of *nitrogen fixation* by specialized
bacteria belonging to the genera *Azotobacter* (aerobic) and *Clostridium* (anaerobic), which are free living, and *Rhizobium,* which
live symbiotically in root nodules on certain higher plants, notably:
locust trees, alfalfa, clover, beans, peas, and other legumes. These
bacteria take in free nitrogen, build it into their bodies and, in the

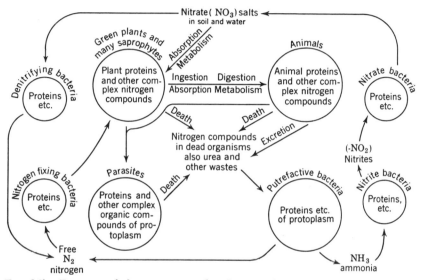

Fig. 8.5. Diagram of the nitrogen cycle, showing the principal components and
processes. Compounds not included in circles are free in the environment.
(Modified from *Principles of Modern Biology* by Marsland and Plunkett. By
permission of Henry Holt and Co., Copyright, 1945.)

case of the symbiotic forms, pass it on to their hosts. After these
bacteria or the tissues of the host plants die and decompose, the supply of fixed nitrogen that they contain is made available through the
activities of the nitrifying bacteria. Free nitrogen can also be fixed
by certain photosynthetic bacteria, sulfate-reducing bacteria, and
blue-green algae. Other types of bacteria cause *denitrification,* or
the loss of fixed nitrogen from the environment, by reducing nitrate
to nitrite and nitrite to nitrogen, or even to ammonia (Frobisher,
1944, Ch. 25; Welch, 1952, Ch. 10).

Thus nitrogenous material derived from dead animals and plants is decomposed and transformed by different microorganisms into inorganic compounds that can be utilized once more in the growth of phototrophic plants. The various steps—some of them reversible—involved in this vital nitrogen cycle are indicated in Fig. 8.5. An example of the quantitative changes in successive nitrogenous products is shown in Fig. 8.6 depicting the course of an experiment in

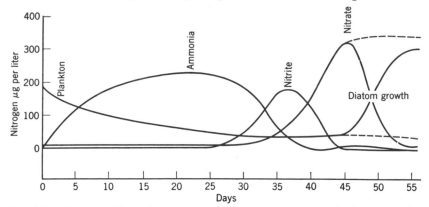

FIG. 8.6. Decomposition of nitrogenous organic matter in mixed plankton under laboratory conditions, showing the successive appearance of soluble nitrogen compounds. One portion inoculated with diatoms after 45 days; dotted lines represent uninoculated portion. (Von Brand, Rakestraw, and Renn, 1937, *Biological Bull.*)

which marine plankton decomposed and a new growth of the plankton took place after regeneration of the nutrients. Phosphorus, carbon, sulphur, and other elements entering the living complex take part in similar cyclic movements between the organism and the environment. The carbon cycle is represented diagrammatically in Fig. 8.7.

Place of Decomposition

In the terrestrial environment the decomposition of organic matter takes place on and in the soil. Material in particulate form is carried beneath the surface by organisms and by rain to depths varying according to the ecological conditions as discussed in Chapter 3. Material in solution may be transported still further by percolating water. The decomposition of this organic matter thus may take place at a variety of levels within the soil profile, although most of it goes forward in the A horizon. As we have mentioned earlier, a good portion of the products of decomposition may be retained in the soil when the vegetation is suitable and the rainfall moderate, but some loss of mineral salts takes place under the best of conditions. However, serious amounts of these valuable nutrients are leached from soils that are acid and subject to excessive rainfall or that exist under other unfavorable circumstances. Farm or forest practices that permit soil erosion to take place have resulted in accelerated and often irreparable loss of mineral nutrients and humus from the land.

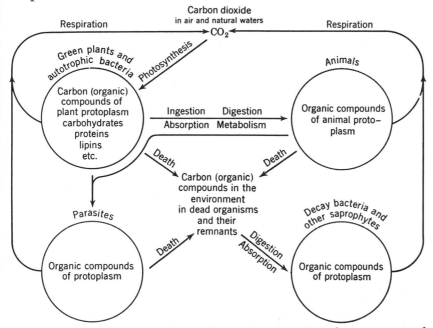

FIG. 8.7. Diagram of the carbon cycle, showing the principal components and processes. Compounds not included in circles are free in the environment. (From *Principles of Modern Biology* by Marsland and Plunkett. By permission of Henry Holt and Co., Copyright, 1945.)

In the water environment dead organisms tend eventually to sink even though they may have a period of buoyancy. After the organism's substance has gone into solution, no further tendency to sink exists. During the period of sinking the decomposing material may have been displaced horizontally by currents for considerable distances. By the time that the organic matter has been decomposed and transformed, the resulting nutrient materials may be very far removed both horizontally and vertically from the spot originally inhabited by the organism from whose body they were derived.

In deep areas of lakes or of oceans the bodies of many dead plants and animals sink to depths below the euphotic zone before they decompose. Under these circumstances, when the phosphate and nitrate are released in form suitable for absorption by green plants, they will be at levels where light is too weak for photosynthesis. These nutrients cannot be used again for plant growth until they have been returned to the euphotic zone by vertical currents and mixing, as will be discussed in the next section. A cycle thus exists involving this movement of nutrient materials to the deeper parts of water bodies and the restoration of the decomposition products to the upper

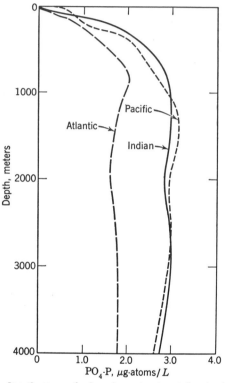

FIG. 8.8. Vertical distribution of phosphate in the Atlantic, Pacific, and Indian Oceans. (From *The Oceans* by Sverdrup et al., 1942, Copyright, Prentice-Hall, N. Y.)

layers by vertical transport. In deep lakes and in the ocean the concentration of nutrient salts is much greater in the lower strata than it is near the surface, as may be illustrated by the condition in the Pacific (Fig. 8.8). The rates of upward and downward transport for the year as a whole are presumably in approximate balance, and the cycle tends toward a steady state. However, mineral salts are continually being added to the ocean by run-off and river discharge—a process constituting a loss of nutrient material from the land. These nutrients enter the marine cycle and the major portion of them is eventually distributed to the huge reservoir of nutrients in the deep sea. These critically important materials are thus being drained away inexorably from the land environment and being added to the accumulation in deep water which is unavailable, except for that portion brought to the surface again by vertical circulation.

Stagnation in Cycles. Materials move from the environment into the bodies of plants and animals as they grow, return to the environment when they die and decompose, and in some instances undergo complicated transformations and translocations in the environment before they are again taken up by living organisms. The study of the geographical distribution of materials used by plants and animals and their cycles is known as *biogeochemistry*. A further discussion of these circular causal systems in ecology is presented by Hutchinson (1948). Materials are not equally abundant in the different phases of these cycles, nor do the various steps take place at uniform rates. Biogeochemical investigations show that materials of critical concern to plants and animals have accumulated in certain places and represent points of stagnation in the cycles. The gradual augmentation of nutrient materials in the deep sea is an instance of this phenomenon. Nutrient substances may thus be withdrawn from circulation for longer or shorter periods.

A relatively temporary stagnation is represented by the organic matter in the soil or on the bottom mud of natural water bodies. The nutrient minerals contained in this organic matter are unavailable for plant growth until the material decomposes. In many soils this retardation of the cycle is beneficial because, as explained earlier, the formation of humus in the soil has valuable physical effects besides providing a slow, steady release of nutrients. Guano deposits, such as those on the islands off Peru, illustrate a long-term accumulation of nutrient materials (Hutchinson, 1950). The many cubic miles of peat, lignite, and coal buried in the earth's crust represent stagnation in the carbon cycle for hundreds of millions of years. A similar stagnation in the calcium cycle is represented by the deposits of chalk, limestone, and coral material.

Great differences exist in the total supply of the various building materials needed by plants and animals as well as in their availability. When stoppages occur in cycles of elements likely to be scarce in available form, such as nitrogen and phosphorus, critical conditions may arise. An inexhaustable supply of nitrogen exists in the earth's atmosphere, but this represents a reservoir that can be drawn upon only slowly by certain physical and biological agents. Phosphorus, on the other hand, is a rare material: only about $\frac{1}{100}$ of the earth's crust is composed of this element. The only ready sources of phosphorus are the products of decomposition of the bodies of organisms. We have seen that the supply of phosphate in the rocks and in the deep sea can be obtained at only a very slow rate. Therefore the acceleration of the loss of this element from the land by soil erosion is a critically serious matter for life in general, and for our agriculture in particular, since our food supply is chiefly derived from the terrestrial environment. Wells, Huxley, and Wells (1939) have said: "Phosphorus is the weak link in the vital chain on which man's civilization is supported."

Regeneration

The return process in the cycle of materials in natural environments, by means of which nutrients once used are made available again for the further growth of organisms, is known in ecology as *regeneration*. There are two aspects of regeneration: first, nutrients must be rendered available chemically through the processes of decomposition and transformation that we have traced in the preceding sections; second, nutrients must be rendered available spatially, that is, restored to zones where green plants can grow and resynthesize organic material. Critical minerals that have been carried below the level of plant growth must be brought up again before they can be used.

Mention has been made earlier of the favorable situation in prairie soils in which rainfall is not sufficient to cause serious leaching, and in semiarid soils in which an upward movement of the ground water takes place. These effects, augmented by the activity of the roots of grasses, account to a considerable degree for the restoration of nutrients to the surface layers in pedocal soils. Regeneration of nutrients in the pedalfer soils is less complete. In the deciduous forest region, however, some restoration of materials to the surface is accomplished by the fall of leaves and other litter, and by the mining activities of earthworms and other animals. In the podzol regions the greater rainfall produces excessive leaching with the result that nutrient salts are carried beyond the reach of plant roots.

Here we have an analogous situation to that in the deep parts of the aquatic environment, where decomposition is often completed at depths below those at which green plants can grow. In water habitats the return portions of the same currents that carry oxygen down to the deeper levels in lakes and in the ocean bring nutrients up from the richer reservoirs in the lower strata. This upward transport of nutrients by wind stirring, eddy conduction, or mass circulation which also affect other properties of the water is another manifestation of the principle of common transport.

Rate of Regeneration. The rate at which regeneration takes place varies very widely and depends not only upon the speed of decomposition but also upon the rapidity of restoration of nutrients to the growth zone. The rate of regeneration is rapid in some instances and slow in others. The rapidity with which the processes of decomposition and transformation go forward depends upon temperature, supply of oxygen, and other conditions that influence the industriousness of the various kinds of bacteria required. In very cold regions and in poorly aerated soils and muds the chemical steps in regeneration take place at a sluggish rate and sometimes come to a standstill. Under these circumstances undecomposed, or partially decomposed, organic matter accumulates and, if time and circumstances are right, deposits of peat, coal, or oil may be formed.

When decomposition and transformation to inorganic compounds have taken place, the rate at which nutrients are restored to surface layers depends on the physical conditions in the soil and in the water. In oceanic areas of active upwelling of water from deeper layers the regeneration of nutrients may take place as fast as the plants can use them. The extensive regions of permanent upwelling off the west coast of Africa and the west coast of North and South America are characterized by water rich in nutrients, and consequently they support a vigorous plant growth at all seasons. In most temperate waters vertical circulation is retarded or stopped completely during the summer. The deep stirring in temperate seas during the winter period brings a new charge of nutrient-rich water to the surface and gives rise to the expression: "Once a year the sea is plowed." In deep lakes of the temperate region phosphate and nitrate are restored to the euphotic zone during the spring and fall overturns.

During periods when virtually no vertical circulation takes place plant growth in natural waters must depend upon the nutrients furnished by decomposition within the surface layers and by the relatively slow eddy conduction from deeper strata—often further retarded by the presence of a thermocline. An adequate rate of replacement is just as necessary as an adequate concentration of nutrients. A single measurement of the phosphate and nitrate in the water might indicate the presence of adequate amounts of these substances, but in view of the rapidity with which the nutrients are used by a growing plant population, the supply of nitrate and/or of phosphate will soon be exhausted unless regeneration keeps pace with utilization. Quantitative data on the rates of decomposition, regeneration, and assimilation of phosphate by phytoplankton are available from controlled experiments in outdoor tanks (Pratt, 1950) in addition to laboratory tests (Rice, 1949). Analysis of the seasonal cycle of phosphate in the Gulf of Maine by Redfield, Smith, and Ketchum (1937) gives the following approximate estimates for the fractions of this nutrient assimilated by the phytoplankton from the various sources of supply: 2 per cent from the original inorganic phosphate in the surface water layer, 73 per cent from vertical transport, and 25 per cent from decomposition and animal excretion within the surface layer (Ketchum, 1947). Similar experiments in the terrestrial environment have been carried out principally in relation to cultivation of crops, and relatively little is known about the rate of regeneration in wild areas. For further information on this subject for cultivated areas the reader may consult the *Yearbooks* of the United States Department of Agriculture.

Ratio of Regenerated Materials. The proportions of the materials provided by the regeneration process are limited by the relative abun-

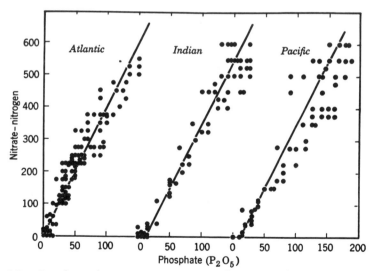

Fɪɢ. 8.9. Correlation between concentrations of nitrate and phosphate in waters of the Atlantic, Indian, and Pacific Oceans expressed in milligrams per cubic meter (Redfield, 1934, Copyright, Univ. Press of Liverpool.)

dance of the elements in the organic matter that has decomposed. Only those nutrients will be provided by decomposition that were present in the dead organisms. The fact that chemical fertilizers added to the soil do not replace all the nutritive substances, nor furnish them in the same proportions as those removed by the growth of the farm crops, has already been mentioned. Procedures recommended by "organic farmers" in which the unused portions of the crops are returned to the soil as a green manure and in which animal manure is used extensively go far toward maintaining a proper balance of organic matter and the various mineral nutrients, but further correction of proportions or the addition of trace elements may also be necessary.

The interdependence of the ratios of materials regenerated and those of nutrients assimilated is also demonstrated in the aquatic environment. Analysis of samples of sea water from many localities in the Atlantic, Indian, and Pacific Oceans reveal a striking parallelism in the ratio of phosphate and nitrate in spite of the great fluctuations in the concentration of each (Fig. 8.9). The ratio of carbon to the other two elements also tends to remain constant, giving the following average values:

$$C:N:P = 41:7:1 \text{ grams} = 106:15:1 \text{ atoms}$$

The ratios of these three elements in the plankton are found to be very closely the same. Plankton is thus known to take up nutrients in the ratio in which they are provided in the water; when the plankters die, these materials are restored to the water in the same ratio (Redfield, 1934). It is not easy to decide how this unique situation arose. Do these ratios represent the composition of the primitive ocean in which species of phytoplankton evolved that could assimilate nutrients in just these proportions? Or do the ratios represent an equilibrium reached and maintained by the activity of nitrogen-fixing and denitrifying bacteria in the sea? The answer to these questions must await further investigation.

Let us cast a backward glance over the web of interdependencies involved in the nutritive relations between the organism and the environment. We have seen that the lack of nutrients in quantity or quality, or in chemical or mechanical availability, limits the growth and distribution of both plants and animals. As living things grow, they reduce the supply of nutrient materials in their environment; but, when they die and decompose, their substance adds to this supply directly or indirectly. In situations in which either the organisms or the nutrients are mobile the shortage of food affects the whole population, not merely the individuals most recently added to the population. For a replenishment of certain critical nutrients the chief source is the dead bodies of the animals and plants themselves. The presence of other sets of organisms—the decomposers and transformers—is required to convert the organic materials to forms suitable for the growth of green plants, and frequently physical agents are necessary to restore the nutrients to zones where growth can take place once more.

9

Relations within the Species

Our discussion of nutrients in the previous chapter leads directly to a consideration of the presence of other organisms as a part of the environment. No individual animal could live by itself because it is dependent upon other organisms for food as well as for other requirements. Certain green plants could conceivably exist in isolation for a period, but, if the species is to be maintained, progeny must be produced. The plant would soon be surrounded by young with which it would be in competition, or in some other relation, so that it would no longer be living as an isolated individual. As the population of each species increases and as groups of animals and plants are formed, new relations appear—in ecological situations as well as in others the whole is more than the sum of its more obvious parts. In this chapter we shall deal with intraspecific relationships and in the next chapter with interspecific relationships.

ORIGIN OF GROUPS

Groups of individuals of the same species may arise in several ways: (1) as the result of reproduction, (2) as the result of passive transport, or (3) as the result of active locomotion.

Reproduction

Some groups are the result of the breeding activity of one breeding unit—either an individual in the case of asexual reproduction, or a pair in the case of sexual reproduction. If the progeny of this breeding unit stay near together, a group will be formed. In some types of animals and plants the young remain attached to the adults. This situation is seen commonly in the cryptogamic plants, but instances are also found among the higher plants. Strawberry plants, for example, send out runners that take root, producing new plants, and these in turn send out more runners. In this way dense aggregations of the species are formed. Unfortunately for man, briars and poison ivy also produce thick clumps of individuals by this very successful vegetative reproduction.

Similar attached aggregations are formed by certain sessile organisms of the animal kingdom. Many sponges, bryozoans, tunicates, hydroids, and other invertebrates grow in colonies, and coral animals produce extensive formations as a result of colonial development. Animals displaying this growth habit are sometimes very numerous, but they are not capable of free locomotion, and they have not attained as high a degree of development as non-colonial animals.

In other groups formed by the progeny of a breeding unit the individuals are unattached but remain together. The parents and their immediate offspring constitute a family among animals, and the same term is sometimes applied to the progeny of a single plant. A few relatives may join the family unit, as has been observed in a den of wolves (Murie, 1944). Larger aggregations result from a further extension of family groups. An animal and "his sisters and his cousins and his aunts" may remain together as a clan, and unrelated members of the species may subsequently join the group to form a larger herd, pack, or flock. Seals, sea lions, wolves, monkeys, prairie dogs, many ungulates, and various kinds of birds are examples of animals that form units of this sort. More complex groups of related individuals are represented by colonies of social insects, such as ants, bees, wasps, and termites. In the plant kingdom the progeny of neighboring adults may join to form larger groups of the same species. If such a group is invading a bare area, it is termed a plant colony, as will be discussed more fully in Chapter 12 in relation to ecological succession.

In other instances groups resulting from reproductive activities are not necessarily the descendants of one breeding unit. Aggregations of young are frequently formed by the simultaneous release of eggs or larvae within a restricted area. The coincident production of young by neighboring adults is often set off by some common environmental stimulus, such as the occurrence of a critical illumination or temperature. The nearly simultaneous spawning of oysters, triggered by temperature conditions as described in Chapter 5, results in the sudden appearance of swarms of oyster larvae in estuaries of the Atlantic coast.

Passive Transport

A second, and entirely different, mode of origin of groups of the same species results from the passive transport provided by the medium. Wind often sweeps mosquitoes and other insects from exposed terrain and thus indirectly concentrates them in sheltered places. Most commonly this mechanical action of the medium in bringing about aggregations is seen in the aquatic environment. Inhabitants of streams tend to be swept together in eddies, and the currents of lakes and oceanic areas often concentrate phytoplankton and zooplankton in the same way, but more slowly. The current system in the Gulf of Maine, for example, plays a major role in the accumulation of certain types of plankton in the water mass overlying Georges Bank. The clockwise circulation of water around the margin and the relatively quiet eddy of homogeneous water over the center of the Bank have produced conditions in the central area that favor the development of *Sagitta* and of the copepod *Pseudocalanus* but are unfavorable for *Calanus,* a closely related copepod. The current system tends to concentrate the two former species in the central part of the Bank and to exclude immigrants from populations of *Calanus* and other species developing beyond the margins of the Bank (Clarke, Pierce, and Bumpus, 1943).

Another example of the concentration of animals by passive transport is the occurrence of "plankton traps" found particularly in Scandinavian fjords but also to a lesser extent in other estuaries. Characteristically, a considerable amount of fresh water enters from rivers at the head of the fjord, and this flows out at the surface over the more saline water beneath. Water from offshore moves in at the bottom, gradually rises at the head of the fjord, and mixes with the outward flowing water. Plankton organisms that tend to remain in deeper water layers because they are positively geotactic or negatively phototactic are drawn into the fjord by the deep circulation but are not carried out again by the surface flow. The result is that a mechanical concentration of the plankton takes place in the lower layers of the fjord. In any species in which tactic responses cause the young stages to move toward the surface, a horizontal separation of the age groups results from this current action. The transport of the larvae of sessile invertebrates to the upper portions of tidal estuaries, as described in Chapter 2, is another manifestation of the concentrating action of this type of differential water movement.

Active Locomotion

Groups of the same species brought about by the active locomotion of the individuals may arise (1) from the guidance of the organisms towards the same area by oriented responses to inanimate features of the environment or (2) from the attraction of the organisms to others of their own kind. The formation of groups by active locomotion is, of course, found most frequently in the animal kingdom, but certain motile algae and the swarm spores of aquatic plants also exhibit this behavior.

Common Orientation. If the individuals of a species react in the same way to some physical stimulus in the environment, their locomotion will bring them to the same locality with the result that an aggregation will be formed. A familiar example is the clustering of insects about a source of light at night as a result of their positive phototaxis, or the attraction of fish and invertebrate animals to a torch held over the water (Maéda, 1951). Since land isopods, such as the wood louse, move more slowly, or stop creeping entirely, under moist conditions they tend to collect in damp places. A dead fish on the shore or a dead deer in the forest acts as a lodestone to which a large num-

Fig. 9.1. Aggregation of mud snails (*Nassa obsoleta*) exposed at low tide in Barnstable Harbor, Mass.

ber of scavengers will be attracted. Other sources of food or shelter similarly serve as a focal point at which animals from the surrounding areas tend to congregate (Fig. 9.1). In these instances each individual reacts independently, and the group is formed as a secondary consequence.

Sometimes the aggregation is the result of more complex and long-continuing reactions. Several kinds of marine worms form aggregations by reacting individually to some aspect of the lunar cycle and swimming to the surface of the sea, as described in Chapter 6. When the animals have formed a huge swarm in this way, they initiate their breeding activity. Since the eggs and sperm are thus discharged into the water at the same time and at close quarters, the chances of successful fertilization are much improved. Consequently, the reaction of the animals to the physical stimulus that leads to the formation of the aggregation has survival value in this instance.

The dense schools of salmon preparing to breed in the headwaters of streams have come into being following the orientation of each individual separately during the previous weeks while the fish was finding its way for hundreds of miles up from the ocean (Fig. 9.2).

Photo International Pacific Salmon Fisheries Commission

FIG. 9.2. Sockeye salmon in Adams River, British Columbia, schooling near bank before moving onto the spawning beds. Note dead, spawned-out salmon washed up on the bar.

When a large number of salmon have arrived at a suitable spawning place, the fish react more definitely to each other, pair off, and begin their breeding activity. After spawning the adults of the Atlantic salmon eventually return to the sea, but in the Pacific species the adults die in the stream and huge numbers of dead fish may choke the narrow waterways. The great quantity of decomposing organic matter thus added to the streams may deplete the oxygen supply locally and produce further ecological consequences. Nutrient materials resulting from the decomposition may possibly stimulate the growth of plankton on which the young fish depend. When the eggs hatch, a large number of young fish appears simultaneously in the headwaters of each salmon stream and represents another occurrence of aggregation in this species. A further discussion of the ecological problems involved in the life history of the salmon will be found in a symposium sponsored by the American Association for the Advancement of Science (1939).

Mutual Attraction. Another manner in which aggregations of the same species are formed is by an initial direct attraction of the individuals to each other. Mutual attraction of individuals is found among lower animals, but frequently the reaction is largely non-specific. If isopods are distributed over a surface of uniformly low moisture, the animals stop against the first individual to come to a halt and soon a dense cluster will be built up. Brittle starfishes placed in a bare aquarium will move to form closely entwined aggregations, but, if the aquarium contains eel grass, or even glass rods simulating eel grass, the starfishes will remain spaced out in contact with these objects. In these instances the other individuals present are merely satisfying physical needs of moisture or of contact. In schools of fish, flocks of birds, and herds of mammals the origin of the group results from mutual attraction on a highly or a completely specific basis. "Birds of a feather flock together" because of a definite attraction to others of the same species. The members of these groups are not necessarily from the same parents and are usually quite unrelated, but during the breeding season units are formed within some populations in which the members are breeding partners and family relatives, as discussed above.

Sometimes the reaction to keep in close contact, or to follow others of the same species, is very strong indeed. The manifestation of this in groups of ungulates, such as sheep, has given rise to our term "sheep-minded." Anyone who has visited sheep country knows the very great strength of the tendency of these animals to keep close together. So strong is this reaction that if the leaders of a flock stumble in a ditch, the remaining sheep will continue crowding forward causing a "pile-up." Sheep men greatly fear the occurrence of these pile-ups in which as many as 500 sheep may be killed within a few minutes.

Animals forming groups recognize others of the same species most commonly by vision, but various other means are also used. Birds migrating in darkness or fog, or moving through thick vegetation, probably rely on call notes for keeping in touch with one another. Sound is probably used in the aquatic environment also, to a much greater extent than has been realized. Sound travels through the water medium much more effectively than through the air medium —quite the reverse of the relationship for other orienting stimuli, such as light and odor. Various crustaceans, a great many fishes, and certain cetaceans, including blackfish and porpoises, produce grunts, whistles, squeaks, and other noises that can be heard under water for great distances and are undoubtedly useful for recognition among aquatic animals (Kellogg, Kohler, and Morris, 1953).

Some species of ants which are totally blind nevertheless manage to keep close together by the use of their "contact odor" sense. In tests with bullhead fishes each individual was found to move toward any object of the same size and color as itself. The fish would then touch the object with its barbels, and, if the sense organs encountered a paraffin model, the fish would move away. In this instance the first reaction causing the fishes to move together was a visual one; other reactions came into play subsequently. Among land vertebrates many mammals use odor for recognition.

Sometimes the reaction to school or to form flocks is so strong that, if no others of the same species are available, the animal will join a group of another species. Thus we commonly find a few isolated gulls flocking with a group of terns on the shore, or a single sanderling hurrying along the beach in company with a flock of least sandpipers. Examples among other types of animals will occur to the reader. An amusing illustration of this tendency to associate with a group, even of another species, was observed in the large basement tank at the laboratory of the Woods Hole Oceanographic Institution. A number of squid had been kept in this tank for some time, and these animals always moved together in a dense school. One day a small mackerel of about the same size was placed in the tank. Since no other mackerel were present, this fish immediately joined the ranks of the squid, swimming along with them at the same rate in close formation. As the observer approached the side of the tank, the squid were startled and shot backwards. Since the mackerel was quite unable to move in this direction, he was left isolated and apparently bewildered, turning to right and left. Never was there such a frustrated mackerel!

The groups that have arisen in the various ways described above show all gradations of integration and permanency. In brief, we may note that some groups are brought together mechanically and often the individuals have no direct relation to one another. In other groups, such as insect colonies, a definite organization of the members exists. Some of the aggregations are of a temporary nature, lasting for only a few hours, days, or weeks. Starlings are commonly observed to gather in noisy flocks in the evening and to roost together in certain large trees, belfries, or other favorite spots; but the birds usually disband at daybreak, flying about independently or in small groups during the daylight hours. Bats follow a reverse daily schedule, coming together to roost during the day and dispersing during the night. Some aggregations exist only during the breeding season, whereas in other species flocking or herding takes place for the period of migration only. On the other hand, many herds of large mammals and many insect colonies are essentially permanent—outlasting the lives of individual members and remaining in existence until destroyed by some unusual environmental change. For a fuller discussion of this subject and of other aspects of animal aggregations, the reader is referred to the more extended treatment by Allee (1931).

EFFECTS OF INCREASED NUMBERS

An increase in the abundance of a species originating in any of the ways discussed in the previous section results in consequences of concern to the species itself and also to other interdependent species of the habitat. The repercussions from the numerical increase of one species on other species will be taken up in subsequent chapters. Here we shall consider the results of population increase within the species, dealing first with relations that are generally harmful and later with beneficial relations. Our present discussion will be centered on contemporary effects, that is, on effects within the life span of the individuals or of the populations considered. Long-term effects on the species may be quite different. Competition, for example, is usually harmful to the individuals concerned, but its selective action in guiding the course of evolution may result in an eventual benefit to the species as a whole.

Harmful Effects

An increase in numbers means an increase in competition for the necessities of life. Rivalry between members of the same species is typically keener than that between members of different species. In the words of Darwin (1859), "the struggle will almost invariably be most severe between the individuals of the same species, for they frequent the same districts, require the same food, and are exposed to the same dangers." Overpopulation therefore results in a serious interference of one individual with another—sometimes in a passive or indirect way, at other times as direct aggression or even cannibalism. The accumulation of metabolites often curtails the further growth of the species within the area, and the simple matter of occupying available space imposes a mechanical limitation on some populations. Since established land plants are fixed in position, the sphere of influence of each individual, and the area from which it must draw its necessities, are sometimes easier to observe than those of active animals. When a population of plants has increased so that the individuals are growing close together, their roots compete for nutrients and for water and their tops compete for light. As competition becomes more intense, growth rate is correspondingly retarded.

A ready-made record of the effects of competition was found in the cross section of the trunk of a locust tree that had grown in Belmont, Mass., and was blown down in the hurricane of 1944 (Fig. 9.3). By counting growth rings the date of the first year of the tree's life was determined as 1929. At that time an open field was abandoned and a few trees seeded themselves in the area at widely spaced intervals. For the first few years thereafter, the tree grew rapidly, but, as size increased, competition with neighboring trees for nutrients, for water, and particularly for light became progressively more serious. The result may be observed in the diagram as progressively smaller growth rings in 1934, 1935, and 1936. In the spring of 1937 the land was cleared of most of the trees for the construction of a house. With competition removed the growth of this locust tree was "released," to use the term of the forester. More wood was added during the growing season of 1937 than had been added in any of the previous 4 or 5 years, and growth continued at a high rate for the remainder of the life of the tree.

The form of development of plants as well as their growth is affected by competition. The growth form of a solitary tree is completely different from that of a tree of the same species that has developed in a stand closely surrounded by other individuals. In the latter situation the lower branches are killed by the reduction of light, or the growing buds and branchlets are knocked off by the branches of trees near by, as they whip about in the wind. The smaller, neighboring trees that bring about this pruning action are referred to as "trainers" by foresters, since they cause the tree to develop without lateral branches in a form that will later be suitable for saw timber.

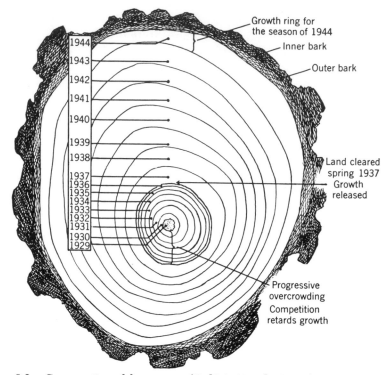

Fig. 9.3. Cross section of locust tree (*Robinia Pseudo-Acacia*), 17 cm in diameter, grown in Belmont, Mass., showing effects of early overcrowding and subsequent "release."

Many examples of the harmful effects of overcrowding could be cited for other types of plants and for animals. We find the same principles of competition at work among populations of microbes as among forest trees. Bacteria deplete their supply of nutrients as they multiply and produce an accumulation of metabolites, until the further growth of the colony is prevented. Organisms continuing to live in the same medium tend to change or to "condition" it. Conditioning of flour by laboratory populations of the flour beetle *Tribolium confusum* has been shown to cause reduced fecundity, extended duration of metamorphosis, and increased mortality (Park, 1941). The same kinds of harmful changes are brought about by overcrowding under natural conditions. In some situations aquatic animals may aggregate to such an extent as to exhaust the oxygen supply; elsewhere they may exhaust the food supply, produce harmful metabolites, or displace one another mechanically. Of several hundred oyster larvae originally setting on an old shell or other small object, only a few will find sufficient space to develop into full-sized oysters; all the others will eventually be killed by crowding. Where competition for space is keen, oysters grow in a long slender form, undesirable for the market. Oystermen in cultivating their beds com-

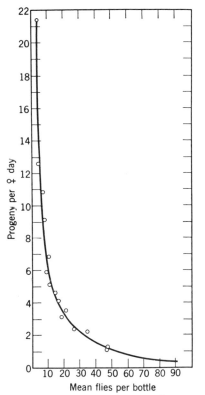

Fig. 9.4. Curve showing decrease in rate of reproduction in *Drosophila* as cultures become more crowded. (Pearl and Parker, 1922.)

monly break clusters of young oysters apart to insure that the animals develop in the well-rounded form characteristic of solitary oysters.

The harmful effect of excessive numbers of animals is sometimes manifested as an interference with breeding. The progressive reduction in the reproductive rate of *Drosophila* with increased density of the population is shown in Figure 9.4. As the flies become more crowded, interference with feeding and possibly also with oviposition is experienced. Frequent collision and interruption of feeding result in inadequate nourishment and lowered fecundity although the supply of food may be ample (cf. Robertson and Sang, 1944). In some kinds of animals the ratio of males to females is also significant in controlling success of reproduction. Although many animals do best when the two sexes are present in equal numbers, a one-to-one ratio is detrimental for some polygamous species. Among pheasants, for example, each cock normally maintains a harem of about five hens, and, if more males are present in the population, the consequent fighting and disturbance of the incubating females greatly reduces the success of the breeding. With species requiring highly specialized places for breeding or nesting, the first effect of an enlarged population may be a critical shortage of breeding sites.

Photo by Swem

Fig. 9.5.   "Deer-line" formed by denuded branches of Douglas fir and Ponderosa pine, caused by browsing of overabundant deer in Oregon.

Perhaps the most generally harmful effect of increasing numbers among animal populations is the competition for food. In the photograph, Fig. 9.5, a "deer-line" is distinctly visible on the vegetation at a height of about 2 m. This denudation of the trees has been caused by the browsing of an excessive number of deer. With the shortage of food the growth of the deer population will be curtailed, and, if all the edible vegetation throughout the area is removed, the deer will be in danger of starvation. In extreme instances the vegetation may be permanently injured with the result that the area will subsequently not support as many deer as previously.

The effect of competition for food on the growth of bluegill sunfish is well demonstrated by records of farm fish ponds. In one test a pond was stocked in March with fish averaging 5.7 g. When weighed again in June of the same year, the average size of the fish had increased to 76 g. During this month each pair of sunfish produced an average of 4000 young. Since the young were not removed either artificially or by a predatory species of fish, the new generation entered into direct competition with the adults for food. When the pond was drained in November of the same year, the average weight of the parent group had decreased from 76 g to 54 g, showing that

Swingle and Smith, 1942

Fig. 9.6. Effect of overcrowding on the growth of bluegill sunfish. Both fish are 1 year old: upper specimen from a pond stocked with 3750 fish per hectare (1500 per acre); lower specimen from a pond stocked with 450,000 fish per hectare (180,000 per acre).

these fish had not only failed to gain but had actually lost weight as a result of excessive competition. Another instance of the curtailment of growth of sunfish brought about by overpopulation is shown in Fig. 9.6.

Beneficial Effects

In the previous section we have seen that, if the population of a species within any area continues to increase, a point will eventually be reached at which harmful effects are produced. Before this point is reached, the members of the population may receive definite benefit from the presence of others of the same species. An isolated individual or a single pair of organisms is often not as able to deal successfully with the environment as a group. This subject has been extensively discussed by Allee (1931 and 1951). Moderate increase in abundance of a plant or an animal may afford protection from enemies or from physical features of the environment. It may accelerate reproduction and improve survival. The degree and nature of activity is also influenced by the density of the population (Schuett, 1934). Learning by fishes and other animals has been shown to be more rapid when other individuals are present than when they are isolated (Welty, 1934). Groups of the same species also make possible a certain division of labor and the beginnings of social organization. Some of these effects of increased numbers that are beneficial within the species will be considered in the following sections.

Protection. Animals and plants in groups often protect each other against harmful features of the environment without any special group organization. In a thick stand of trees a higher humidity will be maintained and a better resistance to wind and water erosion will be experienced than if the same individuals were growing in a widely spaced manner. Furthermore, since the blowing away of fallen leaves is largely prevented in a dense grove, the humus and moisture content of the soil is increased. Groups of animals have been shown to be less susceptible to poisons, oxygen lack, extreme temperatures, and other environmental dangers than single individuals.

The large number of honeybees living close together in a hive enables these insects to modify the temperature inside their microhabitat to an extent that would be utterly impossible were the bees living as solitary individuals. As winter conditions arrive, the bees are able to maintain the temperature within their cluster in the hive at 25 to 30°C by increased muscular activity. During hot days in summer the bees force air through the hive passages with their wings, thus increasing evaporation and lowering the inside temperature. Owing to this primitive "air-conditioning" temperature inside the hive fluctuates only slightly in spite of extreme external conditions (Uvarov, 1931).

A group of animals is often protected against its predators by the simple effect of numbers. A flock of small birds does not attempt to fight off an attack by a hawk and probably could not do so; hawks generally obtain their prey by picking off stray individuals. Perhaps the hawk is less likely to be successful in catching his prey from a flock because of the confusion of numbers, just as a tennis player is distracted by having his opponent throw three balls to him at once, with the result that he does not succeed in catching any one of them.

A favorable effect on survival of an optimal degree of crowding has been found in laboratory cultures of *Drosophila* and of *Daphnia* and in natural populations of the sessile rotifer, *Floscularia*. At population densities of 5 and 10 per 50 cc of culture medium *Daphnia* lives considerably longer than at densities of either 1 or 25 per culture unit in tests at 25°C. At 18°C mortality appears to be least at a density of about 75. Lower metabolic rate or better control of harmful bacterial contaminants by the supraminimal populations are suggested as possible explanations (Pratt, 1943). The mean length of life of *Floscularia* is practically doubled if the young rotifer, instead of living a solitary existence on a water plant, attaches to the tube of an older *Floscularia* and thereby establishes a small colony. No explanation of this striking fact has come to light (Edmondson, 1945).

Influence on Reproduction. Since most animals and plants reproduce by sexual methods, it is obvious that too great a scarcity of individuals of the opposite sex will reduce the rate of breeding. In an earlier chapter we have called attention to the probability that this constitutes a serious limitation for deep sea fish and perhaps also for whales and other aquatic animals of low population density. Luminescence and underwater sound have been suggested as possibly serving as aids for males and females to find each other in the huge expanses of the ocean. The same limitation affects land animals and plants that are very sparsely distributed.

A similar situation on a much smaller scale is presented by flour beetles dispersed in a large uniform volume of flour. Investigations with *Tribolium confusum* have shown that when only two individuals are present in a "microcosm" of 32 g of flour, the number of young produced per female is considerably less than when four individuals inhabit the same volume. The explanation is that fecundity is increased by recopulation, and recopulation increases with the density of the population. At densities higher than four, however, the fact that the beetles eat their own eggs progressively curtails the success of reproduction. This cannibalism eventually sets the upper limit of the population (Park, 1941). In experiments with ciliates the reproductive rate was found to increase with the size of the initial population. This effect may be due to the release into the medium of a beneficial substance produced by the protozoans, to the low absorption per individual of some inimical material originally present, or to more adequate control of the bacterial population (Mast and Pace, 1946; Allee, 1951).

Another effect of numbers on success in reproduction involves reactions, some of which may be considered to be in the realm of group psychology. In many animals breeding activity is initiated only when an aggregation of more than a certain minimum size has been formed. The necessity for the existence of a sizable group in order that reproductive behavior will be called forth is clearly seen among social insects and among certain fishes, birds, and mammals, as well as among other types of animals.

This effect of numbers is particularly striking in birds that breed in colonies (Darling, 1938). Anyone who has visited an island where terns are nesting or a cliff where gannets have established a rookery (Fig. 1.2) will have obtained an indelible impression of the atmosphere of excitement caused by the sight of thousands of wheeling and darting birds and by the sound of their screaming calls. The visual and auditory stimuli produced by this uproar are necessary, or at least valuable, in preparing the birds psychologically for mating as well as for setting off and integrating the elaborate behavior patterns involved in nest building, incubation, and feeding the young. If there are too few birds in the colony, the reproductive cycle will not be successfully completed. Furthermore, the large concentration of birds often induces synchrony in reproduction, and this provides a certain amount of protection since predators cannot destroy a serious proportion of the eggs and young if they all appear within a short period. Even without synchronous reproduction large colony size has the advantage of a relatively smaller periphery where young may wander away or be attacked by enemies. This need in certain species for group stimulation accounts for the failure of isolated pairs to breed and for inefficient breeding as seen, for example, in small colonies of gannets (Fisher and Vevers, 1944). An extreme illustration of these principles is the report that a minimum of 10,000 birds, nesting at a mean density of 3 nests per sq m, is necessary for the establishment of a successful breeding colony of the guano-producing cormorant on islands off Peru (Hutchinson, 1950). Among mammals, populations of muskrats smaller than about 1 pair per linear mile of stream or per 35 hectares of marshland appear not to breed successfully (Errington, 1945).

Degree of crowding can influence the sex and structure of some species and the coordination of these features with the natural life cycle. Crowding has been shown to influence the sex ratio in certain cladocerans, in *Bonellia*, and in *Crepidula*. *Moina*, a common cladoceran inhabiting temporary ponds, reproduces parthenogenetically under ordinary conditions with the production chiefly of females. If the population becomes crowded, however, males begin to appear. This reaction is obviously related to the reduction of space attending the drying up of a pond and necessitating the production of resistant eggs if the population is to survive. Since resistant eggs are produced only sexually, males must be present in the population. The production of males by crowding is thus nicely attuned to the needs of these animals under the exigencies of life in temporary ponds.

In the aphids, or "plant lice," which attack vegetation, the winter eggs hatch into wingless females; these reproduce parthenogenetically under ordinary circumstances, with the result that the population on each plant grows rapidly. If the plant host becomes overcrowded and consequently withers, the destruction of the whole group of aphids is threatened. However, crowded conditions react on the aphids in such a way as to bring about the production of winged females. This extraordinarily neat adaptation makes possible the migration of many of the aphids to other plants, relieving the congestion at home and establishing new centers of population growth. Later in the season males appear and sexual eggs are produced that tide the population over the winter period and complete the cycle.

Another effect of the size of breeding population is in relation to genetic elasticity and, hence, the adaptability of the progeny of a species to varied conditions. Most species of plants and animals in nature are composed of a great many *biotypes*, that is, types of individuals that grow and react differently because of different genetic constitutions. Owing to varying environmental conditions certain biotype groups become established in different ecological regions of the range of each species. These ecological subdivisions of the species are known as *ecotypes* and are genetically distinct races. Since the ecotypes are interfertile, they are placed in the same taxonomic species. Ecotypes are sometimes recognized as subspecies, but in other instances they are not sufficiently distinct morphologically to warrant that designation. Each ecotype is the result of selection by its environment and has become specially adapted for a particular set of conditions. Wide-ranging species are represented in different parts of their ranges by different ecotypes.

A small population of an ecotype, particularly if it is isolated, will tend to become less variable genetically because of inbreeding; that is, it will come to contain fewer biotypes. With less adaptability the population will be less likely to survive bad conditions and will fail to respond quickly to the occurrence of good conditions. In contrast, a larger population with more biotypes is more likely to include some individuals that can withstand adverse circumstances and that can take advantage of new variations in the environment. These relations probably account, in part at least, for the fact that certain reduced populations fail to spread widely or to recover a former abundance although environmental conditions appear favorable (Cain, 1944, Ch. 16; and Allee, 1951, Ch. 4). The isolation of segments of a varying population also plays a major role in influencing the course of evolution. This large topic, which is beyond the scope of the present book, is considered in the works referred to above and also by such authors as Elton (1930), Mayr (1942), and Lack (1947).

An example of the failure of a small population of an ecotype to spread readily is furnished by the distribution of wild irises in Canada (Fig. 9.7). *Iris setosa* has considerable morphological variation and is distributed widely in western Canada and Alaska. The subspecies *Iris setosa* var. *canadensis*, however, exhibits high morphological constancy and is limited to the Gulf of St. Lawrence region. This subspecies survived the ice age, during which other luxuriant types may have succumbed, but as a relict ecotype it emerged so uniform genetically that during the intervening centuries it has been able to repopulate only the immediate area and is slow in adapting itself to other environments.

The disadvantage of low numbers may also be illustrated from experience in the oyster fishery. Around the shores of Great Britain, and elsewhere, oyster populations have been greatly reduced by overfishing. However, after restrictions were placed on the amount of the oystermen's harvest, or in other areas after fishing had been abandoned entirely because of unprofitable yields, the populations often failed to rebound to their previous large sizes. Gross and Smyth (1946) believe that the explanation is to be found in the lack of genetic flexibility in the small isolated groups of these sessile animals.

A small population not only may be unable to grow rapidly and to spread but also, after it has been reduced below a critical size, it may be unable to hold its own. This latter possibility introduces the *principle of the minimum population* which states that in order for a population to survive indefinitely in an environment its numbers must be maintained above a critical minimum.

A classic illustration of this principle is furnished by the fate of the heath hen, a bird that was formerly abundant in Massachusetts and may have been distributed from Maine to Delaware (Gross, 1928). By 1880 the heath hen was restricted to Martha's Vineyard Island, and a realization of its low abundance led to the establishment of a large reservation for the birds on the island. The heath hens increased to about 2000 in 1916, but a fire, a gale, and a hard winter with a great flight of goshawks decimated the population, leaving fewer than 50 breeding pairs. Numbers continued to decline irregularly until only 20 birds were counted in 1927, and the last bird was seen in 1932. In spite of elaborate protection this species could not be saved from extinction once the population had been reduced below its critical size.

Division of Labor. Beneficial effects of increasing numbers may also be brought about by a division of labor made possible within

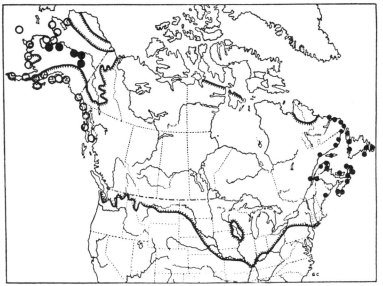

Fig. 9.7. The discontinuous range of *Iris setosa* (open circles) and its varieties: *canadensis* (small black dots) and *interior* (large black dots). Hatched lines indicate the maximum extent of the Pleistocene glaciations. (Cain, 1944, modified from Anderson, Copyright, Harper and Bros., New York.)

the group. In some sessile colonial animals, such as certain of the
coelenterates, different individuals are specialized for definite functions. This differentiation of zooids permitting a division of labor
within the colony reaches its highest development in siphonophores
such as the Portuguese man-of-war. Different zooids of this animal
are specialized for flotation, protection, nutrition, or reproduction.
In some siphonophores zooids are also specialized for locomotion and
produce a movement of the whole colony by rhythmic ejection of
water from their cavities. Certain colonial Protozoa and Protophyta
also show a division of labor. Although this development among
unicellular colonial forms is very primitive, its advantages may have
led in the past to the evolution of multicellular organisms.

Among organisms that form groups but in which the individuals remain separate we find other types of division of labor. The most
fundamental and widespread of these is the differentiation of the
species into two sexes. This division of labor has arisen in both the
animal and plant kingdom, and interestingly enough the appearance
of sex occurred long after plants and animals had evolved from their
common ancestral unicellular form. We have here a remarkable case
of parallel evolution in which the same adaptation arose independently on at least two occasions.

A variation in activity among members of a group without any
special morphological adaptation is seen in the phenomenon of *social
dominance*. This is the establishment within the group of a social
hierarchy in which an animal of higher position outfaces or drives
away an animal of lower position (Allee, 1951). Such "peck orders"
were first recognized in flocks of fowl, but now dominance-subordina-
tion relations are known to exist among certain groups of fishes,
lizards, rodents, ungulates, carnivores, and other animals (Collias,
1944, 1952). The peck order among hens establishes the social position of the birds in the flock. A dominant hen has attained the right
to peck a subordinate hen without being pecked back. When the
social organization of a flock has become established, the group functions more smoothly and less fighting occurs, since protocol is recognized by all members for all group activities.

Another type of division of labor in a group is *leadership*. Within
a flock of goats one animal will become recognized as the leader in the
wanderings of the group; but this animal is not necessarily the dominant individual in the sense of the term used above. The existence
of a definite leadership was also demonstrated in a band of monkeys
inhabiting a tropical island. One individual always led the way when
the band moved through the aerial pathways of the treetops. When

the leader was shot, the band was reported to remain in a confined area of the island, and did not take its usual trips to other parts of the island.

Cooperation without any special morphological modifications among the individuals and with a minimum of organization is another advantage often resulting from the formation of groups. When attacked, musk ox form in a circle with their horns extending outward and thus secure for themselves a protection that would not exist if each animal attempted to defend itself individually. A group of beavers working together can dam a stream that could not be successfully dammed by animals operating singly. In a penguin colony some adults guard not only their own young but also the young of others while the remaining parents leave the area in search of food. Feeding cormorants are observed to maintain a rough line as they swim and dive and thus presumably improve the effectiveness of their fishing (Bartholomew, 1942).

A somewhat more elaborate division of activity within the group is found in certain species during the breeding season. In sea lions (Fig. 9.8), fur seals, elk (Fig. 9.9), deer, and other mammals, as well as various game birds, the population of a region becomes organized into breeding units each consisting of a male, his harem, and subsequently their young. After the mating season the harem groups are broken down, and the animals may reorganize themselves into separate bands of males, females, and young for the remainder of the year. Group organization in the fur seals (*Callorhinus ursinus*) may be taken as an example. The bulls arrive first early in May at the breeding grounds on the Pribilof Islands, and each stakes out a breeding site for himself which he jealously guards. When the cows arrive in mid-July, each of the larger and more senior of the bulls collects a harem for himself within his own territory. The remaining bulls, kept away by ferocious fighting, form a group of disappointed bachelors. Bulls with harems are continually being challenged by the bachelors, and, although each established bull drives off the intruders for one or more seasons, eventually each bull ages and after losing a fight or a series of fights he is forced to relinquish his harem to a new master. Soon after the females are organized into harems the pups resulting from the previous breeding season are born, and subsequently mating with the bulls takes place. When breeding has been completed, the harems disintegrate. After a period of feeding and of nursing the pups, the seals reorganize themselves in groups consisting of males only, and other groups made up of females and pups. In these groups the seals leave the Pribilofs

Photo Alfred M. Bailey, National Audubon Society

Fig. 9.8. Breeding groups of sea lions on San Benitos Island off the west coast of Mexico. Each bull sits erect guarding his territory and presiding over his harem and pups.

Photo U. S. National Park Service

Fig. 9.9. Bull elk and his harem in Rocky Mountain National Park in late September.

in October and travel to their winter quarters along the California coast (Allen, 1870). With this social organization in operation among the fur seals, the non-breeding males can be killed for their pelts without reducing the productivity of the herd; hunting is restricted in this way by international agreement. Similar organization of the herd into harems during the breeding season and into larger non-family groups during other parts of the year is found among the European red deer, *Cervus elaphus* (Darling, 1937) and among the American elk or wapiti, *Cervus canadensis* (Murie, 1951).

The most complex types of division of labor are exhibited by man himself and by certain insects. The division of labor in man is a learned behavior and occurs without structural modification. In complete contrast, the behavior exhibited by members of an insect colony is instinctive and the individuals performing various functions in the colony are specialized morphologically and physiologically (Fig. 9.10). This differentiation of members of the same species is developed to its greatest extent among the termites and ants (Wilson, 1953). Since the division of labor in an insect colony is accompanied by structural specializations and instinctive behavior, it is less flexible than that occurring in mammalian groups, and especially in man's society. This fact and their size limitations have no doubt largely prevented the insects from attaining a more dominant position in the world.

Among groups of animals all degrees of integration exist from aggregations with no organization to highly elaborated *societies*. Allee (1951) has developed the theory that societies have evolved from aggregations. If the existence of a group confers definite survival value on the individuals, the group will tend to persist. Those reactions that lead to the formation of the group will also persist, and these will constitute the beginning of social behavior. The cooperation that we now observe among the individuals may have resulted as a consequence of the formation of the group. The division of labor appeared as chance variation and persisted because of its survival value; it is not necessarily conscious nor purposeful.

According to the foregoing ideas the elaborate social organization found among a few species may therefore have evolved through the following steps. First, others of the same species are tolerated in a restricted space and then definite reactions to their presence are developed. If survival values result either through behavior or physiological adjustments, a tendency for an increase in the permanency of the group will exist. Following this, a further development of the organization of the group may take place with the appearance of leadership, dominance, and/or the division of labor. It is impossible to say just when an aggregation becomes sufficiently organized to be termed a society—all gradations exist. The evidence is strong, however, that the beneficial effects of increased numbers have played a considerable part in the development of organized groups and fully differentiated societies.

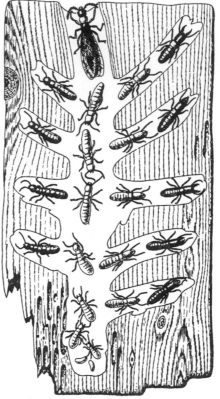

FIG. 9.10. The various forms of the termite *Kalotermes flavicollis* and their developmental origins. The eggs (*bottom*) hatch into young nymphs which after 5 to 7 molts reach the pseudergate stage (individual in center). From this stage the termite can change into a winged reproductive (*top*) by way of two wing-padded nymphs. At intermediate stages environmental influences may cause the nymphs to change into supplementary reproductives (*left*) or, by way of soldier nymphs, into soldiers (*right*). Most of the nymphs do not differentiate and these function as workers. All these stages are present in the termite colony, and their activities are integrated in its maintenance. (Lüscher, 1953, *Sci. American*, drawing by E. Mose.)

POPULATION DEVELOPMENT

The organisms inhabiting an area at a given time constitute a *population.* If the organisms all belong to one species, they form a *single-species population.* In most natural situations several to many kinds of plants and animals coexist in the same habitat. The inhabitants may then be regarded as composing a corresponding number of single-species populations that are intermingled, or alternatively, as forming one *mixed* or *multi-species population.* The interspecific relations of mixed populations will be treated in the next chapter Here we shall discuss the quantitative relations that arise during the growth and fluctuation of single-species populations under the influence of the harmful and beneficial interactions considered in the foregoing sections.

Principles governing population dynamics are found to apply equally to special situations, such as laboratory cultures, in which only one species is present, and to natural areas in which many populations exist together. The presence of other species acts as part of the environment in influencing the changes in the population of the species under consideration.

Natality and Mortality

The abundance of a species in an area tends to increase because of reproduction, and to decrease because of death. The rate of reproduction depends upon the birth rate or *natality,* and the rate of death is referred to as *mortality.* The *dispersion* of members of the species also affects abundance—positively in the case of immigration, and negatively in the case of emigration. We shall consider first the simplest situation in which no dispersion is taking place, leaving a discussion of the influence of migration into or out of the area to a later section. The maximum possible rate of reproduction for a given species under optimal conditions is termed the *potential natality.* In natural situations the potential natality is rarely, if ever, attained because the birth rate is inevitably reduced by one adverse circumstance or another. The actual birth rate under the existing conditions is referred to as the *realized natality.* In parallel fashion the lowest possible death rate for a given species in the best of circumstances is the *potential mortality,* and the actual death rate is the *realized mortality.*

Natality and mortality vary not only from species to species but also according to the age of the individuals. Natality is usually highest during the middle of the life span after the individual has become mature and before it has become senile. Variation of mortality with age or life stage differs greatly among different kinds of animals and plants. In some species extremely high mortality is experienced in the egg, larval, or seed stages; in others high mortality does not occur until late in life.

The potential natality of every species of plant and animal is greater than its potential mortality, and hence, under favorable conditions, every species always has the capacity to increase. If under existing conditions the realized natality also is greater than the realized mortality, the population will actually increase. If the two rates are equal, the population will be stationary; but, if the realized mortality is greater, numbers will diminish. A birth-death ratio defined as $100 \frac{\text{births}}{\text{deaths}}$ is known as the *vital index*.

Biotic Potential and Environmental Resistance. The maximum possible rate of increase (highest vital index) for a population of a species occurs under ideal conditions in which the birth rate is the highest possible for that species (potential natality) and the death rate is the lowest (potential mortality). Maximum birth rate is determined by the largest number of viable progeny (spores, eggs, young, or seeds) that an animal or a plant can produce and the frequency of reproduction. Minimum death rate is determined by internal factors controlling survival when environmental factors are all completely favorable. The values of maximum birth rate and minimum death rate are thus fixed by life processes inherent within the organism, and the maximum rate of population increase, or the *biotic potential*, is an innate characteristic of each species. The value of the biotic potential, or *potential increase* as it is sometimes called, differs widely from species to species; contrasting examples of differing rates were given in Chapter 1. As will be more fully discussed subsequently, evolutionary processes have established certain relations between the biotic potential of each species and the exigencies of its existence.

Under natural conditions the full biotic potential of an animal or a plant population is ordinarily not realized since conditions are rarely completely favorable. Harmful climatic changes, attacks by predators and diseases, and other external circumstances curtail the growth of the population. As the population grows, the increase in numbers itself produces changed conditions. A moderate increase in density may sometimes have an ameliorating effect, as we have seen, but sooner or later the detrimental effects of overpopulation—scarcity of food supply or of breeding sites, accumulation of metabolites, and the like—will appear. The combined effect of these factors tending to curtail population growth is called *environmental resistance*. The capacity to increase resides within the species, but the degree to which it is realized is determined by the environment, including the changes in the environment brought about by the species itself, and aspects of the environment consisting of other members of the species. Thus the actual rate of the increase of a population is determined by the balance struck between biotic potential and environmental resistance.

Certain features of the environment are largely or entirely unaffected by changes in the density of the population. These are *density-independent factors*. For example, an increase in the abundance of a species in a marine area does not affect the temperature or the salinity of the water, but changes in these factors, harmful or otherwise, are brought about by agents unrelated to the density of the population. Other changes in the environment are directly related to the abundance of the animals or plants concerned; these are *density-dependent factors*. Scarcity of such necessities as food, oxygen, or breeding sites may become increasingly acute as a population of animals grows; lack of nutrients, excessive pH values, or other inimical condition may be brought about by the growth of a plant population. In addition, the susceptibility of organisms to disease as well as the ease of transmission is often increased as the density of the population grows. Generally speaking, the physical features of the environment tend to be density-independent and the biotic influences are often density-dependent factors, but the reverse is sometimes true, and certain factors may change from one category to the other according to circumstances. For example, the predation of a tawny owl (*Strix aluco*) on a population of mice in an English woodland was found to be a density-independent factor since the owl was observed to eat only 4 to 6 wood mice (*Apodemus sylvaticus*) each day, regardless of the size of the prey population (Miller, 1951). But in other situations predation will be a density-dependent factor if each predator kills more prey when the prey are abundant. During periods of plenty many predators are known to kill more than they can eat. Increased density of prey may also cause increase in the predator factor by making possible increased reproduction and growth of the predator population as well as by attracting predators from neighboring areas.

The question just discussed of whether the density of a population controls or modifies a certain environmental factor must be carefully

distinguished from the question of whether the *influence* of the factor
on the population is related to the size of the population. For example, the winter temperature in most habitats is a density-independent factor since its value is not affected by the number of organisms
present, but the effect which the temperature has may or may not be
related to the size of a population of animals. In some habitats extreme cold will kill the same *percentage* of a large population as of
a small one, with the result that the number of animals succumbing
is proportional to abundance. In other instances the habitat will
provide adequate shelter (from extreme temperature or other danger)
for a small number of animals but inadequate shelter for a large number. As a consequence a much greater fraction of the large population would be harmed than of the small population. If in another
situation a factor killed off a constant number of animals in an area,
it would have a greater *relative* effect on a small population than on
a large one.

Form of Population Growth

When plants or animals reproduce, they add more individuals to
the population, and the enlarged breeding stock then has the capacity
to produce a still larger number of progeny. Thus the population
tends to grow at an ever-accelerating rate. Sooner or later, however,
harmful density-dependent influences begin to take effect. If we
assume for a moment that no other interfering factors are present, the
growth of the population will follow a mathematically prescribed
form.

Let us take a simple numerical example. Suppose we assume that
under the most favorable conditions a certain pair of animals can produce 6 young during a year and that the resulting population suffers
a mortality of 2 during the year. We then have:

$$N_0 + A - M = N_1$$
$$2 + 6 - 2 = 6$$
$$\frac{N_1}{N_0} = R = 3$$

in which N_0 and N_1 represent the populations at the beginning and
at the end of the year, respectively, A is augmentation, M is mortality,
and R is the biotic potential or rate of potential increase per generation. The generation time in this example is one year. At the beginning of the second year our sample population stands at 6, and,
since there are more individuals to breed, a larger number of progeny

will be produced during the second year than during the first. Assuming the same rates of reproduction and mortality, 18 young will be produced, 6 will die, and the total population at the end of the second year will be:

$$N_1 + A - M = N_2$$
$$6 + 18 - 6 = 18$$

or

$$RN_1 = N_2$$
$$3 \times 6 = 18$$

If the same rate of increase continues unimpeded, the population will have grown to 54 at the end of the third year, 162 at the end of the fourth year, and so on, as shown in Table 18. The population, which under these circumstances is exhibiting a geometric or "logarithmic" increase, is represented by the equation:

$$N = N_0 R^t$$

where t in years starts at 0. This is indicated graphically by curve (A) Fig. 9.11. The *rate of change* of population size is given by the equation:

$$\frac{dN}{dt} = N \log_e R$$

which means that growth rate is proportional to size of population.

TABLE 18

GROWTH OF HYPOTHETICAL POPULATIONS IN WHICH INCREASE IS
(1) UNIMPEDED AND (2) SELF-LIMITED

Unimpeded Increase

Years	0	1	2	3	4	5	6	7
Total population	2	6	18	54	162	486	1458	4374
Numbers added		4	12	36	108	324	972	2916

Self-limited Increase

Years	0	1	2	3	4	5	6	7
Total population	2	6	14	27	39	46	48	49
Numbers added		4	8	13	12	7	2	1

Logistic Curve. Since the full biotic potential of a species is not realized under most natural conditions, the population does not in fact increase as fast as it could if its growth were completely unimpeded. However, if the natality rate remains above the mortality rate, the population will continue to grow and will increase at an accelerating rate. Nevertheless, the increase in the population will eventually produce conditions harmful to itself—density-dependent factors will come into play. The rate of growth will then be progressively curtailed until it reaches zero when the population reaches the largest size possible for it within the area concerned. If the harmful effect of crowding increases proportionally, the *rate of change* of population size can be expressed as follows:

$$\frac{dN}{dt} = \left(\frac{K - N}{K}\right) N \log_e R$$

where R is the biotic potential per generation, N is the size of the population at any moment, and K is the ultimate maximal size possible for the population in the given area.[*]   In words, the equation simply says that the rate of increase of the population is equal to the potential

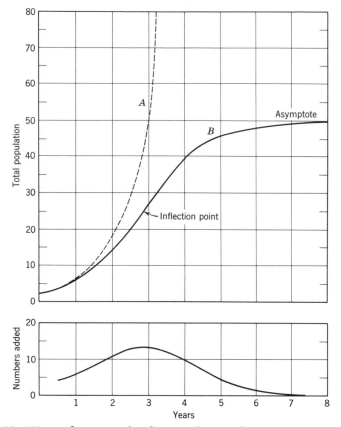

Fig. 9.11. *Upper figure:* graphs showing theoretical increase in total numbers during (*A*) unimpeded and (*B*) self-limited population growth (logistic curve). *Lower figure:* graph of numbers added to population in each time interval during the logistic growth shown by (*B*) above (values plotted at midpoint of each time interval).

[*] For further discussion of these relations reference may be made to H. C. Andrewartha and L. C. Birch. "The Distribution and Abundance of Animals" 1954, Univ. of Chicago Press.

increase limited by the degree of realization of maximal size. When the growth of a self-limiting population is expressed graphically, a typical S-shaped curve is obtained known as the *logistic curve,* shown as (*B*) in Fig. 9.11. The curve is truly logarithmic only at its beginning, departs from the logarithmic increase as impeding factors become effective, reaches an *inflection point* at which the acceleration of growth becomes negative, and approaches an *asymptote* representing the limiting size (*K*) of the population.

If we now apply to our previous numerical example the more realistic condition that increase is progressively curtailed as the population grows, we obtain the growth values, rounded to integers, indicated in the lower part of Table 18 with a maximal population size in this case assumed as 50. Besides the population totals at the end of each year (or other period) we are also interested in knowing the numbers added to the population during each unit of time. With unimpeded growth the annual increment becomes larger and larger indefinitely; but with self-limited growth the annual increment passes through a maximum at the time when the logistic curve reaches the inflection point. In our example the numbers added per year increase to a maximum of 13 during the third year and then drop off nearly to zero in the seventh year. A curve showing these changes in the increments to the population and their relation to the logistic curve is presented in the lower portion of Fig. 9.11. The fact that the population has approached its asymptote with annual increment approaching zero does not necessarily mean that little or no reproduction is taking place in the population—it simply means that births are completely offset by deaths, natality is equaled by mortality, or $A = M$. Under these circumstances reproduction may continue to be high accompanied by high mortality, or reproduction may be low with low mortality; as long as A and M are equal the size of the population will not change.

Early in the history of the population only small numbers are added each year because the breeding stock is small. During the middle period annual increments are large, but, as the population reaches its maximum size, small annual increments again occur either because breeding is sharply curtailed or because the young produced suffer severe mortality. The reader should particularly notice that the largest annual increment is not found when the population is at its maximum, but occurs at the inflection point of the logistic curve, that is, at the time when the population is growing most rapidly.

Populations of a wide variety of organisms, ranging from bacteria to whales, have been found to follow the logistic curve in their growth form. Illustrations of such curves of growth for laboratory cultures of Protozoa, yeasts, *Drosophila,* flour beetles, and water fleas, and for natural populations of bees, ants, thrips, sheep, and other animals are discussed in further detail by Allee et al. (1949, Ch. 21). The growth of man's population follows a similar pattern whether examined in individual regions or in the world as a whole. A plot of the census records for the United States for the years up to 1940 is shown in Fig. 9.12, and the curve has been extrapolated by fitting the logistic func-

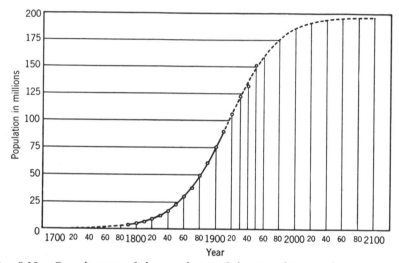

FIG. 9.12. Growth curve of the population of the United States, showing census counts from 1790 to 1950. The logistic function has been fitted to the counts from 1790 to 1910 and extrapolated to 2100. The agreement of the extrapolation with the counts for 1920 to 1950 is shown, and a cessation of growth about the year 2100 is indicated. (Modified from Pearl, Reed, and Kish, 1940.)

tion. The agreement of the 1950 census figure of 151 million with the extrapolated curve and the indication of an asymptote at about 184 million in the year 2100 may be observed.

Equilibrium and Fluctuation

The logistic curve discussed in the previous section applies only to periods of population growth (when $A > M$) and to situations in which the rate of increase is controlled only by density-dependent factors. Since the inhabitants of a natural area have mostly been present for a long time, we see the initial stages of population growth only in special instances. The early part of population increase is observed when a bare area is invaded, when a new species is introduced, or when a check holding a species to a low number is suddenly removed. Aside from these special situations the changes observed in population size involve the action of both density-dependent and density-independent factors usually long after the original growth of the population. In both laboratory cultures and in natural habitats, after the initial attainment of maximal size, a population will (1) maintain itself at about the same level for a long period, (2) decline and eventually become extinct, or (3) fluctuate regularly or irregularly.

If the population approaches its asymptote in such a way that the supply of food, and other necessities, and the removal of harmful by-products keeps pace with growth, then the population will maintain itself at or near this equilibrium level ($A = M$) until outside conditions are altered. Under these circumstances the reproductive rate may be high or low, but, as long as it is exactly offset by mortality, the population size will not change. Nevertheless the magnitude of A and M may exert an important ecological effect on evolution. If A is very large, as is true of many invertebrate animals, the accompanying high mortality will generally take place when the progeny are young and usually before reproduction has occurred. On the other hand, if A and M are small, a much larger proportion of the young animals may live long enough to reproduce before they are eliminated from the population. In the former circumstance, most of the mutations appearing in the population will be lost, but in the latter case a larger percentage will be retained long enough to affect the next generation. We find that the possible effect of this difference corresponds to the generally more rapid evolution of mammals, for example, than that of invertebrates.

In other populations the harmful conditions that were produced by increasing numbers and that brought the growth of the population to a stop may progressively intensify. Under these circumstances the greater and greater scarcity of food, the accumulation of metabolites, or other inimical change will cause a decline in the population either immediately or after a period of time. If the changes in the environment brought about by overcrowding are irreversible, extinction of the population will eventually follow. This result is commonly seen in laboratory cultures of bacteria, Protozoa, and other organisms. In nature a similar fate may overtake a population developing on a small island as a result of the introduction of breeding stock by natural processes of dispersal or by man. Rats, goats, rabbits, or other animals, escaped from explorers' ships or introduced by colonists, often find conditions suitable for rapid growth and reproduction. Unimpeded, geometric increase in the population ensues until all suitable food or other necessity on the island is exhausted. Thereupon starvation, and often disease, decimate the population, and the death of all, or nearly all, of the animals quickly follows.

More usual than either of the foregoing is the third type of situation in which the population overshoots its equilibrium level, but, after a reduction in numbers, conditions are ameliorated sufficiently for the population to increase again. The repetition of this process causes fluctuations. If these are small, the population curve is designated as *flat;* if the amplitude is large and regular, the curve is termed *cyclic,* and, if irregular, especially with sudden periods of great increase, it is called *irruptive* (Fig. 9.13). Some ecologists refer to

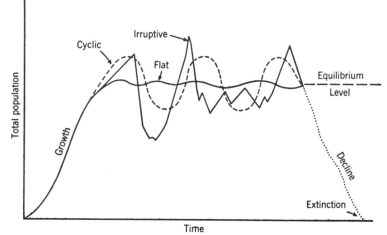

Fig. 9.13. Diagram of types of fluctuations in populations.

regular changes in abundance as oscillations and to irregular changes as fluctuations, but the more specific terminology given above will be employed here. The reader should understand that all gradations exist between these types of population change.

Fluctuations after a population has approached its equilibrium level may be caused in whole or in part by changes in physical features of the environment or in biotic influences such as the abundance of predators, diseases, or food organisms. These population changes due to the interaction of different species will be considered in detail in later chapters. At this time we wish to emphasize the fact that conditions within the population of a species can themselves be responsible to a greater or lesser degree for the fluctuation in addition to any disturbing influences that may come from the outside. The causes of certain fluctuations can be traced to the reciprocating effects of natality and mortality within the population itself.

A neat illustration of the mechanisms involved in self-induced fluctuations of this sort is found in experiments with laboratory cultures of *Daphnia magna* (Pratt, 1943). Single females were placed in bottles containing 40 ml of water, and as they and their progeny reproduced parthenogenetically the population in each bottle grew in accordance with the logistic function. The culture medium was renewed each day, insuring ample food supply and removal of metabolites, and other external conditions were kept uniform. Following the initial attainment of maximum size, the population sank to a low ebb and then continued to fluctuate in extreme fashion in spite of constant environmental conditions (Fig. 9.14). The explanation is

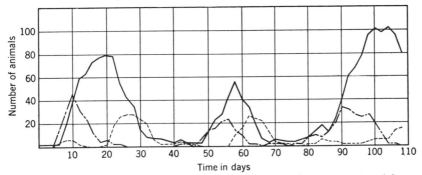

Fig. 9.14. Changes in the abundance (solid line) of *Daphnia magna* in a laboratory culture. The variations in number of births (—·—·) and of deaths (- - - -) that underlie the fluctuations of the population are indicated. (Pratt, 1943.)

seen in the changes in the birth and death curves indicated in the diagram. Although the number of births declined after the tenth day, young *Daphnia* continued to be produced for 18 days with the result that more young were added to the population than could survive when they reached adult condition. As overcrowding continued, the death rate rose rapidly and the birth rate dropped to zero. Even after the size of the population was considerably reduced, no reproduction took place at first and in fact no new young animals appeared until the fortieth day. Animals born in adversity thus did not produce young immediately upon reaching maturity, and the reduction in their reproductive capacity persisted for a long period after favorable conditions had been restored. As a consequence the population continued to overshoot and undershoot a possible equilibrium level. When this experiment was repeated at a lower temperature, the population changed more slowly, with the result that after one or two oscillations an equilibrium value was reached and maintained. Delay in the manifestation of excessive natality and prolongation of the effects of overcrowding similarly act on natural populations and add their influence to that of external factors in causing fluctuations.

The relative abundance of individuals of various ages in the population is known as the *age distribution* of the population. Differences in age distribution depend upon the species and whether the population is changing in size or stationary (Petrides, 1950). A rapidly growing population usually contains an especially large number of young individuals, whereas a declining population includes a relatively high proportion of old individuals. In a stationary population the distribution of ages is more uniform and tends to approach a stable pattern. Since natality and mortality vary with the age of the individuals, the age distribution of the population influences the birth and death rates for the population as a whole. Species that produce large numbers of young generally suffer high mortality during the young stages. A complete description of the mortality of a population is furnished by a *life table* such as has been constructed for man and has long been used by life insurance companies. Life tables and survivorship curves have now been worked out for a number of natural populations and show characteristic differences in mortality patterns among various species (Deevey, 1947 and 1950). For example, mortality in the oyster is extremely high during the larval stage and becomes much lower later in life, in hydra mortality is nearly constant at all ages, and in man mortality tends to be low for a long period during youth and to become high rather abruptly in old age.

Optimal Yield

The foregoing analysis of population development is of interest not only in relation to theoretical considerations but also in connection with practical applications. In the exploitation of natural populations—either plant or animal—a harvest is desired of the largest number of individuals per unit of time that is possible without permanently impairing the breeding stock. In other words, we wish to ascertain the size of the largest sustained yield that can be obtained and learn at what level the population should be maintained to produce this yield. An answer to this question is the formation of the *theory of the optimal yield*. The basic idea underlying this theory is that in the simplest situation with no modifying conditions the population should be maintained at the inflection point of its growth curve since at that point the largest increment is being added per unit of time and the taking of this increment would represent the largest harvest possible without inroad upon the breeding stock. We shall return later to a discussion of special circumstances applying to particular species that modify this basic relation and cause a different density level of the population to be more favorable for the practical exploitation of these species.

To illustrate the basic principle let us imagine a flock of geese from which we wish to obtain as many birds as possible for food. Suppose that the flock originated from the establishment of one pair in a limited area and that the growth of the population followed the logistic curve (Fig. 9.11) with values similar to those indicated in the lower part of Table 18. The largest single yield would obviously be obtained by allowing the flock to grow for 5 or 6 years and then shooting all or most of the birds. For a sustained harvest, however, only the annual increment to the population should be taken; in this example, 13 birds could be taken every year if the flock were allowed to grow to 27 before harvesting. If a hunter considered exploiting this flock without knowing its existing size and found that only 7 or 8 birds were added to the population each year, he would have to determine whether the low growth rate was due to the population being smaller or larger than the optimum. Low yield in any such population may thus be caused by overexploitation—resulting in too small a breeding stock, or in underexploitation—resulting in harmful crowding of the breeding stock. The best conservation procedure often calls for the reduction in size of a natural population. Recognizing this fact, rangers now regularly cut back the populations of deer in national parks whenever numbers become too large because of the absence of wolves, panthers, or other natural enemies that otherwise would keep the deer in check. Consequently, in exploiting a population, it is desirable to ascertain whether density is above or below the level at which increase is most rapid and, if possible, to adjust the size of the population accordingly.

As already suggested, several important modifying considerations must be added to the underlying idea of the theory of optimal yield. Up to this point we have discussed populations in terms of numbers of individuals. Fishermen do not measure their catch by counting the fish, but by weighing them; foresters evaluate their timber by its volume, not by the number of trees. Thus, the growth in size of the individuals must be taken into account as well as the increase in numbers. For such species the growth of the population is measured in terms of weight or volume, and, when plotted in corresponding units, again follows a logistic curve, although the numerical values will, of course, be different. Accordingly, in attempting to ascertain the optimal tonnage of fish to catch we must consider the growth rate of the population in terms of increase in weight rather than numbers. If there are no further modifying considerations in respect to a particular fishery, the optimal catch may be obtained when the population is maintained at the level at which the largest weight increment will be added per unit of time, this increment being due both to an increase in numbers and to the growth of the individuals (Fig. 9.15).

Other practical considerations are the availability of the population for exploitation and its suitability for the market. If game in a forest or fish in a pond are scarce, more time, effort, and expense will be required to harvest the same number than if the population were dense. With sparse populations the *yield per unit effort* is lower. In specific instances, it may be better to allow the population to increase to a somewhat greater density than that which represents the level of most rapid growth in order to increase availability. Often minimum limits and sometimes maximum limits of size exist in relation to marketability. Accordingly, the size composition of the catch must be considered as well as its weight or volume.

Two additional considerations that also may modify the basic plan for obtaining the optimal yield in respect to certain species are: the number of breeders necessary to provide sufficient young, and the rate of natural mortality. In species with a low natality such as most large mammals and birds, the *recruitment*, or number of young annually added to the population, is closely dependent upon the size of the breeding stock. For each new young whale there must be one adult female; but one fish, one oyster, or one termite can produce millions or billions of young in a season. The spat released by only a few clams would provide an ample set for a large area, and, if allowed to grow up, the young produced in one year could repopulate a whole bay under completely favorable conditions. In such species the recruitment usually depends more on the environmental conditions during the early life of the new generation than on the number of breeders, and the optimal level at which the population should be maintained is determined by other considerations.

We have seen that allowing populations to build up by avoiding overexploitation sometimes has advantages in the greater size of individuals, the more concentrated populations, and the larger number of breeders. On the other hand, allowing too great development of

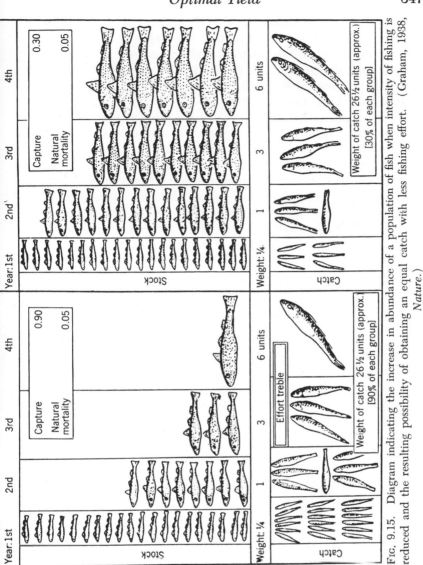

FIG. 9.15. Diagram indicating the increase in abundance of a population of fish when intensity of fishing is reduced and the resulting possibility of obtaining an equal catch with less fishing effort. (Graham, 1938, *Nature.*)

the population will result in the disadvantages of overcrowding. Another consideration is the fact that the longer an animal or a plant remains unharvested, the longer it will be exposed to environmental dangers and the greater the possibility that it will die from other causes or be removed by predators other than man. If natural mortality is very high, the crop may have to be harvested at an earlier age than would be necessary should the reverse be true. The optimal level for the population thus varies widely according to the ecological relations of each species. The optimal yield is obtained when the rates of reproduction, growth, and mortality are so adjusted as to produce the greatest annual increment with due regard to availability and other modifying considerations. More detailed discussion of both the theoretical and the practical aspects of this important topic is available in Russell (1942), Trippensee (1954), and the publications of the United States Department of Agriculture.

SPATIAL RELATIONS OF POPULATIONS

Space Requirements

As a population grows in numerical strength and as its members increase in size, the individuals tend to come closer and closer together as long as the population occupies the same area. In many instances the habitable area is sharply limited, as it is for aquatic populations developing in a pond, or for land organisms multiplying on an island. Although in other instances populations can spread out at their margins for a time as they develop, eventually the unoccupied area is completely taken up and a condition of overcrowding begins to appear.

Every organism requires a minimum amount of space within which it can carry on its necessary exchange with the external world. This minimum space must be sufficient to provide food and other necessities, to absorb metabolites, and to permit reproduction. A relation obviously exists between the size of the organism and the minimum size of the space that it can inhabit. Whales do not live in ponds.

The space required by some organisms is quite small and may be no larger, in one plane, than the actual dimensions of the body. The number of adult barnacles that can inhabit a rock, for example, is determined simply by the number of barnacle bases for which the area of the rock affords room. Barnacles can grow with their sides closely appressed to their neighbors because water currents bring food particles and oxygen and take away metabolites and progeny.

Most species require more space than their physical dimensions. The actual amount of room needed varies greatly from species to species, but frequently the space required is very large either because some necessity is sparse in its distribution or because of certain, often poorly understood, psychological relations.   A census of the fishes inhabiting the shore zone of Morris Cove, New Haven, Conn. revealed the presence of representatives of 32 species, but few specimens longer than 100 mm were found.   Although the adults of small species were taken, only the young of the large species were present.   The depth of water was ample for more sizable fish to move about in, but fish larger than the critical size were definitely excluded from this habitat regardless of age although the mode of action of the space requirement in this instance is not known (Warfel and Merriman, 1944).

The manifestations of the space requirement may also occur in relation to breeding, hostility, or other reaction.   Insects such as the Canna Leaf Roller (*Calpodes ethlius*) have been found to breed satisfactorily under laboratory conditions if placed in containers of certain size.   They will not breed in smaller containers, nor in much larger confined areas such as greenhouses, which appear to be otherwise suitable.   Cannibalism among insects often occurs when they are crowded together, whereas members of the same species do not attack each other when they meet at other times under uncrowded conditions.   The English sparrow, a partially domesticated bird, will breed regularly in large aviaries but will not breed in small cages. The foregoing examples suffice to illustrate the point that definite space requirements exist not only in relation to the physical needs of the organism but also in relation to reactions essential in their life cycles.

For sessile forms, such as the majority of plants and non-motile animals, the provision of minimum space is automatic to some extent. As crowding continues to increase, competition brings about the stunting and eventually the death of a portion of the population. This process can be readily seen in the development of a stand of trees from a bed of seedlings.   Root competition, shading, and diseases gradually thin out the population.   Young white pines in New England, for example, sprout from seeds to form a bed with a density of perhaps 75,000 seedlings per hectare (30,000 per acre).   When these pines have attained an age of 60 to 80 years, they will form a mature stand in which the density has been reduced by natural processes to about 750 trees per hectare (300 per acre), or even less, without any treatment by the forester.   Similar examples may be found among oysters, mussels, and other sessile animals growing on substrata of limited dimensions; a few individuals, growing faster than the rest, gain the upper hand and smother their more retarded brothers. This automatic reduction of the population by the growth of its own members produces at least the minimum spacing necessary for survival, but it usually does not provide the most favorable spacing for the best development of the individuals. Man can often improve growing conditions for particular species in which he has a special interest by further thinning—and this is done regularly, of course, by professional growers, such as oystermen, farmers, and foresters.

For motile animals the danger exists that during favorable conditions the members of a species inhabiting a region will move too close together, with the result that wholesale destruction will take place when conditions become unfavorable again. In some species we find an instinctive reaction causing the animals to space themselves out to a certain extent at least; and the existence of this response helps to avoid overcrowding, as will be discussed in the ensuing section.

Home Range and Territory

Many kinds of animals are known to establish a center of operations for themselves and to confine their roamings within certain boundaries. The area within which an animal tends to stay is known as its *home range*. Sometimes other members of the same species are not allowed to enter the area, or a portion of it, and any trespassers are forcibly driven out. The inner sanctum that is actively defended is called the animal's *territory*. The territory may be established by a social group, such as a hive of bees or a colony of ants, by a breeding pair, or sometimes by a single individual. The existence of territories with "exclusive rights" was recognized in an old Chinese proverb that states: "One hill cannot shelter two tigers." A dog's own yard is his territory, and he drives other dogs out with a self-assurance that is familiar to all of us. Within their own territories animals typically acquire a heightened position of dominance in relation to other members of the same species.

The concept of territory was first delineated for birds. It was observed that in many species each male established a territory at the beginning of the breeding season. The male then isolates himself, and confines his movements to his own territory He becomes hostile to other males of the same species, with which he was on amicable terms only a short time previously. This bird drives others of his kind out of his territory, but pays little or no attention to birds of other species that wander by unless they actually intrude on his intended nesting site. Characteristically, the male bird chooses a singing perch, makes himself conspicuous, and, when a potential mate comes to the area, goes through the courtship display. In some species, as for example the house wren, the male may even start building a nest before the female arrives. (No doubt he has to do it all over again when she appears on the scene!) After the nest is completed and during the period when eggs or young are in the nest, the territory is defended with particular fierceness.

By carefully observing the movements of a pair of birds for a period of time, the ecologist can determine the position of the unseen boundary lines of their territory. If the birds build a second or a third nest during the same season, these later nests are placed somewhere within the original territory. The division of a region into territories by pairs of breeding birds is illustrated in the diagram of Figure 9.16. It will be noted that the territories of birds of the same species do not overlap—indeed, a neutral zone usually exists between them—but the territory of one species may overlap that of another species if no reaction of antagonism occurs between them.

In a 16-hectare tract of spruce-fir forest in northern Maine 148 male birds of various species were found to have established breeding territories by a census conducted during a week in June. During the ensuing 3 weeks a total of 302 territorial males were removed from the tract by shooting. Study of the area indicated that new males from a "floating" unmated population moved in and established territories as rapidly as the former inhabitants were removed. Thus the number of sites suitable for the establishment of territories was shown to be the chief factor limiting the number of birds that could breed in the area (Stewart and Aldrich, 1951).

The dimensions of the territory or home range may be measured in kilometers in the case of large mammals or birds of prey or in meters or smaller units in the case of smaller animals. Bears may roam over distances of 30 or 40 km, whereas porcupines confine their home activities to trips of a kilometer or so and the home range of beavers is ordinarily less than a kilometer in diameter. The home ranges of the whitetail deer vary in size from about 80 to 120 hectares (200 to 300 acres), of the cottontail rabbit from 1 to 3 hectares, and of some kinds of mice from less than ½ to more than 1 hectare. The daily roamings of prairie deermice in southern Michigan were found to be confined within 2 or 2½ hectares, but on different occasions during a breeding season both male and female deermice may travel over an area as great as 4 hectares (Howard, 1949). The home ranges of box

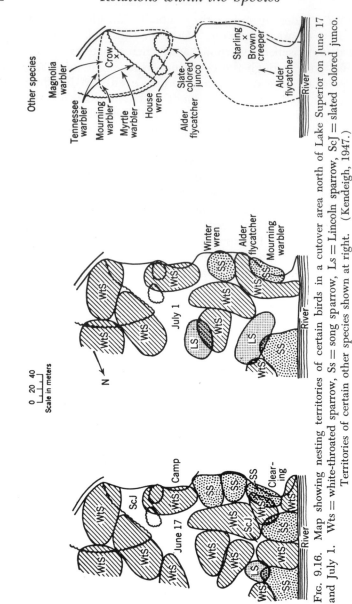

Fig. 9.16. Map showing nesting territories of certain birds in a cutover area north of Lake Superior on June 17 and July 1. Wts = white-throated sparrow, Ss = song sparrow, Ls = Lincoln sparrow, ScJ = slated colored junco. Territories of certain other species shown at right. (Kendeigh, 1947.)

turtles in Paxtuxent Research Refuge, Maryland, investigated by Stickel (1950), were found to average 100 m in diameter and to overlap considerably. Chameleon lizards were reported to establish territories of 20 to 25 sq m in area. The arrangement of territories of the wood ant is illustrated in Fig. 9.17. In this instance the ants' nests were found to be only a meter or so apart. The ants foraged for distances of 70 m or so, but in no instance did the members of one colony encroach upon the territory of another colony. In colonies of breeding birds the private domain around each nest site may be very small indeed, but this may be jealously guarded (Fig. 9.18).

Wood mice apparently do not establish territories that are actively defended, but home ranges are delineated. Some avoidance response keeps the animals confined to their home ranges. The reality of this action of population pressure has been demonstrated by trapping experiments. When an area is cleared of one species—thus creating a "social vacuum"—animals from neighboring areas will move into the vacant area within a few days. Obviously then, the animals on the periphery of the area in question did not fail to enter the area because it lacked food or other necessity, or because they lacked the inclination to move the distances involved. The neighboring mice were kept out of the area by "social" pressure of some sort resulting from the presence of other members of the same species. Although animals avoid entering the territory of others, peripheral contacts with neighbors are presumably a normal condition. The rapid entry of the mice into a cleared area may be due in part to a movement of the animals "as if in an attempt to encounter again the stimuli produced by neighbors" (Calhoun and Webb, 1953).

The size of the territory or home range is usually larger than that which would be needed for the food supply of the individual establishing it. In the case of territories staked out at the beginning of the breeding season, it is obvious that the food supply must be adequate for the young that are to be raised. Apparently during the course of evolution reactions for establishing the territory have come into existence that cause the breeding pairs to space themselves out sufficiently to anticipate the food needed by the new family. The size of the home range or territory has probably come to be based primarily on the food supply, but in some instances it may be determined by available breeding sites or other needs of the species.

Homing. Frequently the attraction of an animal to the location of its home is very strong; this is particularly true if the territory is established in relation to a breeding site, and the reaction is further intensified if young are present. The return of an animal to its ter-

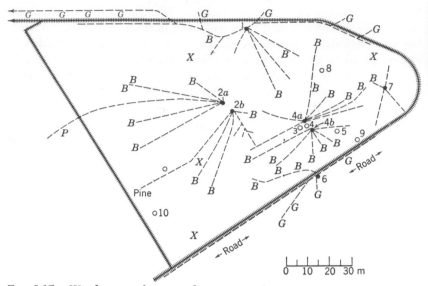

FIG. 9.17. Wood-ant trackways and nests at Picket Hill, Oxfordshire, England.
• = nests, o = former nests, B = birch trees, G = gorse bushes, x = nests of willow wrens. (Elton, 1932, Copyright, Cambridge Univ. Press.)

Photo R. H. Beck, Am. Museum of Nat. Hist.

FIG. 9.18. Territorial dispute in penguin colony, Bleaker Island, Falklands.

ritory or breeding site is referred to as *homing*. The reaction is particularly familiar among birds, but other types of vertebrates, many species of insects, certain Crustacea, and some other invertebrates are known to home. Even the pulmonate snail *Onchidium*, after leaving its home crevice in the rocks to feed in the surrounding area, returns to its own particular crevice and cannot be induced to enter any other (Arey and Crozier, 1921). Bees fly unerringly back to the hive from distances greater than 6 kilometers.

Homing is especially well developed among birds. The distances covered are often spectacular, and the precision with which the home territory is located is little short of miraculous. Although small perching birds may travel only 100 m or so to procure food, hawks and eagles forage for many kilometers, and sea birds often range widely over the ocean before returning to the home site. When investigators have carried parent birds great distances away from their nests and released them in unfamiliar surroundings, the prompt return of the birds to their breeding sites has demonstrated the extraordinary strength of the homing reaction as well as the existence of some highly successful method of orientation. The fact that the performance of domesticated homing pigeons improves with training and familiarity with the terrain indicates that these birds use landmarks to some extent, but other methods of orientation must also be employed (Matthews, 1950).

In nature birds will home across unfamiliar country and over water where no landmarks exist. Perhaps the most spectacular instance of homing is that of a Manx shearwater that was taken from its nesting burrow on the Island of Skokholm, Wales, banded for identification, and transported across the Atlantic by airplane. This bird was released from the Logan International Airport, Boston, Mass., on June 3, 1952, and arrived back at its burrow in Wales 13 days later, having traversed 3000 miles of ocean. We do not know whether birds and other animals use the same methods of orientation for homing as they do for seasonal migrations. The whole fascinating subject awaits further study. A general discussion of orientation was presented in Chapter 6.

Return Migration. Many birds, mammals, fishes, and other animals move seasonally from one habitat to another, sometimes traversing great distances. Journeys of this sort in which at least some of the population completes a round trip are known as *return migrations*. The most spectacular movements of this sort are found among the vertebrates, but return migrations also occur in the invertebrates, as exemplified by certain crabs and by butterflies (Williams et al., 1942).

Among many species the instinct to return to a certain area is exceedingly strong, as will be realized, for example, by anyone observing fish migrating up a river. According to an early colonial report in New England: "Alewifes continue to move up the stream, yea though ye beat at them with clubs." Perhaps some of these migrations may be thought of as movements out from and back to a home territory and hence an extension of the homing reaction. Return migrations as adaptations to (1) climatic conditions, (2) feeding needs, or (3) breeding activity, have been discussed in previous chapters.

In some of these migrations members of the population come back to the same general area or even to the same locality. Birds return to the same region after journeys of several hundred or several thousand miles and after absences of 9 months or more. Frequently a pair of banded birds uses the identical nest site for two or more summers in succession although the birds have journeyed to the tropics during the intervening winters. The greater shearwater roams widely over the North and South Atlantic Oceans during most of the year, but its only known breeding place is on the Island of Tristan da Cunha about 2000 miles south of the equator (Murphy, 1936). In some similarly mysterious way slender-billed shearwaters ("mutton birds") from all over the Pacific Ocean locate two tiny islands between Australia and Tasmania and all descend on the islands on the same day in a huge flock to begin the breeding season (Griscom, 1945). Alaskan fur seals breed only on the Pribilof Islands in the Bering Straits, and they manage to locate in some unknown way these tiny bits of rock in the vast ocean after swimming for a 1000 miles or more from regions off the coast of California where they spend the winter.

In some of these breeding migrations the reaction to the home territory may persist over the winter and stimulate the animal to return to the breeding area at the next season. It is difficult to believe, however, that after several years in inland streams adult eels retain any homing reaction to the area in the Sargasso Sea where they were hatched—yet they do return there. The same might be said of the Pacific salmon that ascend the rivers to spawn after spending 4 to 7 years in the ocean, but something does stimulate the salmon to undertake the migration and something orients the fish to the very tributary in which they developed as larvae (Hasler, 1954). Perhaps migrations taking place after long intervals and also those correlated with climatic changes and feeding activities are unrelated to homing or only secondarily related to it. In these instances, external or internal factors may stimulate the animal to migrate at a certain time, and conditions along the way may orient the animal back to the region of its origin with the retention of no specific homing reaction or of one that is operative only after the animal has arrived within the general area of its original home territory.

Emigration

When animals leave their home range never to return, the movement is spoken of as *emigration*. This type of migration may take place either as a drift of individuals or of small groups, or as a mass movement. The young of many species of birds—and also to some extent the adults—wander in all directions after the breeding season and before the autumnal migration to the winter range begins. An example of this centrifugal movement is obtained from the returns of banded ducks (Fig. 9.19). Drift emigration of this sort is very widespread in its occurrence, but it often escapes notice because the animals or birds move inconspicuously in small numbers. Some kinds of animals wander about for long periods of their lives, seeking primarily perhaps food or water, without definite return to any given place; such irregular roaming is spoken of as *nomadism*. This and other types of animal travels are discussed fully by Heape (1932).

In contrast to the foregoing, mass emigration is often spectacular although it occurs in relatively few species. At more or less regularly recurring intervals such animals as the mouselike lemmings of Scandinavia and Canada, the springbucks of Africa, and the locusts of Egypt and India undertake mass movements involving millions or billions of individuals. The causes of these mass emigrations are not clearly understood: in some instances they may be due to climatic changes; in others they may be due to lack of food which may or may not be the result of overproduction of the species itself. The onset of acute hunger, nervous disorder, or other conditions occurring at the time of mass emigration often profoundly alter the behavior of the animals. For example, according to Heape (1932), some such internal change "transforms the shy and timid springbuck into a fearless creature with no regard for danger of any kind, and converts the no less shy and timid lemming into a truculent swashbuckler."

An instance of a mass emigration of lemmings was witnessed in 1937 by the manager at the Perry River post of the Hudson's Bay Company, Northwest Territory, Canada, and an excerpt from his account follows (Gavin, 1945):

· · · While camped at the old post site on April 27 and for about four days subsequently, the onset of the migration was noticed. The whole tundra was a mass of moving lemmings and each time we went into the tent there would be a dozen or more inside. The migration went on night and

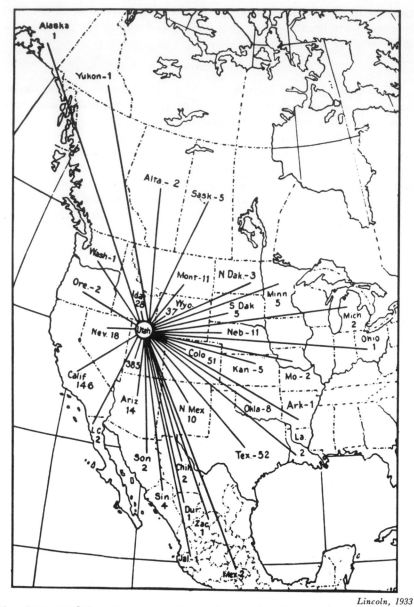

Lincoln, 1933

FIG. 9.19.   Radial emigration of ducks after the breeding season, plotted from
reports of banded birds.

day; my 13 dogs outside the tent could be heard killing them at frequent intervals during the night.

When we started for the new post, the sea ice was covered with a moving mass of lemmings, all headed in an easterly direction. They stopped at nothing. Untold thousands plunged over the ice into the water of a lead, about a foot below, and swam the 10 or 15-foot channel, but were unable to climb up the sheet ice on the other side. They perished in large numbers in these leads, but here and there, they found passages up the ice and blindly continued their journey. Around the ends of the leads they pressed on without interruption going through the pools of water, lying on the surface of the ice without deviation and without the slightest hesitation. This scene extended as far as we could see in any direction. The natives later informed me that at Kol-gyuak—a river 45 miles east of Perry—the same thing was going on at the same time. I do not know how far west it extended, but it was the same for at least 15 miles west of the post. This mass migration lasted for about 10 days and reached its peak about May 3 or 4.

In travelling from the old post to the new, my dogs grabbed up and ate so many lemmings while they were running that their stomachs distended to a noticeable degree. They were so surfeited that they were useless for further work until they had gotten over their abnormal feeding. I had to rest them for 24 hours to allow them to get over their gluttony. An estimate of the average density of lemmings during this migration would be one to the square yard.

Studies of the migratory locust have shown that under ordinary conditions this insect exists exclusively in a form known as the solitary phase. Particular conditions of temperature or dryness cause a great increase in the numbers of the species, and this is followed by the development in the population of the swarming phase of the locust, differing in color and in structure from the solitary phase. With the appearance of the swarming phase, emigration of great numbers of locusts begins (Fig. 9.20). Huge swarms of locusts, such as were recorded in Biblical times, spread into surrounding areas and do untold damage to crops and other vegetation. Since the newly invaded regions are less favorable for the maintenance of the species, fewer of the young survive, and numbers are also reduced by enemies that have been attracted by the plentiful food. As the density of the locust population diminishes, the swarming phase disappears and the solitary phase reappears. Gradually the locust dies out of the invaded areas, and the species shrinks back to its original range (Uvarov, 1931).

In this chapter we have considered the wide variety of relations among members of the same species. Other individuals of the same kind become abundant in an organism's environment as a result of reproduction, of passive transport, or of active locomotion. We have seen that, as numbers of a species increase, eventually harmful effects

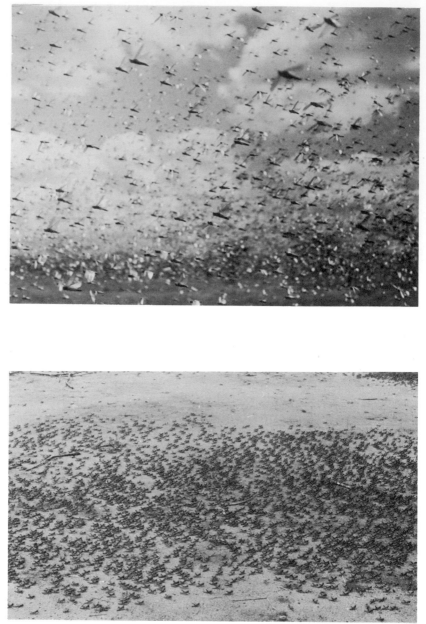

Photos D. L. Gunn, reproduced by permission of the Anti-Locust Research Centre
FIG. 9.20.   (*Upper*) A small swarm of migrating desert locusts in Kenya (density
estimated at 14 insects per cu m).   (*Lower*) Desert locust hoppers (fifth instar)
marching.

of competition, interference, or aggression always come into being. However, a moderate amount of crowding may be beneficial to members of a group, and this result may have favored the evolutionary development of integrated social organization in animals. The fact that an increase in a population progressively curtails its own growth makes possible a mathematical formulation of population development and provides a basis for deducing the optimal yield that can be obtained by exploiting a population. Numbers of a species always fluctuate to a greater or a lesser extent. Every species has definite space requirements, determined either mechanically or by avoiding reactions related to home ranges, and overpopulation is relieved by the destruction of the extra individuals or by emigration. The presence of others of the same species thus forms a critical aspect of the environment, and each organism is involved in many reciprocal relations with individuals of its own kind.

10

Relations between Species

In natural situations the presence of other organisms of different species is an unavoidable and also a necessary part of the environment. The existence of other species may be crucially important in the provision of food, shelter, or some other necessity. Contrarywise, various kinds of animals and plants are undesirable neighbors; but the presence of these species must nevertheless be dealt with as an influence received from the surroundings. Certain interactions among species in an area are prominent and clearly discerned, but others are of a subtle nature not easily studied. Some of the relationships form an integral part of the operation of the ecological complex as a whole, whereas others may be of only minor consequence. In this chapter we shall continue our analytical approach to ecological problems by surveying the various types of relationships between species and considering the operation of each separately. In subsequent chapters the combined operation of these interactions will be considered in relation to the composition and adjustment of the community and to the functioning of the ecosystem as a whole.

In attempting to delineate the various types of interrelations between species one realizes that a great complexity exists. Animals have relations with other animals, plants with other plants, many animals are dependent upon plants in their environment, and some plants are dependent upon animals. All gradations exist from relationships that are vital and lifelong to those that are casual and temporary. Interdependency may exist between species of widely different kinds and sizes—as between mighty redwood trees and microscopic bacteria, or in the animal kingdom between elephants and fleas. In some instances one species has an exclusive relation with another—sometimes with one short life stage of the other species; but in other instances species are quite flexible in their dependencies upon their neighbors.

Interrelations between species may be beneficial to both parties, harmful to both parties, or beneficial or harmful to one and neutral in respect to the other.   Every gradation may be found between these conditions.   The beneficial effect of the presence of another species is sometimes a vital necessity; but in other instances in which only a trivial advantage is provided, decision is often difficult as to whether the relationship is actually beneficial or merely neutral.   Positively harmful relations grade off in similar fashion to those that produce only a minor inconvenience or are essentially neutral.   The nature of the relationship may change during the life cycle of one or both of the species concerned.   Furthermore, as with intraspecific relations, the classification of an interaction between two species as beneficial or harmful depends upon whether consideration is given to the immediate effect on the individual or to the long-range effect on the species as a whole.   In our present discussion we shall consider first the nature of interspecific relations as they act within the life span of the individual, and subsequently their more remote consequences to the success of the population and to the evolution of the species.

With the foregoing qualifications in mind, we may divide the interrelations between species into two main categories: (1) *symbiosis,* in which one or both species are benefited and neither species is harmed; and (2) *antagonism,* in which at least one of the species is harmed.   Some authors extend the meaning of symbiosis to embrace all types of interrelations including harmful ones; other authors, taking the other extreme, limit the term to relations between a plant and an animal, or to relations that are mutually beneficial.   The present definition of symbiosis, which literally means "living together," seems more logical and more in keeping with established usage.   Symbiotic associations are divided into those of mutualism (both species benefited) and commensalism (only one species benefited).   Relationships of antagonism between species embrace antibiosis, exploitation (including parasitism and predation), and competition.

Various ecological aspects of the foreging subdivisions will be discussed in the following sections.   E. F. Haskell's more elaborate classification of "coactions" between species is discussed and illustrated by Burkholder (1952).   A simplified arrangement of these interspecific relations may be represented as tabulated on page 364.

In this scheme (+) indicates an increase in a beneficial life process as the result of the association, (−) indicates decrease or harm, and (0) indicates no significant effect.   Since these relationships grade into one another and sometimes change, and since it is often difficult to determine whether the effect on one of the species is essentially neutral, attempts to classify many actual associations in these sub-divisions may not be profitable. The scheme is chiefly useful in clarifying the types of relationship to be kept in mind while interspecific reactions are being examined.

Species A	Species B	Relation	
+	+	Mutualism	⎫ Symbiosis
+	0	Commensalism	⎭
0	0	Neutrality, toleration	
0	−	Antibiosis	⎫
+	−	Exploitation (inc. parasitism and pre-dation)	⎬ Antagonism
−	−	Competition	⎭

SYMBIOSIS

When members of two species are living together in a symbiotic relationship, the benefit received by one or both of them most frequently involves the provision of food, but it may also involve shelter, substratum, or transport. The association may be continuous or transitory, obligate or facultative. The two symbionts may be in close contact, with their tissues actually intermingled, or one partner may live within a cavity of the other or attached to its surface. In some instances contact between the individuals is transitory, and in some the two species may influence each other without actual contact. Associations in which both species derive benefit are termed *mutualism;* those in which only one species is benefited and neither is harmed are termed *commensalism.*

Mutualism

Mutualism with Continuous Contact. The most intimate type of mutualism is seen in those associations in which contact between the symbionts is close and is often permanent as well as obligatory. A classic example of this sort of relationship is furnished by the lichens, which are composed of a matrix formed by a fungus within which cells of an alga are embedded. The fungus holds moisture and makes minerals available for both partners, in return for which the chlorophyll-bearing alga manufactures carbohydrates for itself and also for the colorless fungus. The fungus of a lichen can never grow in nature without the associated algae, and the algae, although generally similar to independent species, are probably dependent upon the fungus under natural conditions. The dual personality of the lichen may be demonstrated in the laboratory by suitable techniques that permit the algal and fungal components to be cultured separately, as is suggested in Fig. 10.1. Many lichens grow abundantly on bare rock surfaces where the lack of moisture and of organic matter would make life impossible for most independent algae and fungi.

Other equally fascinating instances of mutualistic symbiosis involving two plant species are to be found in nature. A well-known example, and one already mentioned as of great ecological importance in relation is nutrients, is furnished by the bacteria of the genus

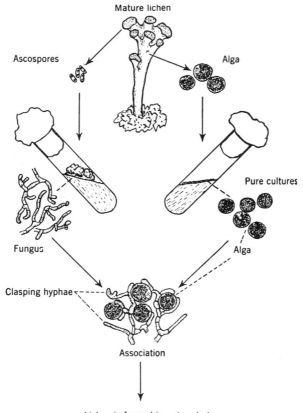

Fig. 10.1. Diagram illustrating the symbiotic partnership represented by the lichen *Cladonia cristatella* and its separation in the laboratory into algal and fungal components. When the components are recombined in the laboratory, the typical morphology of the lichen is not developed, evidently because of the lack of certain environmental conditions found in nature. (Burkholder, 1952, Copyright Baitsell's *Science in Progress*, Yale University Press.)

Rhizobium, which form nodules on the roots of leguminous plants and live symbiotically with their hosts (Fig. 10.2). The bacteria are somewhat specific as to host, and obtain carbohydrate and other substances from its juices. In return the rhizobia fix gaseous nitrogen and pass it on to their plant host. If available fixed nitrogen is absent from the soil, the plant is completely dependent upon its symbiotic nitrogen-fixing bacteria.

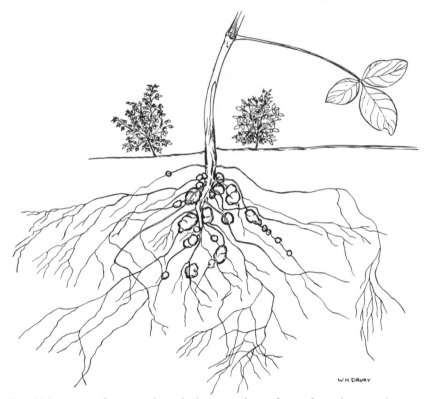

W.H. DRURY

Fig. 10.2. Vertical section through the root of a soybean plant, showing the root nodules within which live symbiotic bacteria (*Rhizobium japonicum*).

A somewhat similar mutualism is seen in the fungi that form mycorrhizal structures either inside the roots of certain plants or on their outside surfaces (Fig. 10.3). Ectotrophic mycorrhizae are found on various kinds of trees such as pines, oaks, hickories, and beech; endotrophic mycorrhizae occur in the red maple and are particularly common in roots and other tissues of many orchids and heaths. Fungi of this type are nourished by organic material that they absorb from their hosts. The ectotrophic mycorrhizae commonly take the place of root hairs and function in the absorption of water and nutrient salts from the soil. The degree of dependency of the host plant upon mycorrhizae is very variable, but pine seedlings, at least, appear to be quite unable to grow in soils normally deficient in one essential nutrient without the aid of these symbiotic structures. Since the beneficial mycorrhizae of the blueberry, rhododendron, and heather

Photo by Somerville Hastings, from McDougall, 1949, Copyright, Lea and Febiger
FIG. 10.3. Ectotrophic mycorrhizae seen as whitish sheaths over the branching rootlets of the hornbeam (*Carpinus betulus*) growing in leaf mold.

flourish only in an acid medium, the growth of these plants is improved by a soil of low pH (McDougall, 1949). It is reported that settlers moving west in the United States were at first unsuccessful in establishing certain kinds of trees around their homesteads because of the absence of suitable fungi. The seeds that they brought with them sprouted, but often the young trees would not grow. When fungal spores accidentally reached the plantations in soil samples carried from the east, many of the necessary mycorrhizae were supplied and better tree growth became possible. Subsequently deliberate inoculation was practiced, especially for the growth of pine trees.

Even more remarkable associations involving the intermingling of tissues are those in which one partner is an animal and one a plant. Unicellular plants live symbiotically in the outer tissues of certain sponges, coelenterates, mollusks, and worms. Some of these unicellular forms are green algae known as zoochlorellae; others are brown or yellow cells, believed to be flagellates, and are termed zooxanthellae. Partnerships called plant-animals by Keeble (1910) are formed by a turbellarian worm (*Convoluta roscoffensis*) and large numbers of zoochlorellae. The algal cells, often growing in the tissues of the worm in such profusion as to give it a greenish appearance, release oxygen during photosynthesis and produce nitrogen compounds that are nutritionally beneficial to the host. In exchange the algae obtain a suitable matrix for their growth and receive a supply of nutrient material resulting from the animal's metabolic processes. This balanced symbiotic relationship is thus able to persist indefinitely, and the nourishment furnished by the algae enables the worm to live and grow for long periods without taking in solid food.

Zooxanthellae are found abundantly in the body wall of coral polyps. These unicellular organisms serve the useful function of removing nitrogenous wastes and carbon dioxide from the coral and providing it with oxygen produced as a by-product of photosynthesis. The zooxanthellae in turn benefit by the absorption of the metabolites containing nitrogen and phosphorus, which are scarce in tropical waters, as well as by the absorption of carbon dioxide resulting from the catabolic processes of the coral animal. The fact that coral polyps placed in the sea in sealed glass containers survived for 2 weeks is evidence that the symbionts in this instance had approached a state of balance, in regard to their respiratory exchanges at least, and perhaps also to some extent in regard to other needs.

The giant clam *Tridacna* (Fig. 7.11) grows on shallow coral reefs with the opening between its shells directed upwards and the broad edges of its mantle, containing vast numbers of zooxanthellae, spread out horizontally where they receive intense radiation from the sun. The mantle also contains great numbers of small lens-like organs which probably serve to focus light into the tissue, making photosynthesis possible for the deeper-lying zooxanthellae. Since phagocytic blood cells regularly engulf and digest large numbers of the zooxanthellae, the giant clam may be thought of as "farming" these symbiotic algae and deriving a considerable portion of its nutrition from them (Yonge, 1944).

Some symbionts reside in cavities of their hosts rather than in their tissues. Ruminants and other animals living on a diet high in cellulose are unable to digest this material without the enzymatic action of cellulase produced by microorganisms in their intestines. Symbiotic bacteria fulfill this function in cattle and other grazing animals.

Certain cockroaches and termites can digest wood only with the aid of a special type of flagellate that is harbored within their guts. Symbiosis in these instances is mutually beneficial and obligatory for both parties. Some of the bacteria living in the intestines of animals also produce various B vitamins and other special materials.

Another manifestation of mutualism in which the symbionts are in permanent contact, but one in which the contact is entirely external is the attachment of certain marine sponges and coelenterates to the shells of crabs. The attached animal benefits by being carried about to fresh feeding areas and by avoiding being stranded in the tidal zone or in stagnant water, as well as by obtaining fragments of food from the meal of its host. The crab, for its part, is camouflaged to some extent by the presence of the attached animals on its back and is often protected by them from attacks by its enemies.

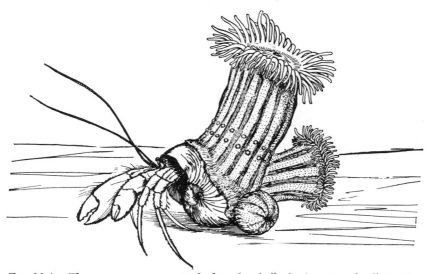

Fig. 10.4. Three sea anemones attached to the shell of a hermit crab, illustrating mutually beneficial symbiosis. Note the growth of the foot of the anemone over the surface of the shell. (Modified from Borradaile, 1923.)

The classic example of this type of partnership under the sea is furnished by the sea anemone *Adamsia palliata* which grows on the shell of the hermit crab *Eupagurus prideauxi* (Fig. 10.4). Further interspecific relations result in this instance from the fact that the shell inhabited by the hermit crab is the abandoned house of a snail and from the fact that the same shell may also furnish the abode of the annelid worm *Nereis*. The hermit crab starts the enterprise by obtaining a sea anemone from a rock and placing it on the back of its shell. When the growth of the crab causes it to move to a larger shell, the crab loosens the base of the anemone with its claws and transfers it to the new shell. In some species the base of the anemone grows over the entire shell and extends beyond it; sometimes the original shell is largely dissolved away so that the crab's house consists almost entirely of the anemone's base. The stinging nematocysts of the sea anemone are a powerful deterrent to predaceous fish and protect the members of the partnership from being eaten. When *Nereis* is also present as a junior partner, it is said to help keep the inside of the shell clean and, as payment, to snatch fragments of food from the pincers of the crab.

Mutualism without Continuous Contact. A great many instances exist of mutualism in which the partners are not attached to each other or in which they are in contact intermittently or for only a short period. In most mutual benefit associations of this sort the fulfillment of a nutritional need plays a prominent role for at least one of the species; but the other species, and sometimes both, may derive an entirely different type of advantage.

A commonly cited example of mutualism of two animal species involves birds that alight on the backs of large grazing animals and pick off the ticks or other external parasites. The cowbird in North America, the oxpecker, the little white heron in Africa, and certain other birds obtain a ready supply of food in this way. The host animals are rid of their pests and are frequently warned of approaching danger by the activity of the birds as watchmen. An amazing kind of pest-control service is rendered by the crocodile bird in removing leeches from around the teeth of the crocodile, which allows the bird to enter its mouth for the search. Mixed groups of ostriches and zebras are said to derive mutual benefit in guarding against attack by the keener sense of sight of the ostrich and the greater powers of scent possessed by the zebras.

In the subterranean world we find various extremely complex reciprocal relations between species. Various ants maintain a population of aphids in their nests. The ants obtain a nutritive exudation from the hind end of the alimentary tract by stroking the aphid's abdomen with their antennae. This furnishes the basis for popular accounts that ants "keep cows" and "milk" them. The aphids feed on the roots of plants, or they are carried by the ants out of the nest and allowed to feed on leaf stalks. The aphid eggs are laid on the plants above ground, and, although of no immediate use to the ants, they are carried down into the nest where they are sheltered during the winter until they hatch and the young aphids repopulate the dairy farm (Fig. 10.5).

An equally extraordinary agricultural technique practiced by insects is the cultivation of fungi by certain beetles, ants, and termites. Various kinds of fungi are grown for food by these animals, and some species are known only in insect gardens of this sort. In the tropical forest one may see a band of green moving across the ground; this is formed by a line of leaf-cutting ants (*Atta*) carrying pieces of leaves

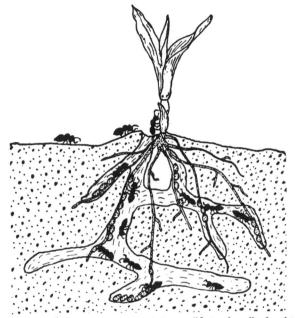

Fig. 10.5.   Diagram of an ant nest containing a "dairy farm" of aphids.   (Burkholder, 1952, Copyright, Baitsell's *Science in Progress*, Yale Univ. Press.)

over their backs like so many umbrellas.   The leaves have been cut from a shrub and are being transported to the ant's underground nest where they will be chewed into a pulp and spread out to form a bed in which a particular kind of fungus (*Rozites gongylophora*) is planted.   The ants cultivate the garden with great care; they weed out unwanted species of fungi and prevent the fruiting of their fungus, but encourage it to develop special mycelial outgrowths on which they feed (Brues, 1946).   The fungi that live symbiotically in termite nests are nourished by the insects' excreta rather than by leaf pulp.   The cultivation of fungi by ambrosia beetles (*Scolytidae*) is carried on within the tunnels drilled in wood by these insects (Chamberlin, 1939). Sometimes the development of the fungi is sufficiently luxuriant to clog up the tunnels completely, and the beetles are killed unless they can eat their way out faster than the fungi grow!

The perpetuation of this mutualistic relation between insects and fungi is assured by elaborate structures and reactions by which the fungi are transferred to the habitats of new generations. The fungus-growing beetles, for example, possess certain external or internal structures by means of which they carry spores or fragments of the fungi from the old burrow, where the larvae were hatched, to the site of a newly founded colony. Among the leaf-cutting ants the virgin queen carries a pellet of fungus in a pocket below the mouth and deposits the inoculum in her new bridal chamber. These arrangements by the host for transmission are strong evidence that the guest species are beneficial, and hence are symbionts. With parasitism, the problem of transmission is always arranged for by the parasite in one way or another and is resisted by the host. A more detailed consideration of these relationships among insects will be found in the summary by Steinhaus (1946).

The pollination of flowers by bees, moths, and butterflies, and occasionally by hummingbirds, is another manifestation of mutually beneficial symbiosis, but one in which the species concerned may be in contact for only a few seconds. The insect derives food from the nectar, or other product of the plant, and in return carries pollen from the anthers of one flower to the stigma of another, thus ensuring cross pollination. The coordination of the elaborate behavioristic and anatomical adaptations that have been evolved in the insect and in the flower in relation to this cooperative activity is truly remarkable. The flowers open, producing odors and displaying colors that attract suitable insects, only at the time when they are sufficiently mature for fertilization. In various ingenious ways the flower is so shaped that the insect cannot get its food without dusting the stigma with pollen carried from another flower and then picking up fresh pollen to be carried to the next flower. The reactions and the structure of the pollinating insects are correspondingly adapted. Bees, for example, continue to visit the same species of flower as long as a supply of mature blossoms is available and thus avoid mixing pollen from different species.

The mutual dependence of insect and flower is frequently highly specific and sometimes involves the reproductive cycle of the animal as well as that of the plant. The peculiarly enclosed flowers of the commercial fig are pollinated only by wasps of the genus *Blastophaga,* and special floral structures called caprifigs provide the only place in which these wasps can lay their eggs. A similar dually obligate and specific symbiosis is found in the relation between the yucca plant and the yucca moth (Fig. 10.6). The female moth visits the yucca flower in the evening and collects a ball of pollen from the anthers. Then, holding the pollen ball in specially adapted mouth parts, she flies to another plant and pierces the ovary of the flower with her

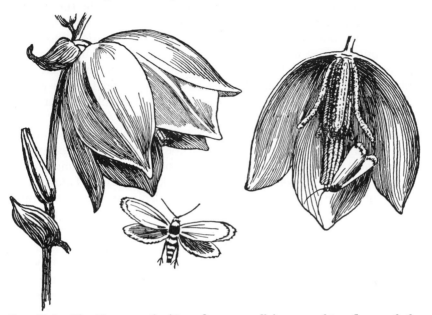

Fig. 10.6. The Yucca moth (*Pronuba yuccasella*) approaching flower of the yucca plant (*left*). Flower cut open (*right*), showing the moth placing pollen on the stigma. (Modified from Borradaile, 1923.)

ovipositor. After depositing eggs within one of the ovules, the moth creeps down the style and stuffs the ball of pollen into the stigma. When the moth eggs hatch, the larvae feed on the tissue of the ovule, and eventually mature to repeat the process for the next generation. It is difficult to imagine in such complex interdependencies how the behavior pattern and anatomical structures vitally necessary to both species have evolved.

Other two-way benefits in the relations between species involve transport and dispersal of seed. The fruit eaten by birds, mammals, and other animals provides them with a source of nourishment, and the contained seeds are subsequently dropped in their excrement at varying distances from the original site. The activity of squirrels in carrying and burying acorns, hickory nuts, and the like may play a significant role in the establishment of trees in new areas. Many other illustrations of mutualism, both of an intimate and of a casual nature, will occur to the reader.

Commensalism

When members of different species are associated in such a way that only one of the organisms is benefited but neither is harmed, the relationship constitutes commensalism. Such associations no doubt began by the mere toleration of "guests" near the usually larger host species, or on or in its body. If the guest derived some benefit without interfering with the host, the relationship would tend to persist. Casual association may have led to a partial or a complete dependency on the part of the guest. Obligate commensalism established in this way may have evolved further in some instances to give rise to mutualism, on the one hand, or parasitism, on the other. If the host species became adapted to take some advantage of the close proximity of its guest, a mutualistic symbiosis would result. However, if during the course of evolution the guest species imposed more and more upon its host, finally overstepping the bounds of hospitality and inflicting harm upon the host, the relationship would change to exploitation and perhaps to parasitism.

The advantage derived by the commensal involves the provision of substratum, shelter, or transport, and very frequently of food. Commensalism means "eating off the same table" as guest messmates. "The messmate does not live at the expense of his host; all that he desires is a home or his friend's superfluities" (Pearse, 1939). As would be expected, the circumstances of commensalism are more variable than those of mutualism. Although in some instances the commensal is in continuous contact with its host—attached to a surface or retained within a cavity—more frequently the guest is free to come and go at irregular intervals. Sometimes the commensal species can associate with only a single host species, but often considerable species flexibility is observed.

Commensalism with Continuous Contact. Commensals in more or less permanent contact with their hosts are represented by a great variety of *epiphytes* and *epizoans*. Many tropical orchids, bromeliads, and other "air plants" grow perched on horizontal branches or in forks of trees or hanging in streaming festoons (Fig. 10.7). Familiar in the northern coniferous forest are the hanging "mosses" *Usnea* and *Alectoria* that gave rise to Longfellow's well-known lines:

This is the forest primeval.   The murmuring pines and the hemlocks,
Bearded with moss, and in garments green, indistinct in the twilight,
Stand like Druids of eld, with voices sad and prophetic,
Stand like harpers hoar, with beards that rest on their bosoms.

Each of these mosses consists of two species forming a lichen, and
this grows as an epiphyte upon the conifers, thus creating a three-way
partnership.   Epiphytes sometimes show distinct preferences for one
host species, as may be seen, for example, in southeastern United

Photo by H. B. Moore

Fig. 10.7.   Bromeliads, including the pendant Spanish moss (*Tillandsia*), growing
as epiphytes on the branches of the live oak in Florida.

States where the Spanish moss grows more abundantly on the live
oaks than on the pines (Fig. 10.8).

All these epiphytes use the trees only as a point of attachment amid
suitable light and other conditions, and manufacture their own food
by photosynthesis.   Since they do not obtain nourishment from the

tissues of the tree, they are not classed as parasites. For the most part the epiphytes do no harm to the host plant but occasionally they become so numerous as to break it down or to. stifle its growth (Fig. 10.8). Orange growers in Florida are forced to spend large sums every year for the removal of Spanish moss from their trees.

Fɪɢ. 10.8. Spanish moss (*Tillandsia*) growing in harmful abundance on a live oak tree in South Carolina but practically absent from a neighboring pine.

Some plants live as attached epiphytes on the surfaces of animals. One extraordinary example is the green alga that grows on the long, grooved hairs of the sloth. Since this alga often becomes sufficiently abundant to give the animal a greenish appearance, the sloth presumably derives some advantage in concealment as it sleeps in the tree tops. Equally remarkable in its habit is the green alga *Basicladia*, a genus of the Cladophoraceae, which grows only on the backs of freshwater turtles (Leake, 1939). The specific relation here appears to be due to a dependence on keratin, since the alga can be cultured in the laboratory only if this substance is provided. To the extent that the host receives benefit from such epiphytic algae, the relationship approaches mutualism.

Many kinds of microorganisms take up residence within tissues or cavities of larger plants and animals without causing any trouble for the owner but without paying any rent. Since no light is available for photosynthesis these commensals are represented by saprophytic fungi and bacteria and by Protozoa. Many such organisms are found in the lower intestines of animals where they consume undigested food and secretions and complete their life cycles unnoticed by their hosts. The bacteria in the human colon, notably *Escherichia coli,* are a familiar example. As already mentioned, these commensals may represent a mode of life that is transitional between that of the parasites and the beneficial symbionts also found in such habitats.

Permanently fixed commensals in the animal kingdom are represented by sessile invertebrates that grow attached to plants or to other animals. Sometimes a highly specific relation exists between the epizoan and its host, although the reason for this is often hard to discern. The oyster-like bivalve *Ostrea frons* grows almost exclusively on the roots of the red mangrove in the shallow waters off the coast of Florida; special hooks develop on the lower shell of this animal by means of which it clings tenaciously to its host and is not displaced by surf. Certain barnacles are found only on the backs of whales where they benefit by a free ride; since they do not feed upon the whale's flesh, they are not parasites in the strict sense of the term. The marine environment furnishes many other instances of attached commensals (Wilson, 1951, Ch. 11). Anyone who has an opportunity to catch an elderly horseshoe crab (*Limulus polyphemus*) in the shallow water off the New England coast is likely to find several species of mollusks, barnacles, and tube worms attached to the shell and a number of more motile commensals living in the "book gills" or other anatomical nooks of this strange animal.

Commensalism without Continuous Contact. The category of commensals that are in temporary contact with their hosts or that are associated without being in actual contact is also a large one. Intermittent contact between animal commensals and plant hosts is displayed on land by squirrels, monkeys, tree frogs, and snakes, and by a great many birds, insects, and other animals that use trees or other plants for substrata, for shelter, or for breeding sites without harming the host plant significantly. Many examples of partial or complete specificity in commensalism of this type will occur to the reader. An intriguing three-cornered relationship is that of the elf owl that nests only in abandoned holes made by the Gila woodpecker in the stems of the large Sahuaro cactus found in Arizona and neighboring regions.

Temporary or intermittent contact between two animal commensals is seen in such special associations as that of the remora fishes and the sharks, whales, or sea turtles to which they attach. The dorsal fin of this "shark sucker" has become modified in the course of evolution into a most effective suction disc by means of which the fish attaches itself to the under side of a shark or other large animal. The sucker can release its grip at will, swim about gathering fragments of food resulting from the shark's meal, and return to hook another ride on the body of the host. Several suckers may be found attached to the same shark, but they do not seem to hinder the powerful fish appreciably.

Commensalism involving close association between two species but without the attachment of the guest to the host occurs in a wide variety of animal groups. The guest may live in a burrow or other retreat of the host species, and sometimes the relation is highly specific. Certain beetles, for example, are known exclusively from the nests of meadow mice. The burrowing owl which often nests in the burrow of a prairie dog is an accepted member of the prairie dog "village" while the village is actively populated by these rodents. Many such uninvited guests take up residence in the burrows or tubes of aquatic animals. The decapod crustacean *Polyonx* lives in the "back entry" of the U-shaped tube of the marine annelid *Chaetopterus*, where it is well hidden from enemies and where it can obtain particles of food as well as a supply of oxygen from the water forced through the tube by the pumping action of the worm's parapodia (Fig. 10.9).

Other marine commensals live within a water cavity of their host. In certain instances in which the relationship is highly specific the commensal has been shown to be guided to the proper host by chemical emanations or to be kept within the host by definite tactic reactions (Davenport, 1950). The oyster crab is a familiar example of this type of commensalism and one among several of a similar nature in which the commensal eventually becomes a prisoner. The oyster crab is originally carried as a planktonic larva into the mantle cavity of the oyster by incoming water currents produced by the feeding and respiratory activity of the host. The tiny larva metamorphoses, and eventually grows into an adult about a centimeter in length and too large to escape through the narrow opening between the valves of the oyster. The crab leads a completely sheltered life, stealing particles of food from the oyster, to be sure, but apparently doing its host no significant amount of harm. The commensal is still within the cavity of the shell when the oyster is opened in the kitchen, and the crab sometimes startles an uninformed diner by appearing in his oyster stew. (Oyster crabs are perfectly edible and are regarded as a delicacy by some, including many who are not ecologists.)

Perhaps the most extraordinary instance of a commensal living within its host is that of the small tropical fish *Fierasfer* which finds

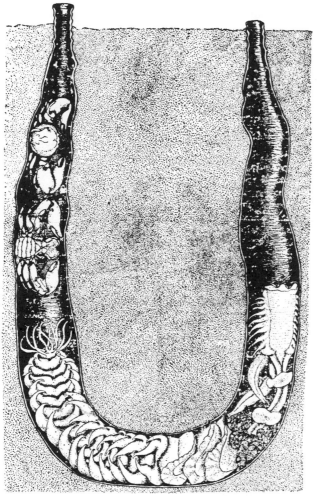

Fɪɢ. 10.9. Diagrammatic vertical section of a *Chaetopterus* tube in the mud bottom of the littoral zone, showing the position of the worm and two commensal crabs (*Polyonyx*). (By permission from *Animal Ecology* by A. S. Pearse, Copyright 1939, McGraw-Hill Book Co.)

shelter within the cloacal cavity of a sea cucumber (Holothuroidea). The fish occasionally emerges to feed in the neighborhood. When it wishes to reenter its strange retreat, it pokes its nose against the opening of the cucumber's cloaca, then quickly reverses its position, and allows itself to be drawn tail first inside its host.

Some species appear to derive protection by acquiring a big brother, that is, by associating themselves with other species recognized in the community as being voracious or poisonous. Pilot fish (*Naucrates ductor*) follow along beneath sharks as closely as shadows, but cannot attach to the surface of their hosts since they have no suction discs as do the remoras. For some reason they are never eaten by the sharks. In similar fashion particular kinds of fish find shelter under the umbrella of poisonous jellyfish; one species somehow manages to live unharmed among the tentacles of the Portuguese man-of-war, whose stinging cells instantly paralyze other kinds of fish, which are used for food. Another commensal fish has acquired a type of swimming motion that allows it to move among the tentacles of large sea anemones without causing the discharge of the poisonous nematocysts.

Other instances of the protection gained by the weak through association with the strong are furnished by scavengers and mimics, although their modes of life should perhaps not be termed commensalism because of the absence of toleration or even awareness. In the tropics the hyena lives as a scavenger on leavings from the lion's meal, which consists of animals that the hyena could not possibly have killed for itself. Similarly, in the far north during the winter the arctic fox lives largely upon the remains of seals killed by polar bears. Another type of protection is attained by weaker species through mimicking in appearance and behavior certain species recognized as voracious or poisonous by other members of the community, as described in Chapter 6. The mimics, as well as the truly dangerous models, are presumably avoided by the predators.

The foregoing account of symbiosis is sufficient to indicate the widely separated types of animals and plants that may be associated in relations of advantage or of toleration. We have also reviewed the great range that exists in the degree of dependence and of specificity in these relationships. However, many fascinating questions await future study as to the exact nature of the behavior patterns that bring the symbionts together and of the physiological interdependencies between them. The examples described show how these associations may have arisen from casual contacts between species, which then led to a recognizable commensalism. Subsequently the relation may have evolved in some instances into mutualism and in others into parasitism. The possibility of evolutionary transformation in either direction may be imagined from such flexible associations as those of the various mycorrhizae.

The interspecific relationships described in this section are flexible, and their nature may change even within the lifetime of the individuals concerned. At one moment the tissue of the giant clam is providing a favorable environment for the growth of zooxanthellae; at another moment it is digesting these unicellular organisms. Fungi associated with the roots of the tomato plant are ordinarily harmless, or even beneficial; but under certain conditions these fungi become definitely parasitic on the same plant. Another turn-about relationship, which will be more fully described in Chapter 12, occurs in stands of "old field" pine. The grass in abandoned fields in central New England forms a favorable bed for the development of seeds that blow in from white pine trees. When the pines have grown into a dense grove, however, the resulting deep shade and thick carpet of fallen needles will kill the grass beneath. These examples will suffice to indicate how easily the line between symbiosis and antagonism may be crossed.

ANTAGONISM

Relations between members of different species in which one or both are harmed during the life span of the individuals concerned are included under the general heading of antagonism. These antagonistic relations are not necessarily harmful for the population or for the species as a whole. From the broader viewpoint interspecific antagonism may have beneficial effects through controlling abundance or influencing the course of evolution. Exploitation and competition are necessary for the very existence of the community, and, when kept in suitable balance, make possible its perpetuation. Our scrutiny of the relations between individuals of different species therefore will lead to a consideration of the relations between interacting populations. The latter are involved in functional adjustments of the community as a whole which will be discussed in subsequent chapters. As with other ecological factors, when the interaction between species is extended from individuals to populations and the entire community, additional relations with new significance emerge.

Antagonistic relations of one species toward another involve harm that may be inflicted in one or more of several ways: (1) Species A may produce a poisonous substance or a change in environmental condition that is inimical to species B without species A deriving any benefit (0, —). *Antibiosis,* the production of harmful secretions, is the outstanding example of this type of relationship. (2) Species A may inflict harm by direct use of species B for its own benefit in a relationship of *exploitation* (+, —). Species A may exploit B by gaining support or shelter for itself, or it may obtain nourishment directly from B as a *parasite* or as a *predator.* (3) Both species may be harmed in a reciprocally unfavorable relationship (—, —). This situation is commonly found in the indirect rivalry, or *competition,* of two species for some feature of the environment that they both need and that exists in short supply. The space, food, light, oxygen, or other necessity taken by one species reduces the amount available for the other. In some situations considerable harm is suffered by both competing species; in other instances the injury may be serious for one species and relatively minor for the other. A reciprocally harmful effect will also occur if species A produces an antibiotic harmful to

FIG. 10.10.   Roots of strangling fig enveloping the trunk of its host in a Florida hammock.

species B and at the same time an antibiotic secreted by B is harmful to A.

In the foregoing paragraph the term competition was used in a restricted sense referring to the indirect rivalry of two species striving for some necessity from a limited supply. The aggression between species that prey on one another or exhibit some other form of direct antagonism may also be considered competition in the broad sense. The ecological effects of competition as both direct and indirect antagonism will be considered both from the point of view of the individual and of the population and the species.

All gradations exist between relations that are harmful to one species and neutral to the other, those that are harmful to one and beneficial to the other, and those that are harmful to both parties. Associations between species that are at first neutral or even beneficial may change during the life of the individuals to become harmful to one species, as already mentioned, and this relationship may change further to bring disadvantage to both parties. For example, the strangling fig starts life as a harmless epiphyte on a palm or other tree, but after a time its dangling roots reach the ground. Deriving nutrients from the soil and energy from sunlight, the fig rapidly envelops the trunk of its host with a network of anastomosing roots (Fig. 10.10). The luxuriant growth of the upper part of the fig gradually shades out the palm, and, after the death of the host tree, the fig eventually falls to the ground from lack of support. In similar fashion a parasite or a predator may bring about its own destruction under certain circumstances by killing its host or consuming all of its prey.

Antibiosis

Many substances produced by organisms, or conditions resulting from their metabolism, are generally harmful to others. Thus the generation of carbon dioxide or of organic acids may harm more sensitive species to such an extent that they are unable to continue to live in the area, and excessive shading by one kind of vegetation will kill off species intolerant of low illumination. The term antibiosis applies more particularly to the production of materials that are specifically antagonistic to other species. Such antibiotic substances are known to be generated by many kinds of fungi and bacteria. The action of penicillin, streptomycin, aureomycin, and other antibiotics produced by fungi in destroying various pathogenic bacteria is familiar to the reader through the practical use of these substances—either natural or synthetic—in medicine.

Bacteria, molds, and actinomycetes that produce antimicrobial substances have now been shown to be widespread in nature. Burkholder (1952) reports that about half of the species of actinomycetes and half of the lichens as well as large numbers of higher plants produce substances that inhibit certain molds and bacteria. Under some natural conditions antibiotics are believed to protect the species producing them from bacterial marauders, but this ecological aspect of the subject is largely unexplored.

Antagonistic substances formed by algae have been shown to affect other algae adversely in the laboratory and undoubtedly also do so in nature under some circumstances. Some substance accumulating in cultures of the green alga *Chlorella vulgaris* was found to inhibit the growth of the diatom *Nitzschia frustrulum* to a greater extent than its own growth; similarly, an antibiotic produced by dense cultures of *Nitzschia* retarded the division rate of *Chlorella* grown in the same culture or in conditioned water filtered off from the diatom culture. Interspecies antagonism of this sort probably exerts control on the abundance of different kinds of phytoplankton in ponds or other aquatic areas, and in some instances it may influence the seasonal sequence of species commonly observed in nature (Rice, 1949).

Similar products of plant growth have been found to be harmful to certain animals. Substances produced by senescent cultures of *Chlorella* and of the diatoms *Navicula* and *Scenedesmus* inhibit the filter feeding of *Daphnia* in laboratory tests. A reaction of this sort may account in part for the curtailment of the growth of zooplankton sometimes observed in natural waters containing senescent populations of phytoplankton (Ryther, 1954b). Pond "blooms" of blue-green algae, especially of the genus *Microcystis,* are known to produce toxic substances, such as hydroxylamine, which cause the death of fish and even of cattle that drink the water (Prescott, 1948). In the marine environment toxins produced by huge populations of certain microorganisms, popularly known as "red tide," cause the catastrophic destruction of fish and other animals. An outbreak of the dinoflagellate *Gymnodinium brevis* off the west coast of Florida in 1946–1947 resulted in the wholesale death of fish throughout an area of several thousand square miles (Gunter et al., 1948).

Certain land plants are similarly harmful to animals, but they usually exert their poisonous effects only when eaten. For example, a semidesert bush (*Halogeton glomeratus*) found in Nevada and neighboring states kills the sheep that eat it. The spongy leaves of this weed are filled with oxalic acid, which combines with the calcium in the blood and causes death within a few hours.

Many other instances of poisoning are known, some of them acting in a highly specific manner. The harm done in this way by one species to another may be completely fortuitous in some instances, but it may have evolved as a protective adaptation in others. The ecological consequences of this type of antagonism, involving the production of poisons or of harmful metabolites, have been discussed in further detail by Lucas (1949).

Exploitation

We shall now turn to relations of exploitation in which the members of one species benefit by the utilization of another species. The most common manifestation of interspecific exploitation is the use of a neighboring species as a source of food, and this will be discussed under the headings of parasitism and predation. However, an organism may employ another species of plant or animal in the environment for attachment, support, or transport, as already mentioned, and such activity often results in harmful consequences to the host.

Certain highly specialized kinds of exploitation occur, and one of the most astonishing of these is the enslavement of one species of ant by another (Talbot and Kennedy, 1940). *Polyergus* is an obligate slave-making ant that is unable to maintain its colony without the presence of members of certain species of *Formica*. *Polyergus* workers raid neighboring nests of *Formica* and carry home larvae and pupae. After maturing into the worker stage, these captive ants undertake feeding and nest building for their masters. *Polyergus* ants will starve even in the presence of abundant food if this slave labor is not available.

Another special type of exploitation is that practiced by so-called "parasitic birds." The cuckoo in Europe and the cowbird in the United States never build nests of their own; each female lays an egg in the nest established by birds of another, usually smaller, species. The cowbirds' habit perhaps arose as a result of their nomadic wandering after grazing animals, which left them insufficient time in one place for such domestic matters as raising a family. The pair of birds thus imposed upon is sometimes able to throw out the foisted egg or to cover it by building a new nest bottom over it, but more frequently the unwanted egg hatches out along with the host's own eggs. The young cuckoo soon pushes the other fledglings out of the nest, and the young cowbird is able to starve out its nest mates by grabbing all the food. After the young imposter has left the nest, its squawking still calls forth in its foster parents the behavior pattern of feeding and caring for it even in the absence of the rightful young. The spectacle of a small sparrow or warbler frantically trying to satisfy the hunger of an adolescent cowbird perhaps four times its size is an amazing sight.

The "parasitic" activities of other kinds of birds are really in the nature of "hold-ups." The reader may have witnessed the spectacular sight of an eagle attacking an osprey high in the air, forcing it to drop a fish from its talons, and then catching the fish before it reaches the ground. Similarly, a skua or a jaeger will chase a gull or a fulmar until the pursued bird drops its fish, or disgorges a meal already swallowed, and then the bully secures the food for itself. Various other kinds of animals are professional highwaymen, including some that compound the felony by robbing thieves. Such hijacking is carried on by certain flies (*Bengalia*) that waylay ants returning from a raid on a termite nest. The fly attacks an ant carrying away a termite, causing it to drop its booty, whereupon the fly quickly consumes the stolen goods.

Parasitism. Strictly speaking, a parasite is an organism that resides on or in the body of a larger living organism and derives nourishment from its tissues. Accordingly, the foregoing instances of exploitation are not regarded as parasitism in the more precise meaning of the term, either because nourishment is not involved or because one organism does not live in contact with the other. Thus barnacles growing on the back of a whale, as well as other kinds of epizoans and epiphytes, are not true parasites since they do not eat the host's tissue. However, the limits of parasitism even in the strict sense are not sharp. Just as gradations exist between parasitism, commensalism, and symbiosis, so also many borderline situations exist between parasitism and predation. Some organisms derive only a part of their nourishment from their hosts and some are in contact with their hosts for only a part of their lives. The typical parasite lives in its host without causing its death, and the typical predator kills the prey upon which it feeds. Yet some parasites regularly kill their hosts, and some organisms classified as predators eat only a part of their prey—sometimes without causing significant harm. Generally speaking in parasitism the weak benefit at the expense of the strong, whereas in predation the relations are reversed and the strong exploit the weak.

Examples of partial parasitism are found among various kinds of plants and animals. The mistletoes (Loranthaceae) grow like little shrubs on the branches of trees. Their specialized roots penetrate the vascular tissues of the host whence they obtain water with the contained dissolved minerals. Mistletoe plants may be definitely injurious to the tree on which they grow, but, since they are abundantly supplied with chlorophyll, they photosynthesize their own carbohydrates. Blood-sucking bugs, flies, and leeches and vampire bats may be in contact with their hosts for only short periods, and, although such animals are commonly regarded as parasites, their mode of life is clearly on the borderline between parasitism and predation. Little basis exists for considering mosquitoes, which live on the blood of animals, to be parasites and not so considering aphids, which suck the juices of leaves. But if aphids are regarded as parasites, their use of the material of a living plant is no different in principle from that of caterpillars which eat the leaf substance from the outside as herbaceous predators—or from that of deer which browse on the same leaves from the ground. Many partial parasites can derive nourishment from a wide variety of host species. These considerations bring us to the conclusion that every gradation exists between obligate parasitism at one extreme, in which the parasite is completely dependent upon a living host with which it is permanently associated, and predation at the other extreme, in which a free-living predator catches, kills and devours its prey.

Many kinds of plants and animals have taken up a completely parasitic mode of existence. Although the largest representation comes from the lower organisms, certain members of more advanced groups have also resorted to parasitism. Plant parasites, mostly fungi and bacteria, may attack animals or other plants. Animals that parasitize other animals are found in the Protozoa, in various other invertebrate groups, and rarely in vertebrates. Animals that parasitize plants are represented by gall wasps and gnats. The eggs of these insects are commonly laid on stems and leaves, and the activities of the young cause the formation of galls on the plant host. No organism is known that is not susceptible to attack by parasites of some sort.

Some parasites are restricted to one host species, or to one type of host, whereas other parasites can attack widely different plants and animals. Parasitism may even occur within a species. For example, in the deep-sea angler fish, *Photocorynus spiniceps* the male lives as a tiny permanent parasite upon the head or side of the female and obtains his entire nourishment from her blood supply. Thus does this species solve the problem of the location of one sex by the other in the inky blackness of the deep sea. This type of intraspecific relation occurs frequently in the plant kingdom, as seen, for example, in the growth of the pollen tube—representing the male plant—as a "parasite" on the tissues of the stigma and style of the flower of an angiosperm, or again in the growth of the sporophyte of a moss upon the tissues of the leafy gametophyte. In this chapter, however, we are concerned primarily with the parasitism of one species on another species.

Great variety is displayed among parasites in regard to their location on their hosts, the duration of their dependency, their adaptations, and their methods of transmission. Only brief mention of the more ecological aspects of this large subject can be made here. For a more thorough discussion of parasitism the reader should consult such authors as Pearse (1942), Chandler (1944), or Baer (1951). Parasites may occur on the outside of the hosts (*ectoparasites*) or within their cavities or tissues (*endoparasites*). Certain worms and many bacteria and protozoans are obligate parasites practically throughout their lives; other organisms may be parasitic for only a small part of their existence. Facultative parasitism occurs widely and is found, for example, in mosquitoes that can live their whole lives on nectar and other plant exudates but will readily parasitize any available mammal. However, some species of mosquito must obtain a blood meal before they can reproduce.

Many part-time parasites are parasitic as adults and free living as larvae, but in other species the reverse is true. A rather special condition within the latter category is presented by the parasitic wasps that lay their eggs in the bodies of other insects. When the eggs hatch, the larvae eat the tissue of the host, which at first remains active. Since the host is always killed eventually by the growing stowaway, the term parasitoid is sometimes applied to insects following this life pattern. Certain of the true wasps complicate the procedure further by stinging their victim into permanent paralysis before depositing the egg on it. In this way, the parent wasp provides a living but helpless insect of another species, or a spider, for the nutrition of the larva whose mode of life is thus transitional between parasitism and predation. Perhaps the most extraordinary example of this behavior is the attack of digger wasps, the largest of which have a wing span of about 10 cm, upon the even larger tarantulas. When the female of the giant wasp *Pepsis marginata* is ready for egg laying, she somehow locates a tarantula *Crytopholis portoricae*, and explores it with her antennae to make sure that it is the correct species. The larvae of each species of wasp can be nourished by only one species of tarantula. Although the tarantula could easily kill the wasp, it does not do so, and makes little attempt to escape. After the wasp has dug a grave for its intended victim, she stings it (Fig. 10.11), drags it into the grave, and lays a single egg, which she attaches to the abdomen of the paralyzed monster. At hatching the wasp larva is only a tiny fraction of the bulk of the tarantula, but, by the time it is ready for metamorphosis and independent life, it has consumed all the soft tissue of the giant spider (Petrunkevitch, 1952).

Fɪɢ. 10.11. The giant wasp (*Pepsis marginata*) stinging the tarantula (*Cryto-pholis portoricae*) preparatory to attaching an egg to its abdomen. (Petrunke-vitch, 1952, *Scientific American,* drawing by R. Freund.)

Plants and animals are susceptible to invasion by several to many species of parasites at the same time, and conversely many parasites can or must have more than one type of host during their lives. The fact that parasites infest other parasites has been immortalized by the jingle:

> Fleas have lesser fleas
> Upon their backs to bite 'em,
> And lesser fleas still lesser fleas—
> And so ad infinitum.

In a chickadee nest two cowbirds were found both of which were in-fested with hippoboscid flies. Attached to the abdomen of one of the flies were two mallophagan bird lice that thus obtain transporta-tion from one bird to another, and within the bodies of the lice bac-teria were undoubtedly present (Herman, 1937). As many as five links in chains of such *hyperparasites* and symbionts have been re-ported.

During the perpetual war between parasites and their hosts many special adaptations have evolved on both sides. The anti-invasion tactics of the host include external anatomical features and internal defenses of antibodies and phagocytes. The parasite is usually provided with a protective covering and with special ways for gaining entrance, maintaining position, and avoiding digestion by the host. On the other hand, certain of the parasite's unused organs have degenerated. The efficient parasite gains all the advantage possible without seriously curtailing the life of the host. If the host is killed, or when it eventually dies, the parasite must have the means of reaching a new host. Both host and parasite may become so profoundly modified as to be almost unrecognizable. In its young free-swimming stage the barnacle *Sacculina* has the appearance of a typical crustacean larva, but, as an adult parasitizing the shore crab, it becomes little more than a sac suitable for the absorption of food and for reproduction. The crab host is in turn reciprocally affected by the presence of the parasite for its reproductive glands are caused to atrophy and certain metabolic changes are brought about.

In many instances the transmission of the parasite to new hosts is left to chance aided by a very high natality; in others the parasite is specifically oriented to the host (Thorpe and Jones, 1937) or the host is attracted to the parasite. A remarkable instance of the latter procedure is displayed by the fresh-water mussel *Lampsilis ventricosa* in which the mantle edge is modified to appear like a small fish. When a real fish, attracted by this mimic, swims over the mussel, casting a shadow, the mussel discharges its glochidial larvae. Some of these larvae reach the gills or fins of the fish to which they attach and live as parasites until they are ready to metamorphose into adults. Certain fishes thus parasitized wander upstream where the young mussels drop off and begin a new life as independent bottom animals. In this way these sessile forms are distributed against the current to the upper reaches of the stream.

Many parasites require more than one host for the completion of their life cycles; a large number of instances could be cited for both plants and animals. One familiar example is the white pine rust that is dependent upon members of the genus *Ribes* as a secondary host. The bass tapeworm that causes stunting and sterility in the small-mouthed bass also illustrates the complexities of multiple parasitism. In the spring when the bass swims into the shoal water of a lake for spawning, segments of the tapeworm (1 in Fig. 10.12) living in the fish's gut are discharged into the water where they produce eggs (2). The eggs are eaten by copepods (3), a secondary host, and hatch out within the alimentary tract of these primitive crustaceans. The resulting larvae pass through the wall of the intestines into the body cavity of this host. Meanwhile young bass and other fish (4)

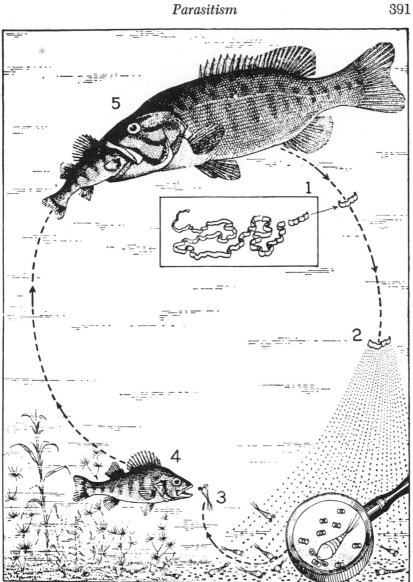

FIG. 10.12. **Life** cycle of the bass tapeworm (*Proteocephalus ambloplitis*, involving adult small-mouthed bass *Micropterus dolomieu*, the copepod *Cyclops*, and young bass or other small fish. (Hunter and Hunter, 1929, New York State Conservation Dept.)

spawned in the same shore area have grown to the feeding stage and eat the copepods harboring the larvae of the tapeworm. A close correlation is thus required between the time for the copepod population to develop, for the larvae of the parasite to hatch, and for the young fish to appear. The larvae taken in with the copepods can resist being digested, as can the other stages of the parasite, and make their way into the body cavity, liver, or other organs of the small fish which is a tertiary host. When the infected young fishes are eaten by the voracious larger bass (5), the tapeworm larvae are passed on, and this transfer from smaller fish to larger fish may take place several times. The larvae do not develop into adults while in the body cavity or internal glands of the small fish. Only if the infected fish is eaten by a large bass at the moment when the larvae are ready to metamorphose, do they develop into adult tapeworms. This final stage establishes itself in the intestine of the primary host and thus completes the life cycle. In another species of fish tapeworm the adult stage is found in man and in other fish-eating mammals. The life cycles of flukes that parasitize birds, snails, and fish successively are described by Hunter (1942). These multiple relations involve many special adaptations of the parasites and of the species in the environment on which they depend.

Predation. The typical predator is free living and catches, kills, and devours individuals of another species for food, in contrast to the typical parasite that lives on or in its host and derives nourishment from it without killing it. Thus the predator is said to live on "capital" whereas the parasite lives on "interest." Although this concept is generally true as far as the individual aggressors and victims are concerned, it does not necessarily apply to the populations as a whole. Parasites may kill a sufficient number of their hosts so that their "capital stock" is very greatly reduced. For example, in the grouse disease, which strikes this game bird periodically, the host population is so depleted by the ravages of the infectious parasite that the parasite population in turn sinks to a low ebb. Similarly, in an area in which the predator and prey populations have struck more or less of a balance we may find that the predators are limiting themselves to "interest" in the sense that they are devouring only the increment to the prey population each year. In such a situation the predator population may continue indefinitely to take a limited number of the prey without endangering the breeding stock of the species on which it depends.

Predatory organisms are almost entirely animals but a few kinds of plants are also included.   Predatory animals that eat other animals are *carnivores,* and those that feed on plants are *herbivores.* Some herbivorous animals kill the plants on which they feed by consuming all or most of each individual.   Aquatic filter feeders necessarily destroy all the diatoms, flagellates, and other algae that they digest, and herbivorous animals on land that feed on small plants may do the same.   However, many insects and many ruminants browse lightly over the vegetation in such a way as to allow the plants to continue life indefinitely.   We have seen that the grazing of sheep, for example may trim the grass harmlessly and prevent the invasion of other plants, thus aiding in the development of a healthy permanent turf.

Usually plants serve as food for animals, but in a very few exceptional instances the tables are turned, and animals fall prey to *carnivorous plants.*   In the terrestrial flora these are also known as insectivorous plants since insects are the usual prey on land.   Plants with this food habit are adapted in various remarkable and intriguing ways to attract, catch, and digest their victims.   The sundew (*Drosera*) for example, has round, reddish leaves provided with hairs that are progressively longer toward the periphery and tipped with glistening drops of a sticky, sweet secretion.   When an insect, attracted by the color or odor of the plant, alights on the leaf, it sticks fast to this little bit of natural fly paper.   The presence of the insect causes the hairs to bend over it; a digestive secretion is produced, and the body of the insect is absorbed.   The vase-like leaves of the pitcher plant are filled with water and serve as death traps for other insects (Fig. 10.13).   Animals that fall into the pitchers are unable to climb out because of the steep sides and downward directed hairs; they eventually drown and are digested by special tissues at the base of the leaf.   Further interspecific relations result from the fact that several protozoans and aquatic insects, including certain mosquito larvae, normally live in the water of the pitchers.   In the larger plants of the tropics frogs station themselves at the openings of the pitchers and spiders spin webs across them to secure their take of the insects that stray past.

Some plants are hunters of even smaller game.   Specially adapted bladders of the aquatic bladderwort *Utricularia* open suddenly when any plankton organism comes in contact with the trigger bristles; the unlucky plankter is sucked inside and digested.   Equally remarkable are adaptations that permit certain predaceous fungi to capture and to consume prey even larger than themselves.   One species produces a chain of cells in the form of a lasso in which a portion of a nematode, or other soil microorganism, becomes ensnared and which then tightens up sufficiently to kill the victim (Bessey, 1950).

Some predators are restricted to one prey species or are dependent upon a small group of food species, whereas others are highly catholic in their tastes, as has already been discussed in Chapter 8. Conversely, certain prey species are attacked by only one predator, but others may satisfy the appetites of many kinds of diners. The special anatomical and physiological adaptations of predator species for securing, devouring, and digesting specific prey species, and the equally elaborate specializations of the prey to avoid detection or to resist capture, have been considered in earlier chapters.

Photo by B. W. Allred, U. S. Soil Conservation Service

FIG. 10.13. A group of pitcher plants (*Sarracenia flava*) in swampy land of Louisiana.

In some animals only the adults are predatory, whereas the young are parasitic or live wholly upon the yolk supplied in the eggs. In other animals, such as many insects, the larvae do most of the eating, and in certain species the adults do not feed at all. Some predators feed upon the adult stage of their prey, some on the larvae, some on the eggs, and some on more than one stage. If members of the prey species are killed before they have had a chance to reproduce, the inroads of the predators on the population will be particularly serious.

The degree to which food "preferences" influence the feeding of predators is of considerable importance, both theoretically and practically in relation to pest control, game management, and fishery biology. The *forage ratio* of a prey species (A) in respect to a predator species (B) is defined as the ratio of the percentage of B's food made up by A to the percentage of the potential food organisms in the environment represented by A:

$$\text{Forage ratio} = \frac{\%A \text{ in } B\text{'s food}}{\%A \text{ in environment}}$$

A forage ratio of 1 indicates that the species is eaten in the same proportion as its abundance in the habitat. An investigation of the feeding of the black-nose dace (*Rhinichthys atratulus atratulus*), for example, revealed a forage ratio of 2.7 for Diptera and of 0.47 for Trichoptera although the latter were about one quarter more abundant in the stream. In this instance the Diptera were found to be of size and in positions that rendered them more accessible to the fish than were the Trichoptera (Hess and Swartz, 1940).

Generally speaking, predators tend to eat the organisms that are most available—either because of their abundance or because of their accessibility. If a predator has a specific food preference or becomes conditioned to continue feeding on the same species, serious consequences may ensue both for the predator and the prey; but usually when one type of food becomes scarce, the predator changes its diet. Top minnows (*Gambusia*) are often stocked in reservoirs because fishes of this type are known to eat mosquito larvae voraciously. Unfortunately for the mosquito-pestered human residents, when the fish have reduced the larvae to low numbers, they turn to other food and thus allow the mosquito population to recover.

Studies by N. Tinbergen showed that during one winter, within a certain locality, when voles (*Microtus*) were abundant, they constituted 86% of the food of long-eared owls (*Asio otus*) and wood mice (*Apodemus*) furnished 7%; whereas in the following winter when voles were scarce, they formed only 30% of the owls' food, wood mice furnished 15%, and other animals made up the difference. A more elaborate investigation of the forage ratios of the sparrow hawk by L. Tinbergen has been reviewed by Hartley (1947). These quantitative aspects of prey-predator relations will be considered further in the section on competition and in subsequent chapters dealing with the interdependencies of the community as a whole.

Competition

In the foregoing sections we have discussed certain categories of antagonism in which one species harms another by parasitizing it, by preying upon it, by poisoning it, or by taking some other direct advantage of it. In this section we shall consider first the aspect of competition that involves the "cold war" between species that are contending for "lebensraum" or for "consumer goods," and then we shall discuss certain generalities in regard to competition involving both direct aggression and indirect rivalry. An organism competes with members of its own species as well as with representatives of other species for space, light, food, or other necessity, but the nature of the competition between species differs because of the variation in precise needs and adaptations of different species.

Lichens compete with each other for space on a dry ledge and also with members of other species; on a submerged rock barnacles similarly compete for space with one another and also with oysters, mussels, and other sessile animals. Tree seedlings vie with small shrubs and herbs for light in the developing vegetation. The roots of a forest tree engage in a continuing but unseen struggle with the roots of other trees for water and for nutrients. Various species of parasites contend for the choicest tissues of their host. Grasshoppers not only compete closely with other insects for grass but also contend to some extent with mice and rabbits as well as with sheep and antelope for the same food. Various carnivorous species similarly are often rivals for the same prey.

The more closely similar one organism is to another the more nearly alike will be their needs—and hence the more intense will be their rivalry in obtaining their requirements from a common environment. This fact means not only that competition between individuals of the same species is particularly keen but also that the intensity of competition between species is directly related to the ecological similarity between them. The rivalry between species of the same genus is therefore usually more severe than that between species belonging to different genera—as pointed out long ago by Darwin.

Various aspects of interspecific competition have been investigated with carefully controlled laboratory populations of flour beetles. When *Tribolium confusum* and *Tribolium castaneum*, for example, are grown in the same "universe" of flour, one species always becomes extinct, leaving the other in sole possession, although plenty of food is available for both. The two beetles are very closely similar in life history, behavior, and requirements, but subtle differences exist in the responses to the conditioning of the medium, in the effects of crowding on natality, mortality, and rate of development, or in the rates at which the beetles eat each other's eggs. Under certain conditions *T. confusum* was found to inhibit the net fecundity of *T. castaneum* more than the latter species inhibits itself, with the result that *T. confusum* drove out *T. castaneum* in competition. Under slightly different circumstances *T. castaneum* gained the upper hand, but never would the two species coexist permanently in the same unit of flour (Birch, Park, and Frank, 1951).

In similar tests involving mixed cultures of two species of cladocerans, *Daphnia pulicaria* always caused the extinction of *Simocephalus vetulus*. Since these species do not directly attack one another at any stage, the displacement of one species must be due to difference in toleration for shortage of food, chemical conditioning, oxygen lack, or physical effects of crowding, but precisely what is the crucial aspect of the competition awaits further investigation (Frank, 1952).

From both laboratory and field studies we learn that two species having essentially the same requirements from their immediate environment do not usually form mixed steady-state populations. The most closely related species of a genus generally have different geographical ranges. If they live in the same region, they inhabit different types of habitat or they obtain their food and other necessities in a slightly different way—in other words, they occupy different habitat niches, as discussed more fully in Chapter 13.

When two closely competing species are unable to continue living in the same habitat, the determination of the species destined to survive depends upon which species is favored by the existing environmental conditions. If conditions change, as they do regularly with the seasons in temperate regions, for example, a different species may come to be favored. When conditions are not optimal in respect to one ecological factor, the range of tolerance is often reduced with respect to other factors. These general relations help to explain the fact that different species succeed one another during the season, as is seen in phytoplankton populations, with no one species holding numerical superiority throughout the year.

The type of competition between species that vie with one another by direct aggression has been given mathematical formulation by Volterra (1931) and Lotka (1934) for various cases in which one or more species feeds upon another species. When the population of one species grows at the expense of another, as in the predator-prey relation, the populations of the two species have certain reciprocal relations. These may be illustrated by the well-known investigations of Gause (1935) in which the interactions were demonstrated in laboratory populations of protozoans (Fig. 10.14). Gause prepared cultures in which the ciliate *Paramecium caudatum*, as prey, was eaten by another ciliate *Didinium nasutum*, as predator. An ample

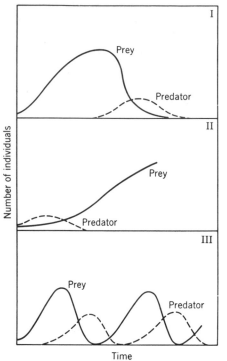

Fig. 10.14. History of prey (*Paramecium caudatum*) and predator (*Didinium nasutum*) populations in (I) homogeneous microcosm with initial seeding, (II) heterogenous microcosm providing refuge for prey with initial seeding, and (III) homogeneous microcosm with repeated seedings. (From Allee et al., 1949, after Gause.)

bacterial population was present at all times as a source of food for the paramecia. In the first type of experiment *Paramecium* and *Didinium* were introduced into a medium equally available to both; in the second type the microcosm was heterogeneous so that the *Paramecium* could escape into one part of the medium inaccessible to its aggressor. A homogeneous microcosm was again used in the third type of experiment, but additional seedings of both species were introduced at regular intervals. In the first set of tests the prey population at first grew rapidly, but, as the number of predators increased, the prey gradually became extinct and thus caused the starvation of the predators soon afterward (Fig. 10.14, Case I). In the second experiments (Case II) since the prey could escape, their population continued to grow, but the predators died off. In the third set of tests (Case III), in which the additional seedings simulated immigration, oscillations of both populations were induced with the maxima and minima of the predator population following those of the prey population.

Many illustrations of the interdependencies of prey and predator shown in the foregoing tests are known in natural populations. The removal of predators has allowed certain useful fish populations to increase several fold (Huntsman, 1938; Foerster and Ricker, 1941). The protection of deer from predation in the Kaibab forest resulted first in their great increase and then in wholesale death from starvation, as discussed in an earlier chapter (Leopold, 1943). In most natural situations the predators are unable to find and kill all the prey so that, after the reduction of the predator population, the prey population can increase once more. Furthermore, since in nature not all the prey are successful in finding refuge from their enemies, a small part of the predator population usually manages to survive periods of prey scarcity.

The action of these reciprocating influences may cause oscillations in natural populations of prey and predator even in the absence of periodic immigration. For example, in the Hudson Bay watershed the populations of lynx and of its prey, the varying hare, fluctuate widely and with about the same period of approximately 9½ years (MacLulich, 1937). From the fact that the maxima and minima in the lynx population follow closely those of the hare population, as well as from other observations, the periodicity of lynx abundance appears definitely to be controlled by the availability of its food, and the oscillations of the hare population are influenced to some extent, at least, by the extent of lynx predation. Host and parasite populations similarly affect one another in a generally reciprocal manner (Debach and Smith, 1947, and Utida, 1950). The repercussions of prey-predator and host-parasite fluctuations on the whole community will be considered further in Chapter 12.

To summarize, when two antagonistic species occur in the same environment, these general types of result are possible: (1) If the two species are ecological equivalents making common demand on the environment, and if one inhibits the growth of the other more than its own growth, the first species will cause the elimination of the second from the area. (2) If the two species have somewhat different demands on the environment so that they inhabit different niches, the two species may continue to coexist in the area. (3) If the two species are dependent one upon the other, as parasite and host or predator and prey, the aggressor may eliminate the other species and then turn to other types of food. (4) If the attacking species is unable to destroy all the other species and is able to survive periods of low abundance of the other species, the two species may continue to live in the area in either a steady or a fluctuating equilibrium. For a further discussion of these intricate relations of competition the reader may consult Hutchinson and Deevey (1939), Solomon (1949), or Allee et al. (1949, Ch. 22).

The survey of interrelations that has been presented in this chapter has revealed the extraordinarily varied and complex nature of the dealings of one species with another. We have delineated relations of mutual assistance, of toleration, and of antagonism; we have reviewed the special circumstances of parasitism and of predation and have considered various ecological effects of competition between specific types of organisms. In the natural community many individuals of many species of both plants and animals are typically present. It is our next task to consider the operation, organization, and alteration of the community as a whole in which each individual is responding not only to influences from all neighboring species but also to concomitant influences from others of its own species and from the chemical and physical features of the environment.

11

The Community

In previous chapters we have considered separately the chief physical, chemical, and biological influences of the environment. In all natural situations many physical and chemical factors are in operation simultaneously, and each organism is surrounded by other plants and animals that affect it continuously as a part of its environment. The analytical approach which has been followed is useful in disentangling the complex web of relationships within which the real life of plants and animals is carried on. Furthermore, even though our ultimate interest may be centered in the population or in the community rather than in the individual organism, we realize that the population or community exists only because of sufficient adjustment of each individual member. Having obtained some understanding of each of the important relations between organism and environment, we shall now consider certain of the more significant effects of the concurrent operation of these influences in natural situations.

The interplay of physical and biological forces has resulted in the establishment of characteristic groups of plants and animals in all habitable areas of the world. Each community maintains itself by adaptations that allow it to withstand adverse influences and to obtain its needs by exchange with the environment. The community comprises the living portion of the ecosystem, as explained in Chapter 1. In the remaining chapters we shall discuss the nature of the community, its changes, and the role of the various components of the community in the dynamics of the entire ecosystem.

COMMUNITY CONCEPT

The plants and animals living in any natural area form an assemblage in which each individual finds the environment to be tolerable and to provide at least the minimum requirements. The presence of many of the organisms is necessary for the continued life of other members of the group, and, although antagonisms occur, obviously the individuals that continue to exist in the area have survived any

401

harmful action. Mutual tolerance and beneficial interaction have brought about a certain degree of integration within the group. Such a group of mutually adjusted plants and animals inhabiting a natural area is known as a *community*.

Since the word community is employed in common parlance in many senses as well as in the specific sense described above, considerable ambiguity is apt to result. Accordingly it is often desirable to use the term *biocenose*—a shortened form of the word "biocoenosis" coined in 1880 by Möbius—to distinguish the special meaning attached to the community concept by ecologists. In explaining his proposed term Möbius used an oyster-bed community as an example. Since his statement is of considerable interest as a landmark in the development of ecological thought, an excerpt from it is quoted.

Every oyster-bed is thus, to a certain degree, a community of living beings, a collection of species and a massing of individuals, which find here everything necessary for their growth and continuance, such as suitable soil, sufficient food, the requisite percentage of salt, and a temperature favorable to their development.

Science possesses, as yet, no word by which such a community of living beings may be designated; no word for a community where the sum of species and individuals, being mutually limited and selected under the average external conditions of life, have, by means of transmission, continued in possession of a certain definite territory. I propose the word biocoenosis for such a community.

A biocenose may be composed primarily of animals or primarily of plants, but most biocenoses include both plants and animals (Fig. 11.1) and often many species of each kingdom are present. A biocenose need not necessarily be self-sufficient. The oysters of Möbius's original biocenose require food particles carried to them from other areas by water currents. The animals of a cave form a clearly recognized biocenose, but food must be brought in by streams, by the foraging of bats outside, or in some other way. However, most typical biocenoses include species that fulfill the essential functions of producer, consumer, reducer, and transformer; these communities are thus largely independent of others and, given radiant energy, are relatively self-sufficient.

The general concept of the community or biocenose as a group of mutually adjusted organisms maintaining themselves in an area is clear, but the recognition of specific communities and their limits is difficult. Part of the difficulty is due to the fact that the community concept has both a functional and a descriptive aspect. Every plant and animal necessarily has functional interrelations with a variety

of other organisms in its environment but the particular individuals
that are dependent upon one another are often not clearly distinguishable as a unit. In a large community, such as a forest or an oceanic
area, the spheres of interaction of many of the members will be much
smaller than the area occupied by the whole community. In some
instances the limits of a biocenose as a functional entity are fairly

FIG. 11.1. Salt marsh community at West Falmouth, Mass., consisting principally
of beach grass (*Spartina alterniflora*) and fiddler crabs (*Uca pugilator*). Various
inconspicuous forms are also members of the biocenose. In excavating burrows
in the substratum the crabs have rolled balls of mud and sand out onto the
surface.

definite and discernible, as is generally true of an oyster bed, a pond,
or a small island. In other instances the activities of members of one
community overlap those of another community to such an extent that
no specific margins can be set.

In spite of the difficulties in delimiting communities it is clear that
the members of a biocenose share in common the ability to live under
the conditions existing in the area and to a greater or lesser extent
they are dependent upon one another. Since the community grows,
adjusts, and under some circumstances reproduces itself, it represents

a higher level of integration than the individual plants and animals that make it up. For this reason some ecologists refer to the community as a "superorganism." But it is doubtful if the integration of any community is so closely knit as to justify an analogy with an organism. The composition of each community is determined by the selection of plants and animals which happened to reach and to survive in the area; the activities of the members of the community depend upon the adjustment of each individual to the physical and biological factors operating in the area. According to this "individualistic concept" no community necessarily reaches any prescribed composition or steady state, but each is a law unto itself (Gleason, 1926; Cain, 1947).

Turning from the functional aspect of the community to the descriptive aspect, we find that the community is characterized by having a more or less definite species composition. Often the change in species from one community to another is sharp, and if the principal species of the two communities are conspicuously different, the line of demarcation will be clearly apparent. In other situations one community grades slowly or irregularly into another. Where the species composition definitely changes—signifying the change from one community to another—some controlling environmental change has taken place. This may be an obvious topographic or edaphic change, or it may be a less apparent difference in local climate. From the descriptive view point a community may be recognized (1) on the basis of the habitat it occupies or (2) on the basis of the species of plants and animals present. Both of these bases have been used for the classification of communities into types.

A clearly distinguished unit of the environment showing uniformity of principal habitat conditions is known as a *biotope*. The term may be used to describe an individual area or a type of area. A mud flat, a sandy beach, a sand desert, a mountain brook, and a unit of the ocean are examples of biotopes, and each supports a characteristic type of community. The foregoing biotopes are recognized primarily by the physical features. Other biotopes are determined primarily by living elements, as is illustrated by a spruce forest, a marsh, or a prairie. The spruce forest and the organisms living in it comprise a biocenose, and at the same time the spruce forest serves as the biotope for subordinate communities e.g. the rotting log community.

Although each clearly distinct type of biotope will be inhabited by a characteristic type of biocenose, the species composition may differ widely, depending upon the source of animals and plants available to populate the area. For example, all the communities that de-

velop on flooded soil along the coast of Maine, Argentina, or elsewhere are of the salt-marsh community type but the particular species
of plants and animals present will vary. Differences in species composition will similarly be found in the alpine type community occupying mountain peaks in various parts of the world.

To a certain extent community types can be based on the occurrence of characteristic species (or other taxonomic groups) of plants
and animals. The classification of communities on a taxonomic basis
is difficult because of the variation in species composition from one
community to another of the same general type and because of many
irregularities in occurrence. Furthermore, the composition of a community depends not only upon which species will grow under the
conditions of the habitat but also upon which species happen to have
been successfully distributed to the area. Designation of community type on a taxonomic basis has been undertaken principally in
regions of the middle latitudes where the contrasting biotopes are
often populated by a few characteristic species represented by large
numbers of individuals, so that the communities are relatively distinct.
Nevertheless so many exceptions exist in any of the systems of classification suggested that many ecologists doubt the validity of any
classification and prefer to consider communities on an individualistic
basis, as discussed by Gleason (1926) and Cain (1947). In the
tropics it is extremely difficult, if not impossible, to characterize
communities on a taxonomic basis because the fauna and flora are
made up of a large number of species many of which appear in the
role of dominants (Richards, 1952). In the arctic relatively few
species are present, but over wide areas changes in the vegetation are
not due to the occurrence of different recognizable taxonomic communities but merely to different combinations of the same species
(Raup, 1951).

Where the physical features of the biotope are sharply delineated
and where these features exert primary control over the occurrence
of the organisms, a correspondingly abrupt change in the fauna and
flora takes place. An outcropping of rock in a forested region, for
example, will result in an abrupt shift in the vegetation from trees to
mosses or lichens. In the Florida everglades hammock communities
are sharply delineated on slight elevations of the ground from the
surrounding sawgrass community (Fig. 11.2). Sharp demarcation
among the animals of a community due to physical causes is also
frequently shown by the marine benthos, as for example, in localities
where the bottom material changes abruptly from sand to mud.

Sharp limits to a biocenose or to its subdivisions may sometimes be found in situations in which the climatic or edaphic conditions appear to change only slowly. Such a result occurs when alterations in the environment favor the survival of a new controlling species; it is seen particularly among stands of rooted land plants but is also apparent in the zonation of sessile plants and animals in the tidal zone. Among terrestrial plants, for example, the competition for light, water, and nutrients may be so keen that, at the point in the environmental

Fig. 11.2. Cabbage palm hammocks in the everglades of central Florida sharply delineated from the surrounding sawgrass. The sawgrass community is abruptly separated from the water community by a narrow ecotone in which a red mangrove is developing.

gradient at which the conditions favor a different dominant species, the new species will take over completely, choking out the first species and producing a rather distinct line between the areas dominated by the two species. In approaching a pond in an oak forest, for example, the trees often give way rather abruptly to a zone of high shrubs. Beyond this zone are clearly marked zones of low shrubs, sedges, or grasses, and the last of these gives place to the reeds and other emergent plants at the pond margin. This distinct zonation exists in spite of the fact that a quite uniform gradation in soil moisture may be found from the dry ground on which the oaks stand to the completely saturated soil near the water's edge. An instance of the zonation of dominant plants around a shallow pool near the seashore is shown in Fig. 11.3.

The step-like occurrence of the vegetation within a community, or between communities, may react on the environment to impose a zonation on some of the physical features of the habitat, and this in turn may cause a zonation in the minor constituents of the community. Even without this effect, however, the dependence of certain plants and of many animals upon specific kinds of vegetation for food, shelter, or other needs produces abrupt changes in the distribution

Fig. 11.3. Zonation of vegetation in a semicircle around a shallow pool, and also between the pool and a sand beach at Woods Hole, Mass. (1) Bulrushes (*Scirpus americanus*), (2) marshmallows (*Althaea officinalis*), (3) poison ivy (*Rhus Toxicodendron*), (4) bayberry (*Myrica pensylvanica*), (5) beachgrass (*Ammophila breviligulata*), and (6) wild roses (*Rosa rugosa*).

of the minor inhabitants corresponding to that of the dominating species. Continental and altitudinal tree lines have already been mentioned as illustrations of relatively abrupt limits to communities without correspondingly sharp changes in the physical environment. Many other examples could be cited of the action of the vegetation in complicating the environment and sharpening the transition between biotopes. Thus for a variety of reasons the boundaries of certain biocenoses are clearly distinct, but in many other instances one biocenose gives place gradually and irregularly to another.

Community Dominance

Two general types of situation exist in regard to the manner in which the community as a whole is controlled. In the first type the presence of one or a few species appears to exert a major effect in determining what other species occurs in the area. In the second type the physical features of the biotope tend to control the occurrence of most of the species present more directly and independently. No sharp division exists between these two general conditions. A spruce forest will serve as an illustration of the first category. Here the general conditions of soil and climate are such that spruce trees can grow in abundance and the presence of this species secondarily creates a suitable habitat for a large number of other species of plants and animals. Sometimes two or more species, usually of the same general life form, exert a joint major control, as is seen in the oak-hickory forest. This type of dependency may be represented schematically.

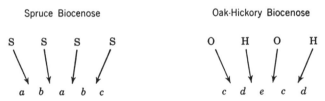

In the spruce biocenose the spruce trees are chiefly responsible for the conditions of light and moisture within the forest. They modify the temperature and affect the structure of the soil together with its acidity and chemical composition. The spruce trees thus influence the species of shrubs, herbs, and cryptogams that will grow on and in the forest floor. They provide food and breeding places for specific kinds of birds, insects, and other animals. Grosbeaks and crossbills feed on the seed cones, and woodpeckers devour the grubs that live in the wood and bark. The trees also provide support for pendant moss-like lichens (*Usnea*), and these are used as nesting sites by the parula warbler. All these species, and many more, dependent directly or indirectly upon the spruce trees, make up the forest community.

In the second general type of control over the community the physical features of the environment tend to influence the principal species independently. Situations of this sort are seen with special clarity where the physical environment is particularly severe, as for example in an alpine region, or is largely unmodifiable as in the open ocean. This type of condition is also seen in communities of marine-bottom organisms in which the chief controlling influences are the mud of the bottom and the water currents. These factors act on the species present more or less directly, as indicated by the accompanying scheme (case 1).

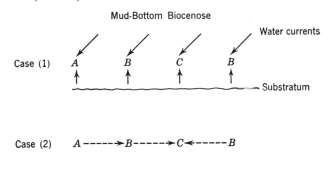

In addition to the major effect of the physical features of the environment a certain amount of interdependency may also exist among the members of biocenoses of this sort. In communities living on isolated rocks the interrelations between the species may be quite minor or entirely absent. When interdependencies do occur, the relations may be specific or non-specific. In case (2) species C is primarily controlled by the physical features of the environment, but it is also influenced by the presence of A and B specifically. An illustration of this situation is furnished by the fresh-water mussels that make use of fish swimming past as transport agents for their larvae. During most of their lives the primary dependencies of the mussels are concerned with the bottom, the water, and the plankton of their biotope, but at the time of reproduction this particular relation with the fish of their community becomes significant.

In a third type of situation the presence of the other species exerts a definite effect but not in a specific way. In other words, as far as C is concerned, A and B may merely be occupying space, and individuals of C could be substituted for them without significant consequence to C as is suggested in case (3) above. Illustrations are found in the competition for space among attached animals on submerged rocks. Similarly, in the competition for light among plants the proximity of other individuals often has its chief effect in cutting off the light with little difference whether the interfering neighbors are of the same or of different species.

In many communities one species is particularly conspicuous because it is the largest or the most numerous. This species is often called the *dominant,* and its name is usually given to the community, as in a spruce forest community. Occasionally two or more species share the honors in respect to dominance, as in an oak-hickory forest. Very frequently the species that is dominant in conspicuousness also appears to exert a controlling influence over the other members of the community, but sometimes a less conspicuous species may have a preponderant influence on the inhabitants of the biotope. In a sphagnum-heath community, for example, the heath plants are the most conspicuous, but the presence of the sphagnum controls the nature of the community as a whole. In some biocenoses microorganisms may play the critical part although they are among the least conspicuous of the species present. The seedlings of pine and some other trees do not grow properly unless suitable fungi are present to form mycorrhizae on their roots. Thus, although the species designated as the dominant frequently does exert the major controlling influence on the biocenose, this is not necessarily true even in those communities in which a high degree of interspecies dependence exists.

In the second general type of situation, in which the members of the community owe their presence primarily to a more or less direct and independent control by physical features of the environment, a species designated as dominant because of prominence or abundance clearly does not exert a critical control over the other inhabitants. For this reason some ecologists refer to such a species as "primary" rather than dominant. Dominance based on controlling influence must be clearly distinguished from dominance based on mere conspicuousness. In communities of low interspecies dependence the relative numbers and prominence of the various species are likely to vary from place to place. Great care must be taken in applying names to such communities to avoid ambiguity and the implication that conspicuous species are necessarily controlling.

Ecotone

The transition zone of tension between communities presents a situation of special ecological interest and is known as an *ecotone.* The border between forest and grassland, the bank of a stream running through a meadow, or the boundaries between any other communities on land or in the water furnish illustrations of ecotones

(Fig. 11.4). In this transition zone of tension the outposts of each community are maintaining themselves in environments that are increasingly unfavorable. The tension may result chiefly from a struggle with physical conditions or from a direct competition between certain species in each community. At the border between a shrub community and a marsh, for instance, the shrubs may compete directly with marsh reeds for light, nutrients, or other necessities of

FIG. 11.4. A distinct ecotone dominated by smooth sumac (*Rhus glabra*) and goldenrod (*Solidago*) between forest and grass communities in eastern Massachusetts.

life in such a way that one type of plant gives way completely to the other. In such a situation and in areas where controlling physical factors change rapidly the transition between communities is abrupt and the ecotone is correspondingly narrow. In other circumstances the two communities may interdigitate to a considerable extent. At the edge of a forest individual trees may pioneer into a scrub community, and the scrub species will invade the margin of the forest as far as they are able to survive.

When one community gives way only gradually to the other community, a wide ecotone results. The transition zones—sometimes more than 100 km in width—between major continental communities are regarded by some as ecotones (Pitelka, 1941), but others restrict the term to areas of smaller scale. Strictly speaking a transition area is an ecotone only if tension exists between the bordering communities, and this is often difficult to demonstrate, especially for large areas. Accordingly, the decision as to what is to be considered an ecotone depends upon the scope of the biocenose as recognized by the individual ecologist.

In the ecotone area the conditions of temperature, moisture, light, wind, and other physical influences are different from, and usually intermediate between, those existing well within either of the bordering communities. These or other conditions, such as food or shelter, may be superior in the region of the ecotone for certain species. These special influences of the ecotone area prevail below ground and high in the vegetation as well as on the surface of the soil. As a consequence various kinds of plants and animals not occurring, or relatively rare, in the bordering communities may become abundant in the ecotone. Shrubs typically grow in profusion at the forest edge and harbor a distinct fauna. At the margin of a pond willows and cattails thrive in the transition between land and water, and here are found such animals as turtles, frogs, herons, red-winged blackbirds, muskrats, and a host of invertebrates that are entirely absent or much less abundant in the center of the pond or in the terrain far removed from the water.

These species favored by the special conditions of the ecotone join with the outpost representatives of the principal inhabitants of the bordering communities in populating the ecotone. The species occurring in the ecotone may thus form a distinct functional community of their own. It must be remembered, however, that the ecotone inhabitants owe their existence to the presence of the particular conditions on each side and that the ecotone assemblage would disappear, or be considerably modified, if the bordering communities or conditions were removed or seriously changed.

As a rule the ecotone contains more species and often a denser population than either of the neighboring communities, and this generality is known as the *principle of edges*. The greater variety of plants in the ecotone provides more cover and food, and thus a greater number of animals can be supported. In measurements of bird populations in a variety of areas in the central part of the United States Kendeigh (1944) and Johnson (1947) distinguished between "forest-edge" species and species which confine their territory, nesting, feeding, and roosting to the interior of the forest.

As conservationists and wildlife managers have become aware of the principle of edges, they have bent their efforts toward increasing the amount of available ecotone area in each region since this usually

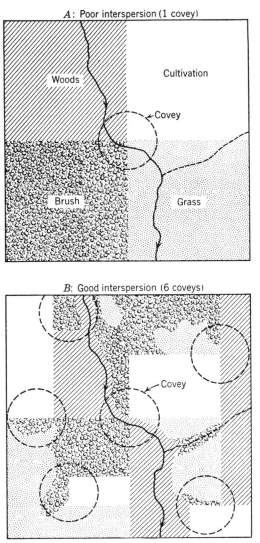

Fig. 11.5. Diagram indicating the increase in number of coveys of quail supported by farmland after increase in the amount of interspersion of the vegetation without change in the total area of each. (Reproduced from *Game Management* by Aldo Leopold, Copyright 1933 by Charles Scribner's Sons, used by permission of the publishers.)

favors the increase in game birds and mammals. Regions that are broken up into many units of different vegetation types are said to have "good interspersion" because the total length of community edge is great and hence a large amount of ecotone habitat is provided. Since coveys of quail tend to establish themselves where several types of vegetation meet, the number of coveys supported by farmland can be increased through a change from a few big tracts of woods, brush, pasture, and fields to a greater number of smaller interspersed tracts without altering the total area of any one type of vegetation (Fig. 11.5).

COMMUNITY COMPOSITION

Communities inhabiting distinctive and commonly occurring biotopes are the most easily recognized, and their composition and interrelations have been more extensively studied than others. A biocenose of this kind is made up of a characteristic, but flexible, assemblage of species without necessarily containing any species that is exclusive to it. Certain types of species invariably occur in a biocenose of a certain kind, but the individual species may vary widely from place to place. In a prairie community grass-like plants are always present and serve as the fundamental plant producers, but in different regions quite different species of grass fill this niche. Among the animals of this community fleet browsing forms, jumping types, and burrowers are commonly present but the species, genera, or even families of these typical members of the biocenose may differ greatly, depending upon the region in which they are located. The ecological relationships are entirely separate from the taxonomic affinities of the species since the latter depend upon the evolutionary history of the area. Species having a common evolutionary origin are placed in "faunal regions" or "floral regions," and these subdivisions may or may not correspond with ecological subdivisions.

Communities may be large or small. Some may cover thousands of square kilometers, such as a spruce forest in Canada, a prairie community in central North America, a pine-land community in southeastern United States, or an oceanic community. Other biocenoses, such as those occupying relatively uniform swamp, desert, or lake biotopes, may have dimensions in hundreds of kilometers. The biocenoses of ponds, tide flats, rivers, balds, alluvial sands, chaparral, mountain meadows, and rocky plateaux typically occupy a more restricted area. Smaller communities inhabit canyons, "hammocks" in the everglades, mountain springs, tidal inlets, and clearings in the forest. The plants and animals living on an isolated boulder, or in a rotten log, or in the debris washed up on the shore of a lake constitute still smaller biocenoses. Characteristic communities occupy even more minute microhabitats in the area such as a crevice in a ledge, or the water in a pitcher plant. We thus have communities within communities. The epiphytes, epizoans, and parasites of an animal or a plant may also be thought of as comprising a biocenose. An apple tree and the plants and animals that live on it and in it illustrate a special community of this sort. A horseshoe crab with the dozen or so species of mollusks, worms, and barnacles attached to its shell exemplify a microcommunity, as do the fauna and flora of a cow's stomach.

The number of species and the population abundance in communities also vary greatly. While maintaining the necessary quantitative relationships among the consumers and the producers in the ecosystem, the inhabitants of an area often include a wide range of densities. Furthermore, each component in the ecosystem may be represented by one, a few, or many species. Biotopes with extreme conditions and little food, such as a rock desert or an ocean deep, generally support few species and relatively few individuals of each species. The relatively small number of both species and individuals in the badlands sections of southwestern United States is familiar to those who have crossed these areas. In other severe habitats sufficient energy and nutritive materials are sometimes available to allow huge populations to develop although only a few species are able to survive. In the relatively simple biocenose on Bear Island in the Arctic Zone some of the smaller plants and animals are very abundant (Elton, 1939).

Under more equable climates larger numbers of species generally become interrelated in community groups; each species is usually rather meagerly represented, but sometimes the abundance of certain species is great. The food relations of the North Sea herring are known to involve a great number of species (Fig. 11.6)—some represented by very large populations—and these food species form only a portion of the whole community of which the herring is a member. A bed of kelp (*Nereocystis luetkeana*) in Carmel Bay, California, was found by Andrews (1945) to form the matrix of a community that included 40 species of invertebrates, several kinds of fishes, and numerous attached algae, protozoans, and bacteria, as well as associated species of phytoplankton and zooplankton.

Few complete enumerations have been made of both the plants and animals in even the simplest situations and none in complicated biotopes—especially in those with elaborate populations of micro-

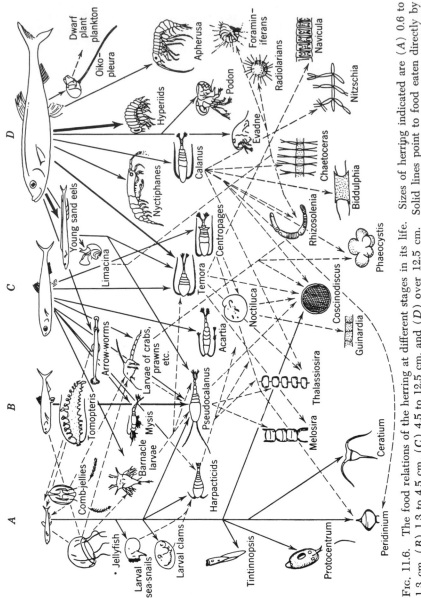

Fig. 11.6. The food relations of the herring at different stages in its life. Sizes of herring indicated are (A) 0.6 to 1.3 cm, (B) 1.3 to 4.5 cm, (C) 4.5 to 12.5 cm, and (D) over 12.5 cm. Solid lines point to food eaten directly by herring; other links in the food chains are dotted. (From Wells, Huxley, and Wells, 1939, Copyright A. P. Watt and Son and Messrs. Cassell and Co., Ltd.)

organisms. The complex ecosystems of temperate and tropical terrestrial areas are particularly difficult to analyze, but some idea of the number and diversity of the living components may be obtained from existing studies of portions of the biota. A comparison of the numbers of species that may be involved in communities of different kinds has been made by Elton (1946); a few examples follow.

The biocenoses of certain British rivers include representatives of as many as 131 species of invertebrates in addition to fishes, amphibians, rooted aquatic plants, and vast populations of algae, flagellates, and bacteria that were not enumerated. A meadow on clay near Oxford, England, served as the biotope for 93 species of invertebrate animals in the soil and surface vegetation, in addition to the plants and the microorganisms. At the other numerical extreme, the biocenose on the sandy shore of Amerdloq Fjord, west Greenland, consisted of only 5 species of invertebrates. In the *Betula odorata* forest in Finmark, Norway, only 29 species of plants were reported, whereas in an ash forest in Yorkshire, England, 72 species were found, and in the red fir forest of the Sierra Nevada, California, 93 species of plants were recorded. The animal components of these forest communities were not recorded, but they would include birds, mammals, amphibians, and a great many species of insects and other invertebrates; the total number of species would be further swelled by a wide variety of protozoans and cryptogamic plants. Even within a single microhabitat a surprising number of animals may be present as evidenced by counts of 111 species of invertebrates found in pine logs and 136 species found in oak logs during investigations in the Duke Forest, North Carolina.

Another observation in regard to community composition is that the species present for the most part belong to different genera. In many biocenoses each genus is represented by only one species; in others certain genera are represented by several species, as is often true, for example, of the sedges, willows, and oaks in communities of temperate and boreal North America. Rarely are more than a few species of a genus found in the same biocenose. Quite exceptional is the occurrence of "species flocks," such as those in Lake Baikal, where, for example, 300 species of gammarid crustaceans are found and these belong to only 30 genera (Brooks, 1950). The typical biocenose is composed of species that are separated by at least generic differences, whereas in the biota of a country or a region many species may be recorded for each genus. Comprehensive surveys of the animals in 55 communities and of the plants in 27 communities from a wide range of habitats showed that 86 per cent of the animal genera and 84 per cent of the plant genera were represented by only one species (Elton, 1946). The average number of species per genus in these widely spread surveys was 1.38 and 1.22 for the animals and plants, respectively. In contrast the average number of species per genus for all British insects, for example, is 4.23.

As a general rule the species of a genus are sufficiently similar so that their demands on the environment are in serious conflict. During the course of evolution this conflict has usually resulted in eliminating all but one species from each genus represented in the area. In contrast to a geographical region, a community is a functional unit and each niche in the community structure is occupied by that species which has been most successful in the competition for it. Adaptations for ecological needs and accessibility determine which species will survive and populate each part of the biocenose. The species that succeed in establishing themselves are almost always sufficiently different to be members of separate genera. Competition within each level of nourishment in the food chain thus produces a certain organization among the species of a community in addition to the organization imposed by the relationships from one link in the food chain to another and by other dependencies. The species composition of each biocenose is therefore determined by relations within the same functional level as well as in successive levels from among the species that are distributed to the area.

To make a census of the inhabitants of a diversified natural community and to ascertain the role of the various species in any complicated ecosystem is exceedingly difficult. Such tasks require the combined efforts of at least several taxonomists and ecologists competent to deal with the various segments of the biota. General accounts of the "plant communities" and the "animal communities" inhabiting the principal types of environment in the world are available in such works as Oosting (1948), Hesse, Allee and Schmidt (1951), and Dice (1952). Detailed studies of the inhabitants of specific biotopes have for the most part been carried out by investigators confining themselves to restricted categories of animal or plant life. To obtain an idea of the total assemblage of organisms making up a biocenose and their integrated activities, it is usually necessary to piece together the results of several investigations carried out in the same region. The reader may obtain rather complete information on the composition of the entire biota of certain specific areas by reference to the collaborative reports of members of expeditions, of government surveys, and of field research laboratories. In many instances the work of areal surveys has been expanded to include

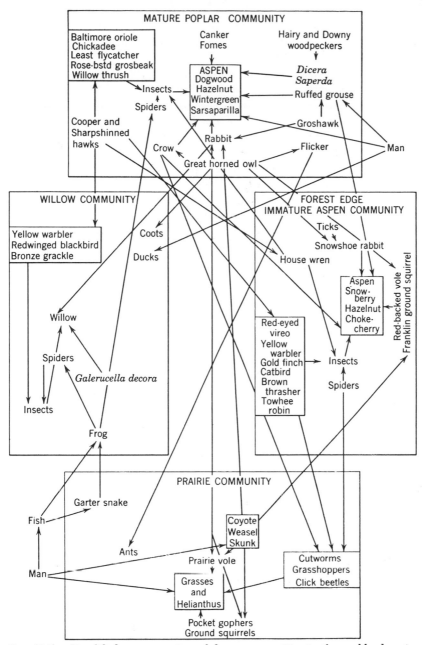

Fig. 11.7. Simplified representation of four communities in the parkland region of Manitoba, showing some of the food relations within and between communities. (Reprinted with permission from Hesse, Allee, and Schmidt, *Ecological Animal Geography*, 1951, John Wiley & Sons.)

studies of the dynamic ecological relationships within the community. The extensive series of investigations on Wisconsin lakes will serve as an example (Juday, 1943).

The foregoing discussion has shown that the biocenose is composed of species characteristic of the area, but these species may not be limited to the area nor is the biocenose limited to a fixed set of species. This concept of the flexibility of the biocenose is well illustrated by studies made by Bird (1930) of the interrelationships of members of communities occurring in the parkland region of Manitoba. The chief food relations of certain of the species within and between communities are indicated in Fig. 11.7. A great many other, smaller species are present in each community represented in the diagram, and many other dependencies exist besides the food relationships. This oversimplified picture nevertheless shows that certain kinds of plants and animals form a characteristic nucleus in each community but many of the individual species occur in more than one biocenose. The principal members of each biocenose have most of their requirements fulfilled within their own biotope but interrelations between the biocenoses are brought about by animals that move from one biotope to another for foraging or other purposes.

STRATIFICATION OF THE COMMUNITY

Many communities exhibit a *structure*, or recognizable pattern, in the spatial arrangement of their members. A community may be divisible horizontally into "subcommunities"—that is, units of homogeneous life-form and ecological relation. The zonations described in earlier pages of this chapter are horizontal structural units of this sort. Of more general occurrence is the aspect of structure that involves vertical changes, or *stratification*, within the community. In some communities a complex stratification is present, but in others the vertical dimension is so much compressed that the entire biocenose consists essentially of only one stratum. Lichens pioneering on a rock ledge represent an extreme example of a one-layered community, but, at a later stage when higher-growing mosses and herbs have become established and bacteria are present in a layer of humus beneath the holophytic plants, the beginnings of stratification are apparent, albeit on a very small scale.

In a grassland community subterranean, floor, and herbaceous subdivisions can be recognized. The subterranean stratum contains the roots of the principal vegetation and forms the permanent residence of the soil bacteria, fungi, and protozoans, as well as a host of insects, spiders, worms, and other invertebrates. In addition, it provides a part-time abode for many other animals including other species of insects, rodents, reptiles, mammals, and a few burrowing birds. The main activity in the soil for both plants and animals occurs in the upper layers, but the longer roots of prairie grasses extend to depths of about 2 meters and the roots of other prairie plants occasionally reach levels of 5 or 6 meters below the surface. In an extensive discussion of the relation of underground plant parts Weaver and Clements (1938) report that 65 per cent of a group of true prairie species studied have root systems that penetrate to depths between 1.5 and 6 m. Prairie ants are active to 3 m, and prairie dogs are known to burrow to more than 4 m.

The floor subdivision of the grassland community contains basal portions of the vegetation, including particularly the rhizomes of the grass plants partially covered by litter and debris of both animal and plant origin. A characteristic group of animals in which insects, spiders, reptiles, and rodents are prominent join with the plants to form this subdivision of the community. Most of the animals inhabiting the grassland floor also usually invade one or both of the other subdivisions. The herbaceous stratum of this biocenose consists of the upper parts of the grasses and herbs and a characteristic assemblage of animals. The vertical dimension of this subdivision is variable, according to the plant species and the local conditions. The area may be covered by sparse, rosetted grass only a few centimeters in height or by coarse tough species growing 2 or even 3 m high. The animals of the herbaceous subdivision include a wide variety of insects, birds, and ruminants.

Stratification of land communities reaches its greatest complexity in the forest. Five vertical subdivisions of the forest biocenose are typically present, namely: the (1) subterranean, (2) forest-floor, (3) herbaceous, (4) shrub, and (5) tree strata (Fig. 11.8). Each of these may exhibit certain further subdivisions in particular situations, and the air above the forest canopy is sometimes considered to comprise a recognizable division of the community. Allee (1926) distinguished 8 strata in the tropical rain forest of Barro Colorado Island. The subterranean layer of the forest is typically damp and contains a large amount of humus that in extreme cases may be prominent to a depth of 2 or 3 m. The effective depth of the subterranean division of the forest community is difficult to determine but in wet forests it appears to be definitely shallower than in dry prairies. The adequate supply of water near the surface, the availability of nutrients, and the inability of roots to penetrate into poorly

aerated soil influence the depth of root growth. In the temperate
forest the tree roots may extend to depths of 3 m, but the bulk of
root development occurs in the upper meter. Animal activity is most
intense in the upper half meter but the larger burrowing forms penetrate to depths of several meters.

FIG. 11.8. Stratification of vegetation in a deciduous forest of the temperate
region. The vertical subdivisions of the biocenose are: (1) subterranean, (2)
forest-floor, (3) herbaceous, (4) shrub, and (5) tree strata.

The forest floor is a complex subdivision of the biocenose in which
great biological activity goes forward involving the decay of plant
material and a web of predator-prey and parasite-host relationships.
Huge numbers of invertebrates inhabit fallen logs and other material
on the forest floor, and they are preyed upon by carnivorous beetles
and hunting spiders as well as by higher animal types. Saprophytes,
including the familiar mushrooms and bracket fungi, are particularly
characteristic here but mosses and other low growing green plants
may be abundant. In general the density of the population of the
floor stratum in the forest is higher than it is in grassland and higher in
warmer climates than in colder climates.

The subdivisions of the forest biocenose above the ground are variable and are determined by the arrangement of the vegetation, but in most instances herbaceous, shrub, and tree strata are distinguishable. The herbaceous stratum varies in height up to a meter or so and frequently overlaps with the shrubs that extend to heights of perhaps 1 to 5 m. The tree stratum occurs between heights of 5 and 15 m in the typical oak forest, but it extends to 25 or 30 m in the coniferous forest and to about 40 m in the rain forests, with individual large-crowned trees towering to 50 m or more. The upper limit of the forest canopy in groves of giant redwoods may surpass 100 m. The herbaceous stratum is poorly represented or absent in some instances as, for example, under a thick stand of pines or spruce, and the shrub stratum may vary greatly in prominence. On the other hand, the tree stratum may be elaborately developed and divisible into sublayers. The trees of the rain forest on the Gold Coast of Africa display a stratification that extends from a height of 2 m or so to about 40 m (Foggie, 1947).

The herbaceous, shrub, and tree strata are each inhabited by a characteristic assemblage of epiphytes and epizoans. Herbivorous insects and web spiders are particularly abundant in the herbaceous stratum. In the higher strata numerical superiority is held by the insect group in enormous variety but snails, lizards, snakes, frogs, arboreal mammals, and many kinds of birds are also present in greater or lesser abundance. Most of the species are primarily associated with one of the principal strata—or perhaps with one of the subdivisions of the tree stratum—but individuals of many of the species range above or below their usual abode.

In certain aquatic habitats vertical gradients in environmental factors cause a recognizable stratification among the members of the community. Such layering may have dimensions of less than a meter in shallow ponds, or it may involve strata many meters thick in the open ocean. Mention has been made in earlier chapters of the sharp limits commonly found for the vertical ranges of attached plants and animals in the littoral zone, and particularly in the tidal zone, as a result of the rapid change in water and light conditions. Where these sessile organisms exert a controlling influence on a variety of dependent species, they cause subdivisions of the community to be formed that may be directly observed (Stephenson and Stephenson, 1949).

The stratification of benthic communities at greater depths is not so easily recognized, but it is being investigated by means of dredges and underwater cameras, and by divers with aqualungs. The situation for communities in the free water contrasts with that for communities on the bottom or on land in the absence of members that are fixed in position. Since the pelagic plants and animals are free to drift or to swim vertically as well as horizontally, subdivisions of the pelagic community are less well defined and are more flexible than those determined by sessile algae or rooted vegetation. Nevertheless, critical changes in the physical environment, as at the lower limit of the photic zone, at the thermocline, at a density discontinuity, or at the margin of an oxygenless stratum bring about a definite stratification within many pelagic communities.

Many investigations have been made in marine and fresh-water environments of the vertical distribution of various taxonomic groups among the plankton, fishes, and benthic organisms. Summaries may be found in such reference works as Welch (1952) and Sverdrup et al. (1942). However, relatively little study has been undertaken of the vertical subdivisions of aquatic communities as functional units. Certain zones of functional dependence are known to exist at various levels along the bottom and in the free water. One such unit of interdependence is formed by the plankton and the fishes of the well-illuminated surface waters, another is composed of the fishes and invertebrates inhabiting the bottom in deep water, and several others may be distinguished at intermediate levels. More intensive study will be required of the interdependencies among all the inhabitants of each stratum before specific functional subdivisions of pelagic communities can be clearly delineated.

Although recognizable stratification does not exist in all communities, its presence is sufficiently common in aquatic situations as well as in terrestrial areas for it to be considered a general characteristic of community structure. Spatial organization may thus be added to the other attributes of the community that have been reviewed in this chapter. Each community has been shown to have a composition and an integration among its members that separate it from neighboring communities. The degree of dominance within the community and the nature of the ecotones between these units of plant and animal life vary greatly from one situation to another. All these characteristics allow the community to maintain itself as a recognizable unit in a specific area for a period of time. Circumstances that sooner or later may cause the replacement of one community by another or that may bring about fluctuations within the community will be considered in the next chapter.

12

Succession and Fluctuation

In the previous chapter the nature of the community was discussed as a characteristic group of plants and animals inhabiting an area. The typical community maintains itself more or less in equilibrium, but the members of the community are never in complete balance with each other or with the physical environment. Changes in the environment over a period of time are produced by variations in climatic and physiographic influences and also by the activities of the plant and animal inhabitants themselves. These modifications of the habitat may cause sufficient changes in the dominant species so that the existing community is replaced by a new community, or they may cause marked fluctuations in the abundance of certain species within the same community. In this chapter we shall consider the progressive changes in communities leading to a relatively stable type of community, the classification of communities, and the oscillations within the community.

ECOLOGICAL SUCCESSION

Progressive changes in communities take place from one geological epoch to another and also within much shorter periods of time. Detailed consideration of large-scale changes in the fauna and flora, such as those caused by the passage of an ice age or the uplifting of a mountain range, or those resulting from the evolution of new species, is beyond the scope of our present task; such alterations in the biota have great long-term significance, and they are discussed in treatments on paleontology, climatology, biogeography, and evolution (Shapley, 1953). Here we shall concern ourselves primarily with the replacement of one community by another in particular areas and within the same general climatic conditions.

Observation has revealed the fact that in given biotopes certain communities tend to succeed one another. The occurrence of a relatively definite sequence of communities in an area is known as *ecological succession*. The change in the communities may be due in part to independent physiographic changes such as alteration of drainage, erosion, or deposition, but more especially it is caused by modifications produced by the action of each community on its own environment. The two types of causes are frequently operating together, as is seen, for example, in the replacement of a pond community by a marsh community. The filling of the pond is brought about by the deposition not only of a certain amount of inorganic silt, but also of a large amount of the organic remains of successive communities, and the accumulation of both types of deposit is enhanced by the presence of the roots and stems of the living community members.

The extent to which ecological succession is self-induced—as distinct from being caused by changes imposed from without—varies greatly in different situations. Similarly, the predictability of the course and speed of succession is variable. In many instances the presumed course of succession is based on inference derived from studies of surrounding areas so that "space is substituted for time"; but in other instances, some of which are described below, the nature of the succession is substantiated by actual records. Self-induced ecological succession is another outstanding example of the organism and the environment acting as a reciprocating system.

Living things modify their own habitat so as to cause one community to give way to another in a variety of ways. All species of animals and plants tend to increase in numbers and/or in size. The conditions of the community consequently change because of the growth of the inhabitants even without any change in species composition. Consider a forest, for example. As the trees increase in size, they provide more shade, higher humidity, and different conditions of food and cover. New types of animals find suitable conditions here; old forms may be eliminated. Wildlife managers have come to realize that the carrying capacity of a forest area for game changes with time because the availability of food and shelter in a stand of saplings is entirely different from that in a stand of mature trees.

When populations grow in respect to numbers or size of individuals, or both, the total weight of living material in the area tends to become larger. As predators and parasites increase in numbers, they tend to reduce the abundance of their prey, but as food becomes scarcer the consumers in turn are curtailed. At the same time the community causes changes in the physical nature of its biotope. Plants withdraw material from the soil as they grow and return it when they die, but the material returned to the soil is not in the same form. Humus accumulates, *p*H changes, moisture content is modified, and other alterations of the environment discussed in previous chapters are brought about.

The changed conditions caused by the varied activities of the inhabitants of the area may favor the growth of species other than those that have been dominating the scene. When this occurs, different species will soon get the upper hand. These may either be species already present in a subordinate capacity, or invaders from the outside. As one or more species take over the dominant position, a new community will be formed; its establishment constitutes a step in the ecological succession of the area.

Dispersal and Invasion

The establishment of the pioneer community on a bare area and the replacement of this community and of subsequent communities as ecological succession goes forward are dependent in the first instance upon the existence of means by which new species can reach the area. The ways in which animals and plants can invade new areas are extremely varied. Certain non-motile forms may be carried by wind or water currents for great distances; other species ride as hitchhikers on or in the bodies of various larger animals. The action of the air and water media in providing dispersal and the many special adaptations of eggs, seeds, and adults for transportation have been described in earlier chapters.

The organism's own locomotion is responsible for the dispersal of many animals and of some motile plants. The success with which the starling extended its permanent breeding range westward in the United States from its point of introduction is indicated in Fig. 12.1. The great distances traveled by ducks after the breeding season and before undertaking the southward migration to winter grounds have already been mentioned (Fig. 9.19). Many other species probably wander radially from the breeding grounds in similar fashion before going to their winter quarters. Animals with such ample powers of dispersal can push rapidly into new areas suitable for their permanent invasion. Although other animals cannot travel at such speeds as those represented by the flight of birds, their incessant pressing against their boundaries nevertheless accomplishes wide dispersal over a period of time. Even non-motile animals and plants are able to extend their ranges with surprising rapidity when conditions are suitable.

Barriers. Against this insistant pressure for dispersal, *barriers* exist that retard or prevent the movement of certain species. Ecological

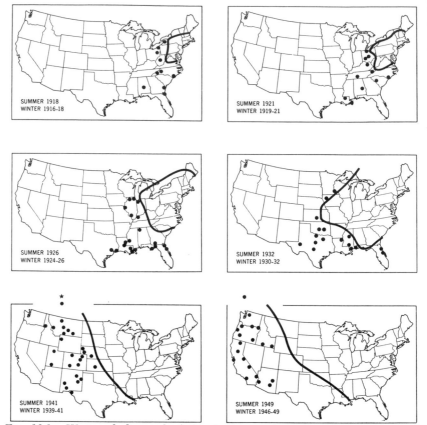

FIG. 12.1. Westward dispersal of the starling as shown by advancing limit of breeding range (solid line) and winter records (black dots) outside the breeding range. Star indicates unusually advanced breeding record in 1934. (Kessel, 1953.)

barriers may be either physical or biological. The action of many physical barriers is easily understood since they may be too wide to cross all at once and unsuitable as a way station because of local conditions. A great expanse of salt water or of dry land acts as an effective barrier against the dispersal of fresh-water forms. A rugged mountain range is a barrier preventing the dispersal of plants that require a warm, moist soil for their growth.

Biological barriers are sometimes more obscure in their mode of operation, but they may be equally effective in preventing the spread of certain species. The action of biological barriers is perhaps most easily seen when larger plants are involved. If an extensive area is completely occupied by trees, for example, other species of trees with closely similar ecological requirements cannot enter the area. If the forested area is large, the dispersal of the other species will be stopped unless their seeds can be carried over or around the barrier. In the same way a grass sod acts as a biological barrier to the dispersal of other herbs from adjacent areas. Undisturbed prairie grass regularly prevents the invasion of trees even though in some situations the climate can "support" trees once the prairie sod is broken. Communities in which all available space for certain types of organisms has been occupied are termed *closed communities* as far as these kinds of organisms are concerned. Although these communities thus prevent the invasion and the dispersal of certain species, they may allow species of very different requirements to enter.

Ecesis. In order for new species to invade an area they not only must have some means of reaching the new locality but also must be able to grow and reproduce under the conditions found there. Ordinarily the first invaders of a bare area are plants, and for them the physical features of the soil and the climate are of primary importance in determining whether or not *ecesis,* or successful establishment, can take place. The pioneer assemblage—usually of plants—first establishing itself in a new area is sometimes referred to as a *colony* but care should be taken to avoid confusion with the use of the same term for groups of social animals. After the ecesis of the pioneers other species will arrive at the area and will gain a foothold if they can. The presence of certain plants is usually a primary factor in determining whether or not invading animal species will be able to establish themselves. Accordingly, the first animals to arrive will be primarily concerned with whether the vegetation which they find is suitable. The general dependence of the distribution of animals upon that of plants is not limited to the early stages of colonization, but applies in more advanced communities, especially in the terrestrial environment.

Later arrivals at the area being invaded must be able not only to tolerate the physical conditions but also to compete successfully with the species already present if they are to establish themselves. The absence of a species in a given area does not necessarily mean that it could not live there as far as the climatic and edaphic conditions are concerned. Finally the newly established species will be forced to defend themselves against additional invaders that continue to arrive. The success with which a species can extend into a variety of new regions depends on its ability to tolerate widely different ecological influences—both physical and biological.

After the invading species becomes established in a new biotope, it may undergo genetic changes. This will further complicate or modify the situation and the effects of such alterations in the inherent nature of the members of the community must be taken into account, especially in any study of an area extending over many generations of the inhabitants. The consequences of mutation and hybridization and the effects of isolation are topics beyond our present scope and the reader is referred to specific treatments such as those of Mayr (1942), Cain (1944), or Anderson (1949).

In summary we observe that from the point of view of the species a tendency for dispersal is always present. When pioneers reach a new area, a struggle for establishment takes place, and, if the struggle is successful, genetic modification or evolutionary change may ensue. Looking at the same process from the point of view of a specific area we may observe the change of inhabitants as time passes. If we watched one spot for a long period of time, we would witness a succession of communities—each one formed from new arrivals, allowed to flourish for a while, and then replaced by a new community.

Succession and Climax

The species that have successfully invaded a biotope dominate the scene for a period and form a closed community; further arrivals cannot at first establish themselves. However, in the course of time conditions become altered with the result that the members of the existing community no longer compete successfully with the invaders. A new dominant type gains a foothold, and a new community succeeds the old. By the modification of the environment one community puts itself at a disadvantage and gives way to another; communities appearing at later stages of ecological succession are established partly or chiefly because of the modifying action of earlier communities.

One community continues to follow another until in many situations a type of community is reached that cannot be displaced under the prevailing conditions. The community that can maintain itself indefinitely in each biotope is known as the *climax*. In other situations doubt exists as to whether the communities would ever be undisturbed for long enough to enable an equilibrium condition or climax to be reached. For example, waterways in the black spruce muskeg of Alaska cause melting of the frozen ground with a consequent destruction of the spruce vegetation through the caving in of the surrounding terrain and a conversion of the area to treeless bogs. In time the spruce forest with frozen ground becomes reestablished and the cycle appears to continue indefinitely (Drury, 1952). In such situations the whole area might be considered as being in the climax condition and the alternation of vegetation types merely fluctuations within the climax. Possibly analogous fluctuations or cyclic changes in the fauna and flora occur in the oceanic community. This type of fluctuation within communities that are apparently in the climax condition will be further discussed in the latter part of this chapter.

When a climax community has become established, it tends to remain in possession of the area because it does not change the environment so as to injure itself or to favor the growth of different dominant species, and because its members can resist all competition from the outside. The succession of communities leading to a recognized type of climax is termed a *sere*. Seres composed of different sequences of communities typify different situations.

On land the type of climax community in which the sere culminates is often determined primarily by the climate, and similar climax communities dominated by plants often extend over large regions. In local areas with special edaphic or physiographic conditions, or subject to recurring fire or disease, a type of community different from the surrounding region may be displayed. Clements (1936) and his followers originally believed that given sufficient time every local area would eventually develop the same type of climax community—the type characteristic of the region as a whole under the prevailing climate, and that the continuing existence of a different type of community in a local area was due to "arrested succession." Subsequently ecologists have abandoned the strict application of the monoclimax theory based on climate alone, and many have adopted a polyclimax theory in which the type of community that maintains itself in each area is regarded as the climax for that area. Since communities do not form a sharply delineated mosaic but grade into one another with many variations of species composition according to local conditions, Whittaker (1953) has proposed a climax pattern hypothesis in which "vegetation is conceived as a pattern of populations, variously related to one another, corresponding to the pattern of environmental gradients."

The climax community remains in possession of the area until some unusual change causes its displacement. The biotope and its biota may be completely destroyed by a cataclysm such as a volcanic eruption or extensive erosion; serious but incomplete destruction may result from a forest fire, flood, or hurricane. On the other hand, the climax community may be displaced less violently by removal of the dominant species through lumbering or the attacks of parasites.

Types of Succession

Primary Succession. Ecological succession that begins on a bare area where no life has existed, or where the previous fauna and flora have been completely destroyed, is known as *primary succession.* Habitats that become available for initial colonization include: new islands, sand bars, deltas, or glacial moraines; recently formed ponds; fresh alluvial, shore, or volcanic deposits; and various types of substrata exposed by erosion. These diverse areas may be classified as xeric, mesic, or hydric according to whether the initial moisture conditions are dry, intermediate, or wet. Seres starting from these types of situations represent *xerarch, mesarch,* and *hydrarch* succession, respectively.

A striking example of primary succession, and a classical one, is the hydrarch succession in which a pond and its community is converted to dry land with an entirely different community. The vegetation rooted along the margins of the pond is able to push out from shallow water into deeper water in a variety of ways (Fig. 12.2). As the vegetation invades the open water, the margin of the pond is reduced. At the same time the growth of the plankton and of other aquatic organisms adds organic matter, and much of this is deposited on the bottom. Beavers, muskrats, and other animals carry material into the pond, deciduous vegetation blows in from the shore, and silt is carried in from surrounding land. Rafts of vegetation from the pond margin drift offshore, strand, and take root, thus establishing islets that grow in size until they meet and also join the shore. At the same time the area available for completely aquatic plants, such as the water lilies, becomes reduced. As the free water is changed to swampy land, the water lilies and similar species give way to sedges and rushes, and these are subsequently replaced by heaths and shrubs. As succession continues, the soil is further built up, so that it becomes drier and is also changed chemically. In time certain smaller species of trees invade the area, taking the place of the shrubs, and eventually full-sized forest trees will dominate the scene. Various stages in such a succession are shown in Fig. 12.3.

The existence of zonation in a community does not necessarily mean that succession is going on since distinct horizontal subdivisions may occur in a static community, as described in the previous chapter. Furthermore, the change in the vegetation is not always self-induced but may be caused by outside influences. Sometimes the conversion of a swamp to dry land is brought about primarily by a lowering of the water table caused by a physiographic change. But in other instances, as in the situation described in the preceding paragraph, the vegetation itself is chiefly responsible for building up the land as ecological succession goes forward.

At the same time that the vegetation is undergoing these profound changes in the hydrarch succession, the animal life of the community is correspondingly altered. Fish, beavers, and muskrats will gradually be excluded and terrestrial vertebrates will enter. Less conspicuous but just as significant will be the manifestations of succession among the invertebrates and the microorganisms. These trends in the animal members of the community are indicated schematically in Fig. 12.4 for a hydrosere in Illinois. The changes in bird species associated with a hydrarch succession are shown in Table 19. The changes in the

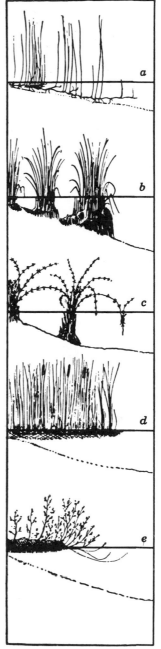

FIG. 12.2. Five methods by which vegetation invades deeper water from the pond margin: (a) spike rush, (b) tussock sedge, (c) loosestrife, (d) cat-tail flag, and (e) sphagnum and heath. (Needham & Lloyd, 1937, Copyright, Cornell Univ. Press.)

433

F<small>IG</small>. 12.3.   Hydrarch succession in Gifford Bog, Falmouth, Massachusetts.   Pond lilies (*Nymphaea*), bulrushes (*Scirpus*), and masses of filamentous algae fill in the open water.   Cassandra or leather leaf (*Chamaedaphne*) forms islets and also invades the bog at its margin, where it is followed by sweet pepperbush (*Clethra alnifolia*) and later by forest vegetation.

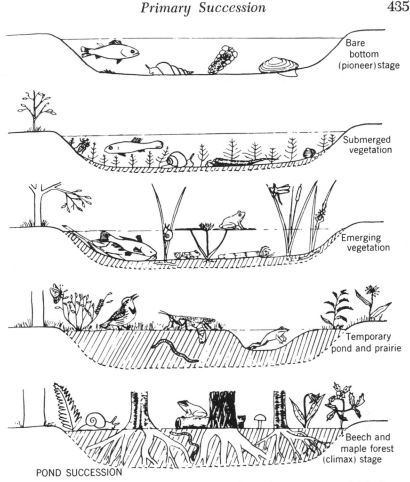

POND SUCCESSION

Fig. 12.4. Schematic representation of some of the changes in animal life during successional stages from pond to forest in Illinois. (Buchsbaum, 1937.)

insect members of seral communities leading to a red oak-maple climax are discussed by Smith (1928).

Secondary Succession. When a natural area is disturbed so as to destroy the community inhabiting it and to set back the course of succession, the new series of communities tending again toward the climax constitutes *secondary succession*. This situation arises when the principal species of the community have been destroyed by fire, disease, tornado, flood, or by human activities such as farming or lumbering. In some instances of secondary succession a community is established that is essentially the same as a stage in the previous primary succession, but in other instances a quite different community is brought into being by the special conditions resulting from the disturbance. However, later stages tend toward the type of community found in the primary succession, and ordinarily the same climax is eventually reached.

An admirable illustration of secondary succession may be observed today in old fields of central New England, and the phenomenon occurred on a large scale during the last century when wholesale farm abandonment took place. The early settlers of this region cut down the forests to build farms and homesteads. Where the land was intensively cultivated, the stumps and roots of the forest trees were

TABLE 19

REPRESENTATIVE SPECIES OF BIRDS PRESENT IN VARIOUS STAGES OF A
TYPICAL HYDROSERE IN NORTHEASTERN OHIO TO SHOW THE CHANGE IN
BIRD LIFE THAT ACCOMPANIES THE CHANGE IN VEGETATION
(Aldrich, 1945)

Stage / Bird Species	1 Water Lily	2 Loose-strife-Cattail	3 Button-bush-Alder	4 Maple-Elm-Ash	5 Beech-Maple
Pied-billed grebe	S	S			
Common mallard	X	S			
Virginia rail		S	X		
Long-billed marsh wren		S	X		
Eastern red-wing		S	S		
Eastern swamp sparrow		S	S		
Eastern kingbird			S		
Alder flycatcher			S		
Eastern yellow warbler			S		
Catbird			S	X	
Eastern goldfinch			S	X	
Northern yellow-throat			S	S	
Mississippi song sparrow			S	S	
Northern blue jay				P	
Eastern hairy woodpecker				P	P
Northern downy woodpecker				P	P
Eastern wood pewee				S	S
Eastern white-breasted nuthatch				P	P
Black-capped chickadee				P	P
Tufted titmouse				P	P
Red-eyed vireo				S	S
Eastern oven-bird				S	S

X = present at times; P = permanent resident; S = seasonal.

completely removed from the soil, and the cleared areas were planted
to crops or used as pastures.   Beginning shortly after 1830 the opening of rich farmlands in the west, the building of railroads, and the
growth of industrial centers, brought about the exodus of the farmer
from the rocky hillsides of New England that were so difficult to work.
The abandoned fields were covered by a thick sod of grass.   In this
turf the seeds of white pine trees blown from neighboring forested
areas found a favorable environment for germination, but other forest
trees were not able to establish themselves effectively in the abandoned fields.   The result was that the white pines grew into a dense,
uniform stand, and eventually produced a forest in which all the
dominant trees were of this species.   A few hardwood saplings later
became established as an understory throughout the pine forest, but
their further growth was suppressed by the pines.

In the course of fifty years or so, the pines had grown to a size that
made a valuable timber harvest possible.   Great areas were lumbered
off; in regions where lumbering was not carried out the even-aged
trees grew old and finally fell.   In both situations the trees which
then grew into dominant position were not white pines but were
hardwood trees that had existed in subordinate position almost unnoticed in the pine forest.   Pines will not sprout from stumps, and,
being an intolerant species, the pine seedlings are unable to develop
in the shade of the mature trees (Fig. 12.5).   The root sprouts and

Fig. 12.5.   View of the forest floor in a stand of mature white pines in southern
New Hampshire, showing the absence of pine seedlings but the presence of beech
and maple saplings.

seedlings of beech, maple, and other tolerant species that existed as minor members of the community grew into mature trees when they were "released" by the removal of the pines. White pine stands formed in abandoned fields of New England were therefore not self-perpetuating. Once the mature pines were gone, the species composition of the forests changed completely, and gave way to a community of mixed hardwoods. Thus, secondary succession originating in old fields of this region produces a transient community of pines but eventually results in the restoration of the typical climax forest.

Convergence. Since the bare areas in which primary succession can be initiated are extremely diverse, it is not surprising to find a correspondingly great variety in pioneer communities. As succession proceeds, however, the different biotopes tend to be modified toward a more nearly uniform condition that will support similar communities. This convergence is particularly clear in relation to the moisture factor—seral communities cause hydric habitats to become drier, and xeric habitats to become moister, so that a trend toward a more nearly mesic condition is followed from either extreme. As a general principal we recognize a convergence in succession such that seres originating in diverse habitats within a region of similar climate tend to progress toward similar climax communities.

An examination of succession in the deciduous forest region of Indiana revealed a tendency to converge that could be traced in seres originating from five kinds of biotopes as shown in the scheme on page 439 from Clements and Shelford (1939). Pioneer communities established on a sand ridge, clay bank, flood plain, shallow pond, or deep pond initiated the successions indicated by the serial numbers with the dominant plants named. The exclusive presence, or relative abundance, of a dominant plant served as a *seral index* to the stage of succession in each sere. An animal species characteristic of each stage could also be recognized, and the names of these animal seral indices appear in the diagram. Succession in each of the widely different original areas tended to bring about the eventual establishment of the same type of climax community in which beech and sugar maple trees and the salamander, *Plethodon cinereus*, are the indices.

Succession in Special Habitats. The instances of succession discussed above are typical of broad areas in temperate regions. Other manifestations of succession occur in special habitats—either large or small. A classical example of succession in a microhabitat is the sequence of bacteria, protozoans, and other microorganisms that follow one another in a hay infusion formed by allowing hay to rot in a quantity of water. The seasonal succession of different kinds of

CONVERGENCE IN SUCCESSION IN INDIANA

SAND RIDGE

1. Cottonwood
   Cicindela lepida
2. Jack pine
   C. formosa generosa
3. Black oak
   Cryptoleon nebulosum
4. White oak-Black oak-Red oak
   Hyaliodes vitripennis
5. Red oak-White oak
   Cicindela sexguttata

5. Hickory-red oak
   Cicindela sexguttata
4. Elm
   Panorpa venosa
3. River maple
   Helodrilus caliginosus
2. Willow
   Succinea ovalis
1. Ragweed
   Tetragnatha laboriosa

FLOOD PLAIN

CLAY BANK

1. Bare ground
   Cicindela limbalis
2. Shadbush
   Polygyra monodon
3. Cottonwood
   Polygyra monodon
4. Hop-hornbeam
   Fontaria corrugatus
5. Red oak-Hickory
   Cicindela sexguttata

BEECH-SUGAR MAPLE

   Plethodon cinereus
5. Soft maple-Tulip
   Plethodon cinereus
4. White elm-White oak
   Anguispira striatella
3. Buttonbush
   Asellus communis
2. Cattail-Bulrush
   Chauliodes rastricornis
1. Water-lily
   Musculium partumeium

SHALLOW POND

5. Birch-Soft maple
   Plethodon cinereus
4. Tamarack
   Hyla crucifer
3. Poison sumac
   Hyla versicolor
2. Cattail-Bulrush
   Sistrurus catenatus
1. Water-lily
   Musculium partumeium

DEEP POND

phytoplankton and of zooplankton in natural waters is in part caused by temporary modification of the medium by the organisms themselves and in part by seasonal changes in the physical environment, as discussed in Chapters 8 and 13. The special circumstances of succession in arctic areas in which the substratum is repeatedly disturbed by frost action are described by Hopkins and Sigafoos (1951).

Succession on a small scale, but of a complex nature, takes place on and in the trunks of fallen trees. The sound wood, cambium, and bark are first attacked by a group of boring insects, saprophytic fungi, and various kinds of microorganisms. This pioneer assemblage is followed by a series of more elaborate communities that cause and accompany the further disintegration and decomposition of the tree trunk. The presence of these organisms attracts predators and scavengers until a very large number of species may be represented in the dead-tree-trunk biotope. Mosses, lichens, ferns, and, later, higher plants find the rotting log a favorable substratum for growth. With the establishment of autotrophic plants a new cycle of constructive growth begins, in which the new pioneers take root literally as well as figuratively from the remains of the previous cycle.

The building up of coast lines is another activity in which the course of succession and the physiographic changes are mutually interdependent. The ecological steps involved in and following the formation of sand dunes along the southern shore of Lake Michigan as one community succeeds another have been studied by a number of ecologists. In simplest terms the course of succession was found to involve the capture of moving sand by grass, and the development of communities dominated successively by cottonwoods, pines, and oaks, leading to the beech-maple forest. Subsequent investigation has shown that the succession is far more elaborate and also more flexible than was at first supposed and that several interlocking channels for advancement or recession may be followed by the various series of communities involved, as indicated in Fig. 12.6.

Along marine coast lines in tropical regions a well-known land-building succession takes place (Fig. 12.7). Here red mangroves (*Rhizophora mangle*) work out from the shore by dropping viviparous seedlings that will root only in water more than about 25 cm deep. By means of spreading, stilt-like roots this species of mangrove can maintain itself in and slightly below the tidal zone in spite of wave action. Mud that collects around the dense jumble of roots builds up the bottom, causing the gradual elimination of the red mangrove, and prepares the way for the establishment of the black mangrove (*Avicennia nitida*), the seedlings of which will grow only in water

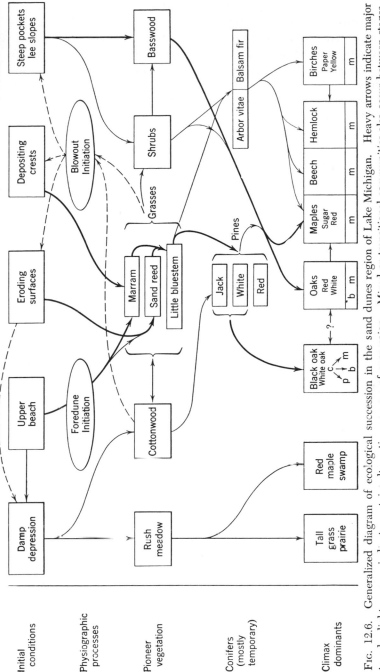

Fig. 12.6. Generalized diagram of ecological succession in the sand dunes region of Lake Michigan. Heavy arrows indicate major trends; light arrows indicate certain alternative courses of succession. Mixed or transitional communities also occur between stages. Depending on fire history and microclimate, contrasting types of undergrowth may develop under the same forest dominants: $p =$ prairie grasses and forbs, $b =$ blueberry-sedge type, $c =$ choke-cherry type, $m =$ mesophytic herbs and shrubs. Broken arrows indicate destruction of pioneer communities by blowout initiation, after which new lines of succession may begin; once started, blowouts may undermine or smother communities at any stage. (Data from J. Olson.)

shallower than about 25 cm. As the bottom is raised and the soil
becomes drier, buttonwoods replace the mangroves, and these are
subsequently succeeded by the climax palm community.

In the situations described thus far the controlling organisms are
plants. On land, plants are usually the dominant members of the
community, and vegetation development is chiefly responsible for
causing succession, but in some communities animals are found to
exert control. For example, birds nesting in colonies are sometimes
so abundant that their activities and their droppings cause a change
in the vegetation. In this way a rookery of herring gulls on Kent
Island off the coast of New Brunswick caused the elimination of a
grove of spruce trees and its replacement by grass.

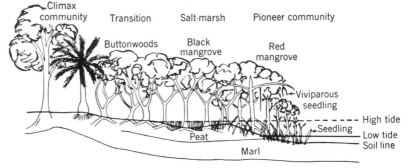

MANGROVE SUCCESSION

FIG. 12.7.   Diagram of succession along the margin of tropical shores as seen in
southern Florida.   (Modified from Davis, 1940.)

Control of the environment by animals is more commonly found
in aquatic habitats where sessile forms are prominent. The photographs in Fig. 12.8 show two stages in an all-animal warfare in the
tidal zone. Oysters became established on the sea bottom in this
biotope, but mussels soon began attaching to the oysters' shells.
Gradually the growth of the mussels smothered the oysters, and the
latter were replaced by an almost continuous carpet of mussels. Subsequently, barnacles became attached to the shells of the mussels in
sufficient numbers to kill them. After the death of the mussels their
shells broke loose from the bottom and the barnacle population was
swept away by wave action so that no enduring change was brought
about in this instance.

Frequently both plants and animals are involved in well-defined
succession in the littoral zone as described by Dexter (1947) for mud-

bottom communities; similar relationships occur on hard bottoms and on submerged surfaces subject to attack by fouling organisms. When a jetty or pier is built, or a boat without anti-fouling paint is left at her moorings, various plants and animals attach in recognizable sequences. Bacteria are the first to establish themselves, and they commonly form a film in which benthic diatoms and various filamentous algae find a foothold. The subsequent course of succession varies according to circumstances, but in some situations Bryozoa appear

From Miner, 1934

Fig. 12.8*a*. Mud flat community dominated by oysters. The shells of these animals provide a suitable substratum for the subsequent attachment of mussels.

From Miner, 1934

Fig. 12.8*b*. Mussels have overgrown the oysters and will in turn be smothered by the barnacles that are seen beginning to attach in abundance to the mussel shells.

next, followed by mussels (Scheer, 1945), whereas in other situations barnacles, tube worms, or tunicates attach at an early stage (Woods Hole Oceanographic Institution, 1952). The varied surfaces of the attached organisms, and particularly the crevices between them, provide abodes for a host of mobile forms that join the community in these later stages and that could not inhabit the biotope if it were not for the presence of the earlier arrivals. Thus, in these small habitats, as well as in the larger areas considered, the early inhabitants change the conditions so as to cause their own displacement and the establishment of successive new communities.

Modification of Succession

The course of succession may be modified by unusual natural circumstances, or frequently by the hand of man. Succession may be changed, for example, by the browsing of an overly abundant population of deer in a forest. Deer do not browse on all species of the vegetation indiscriminately but have certain favorite items. If the deer become numerous, the most appetizing plants will be grazed down excessively and the unpalatable types will be given an advantage. In this way the species composition of the vegetation and the course of succession may be considerably altered. If man permits overgrazing by cattle on the range, the usual sequence of succession may be reversed so that the vegetation is pushed back from perennial grasses to annual weeds (Graham, 1944, Ch. 9).

Repeated forest fires sometimes bring succession to a halt at a community stage that is different from the climax in neighboring areas. In the sandy soils near Plymouth, Massachusetts, and on Cape Cod the prevailing vegetation consists chiefly of pine and scrub oak, and this appears to be a climax condition determined partly at least by fire. On an undisturbed island in a large pond within this region a mature stand of beech, maple, oak, hemlock, and yellow birch has developed. This island has not been burned over during the memory of present residents, and it may well be that because of the protection of the water no fire has occurred on the island for generations. The existence of this island community suggests that other neighboring regions might progress beyond the pine and scrub oak stage if the interference of forest fires was prevented for a sufficient time. The pinelands in some parts of southeastern United States may similarly represent a climax community controlled by fire rather than by climate (Fig. 12.9).

Modification of succession by special factors may also be observed on a small scale in many local habitats. One example is furnished by the activity of certain animals in maintaining open "glades" on the surface of rocks in the tidal zone (Fig. 12.10). The browsing of limpets at the margins of their territories shears away the enlarging basal holdfasts of the red algae that would normally grow over the rock surface in the course of succession. Another animal, *Idotea viridis*, bores holes in the fronds of the algae so that they break away easily and thus assists in affecting succession in this microhabitat.

In contrast to the situations mentioned above the activities of man may sometimes add a stage beyond the usual climax. In certain parts of southern California the climax vegetation formerly consisted of grass or chaparral. When man introduced the eucalyptus from Australia, this tree established extensive stands replacing the former vegetation and adding a forest stage to the previously recognized limit to succession in the region.

Ecologists have taken such an interest in pointing out the occurrence of succession and its importance under various circumstances that emphasis has failed to be laid upon the fact that in some regions

Photo by H. B. Moore

Fig. 12.9. Pineland community in southern Florida, consisting principally of pines, palmettos, and sawgrass. After such an area is burned over, the same type of community is reestablished directly.

no succession appears to take place. Where conditions are not changed by the inhabitants of an area so as to favor other species, succession does not occur. If the existing community is destroyed in many regions of the tropics or subtropics, the area will be repopulated directly by the original species. The communities of the open ocean and of the deep sea may be regarded as being in a climax condition. Since the physical conditions of the sea—and also of large lakes—are essentially unmodifiable by the plant and animal inhabitants, no ecological succession takes place that is comparable to that found on land. In the open ocean seasonal and short-term sequences in the communities of temperate regions occur, as they do on land, but growth of marine organisms in the plankton or on the floor of the deep sea does not change the nature of the physical environment in such a way as to cause a permanent or irreversible replacement of one community by another that regularly extends beyond the seasonal cycle. For a further discussion of ecological succession the reader is referred to Oosting (1948), Allee et al. (1949, Ch. 29), and for special situations to Hutchinson (1941), Dansereau (1951), and Niering (1953).

Photo by C. Davidson

Fig. 12.10. Open "glades" maintained by limpets (*Patella*) on rocks in the tidal zone of the Isle of Cumbrae, Scotland. The browsing of these gastropods (seen on the large rock in the foreground) curtails the invasion of the red alga, *Gigartina stellata*. Barnacles also inhabit the "glades."

COMMUNITY CLASSIFICATION

Since the community is essentially a functional unit, the size of the area occupied by the community, the number of living things included in it, and its organization are variable according to circumstances. As we have seen, the groups of plants and animals that constitute a community may be large or small, and frequently one functional group is contained within another. Furthermore, one community replaces another in the same area as ecological succession proceeds. This situation presents difficulties when we attempt to arrange communities in some sort of order since any practical classification is based on descriptive considerations such as the life form of the dominant species or their position in the terrain. The presence of some types of communities is more strongly influenced by climatic factors than edaphic factors, but for other types the reverse is true.

Studies of the arrangement of communities in hierarchies have been made chiefly in environments where plants hold the dominant position in the biocenose. It is not surprising then that common systems of classifications are based primarily on the vegetation. We shall describe the chief units into which communities are grouped, but unfortunately complete agreement does not exist as to terminology.

Community Type

Communities of a certain dominant life form, such as deciduous forests, coniferous forests, and the like, obviously compose recognizable categories. Some authorities, like Tansley (1939), regard any mature community of distinctive life form as a "formation," but other authorities, following Clements (1936), apply this term to climax communities only. Extreme difficulty is often experienced in ascertaining whether the vegetation in a given region has attained its climax condition, and for many types of investigation it is not necessary to do so. Also there seems little logic in using a different term for, say, grassland that is climax and grassland that is on its way to becoming forest. When the state of ecological succession is known, a modifier may be used for clarity by referring to the community as a climax formation or a seral formation. Until general agreement on usage is reached, it will be necessary to specify the particular sense in which the term formation is used on each occasion, or to avoid it by referring to the life form of the dominant organisms or to the *community type*. Thus we may state that the vegetation in a certain area is a seral shrub formation, is of the shrub life form, or is of the shrub community type.

The Biome

Certain communities whose dominant species have a distinctive life form have become more or less permanently established in certain climatic regions of the earth and are believed to be in the climax condition. Associated with these climax communities are communities in earlier stages of ecological succession and also communities of a type controlled by special local conditions different from the general nature of the region. Such a complex of communities, characterized by a distinctive type of climax community and maintained under the climatic conditions of the region is known as a *biome*. All animal and plant components of each of the included communities are members of the biome. The biomes constitute the great regions of the world distinguished on an ecological basis, such as the tundra, the desert, the grasslands, and the various forests.

The biome consists of a special combination or complex of communities. The essential matrix of the biome is composed of climax communities with dominants of a certain life form that give the biome its particular character. Communities of different life form are present as minor constituents of the biome. The major climax communities in the biome are of the same type but differ in species composition in different parts of the biome. The deciduous forest biome that extends across the eastern part of the United States, for example, is characterized by a community type in which deciduous trees are dominant. Major communities of equal rank in this deciduous forest biome are the oak-hickory forest of the central Atlantic states, the beech-maple forest of the Middle West, the hardwood forest of northern New England, and others of the same life form. These major climax communities that form the essential matrix of the biome have been termed *associations* by Clements and his followers. The life form characteristic of the major climax communities—and hence the general character of the biome—is determined primarily by the nature of the regional climate. Which of several major communities of the same type will be present in each part of the biome is determined by local variations in both climatic and edaphic conditions.

Within each community Clementsian ecologists recognize certain subdivisions. Geographical differences in abundance or in relationship of the dominants in the community are called *faciations*. Within a region occupied by a grass community, for example, variations in climate with latitude and with altitude result in differences in the selection of dominant species. Each of these various geographical combinations of dominants constitutes a faciation of the community. Variations of the dominant species on a more local scale when delineable are termed *lociations.*

The subdominant members of a community may also form recognizable groups. These subdivisions have been called "societies" but this term is unsatisfactory in this connection because of its specific use for highly integrated animal groups within the same species as seen in insect colonies. If we again take a climax deciduous forest as an illustration, the shrubs, seasonal herbs, and cryptogamic plants as well as the various categories of animal life may be regarded as constituting definite groups of subdominants. Many aquatic communities including benthic plant and animal groups may be similarly subdivided, but with the smaller life forms local subdivisions are not as conspicuous as in communities dominated by the larger vegetation. Subdivision of communities involving plankton and nekton are even less clearly defined because of the mobility of the medium and the organisms.

Many ecologists feel that communities and their subdivisions cannot be as clearly distinguished as suggested by the foregoing terms, and that no system of community classification is really satisfactory. Some investigators feel that each community is a law unto itself, as argued by Gleason (1926), since each is composed of whatever plants and animals have reached the area and have found conditions tolerable. As the inhabitants in each situation have grown and multiplied, the community and its environment have changed until a stable condition has been reached. If similar climax communities develop, it is because similar conditions happened to exist, but an indefinite amount of individual variation is possible.

Regardless of the method of classifying communities, each biome is found to consist of several major communities (or associations) in the climax condition and of many minor communities. Between or within the major climax communities the developmental stages of these communities can be recognized and also other community types produced by local variations in the environment. In the deciduous forest biome, for example, grass and brush communities are found that may eventually mature into forest communities. Also present are the communities of ponds, marshes, rock ledges, and sand hills that will not be converted into deciduous forest for a long time but are definite members of the biome. A certain amount of cohesion within the biome is provided by plant species common to two or more communi-

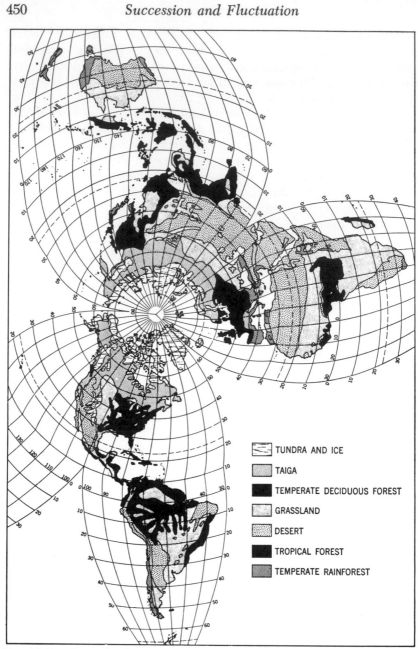

FIG. 12.11.   Generalized representation of the major biome types of the continents.   (Modified from Goode, 1943, Copyright, Rand McNally and Co.)

ties and by the mammals, birds, and other animals that move back and forth between various communities of the biome. For example, beavers are members of a pond community within a forest biome and also are members of an aspen community that borders the pond.

The biomes are the result of the equilibria established by living inhabitants with all aspects of the climate of the region. Since the biomes are characterized by major communities of distinctive life form, they correspond to certain of the life zones that are based on the same life forms. The chief biomes that occur in a series from the equator toward the poles coincide with the principal continental life zones described in Chapter 5. Some biomes tend to be continuous in extent and form a more or less definite unit, but others are discontinuous and the parts may be widely separated geographically. A specific formation of major climax communities is a biome. This kind of formation wherever it occurs is called a *biome type.*

The clearly defined major biome types of the land masses of the world are shown in Fig. 12.11. The sea may be regarded as constituting an additional biome, but the plants of the open ocean do not exert the controlling influence on the biotope experienced on land. All parts of the sea are interconnected, and many kinds of plankton and nekton move readily from one region to another. The biogeographic subdivisions of the sea are therefore based principally on physical features of the environment, as has been described in previous chapters and is further elaborated by Ekman (1953).

The principal biome types on land are: tundra, taiga, temperate deciduous forest, temperate rain forest, grassland, desert, and tropical forest. In certain regions, as in central North America, the dividing line between biomes tends to run longitudinally, but for the most part the chief biomes of the world are arranged in a general latitudinal sequence. For a fuller description of the biomes of the world the reader is referred to the general account of Cain (1944) and Allee et al. (1949, Ch. 30) and to such special treatments as Richards (1952) and Beard (1953).

FLUCTUATION WITHIN THE COMMUNITY

When the climax community has been established, can we then take a long breath and say that at last the ecosystem will be entirely constant? The answer is, No. Even within the relatively permanent and stable climax community fluctuations occur—sometimes of considerable magnitude. It is true that in some situations the community remains relatively steady. Sometimes, the life cycles of the members of the population are staggered so that little change is apparent for the community as a whole. For example, in certain tropical regions where individual trees shed their leaves at different times, the vegetation as a whole remains green throughout the year. Similarly, in tropical waters individual species of plankton in small numbers wax and wane, but the complexion of the community may continue essentially the same for long periods. At higher latitudes where climatic conditions change markedly during the year, the abundance of populations and the composition of the community vary widely with the season. Yet even here the community may in some instances come around each season to essentially the same composition as in the previous year, resulting in a rather faithful repetition of the seasonal cycle.

On the other hand, constancy within a community is the exception rather than the rule, even within the same broad climax condition. Every species in the community fluctuates to some extent in respect to rate of vegetative growth or of reproduction, and sometimes the variations are very large. In earlier chapters we have mentioned the various types of fluctuation of populations of individual species and also the reciprocal oscillations of certain populations of species exploiting one another. We shall now consider fluctuations in component species against the background of the community as a whole. All but the most minor changes in the growth or reproduction of one species of a community is bound to have repercussions among other members of the biocenose. Sometimes the fluctuations are obvious and spectacular, as in a plague of mice or of locusts; on other occasions changes in the community originate in fluctuations among the unseen microorganisms of the soil or of the water, or among pathogenic bacteria or viruses. In either case the effects on the natural community may be serious, and they often have a drastic direct or indirect consequence for man.

It is exceedingly difficult to ascertain the magnitude of fluctuations in the community in any precise terms. Attempts to take a census of wild populations have been made for a relatively small number of biotopes. Even in those instances in which a systematic count has been undertaken, the reliability of the census methods is hard to evaluate, and rarely have population measurements been continued sufficiently long to reveal significant relationships. The best available census data for extended periods are for species that are of concern to man either because they cause damage or because they provide a useful product. Records of abundance in wild populations have been kept for various disease organisms and insect pests, and for certain plants and animals harvested by man. Among the latter the most extensive records are those of trading posts for fur-bearing animals and those of fishery agencies for the landings of commercial fish. We shall discuss some ecological aspects first of irruptive fluctuations in which a population undergoes wide, irregular swings in abundance, and then of oscillations that appear to be cyclic in nature.

Irruptive Fluctuation

Data from the commercial marine fisheries will serve admirably to illustrate the circumstances of irregular fluctuation in a community. It will be agreed that the general nature of the ocean has not changed drastically during the last several hundred years or so; yet during that time certain fish populations are known to have fluctuated in an extreme manner. In the cod fishery off northern Norway, for example, periods of scarcity severe enough to be recorded have occurred as far back as the time of Leif Ericson. In certain intervening years, as in the winters of 1714 and 1715, whole villages along the Norwegian coast are reported to have starved because of the failure of the cod fishery, whereas in the years immediately before and afterward codfish were plentiful. In the same region similar fluctuations have continued to the present day, and equally extreme variations in the fisheries occurred on the American side of the Atlantic. The fluctuation in the catch of mackerel by the American fishing fleet for a period of 150 years shown in Fig. 12.12 may be taken as representative of the change in abundance of the mackerel population in the waters fished. The most spectacular change during this period occurred between

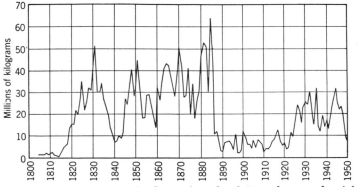

Fig. 12.12. Fluctuations in the landings of mackerel (*Scomber scombrus*) by the fishing fleet from the east coast of North America. (From data of the U. S. Fish & Wildlife Service.)

1884 and 1886 when the catch of mackerel dropped from more than 60 million kg to about 10 million kg. Subsequently the catch fell to a still lower figure but eventually rose again to a value of more than 30 million kg. The seriousness of the ecological, economic, and sociological repercussions of these tremendous oscillations can easily be imagined.

Year-Class Analysis. The economic importance of the fluctuations in the Norwegian herring fishery led the great marine biologist Johan Hjort to examine the annual differences in the population of the herring. By adopting an analytical approach to the problem he was able to trace the source of the oscillations of the entire catch to the special success of fish hatched in certain years. Hjort began by considering a hypothetical, ideal situation in which the same number of young herring were spawned each year and in which mortality caused a uniform reduction in the abundance of each "year-class." Under these circumstances 1-year-old fish would always be the most abundant, 2-year-old fish the next most abundant, and so on. Since herring of 4 years of age and older are taken in the commercial catch, an analysis of the catch under these ideal conditions would show that the 4-year-old fish were always the most numerous, the 5-year-old fish were the next most abundant, and so on.

Applying this reasoning to the catch in 1910, for example, the fish hatched in 1906 should be the most numerous, followed by the 1905 year-class, and then by earlier year-classes, provided always that the same number were spawned each year and underwent the same mortality. When the age composition of the actual catch in 1910 was examined, however, a very different picture was presented, as shown in Fig. 12.13. The 1906 year-class, which was 4 years old in 1910, was by no means the most abundant, but occurred in extremely small numbers, and the 1904 year-class was found to represent more than 80 per cent of the catch. Looking back in the diagram we see that the 1904 year-class dominated the catch in 1909 and in 1908; this same year-class continued to dominate the catch for a good many years after 1910 and remained recognizable until 1921. No other dominating year-class appeared until 1917 when the 1913 year-class entered the scene, but in 1922 the 1918 year-class became prominent. We are confronted then with the surprising discovery that during 20 years only three year-classes were successful. A good year-class is obviously the exception; in spite of the tremendous fecundity of the fish environmental resistance is overpowering in most years. The fluctuation in the herring fishery, and in many others, is now known to be

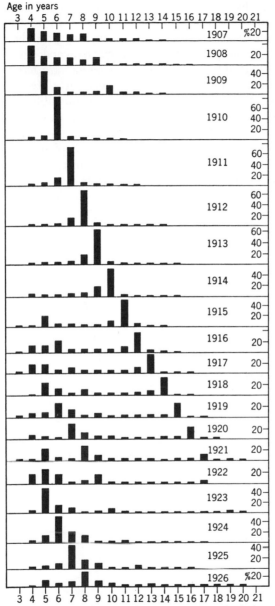

Age in years

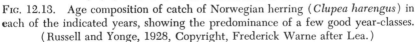

Fig. 12.13.   Age composition of catch of Norwegian herring (*Clupea harengus*) in each of the indicated years, showing the predominance of a few good year-classes. (Russell and Yonge, 1928, Copyright, Frederick Warne after Lea.)

due, in part at least, to the occasional production of a year-class in which many more fish reach commercial size than in other years.

The cause of the varying success of different year-classes is difficult to ascertain. Usually plenty of eggs are spawned every year; rarely does unusual mortality occur after commercial size has been reached. The critical point comes somewhere in very early life. Since the general nature of the ocean does not change, some subtle variation in the environment must arise during a sensitive stage of development. Perhaps an abnormal temperature in the spawning area is to be blamed; possibly a serious change in the abundance of planktonic members of the community—either enemies or food organisms for the young fish— is responsible. Quantitative measurements of plankton in various

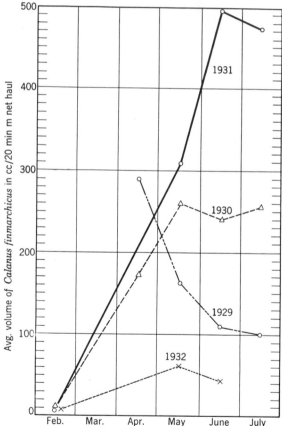

Fig. 12.14.   Annual variation in average volume per standard net haul of a common species of planktonic copepod in the waters between Cape Cod and Cape Hatteras.   (Sears and Clarke, 1940, *Biological Bull.*)

parts of the ocean have revealed great variations in abundance from year to year. As an example, the drastic differences in the seasonal growth of a population of a planktonic copepod during 1929 to 1932 are shown in Fig. 12.14. Presumably these great annual changes in the copepods influenced other members of the oceanic community, but no adequate explanation for these fluctuations in the plankton is known. Possibly the survival of young fish is dependent upon a simultaneous reduction in number of predators and an increase in availability of food. The relation between conditions favoring plankton growth and the abundance of young fish in the English Channel is discussed by Harvey (1950). Search for the factor or factors that control year-class success in specific instances is one of the many fascinating problems in ecology awaiting solution—and obviously one of great practical significance.

Cyclic Fluctuation

The fluctuations of the population in some communities appear to be regular or cyclic. The phenomenon is particularly noticeable in high latitudes of the northern hemisphere among small mammals, certain predators, gallinaceous birds, and some fish such as the salmon. The abundance of certain insect species and the rate of tree growth also exhibit cycles in various parts of the world. In addition, the occurrence of disease epidemics and other biological events are believed by some to be definitely cyclic.

Periodicity among northern mammals may be studied from the records of the Hudson Bay Company and other fur-trading agencies. As with commercial fisheries we must realize that the variations in the take by man may not represent the actual fluctuations of the entire population. Nevertheless the mass of evidence from fur traders is corroborated by other observations and leaves no doubt that oscillations of approximately uniform periods take place over long periods of time (Elton, 1942). Cycles of abundance with 3 to 4 years between peaks are exhibited by mice, voles, and lemmings, and also by arctic foxes, martens, and snowy owls. Many of these cycles can be traced back in the records for a hundred years or more. The snowshoe rabbit, the grouse, and certain insects are commonly reported to fluctuate with a 9- to 10-year cycle. Data for the Canadian lynx are available from 1735, but difference of opinion exists as to the size of the peaks that constitute maxima. If only the "big" peaks are counted, the average period of fluctuation is 9.6 years. If every year in which the population is greater than the preceding and the following year is considered to be a maximum, then analysis of the same records for the Canadian lynx yield an average of 5.8 years for the period of the cycle (Cole, 1951). Lynx populations in Finland oscillate with an average of 3.5 years for the cycle. The 10-year cycle may be interpreted as the average distance between "high peaks" of a basic cycle with maxima 3, 3, and 4 years apart, of which the maximum after the 4-year interval is larger than the others (Siivanen, 1948).

Possible cycles of other periods have been reported and are summarized by Hutchinson and Deevey (1949). The long-haired rat in western Queensland, Australia, appears to display an 11-year cycle. Irruptions of the chinch bug (*Blissus leucopterus*) between 1823 and 1940 occurred with an average period of 9.6 years for the cycle, but individual periods varied from 7 to 13 years and the outbreaks are not considered to be truly cyclic. The population of guano-producing sea birds off Peru undergo catastrophic reductions about every 7 years when the warm current "El Nino" moves farther south than usual, as described in Chapter 5.

Of a different nature is the periodicity of certain other insects in which the cycles are controlled by the simultaneous emergence of the adults after long, but often regular, periods of dormancy. Perhaps the most spectacular is the 17-year cicada (or "locust") *Magicicada septendecim* which in "locust years" swarms over the countryside but during the intervening years remains unseen as a nymphal stage in the ground. During one irruption in an oak-maple forest near Chicago these cicadas occurred at a density of 500,000 per hectare (50 per sq m), equivalent to 77 kg of dry tissue per hectare (Strandine, 1940).

Fluctuation in growth of certain trees as revealed by the width of their growth rings often appears to be definitely periodic. The records studied by Douglas (1936) revealed a recognizable cycle of 9½ to 10 years. The growth of hemlock trees in Pennsylvania, traced for over 230 years and of Douglas firs in Utah traced for about 1500 years oscillated with average cycles of almost exactly 3 years (Schulman, 1948). Nevertheless, during the period 1703 to 1939 when the data for both tree species can be compared, the fluctuations in the two series appear to be completely independent.

Causes of Fluctuation

Discovery of the causes of fluctuations in communities is one of the most desirable objectives of ecological research but also one of the most difficult. We have seen that changes in the size of population are dependent upon the interplay of biotic potential and environmental resistance. Ordinarily the full biotic potential of animals and plants in nature is not reached—environmental factors usually keep a strong check on the population. In some instances, however, even a slight variation in environmental resistance may produce a marked effect on abundance. Consider the accompanying hypothetical example for the annual recruitment of a fish population. From the point of view

Number of fish spawned each year: 1,000,000
1st year: 999,000 die; mortality 99.9%; 1000 left to catch
2nd year: 998,000 die; mortality 99.8%; 2000 left to catch
= 100% increase in number surviving

of the original number of fish spawned the variation in mortality appears to be trivial, but from the point of view of the survival of fish to form the adult population a very great difference is produced in the two sample years.

In addition to variations in physical features of the environment, changes in the living elements, including both food supply and enemies, will produce modifications of the environmental resistance. The biotic potential of the prey is usually greater than that of the predator, but the predator can destroy a much greater supply of its prey than it actually assimilates. As a result predatory animals may sometimes be the chief factor holding prey species in check. When an unusually favorable combination of both physical and biological features of the environment occurs, the species "breaks out" from its controls. If the species possesses a high biotic potential, only a short period of unchecked reproduction will cause the population to irrupt. One North American species of field mouse can breed when it is 3 weeks old and can produce 13 litters per year. A little arithmetic will indicate the size to which the population could expand if most of the young survived for a year or two. Many invertebrates, including notably the insects, can multiply even more explosively. After a population that has escaped from its usual control has increased for a period, its expansion may eventually be stopped by another set of predators, by disease, or finally by a lack of food. The maxima of snowshoe rabbits are brought to an end reputedly by a disease that causes death from shock, possibly induced by shortage of some mineral element in the diet.

Precisely which influence or combination of influences in the environment is responsible for the augmentation of a population and which brings the increase of a population to a halt or causes it to recede is extremely difficult to determine. In attempting to solve the problem as complete a knowledge as possible must be obtained of the interrelations of the species in question with all aspects of its environment at every stage in its life cycle. Apparently correlated conditions must be examined over a period of time and in different parts of the range. When it is feasible, the factor suspected of causing the fluctuation should be tested by laboratory or field experiments.

Many illustrations of the control of growth and reproduction by individual environmental factors, or combination of factors, have been given in previous chapters, and others may be found in reports dealing primarily with this topic, such as those of Shelford (1951, 1951a). Following extensive investigations of the fluctuations in certain forest and non-forest animal populations in the Middle West, Shelford emphasized the fact that environmental influences exert their control chiefly during sensitive periods in the life histories of the species concerned. Forest invertebrates, for example, were found to develop larger populations in years when rainfall is great during late March, April, and May with short dry periods, whereas for certain birds and mammals the conditions in February and March are more significant.

Origin of Cycles. Because of the lack of sufficiently precise data we cannot at present state that the fluctuation of any population is strictly cyclic in the sense that accurate prediction of the times of maxima and minima can be made well into the future. Further study of the possible existence of truly cyclic behavior is very much desired since, in addition to the theoretical interest, prediction would permit precautions to be taken against outbreaks of pests and preparations to be made for glut or scarcity of fish, game, or furs. Since fluctuation may be only approximately cyclic, we must include random variations as a possible explanation. As possible causes of these biological cycles we shall examine self-induced effects within the population, random effects of many external factors, and single controlling influences that themselves fluctuate in a random fashion or are truly cyclic.

Regular oscillation in abundance of a single species might be produced in a constant environment as the result of delays in the effects of excessive or favorable numbers. Such a population would alternately overshoot and undershoot a possible equilibrium level, as described in Chapter 9. When two or more species affect each other's abundance reciprocally, as may occur in prey-predator or host-parasite combinations, oscillations may be similarly set up, as pointed out in Chapter 10. Such oscillations caused by reactions within populations of one or more species are termed *intrinsic cycles*.

As a species becomes more abundant, its metabolites tend to accumulate and other physical and chemical changes are brought about that may curtail the reproductive rate of the population. With increased density of the population predators are attracted and disease parasites can spread more easily. As crowding continues, food and other necessities become scarcer, and the animals tend to wander more extensively. This latter fact causes the further distribution of infectious disease and exposes the animals more frequently to detection by their predatory enemies. Furthermore, with progressive reduction of the vegetation by herbivores less cover for protection against their predators is available. Thus increase in abundance may automatically cause a curtailment of the population in ways that might tend to bring about regular self-induced oscillations. However, the inevitable occurrence of other changes in the environment would be expected to impose irregularities upon any intrinsic cycle.

Approximately regular fluctuations in populations caused by independent changes in the environment—either animate or inanimate—are known as *extrinsic cycles*. Obviously intrinsic and extrinsic types of cycles are not sharply separated since many populations respond both to self-induced and independent variations in their environment. Irregularities in the environment might set in motion regular internal oscillations by a sort of resonance, just as irregular waves can cause a boat to roll in its natural period.

Scrutiny of the data on populations with apparently cyclic fluctuations has led Cole (1951) to conclude that "the oscillations of any hypothetical factor determining population size need only be about as regular as would be expected of a random variable." Since we know that the abundance of every species is affected by many environmental factors, it may be that chance combination of favorable and unfavorable influences in any year will produce apparently cyclic fluctuations. Support for this simple explanation is found in a comparison of certain fluctuations in nature with those of a series of random sampling numbers in which the former are no more convincingly "cyclic" than the latter (Fig. 12.15). Cole also urges that here, as elsewhere, the so-called "law of scientific parsimony" be applied, that is, the avoidance of a more complicated hypothesis than is actually required to explain the observed facts. However, it is unlikely that random fluctuation alone would produce cycles of the same period in widely different species.

In some instances variation in abundance or growth has been definitely related to the variation of some extrinsic factor in the environment, and no doubt many more such relationships will be found in the

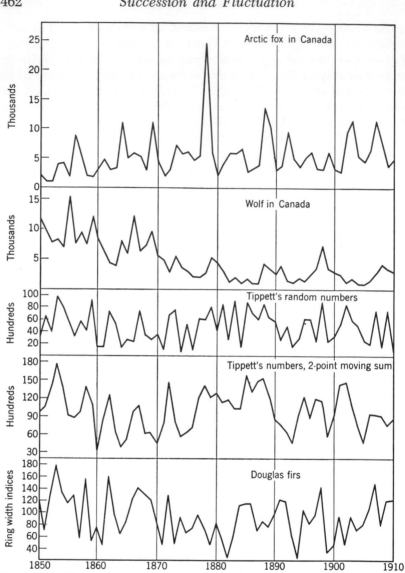

FIG. 12.15. Fluctuating series of animal populations and tree growth compared with series of random numbers. In the 2-point moving sum curve the height of each point depends upon the values of two successive random numbers, much as population size might be affected not only by conditions this year but also by the size of last year's population. (Cole, 1951.)

future. Fluctuation in populations of guano-producing birds is definitely determined by periodic influx of warm currents. The growth of Douglas fir in Utah was found to be closely correlated with precipitation, but the growth of hemlock trees in Pennsylvania during the same years with the same average cycle period exhibited no significant relation to rainfall. The oscillations of the arctic fox (*Alopex lagopus*) and of the snowy owl (*Nyctea nyctea*) are evidently timed by those of the lemmings and mouse-like rodents on which they feed. As the rodent population diminishes, the snowy owls disperse in search of food, and their periodic appearance as far south as New England attracts much interest among ornithologists (Gross, 1947). Maxima of the Canadian lynx follow those of the snowshoe rabbit by a year or so. The fact that the colored fox (*Vulpes fulva*) and the marten (*Martes americana*) exhibit a 4-year cycle in the arctic and a 9- or 10-year cycle farther south is perhaps due to a corresponding difference in the periodicity of its prey in the two regions. In at least some of these instances the fluctuations of the prey are not controlled by the predators as in reciprocating intrinsic cycles. For example, the snowshoe rabbits on Anticosti Island, where there are no lynx, fluctuate with the rabbit population on the mainland where lynx abound.

In the foregoing type of situation the apparently cyclic fluctuation of the species is not due to a random effect of many environmental influences but is controlled principally by the changes in one particular factor. The biological cycle might then be caused either by apparently cyclic random fluctuations of this controlling factor, or by a truly cyclic change in this factor. A long search has been made for a predictably regular cycle in the climate or in some other feature of the environment that might serve as a master timer for biological cycles, but no convincing and generally accepted factor has been found. Sunspots were at one time thought to be correlated with certain population cycles since their average period is about 11 years and is thus closely similar to certain cycles of growth and abundance. However, the sunspot cycle is more variable than the Canadian lynx cycle, for example, since the period of the former has varied from 7 to 17 years as against 8 to 12 years for the latter. In addition, a comparison of the two cycles from 1750 to 1935 shows that, although they correspond for a number of years, they subsequently become completely out of phase (Fig. 12.16).

A satisfactory explanation of these intriguing cycles of growth and abundance accordingly continues to elude us. These fluctuations are another manifestation of the many changes going on within the community that have been reviewed in this chapter. We have seen that

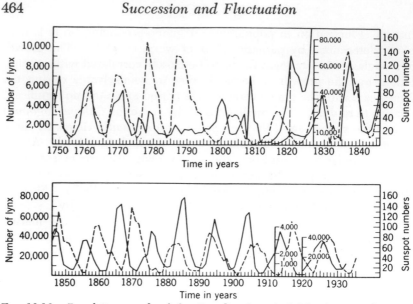

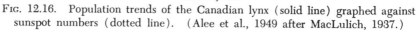

Fig. 12.16.   Population trends of the Canadian lynx (solid line) graphed against sunspot numbers (dotted line). (Alee et al., 1949 after MacLulich, 1937.)

modifications brought about by the life processes of the inhabitants in their reciprocal relations with the environment cause ecological succession to go forward from the initial colonization of a new biotope to the climax condition.   The biomes of the world represent the permanent establishment of the principal climax communities in general equilibrium with their environment.   Within these generally maintained conditions, however, many seemingly regular and many irregular fluctuations continually take place.

13

Dynamics of the Ecosystem

In the two previous chapters we have discussed the composition of communities, their progressive changes, and the fluctuations that occur among their members. We shall now consider the dynamics of the ecosystem as a whole, that is, the operation of the community and its environment as a functional unit. We shall also discuss certain quantitative aspects of the interdependencies in the ecosystem, including the concepts of productivity.

FUNDAMENTAL OPERATION

What natural situation shall we select for the study and illustration of the fundamental operation of the ecosystem? We might take the whole world as a unit. We could measure the energy received by the earth and follow its transformations; we could measure the amounts and kinds of organic matter that are elaborated. In other words, we could evaluate the earth as a mechanism for biological transformations. A study of this sort is of interest and involves subject matter treated in the field of biogeochemistry in which the distribution and transformation of biologically important materials are traced (Hutchinson, 1948). However, we are more often concerned with the operation of particular types of ecosystems, and, in any event, an investigation of the variations from place to place and from time to time would be required before an adequate summation could be made for the entire world.

In selecting an area for study we might go to the opposite extreme and investigate a single plant together with the space immediately surrounding it. Although certain relations of the exchange between the plant and its environment would be revealed, the unit studied would probably not be large enough to include all related influences. Ideally, it would be desirable to study an area that is large enough to be representative and to contain all the fundamental factors, and at the same time that is cut off from outside influences. A completely self-sufficient ecosystem rarely occurs in nature, but situations approaching this condition may be found. A balanced aquarium represents an artificially established, self-contained system in which the number and type of plants and animals are adjusted so that a glass cover can be placed over the top and the organisms within will maintain themselves indefinitely. A pond with no inlet or outlet, or with very little water exchange, may approach self-sufficiency. This idea was first set forth by Forbes (1887) in his classical essay, "The Lake as a Microcosm." In the following quotation it is clear that Forbes was thinking primarily of the animals in the lake and was not taking the complete ecosystem into consideration, but he states the essence of the concept of self-sufficiency, and his essay has become a landmark in the development of ecological thought:

The animals of such a body of water are, as a whole, remarkably isolated —closely related among themselves in all their interests, but so far independent of the land about them that if every terrestrial animal were suddenly annihilated, it would doubtless be long before the general multitude of the inhabitants of the lake would feel the effects of this event in any important way. It is an islet of older, lower life in the midst of the higher, more recent life of the surrounding region. It forms a little world within itself— a microcosm within which all the elemental forces are at work and the play of life goes on in full on so small a scale as to bring it easily within the mental grasp.

If an isolated and self-sufficient microcosm cannot be found, a habitat may be used for study in which exchanges with other areas are slight and regular, or can be measured. Thus, the living and nonliving materials entering a pond by way of the inlet and the substances being carried away by the outlet can sometimes be measured, and suitable allowance can be made. Another possibility is the study of a unit area, or unit volume, within a uniform region. The operation of ecological forces may be investigated in the ecosystem represented by 1 hectare in the middle of a large tract of forest, or in 1 sq km of grassland in range country, or in a certain area of the ocean. In these instances we know very well that the unit we select is not isolated from neighboring units, but we may assume that transfer out of our unit is compensated for by transfer into it from surrounding areas so that ecological activity within our area may be treated as if the study unit were self-contained.

Principal Steps and Components

The fundamental steps in the operation of the ecosystem are: (1) reception of energy; (2) production of organic material by producers;

(3) consumption of this material by consumers and its further elaboration; (4) decomposition to inorganic compounds; and (5) transformation to forms suitable for the nutrition of the producers. If the area is occupied by a self-sufficient community, all these steps will go on within it; otherwise materials must enter from surrounding areas. These steps in the operation of the ecosystem not only involve the production, growth, and death of the living components but also may influence the non-living aspects of the habitat. For example, considerable energy is represented in the organization of the soil that is brought about by the growth of the vegetation.

The diagram in Fig. 13.1 illustrates the fundamental steps in a self-

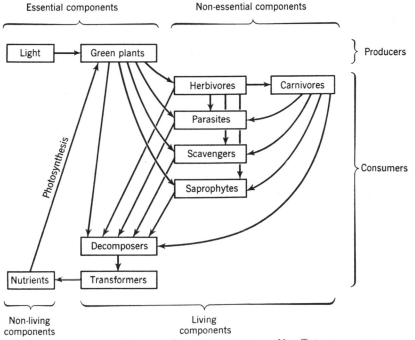

FIG. 13.1. Principal steps and components in a self-sufficient ecosystem.

sufficient ecosystem and shows the nature of the components taking part in the cycle of energy and material. The non-living components that must be present are *light energy* and *inorganic nutrients* for the growth of photosynthetic plants. The living components of the ecosystem consist of *producers* and *consumers*. The producers are represented primarily by green plants but also include synthetic bacteria. The activity of the synthetic bacteria is of minor consequence in most instances, but in specialized situations it may be of quantitative importance. The consumers include all the other types of organisms in the community. Free-living *herbivores* feed directly upon the green plants. The principal herbivores in terrestrial habitats are insects, rodents, and ruminants, and in aquatic habitats they are small crustaceans and mollusks. Since most other prominent types of animal life in the community depend upon these herbivores, the latter have been referred to by Elton (1939) as "key industry animals." The herbivores serve as food for primary *carnivores;* these in turn may fall prey to secondary carnivores, and several more stages of nutritional dependency may exist. The tissues of the various plants and animals in the community may also be eaten by *parasites,* and after the organisms are dead, by *scavengers* and *saprophytes* of many sorts. The plants and animals that depend successively one on another form the links of a *food chain.*

The dead bodies of the producers and of the consumers mentioned above are attacked by *decomposers,* consisting of bacteria and other types of fungi. The decomposers render the organic matter soluble and break it down chemically. The material is then attacked by *transformers*—other types of bacteria that change the inorganic compounds into forms suitable to serve as nutrients for photosynthetic plants once again. Among the living components only the photosynthetic plant producers, the decomposers, and the transformers are essential. Some communities could theoretically maintain themselves indefinitely without the presence of any animals whatsoever, and, although it may injure our ego to state it, we realize that man is not a necessary part of the ecosystem. However, animal life is ordinarily present in most natural communities, and sometimes animals hold a controlling position or take a prominent part in the operation of the ecosystem.

Niches. Different species of animals and plants fulfill different functions in the ecological complex. The role of each is spoken of as its *niche.* The term so used stresses the function of each organism in the community rather than its physical place in the habitat. The term originated, however, from the characteristic location of different types of organisms in the area under consideration, and niche is still used by some ecologists in this sense. The "functional niche" is more fundamental than the "place niche," but both concepts exist and should eventually be given different names.

Niche may be used in a broad sense to refer to the principal functions involved in the operation of the ecosystem, or it may be employed to describe the subdivisions of these and the various methods of "making a living" within each functional category. Among herbivores that feed on trees, for example, some fill the niche of eating the leaves whereas others use the twigs, sap, bark, or roots as a source of food. In different geographical regions each type of niche is often filled by quite different species. Activity in some niches requires extreme and often bizarre specialization of anatomy, physiology, or behavior. Minute differences in function are exhibited by the niches of birds that obtain food organisms from crevices in bark. Small woodpeckers characteristically fly to the base of a tree and climb up the trunk looking for grubs. When they reach the top, they fly diagonally downward to the base of the next tree and again work their way upward. In contrast, nuthatches common in eastern United States ordinarily fly to the top of a tree and work toward the base, clinging upside down to the trunk. In this way woodpeckers readily remove grubs and other food from crevices easily reached from below, whereas the nuthatches obtain their prey from cracks in the bark more accessible from above. In the Galapagos Islands a finch that has evolved toward the woodpecker type fills this niche, but having no barbs on its tongue it wedges grubs out of crevices by means of a thin twig held in its beak.

Trophic Levels and Relations. Each successive level of nourishment as represented by the links of the food chain is known as a *trophic level*. The plant producers within an ecosystem constitute the first trophic level, the herbivores form the second trophic level, and the primary carnivores represent the third level. Additional links in the main food chain, and in side chains such as those formed by parasites, constitute further trophic levels. Three types of pyramidal relations may be found among the organisms at different trophic levels in the ecosystem, resulting in the pyramid of production rates, the pyramid of biomasses, and the pyramid of numbers.

At each step in the food chain a loss of energy and of material from the system takes place because the processes of assimilation and growth are not 100 per cent efficient. This means that the organic matter produced per average unit of time, and the energy represented by it, become less at each successive trophic level. The production rates of the components of a self-sufficient ecosystem may thus be thought of as forming a pyramid. The base of this *pyramid of production rates* is represented by the organic synthesis of the green plant component, and higher levels are represented by the growth rates of the herbivore and carnivore components.

Frequently, the size, growth rate, and longevity of the species making up a particular ecosystem are such that the living weight, or *biomass,* of the members of the food chain present at any one time also form a second type of pyramid. In a land biotope the biomass of the vegetation existing at the moment of observation is commonly the greatest, and the biomasses of herbivores, carnivores, and further links in the food chain are progressively smaller. Thus a *pyramid of biomasses* results, but this pyramid is an indirect consequence of the particular kinds of organisms present, in contrast to the production pyramid which is a dynamic necessity in the operation of the ecosystem. In some aquatic biotopes the biomasses of some of the inhabitants form a pyramid similar to the production pyramid, as in Weber Lake, Wisconsin (Fig. 13.2), and on Georges Bank (Fig. 13.12), but in others the biomasses of fish and particularly of the

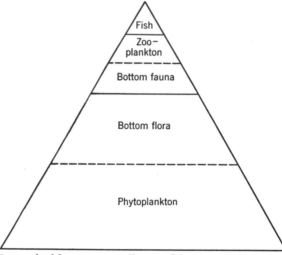

Fig. 13.2. Pyramid of biomasses as illustrated by the weight relationships of the various constituents of Weber Lake, Wisconsin. (Juday, 1943.)

bottom fauna are considerably greater than those of shorter-lived components at lower trophic levels (Harvey, 1950, Table IV). The operation of the ecosystem thus limits the relative amounts of the components that may be produced, but departures from a regular reduction in the biomasses of components present at any one time occur because of special circumstances.

Interdependencies within the ecosystem also exert a certain influence on the size of the individual organisms involved. The essential plant producers vary in size from the very largest organisms in some types of community to the smallest in others. The primary producers in different biocenoses range from giant trees, such as the redwoods, to diatoms, often less than 30 μ in diameter, and green flagellates or photosynthetic bacteria of still smaller dimensions.

The possible size of consumers is generally influenced by the size of their food, but the possession of specialized food-getting equipment enables some consumers to be very different in size from the organism that provides their nutriment. Herbivores may be either larger or smaller than the vegetation upon which they feed. Insects inhabiting forests are characteristically only a minute fraction of the size of their food plants. Some rodents are larger and some smaller than their food; crustaceans and mollusks that filter phytoplankton from natural waters are generally very much larger than the plants upon which they feed.

In the next step in the food chain, namely the subsistence of the carnivores on the herbivores, the predatory species must be stronger in some respect than its prey and is usually larger. Among animals, therefore, a tendency exists for smaller species to form the early links in the food chain and for larger species to form the later links. The maximum size of a prey species that can be attacked successfully depends upon the feeding apparatus of the predator. Thus some organisms in the community may be too large and some may be too small for the consumer to catch or to obtain in sufficient quantity.

Since total biomass tends to become smaller at successive levels in the food chain, and since size of individual generally becomes larger, at least among the animals, it follows that in the typical situation a reduction in the number of individuals comprising successive links in the food chain takes place. A relation of numbers is another consequence of the operation of the ecological complex. Among the animals of a community the herbivores are typically the most numerous; they take in food material synthesized by the plant producers and pass it on to the subsequent consumers. Primary carnivores that prey upon these "key industry animals" are less abundant, and secondary and tertiary carnivores generally exist in still fewer numbers. This numerical relationship with the more abundant species near the base of the food chain and the less abundant species near the top is known as the *pyramid of numbers*. In food chains involving parasites the size relationships are reversed because the parasite is smaller than its host, and hyperparasites must be still smaller. For this reason the pyramid of numbers is reversed for the successive steps of parasite dependency, and the parasites of each link are generally more numerous than their hosts.

An illustration of the pyramid of numbers among mammals and birds inhabiting range land is presented in Table 20. The differences

TABLE 20

ABUNDANCE OF BREEDING ANIMALS ON 1 SQUARE MILE (3 sq km), SANTA RITA
RANGE RESERVE, ARIZONA (After Leopold, 1933)

Species	Number
Coyote	1
Horned owl	2
Redtail hawk	2
Blacktail jackrabbit	10
Hognosed and spotted skunk	15
Roadrunner	20
Cattle (over 1 year old)	25
Scaled quail	25
Cottontail	25
Allen's jackrabbit	45
Gambel quail	75
Kangaroo rat (*Dipodomys*)	1,300
Wood rat (*Neotoma*)	6,400
Mice and other rodents	18,000

in abundance of the carnivores, such as the coyotes, hawks, or owls, and of the herbivores, such as the quail or the mice, are striking; an even greater contrast in numbers would have appeared if the census had included the insects and other invertebrates. An example of the pyramid of numbers on a small scale is furnished by a census of the metazoans inhabiting the floor of a deciduous forest (Fig. 13.3).

In addition to the foregoing relations of biomass, size, and num-

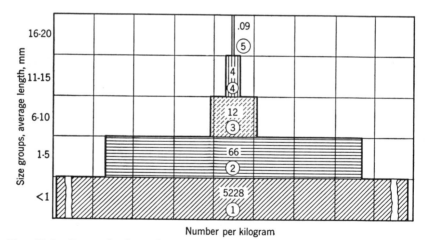

Number per kilogram

FIG. 13.3. Pyramid of numbers among the metazoans of the forest floor in a deciduous forest near Evanston, Illinois. (Park, Allee, & Shelford, 1939, Copyright, Univ. of Chicago Press.)

bers, certain aspects of availability are of crucial concern in the ecosystem. Food organisms must be sufficiently concentrated in relation to their size so that the predator can meet its nutritive requirement within the time available. In other words, the abundance of the food per unit area must be adequate in relation to the possible foraging range of the animal concerned. If there were only one lion in all of Africa and zebras lived 100 miles apart, plenty of food would obviously exist for the one lion, but he would not be able to obtain it fast enough to satisfy his needs. The same general point is illustrated by the facetious remark that in parts of Texas grass is so scarce that the cattle must feed on the run. The necessity for adequate concentration as well as for adequate total amount of food is not so immediately apparent for organisms in which feeding processes are not directly observed. The total amount of planktonic food in an oceanic area may be more than sufficient for the nutritive needs of the clams or oysters living on the bottom, but in order for these bivalves to survive the food must be concentrated to such an extent that the volume of water that they can filter in a day will furnish enough plankton to fill their daily needs.

The necessity for an adequate rate of replacement of nutritive materials is another aspect of availability in the food relations of a community. The growth of terrestrial plants is dependent not only upon the concentration of nutrient salts in the soil at the moment of observation but also upon the replenishment of these nutrients after the existing supply has been absorbed. The same dynamic dependency exists in all natural situations where the nutrition of one step in the food chain depends upon the rate of supply by the previous step. In many situations the amount of nutriment supplied per unit of time is larger than the amount of the material present at any one moment. The same argument applies to the dependency of a carnivore on a prey species. Whether or not the food organism is adequate in amount depends both on its abundance at the moment and also upon the rate of replacement of the population.

Ecological Cycle in the Ocean

The ecological cycle in temperate regions of the ocean will be used to illustrate the principles involved in the general operation of the ecosystem as well as many of the relationships discussed in earlier chapters. The open sea is especially suitable for this purpose since a sampling can be made in the middle of a large uniform area with fair assurance that no serious modification by interchange of materials from surrounding areas of a different sort will take place. As has been pointed out in earlier chapters, the ocean represents a relatively uncomplicated biotope compared to many others, particularly those in the terrestrial environment. In a volume of sea water it is possible to measure with accuracy the physical and chemical factors with which we are concerned and to enumerate the living components with sufficient precision.

Producers. In the open sea the planktonic plants are the essential producers since the reduction in light with depth prevents benthic plants from growing in important numbers in deep water. The main bulk of the phytoplankton is represented by diatoms, but green flagellates and other types of nannoplankton may also play a significant role because of their great numbers and the rapidity of their reproduction. The preponderance of unicellular plants in the oceanic community is related to the retardation of sinking rate resulting from small size and to the increased effectiveness with which widely distributed cells can absorb dilute nutrients. The zones of diatom growth are sometimes spoken of as the pastures of the sea, and the phrase current on land, "All flesh is grass," has been paraphrased for the ocean as "All fish is diatoms."

Since diatoms and other types of phytoplankton represent the producer component of the oceanic ecosystem, we shall consider briefly their typical cycle of abundance and the factors controlling it. In the temperate ocean a sudden outburst of diatom growth generally occurs in the spring months (Fig. 13.4), and this is often called the "spring

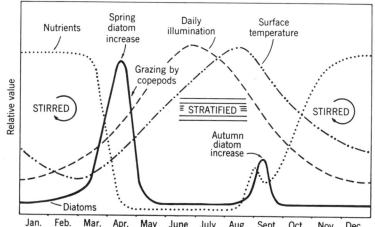

Fig. 13.4. Generalized diagram of seasonal cycle of diatom abundance and certain controlling factors in the temperate ocean.

flowering" or "bloom"—an amusing misnomer since these algae are far removed taxonomically from flowering plants. In the Gulf of Maine, for example, the number of diatoms per unit volume in the spring averages 1000 times greater than the winter population and may be over 60,000 times greater in local regions. Hardly has the diatom population reached its maximum size in March or April than numbers begin to drop off and characteristically continue to fall to a low level.

An intriguing interplay of ecological forces accounts for these enormous changes in the numbers of plant producers. The thorough stirring of the water in the upper layers of the ocean during the winter brings about a replenishment of the nutrients to the euphotic zone from the deeper levels, but the same vertical movement of water also carries the diatoms down to levels below the compensation depth. As the spring comes on, two things happen: the compensation depth extends to deeper levels because of the greater intensity of sunlight, and stirring becomes less because of the progressive stratification of the water. As a result the diatoms remain for longer and longer periods above the compensation depth, until after a time constructive growth of the population becomes possible (Sverdrup, 1953). Under favorable conditions diatoms can divide at a rate greater than once in 24 hours. Exponential growth of the population ensues and the sea may become green with diatoms within a week.

Certain definite ecological reactions bring the spring increase in phytoplankton to an end. As diatom growth goes forward, nutrients are progressively used up until their concentration drops to a point where all the plant cells are starved and either die or form cysts. Furthermore, the great abundance of diatoms has tended to reduce the transparency of the water and at the same time has provided a food supply for a new generation of zooplankton. Copepods and other herbivores "graze" on the diatoms, and, as the zooplankton increases in abundance, the diatom population is consumed at an accelerating rate.

The diatoms of the open sea characteristically remain at a low ebb throughout the summer months because the majority of dead cells decompose and release nutrients again at levels below the compensation depth. Because thermal stratification prevents deep stirring, the euphotic zone remains depleted of its nutrients during the summer. In the autumn when stronger winds and lower surface temperatures allow effective stirring to take place once again, nutrients are restored to the upper layers of the ocean. A rather sudden increase in the diatom population may then take place; this is known as the autumn "flowering" or "bloom." As the diatoms again grow in abundance, they reduce the nutrient supply concomitantly for a time. Following the subsequent complete breakdown of thermal stratification, wind stirring and reduced illumination stop diatom growth as the area returns to its winter condition once more. However, the same deep stirring during the winter brings the nutrient-rich water to the surface. This annual restoration of deep water to the upper layers gives rise to the statement that "the sea is plowed once a year."

Consumers. When we turn to a consideration of the consumer in the typical food chain of the open sea, we are confronted with a situation of special interest because of the nature of the producers. The simple fact that the plants at the base of the food chain are microscopic in size has far-reaching repercussions in the oceanic ecosystem.

(*a*) *Herbivores.* Scarcely any of the larger marine animals are able to feed directly on diatoms because of their small size. The menhaden is one of the few fish of commercial importance that can do so. The gill rakers of this species are usually long and provided with interlocking hooks that form a fine, sieve-like structure by means of which the plant cells can be filtered from the sea in sufficient quantities. The production of the menhaden thus represents a two-link food chain—the shortest possible and a rarity among the large animals of the sea in complete contrast to the situation on land. In the terrestrial environment the availability in respect to size and abundance of trees, grass, and other plant producers is such that deer, elk, sheep, and other large ruminants can feed directly on them. Thus short food chains are common on land.

Since most of the larger animals in the sea are unable to use phytoplankton as food, they must depend for their nutriment upon "middle men" or "key industry animals" of intermediate size. On the sea bottom many mollusks and other sessile invertebrates possess feeding mechanisms that enable them to filter the smaller planktonic forms from the water. In the open sea planktonic crustaceans, especially copepods and euphausiids, fill this niche. Copepods can filter out the smallest diatoms by forcing a current of water through a meshwork of bristles attached to a special set of appendages. We might think of these small crustaceans acting as miniature harvesting machines, packaging the microscopic plant cells. The filter-feeding zooplankton incorporate the substance of the diatoms and represent parcels of food of sufficient size for larger animals (Fig. 13.5).

When the importance of copepods as essential middlemen in the economy of the sea was recognized, special attention was directed toward the factors controlling the food supply of these animals.

However, food dependencies are difficult to determine, and several divergent views have been held as to the critical relations. Since observations at sea indicated that diatoms were often abundant when copepods were scarce and vice versa, some investigators argued that no direct food dependency occurred. The quandary of this apparent contradiction represents the danger of generalizing from isolated observations or from statistical tabulations of the occurrence of animals and plants without due regard to the dynamic aspect of their growth and life cycles. If diatoms are scarce at a given point where copepods are abundant, does it mean that the copepods have just finished consuming the population, or does it mean that copepods are primarily dependent upon some other source of food?

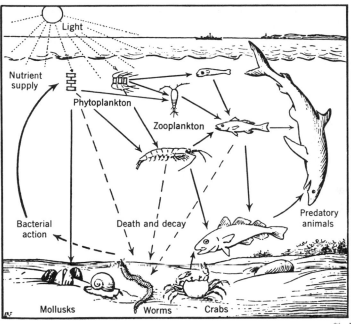

Clarke, 1943

FIG. 13.5. Simplified representation of main ecological cycle in the sea.

As data on this problem were gathered, two theories emerged. One was the *theory of animal exclusion* proposed by Hardy (1936) that high concentrations of phytoplankton are harmful to zooplankton and, therefore, that water masses containing large numbers of diatoms are actively avoided by copepods. Exclusion was originally believed to have taken place chiefly in the vertical direction and thus to curtail the upward phase of the diurnal migration of the zooplankton. Horizontal currents moving differentially at various levels would secondarily bring about a patchiness in horizontal distribution. Subsequently, the scope of the theory has been extended to include other types of exclusion of one population by another. Dense diatom concentrations might be inimical to copepods either mechanically or chemically—possibly through antibiotic effects. Such effects have been demonstrated for oysters and cladocerans in certain instances as described in Chapter 8.

At about the same time, Harvey and co-workers (1935) came forward with the *theory of grazing*, according to which copepods are believed to reduce the diatom population locally by the intensity of their feeding activity. At first sight these theories seemed mutually exclusive, but more extensive investigation has shown that the influences involved in both may be in operation simultaneously without conflict. Copepods depend upon suitable abundance of diatoms for food, but they may avoid thick concentrations of diatoms and, by grazing around the margins of diatom populations, may accentuate the patchiness in the distribution of the latter. The timing of the supply of diatom food in relation to the appearance of new broods of copepods is also critical (Clarke, 1939). Investigation of the production of *Calanus finmarchicus* in the Clyde Sea area gave evidence that those broods of this copepod which hatched during periods of diatom scarcity failed to reach maturity, whereas broods appearing when suitable diatom food was available developed successfully (Marshall et al., 1934).

Another possible source of food for copepods as the key herbivores in the oceanic food cycle is the nannoplankton. Lohmann drew attention long ago to the abundance of such representatives of the nannoplankton as the green flagellates, peridinians, other protozoans, and certain bacteria (Sverdrup et al., 1942). These organisms may occur in concentrations of millions of cells per liter, and, since they are able to divide several to many times a day, they represent a large and rapidly replaced potential food source. The fact that certain copepods at least can sieve these extremely small organisms from the sea is shown by the successful culturing of *Calanus* on flagellates 1.5 to 3 μ in diameter (Raymont and Gross, 1942); and *Calanus* can derive at least some nourishment from bacteria (Clarke and Gellis, 1935). Nannoplankton is undoubtedly of particular importance in the feeding of young stages.

Dissolved organic matter and fragments of dead organisms as detritus have also been suggested as important food sources for primary consumers in the sea. Analyses have shown that more than three times as much organic matter is present in dissolved form as is represented by the phytoplankton. Pütter claimed to have evidence that this material was used extensively for the nourishment of marine animals. However, investigation of the problem now indicates strongly that, if any dissolved organic matter is available to multicellular organisms, it forms an insignificantly small fraction of their total nutritive requirement (Krogh, 1931). We know that some dissolved organic matter in the water can be used by many kinds of bacteria and other saprophytes, but a large fraction of it is resistant even to bacterial attack, and this portion represents an unrecoverable loss for the oceanic ecosystem.

Organic detritus appears in the water directly from the disintegration of dead plants and animals and is also stirred up from muddy bottoms. This material occurs in particles of all sizes, and even the most minute may be removed from the water by animals possessing mucous filtering apparatus. Echiuroid worms can obtain material with dimensions as small as 4 mμ (MacGinitie and MacGinitie, 1949), and *Daphnia magna* is capable of taking in detritus of colloidal size in sufficient quantities for growth (Gellis and Clarke, 1935). Detritus has been shown to form a significant portion of the food of at least certain filter-feeding bivalves (Coe, 1948), and no doubt it does likewise for many kinds of zooplankton. The nutritional dependencies of copepods and other key primary consumers are therefore very complex, but directly or indirectly their food is ultimately derived from the organic material synthesized by the diatoms as the chief plant producers of the open sea.

(b) *Carnivores.* Since the herbivores in the typical community of the open sea are mostly small filter feeders, the primary carnivores—representing the third link in the food chain—are confronted with the problem of obtaining food from prey species that are often less than a centimeter or two in length. Nevertheless, certain sizable fish, such as the mackerel, herring, and shad, are able to feed directly upon the copepods and other primitive crustaceans of the plankton. Interestingly enough, the largest animals in the sea including the basking shark and the whalebone whales are also able to live upon the tiny zooplankton. The great sheets of frayed whalebone attached to the upper jaws of these whales serve as gigantic sieves (Fig. 13.6). When the whales are feeding, they take in huge mouthfuls of the sea and by means of their massive tongues force the water out through the whalebone. The copepods, euphausiids, and other types of zooplankton retained within the mouth cavity are then gulped down. The fact that the food chain of these whales is composed of only three

Photo G. C. Pike

Fig. 13.6a. North Pacific right whale, showing adaptation of mouth for plankton feeding. A cluster of barnacles can be seen on the lower lip.

Photo J. T. Ruud

Fig. 13.6b. Stomach of southern right whale split open, showing mass of euphausiids ("krill") that had been eaten.

links, and hence is relatively efficient, no doubt accounts for the successful maintenance of such large, warm-blooded mammals in the sea.

Most of the sizable marine carnivores are the result of longer food chains. Many adult fish, such as cod, haddock, halibut, and flounders, are bottom feeders and depend upon worms, mollusks, crabs, and other benthic animals for food. As mentioned above, certain of the mollusks are primarily herbivores, but other types of benthos are secondary or tertiary carnivores, scavengers, or mud feeders. Many worms and echinoderms pass large quantities of mud through their intestines, extracting nutriment from its components. Other types of fish feed primarily upon smaller members of their own class; the growth of a shark, for example, may represent a food chain of 5 or more links (Fig. 13.5).

(*c*)*Decomposers and Transformers.* The ecological cycle in the sea is completed by the activities of a large group of decomposers and transformers. Material excreted by living organisms and the bodies of dead plants and animals from every link in the food chain undergo decomposition as the result of the activity of certain groups of marine bacteria. Dead tissue is rendered soluble and decomposed to inorganic form. The material is then attacked by the transformers, as represented by other types of bacteria, and converted to forms suitable for the nutrition of green plants once more. Living members of the oceanic community are thus necessary to carry out each step in the chemical regeneration of the organic material. However, before the resulting nutrient salts can be assimilated again by the phytoplankton, the water containing them must be restored by currents to the euphotic zone where light is sufficient for photosynthesis. On certain submarine banks, such as Georges Bank, and in regions of permanent upwelling, such as along the western coast of the United States, physical regeneration may take place almost continuously. In other regions the deep stirring of winter is required before renewed development of phytoplankton can initiate constructive growth in the oceanic ecosystem once more.

PRODUCTIVITY OF THE ECOSYSTEM

In the previous sections the functional interdependencies between the various living and non-living components of the ecosystem have been discussed. We shall now consider relations of productivity both for the individual links in the food chain and also for the ecosystem as a whole. When reliable methods of measurement have been developed, the productivity of one type of organism may be compared with another, and the productivities of different communities or regions can be evaluated. From the practical point of view it is desirable to ascertain whether the production of a given area is as great as it could be. In order to determine whether an area is being overexploited or underexploited, abundance and growth must be measured in accurate terms, but before this can be done the various aspects of productivity must be clarified.

Concepts of Productivity

The three fundamental concepts of productivity are: (1) standing crop, (2) material removed, and (3) production rate (Fig. 13.7). Failure to distinguish these concepts has resulted in much confusion in attempts to measure and to discuss the production of animals and plants in different areas.

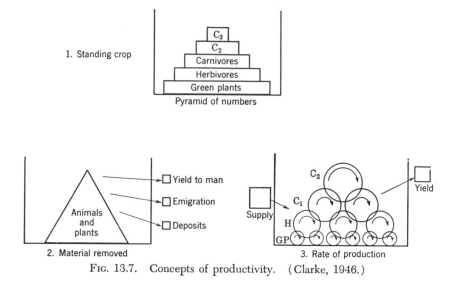

Fig. 13.7. Concepts of productivity. (Clarke, 1946.)

When the early naturalist entered a new area, his interest was at first centered upon the identification and description of the species present. With the growth of the ecological point of view the observer added to his task the enumeration of each species and soon built up a picture of the differences in abundance of the various members of the food chain, leading to the concept of the pyramid of numbers. The *standing crop* is the abundance of the organisms existing in the area at the time of observation; it may be expressed as number of individuals, as biomass, as energy content, or in some other suitable terms.

When the hunter, fisherman, or forester enters an area, he sees the situation from a different viewpoint. The attention of such practical ecologists is directed not so much to the fauna and flora as a whole as to the number of organisms that can be harvested. In addition to the yield taken by man other material may be removed from the area by active or passive emigration or by the withdrawal of organic matter from circulation through the formation of deposits. The second concept of productivity is the *material removed* from the area per unit time, and includes the *yield* to man, organisms removed from the ecosystem by *emigration*, and material withdrawn as organic *deposits*.

When the modern ecologist enters the area, he views the situation in a still different light. He should, of course, be aware of the numbers and types of organisms present, and of the extent of their removal from the area by man and in other ways, but his attention is directed chiefly to the dynamic aspect of the growth and interdependency of the inhabitants as members of a functioning system. The ecologist is concerned with natality and mortality in the various components of the population and with rates of metabolism and growth. He inquires not only into the different types of machinery in the factory but also into the speeds at which the wheels are turning. The third concept of productivity is the *production rate*, or the rate at which growth processes are going forward within the area. Each of the fundamental concepts of productivity will be considered separately in further detail.

Standing Crop

Measurements of the standing crop reveal the concentration of individuals in the various populations of the ecosystem. This information is essential for judging whether the degree of crowding in each species is exerting a harmful or a beneficial effect. Further, in the study of the dependence of one species on another the enumeration gives a measure of the intensity of predation and of the availability of the forage species. The size of the standing crop is also of vital concern in relation to the exploitation of natural populations by man. The abundance of the plant or animal influences the efficiency with which the enterprise is carried forward. However, since a knowledge of the standing crop gives no information on its replaceability, other aspects of productivity must also be taken into account for intelligent use of natural resources of this kind and for a maintained harvest.

Relation to Population Growth. The relation of the size of the standing crop to the rate of growth of the population will be considered for the three types of situations illustrated in Fig. 13.8. In the first a rapid increase in population size is indicated, leading to a

high equilibrium level for the standing crop. In the second situation
the growth of the population is much slower, but the same ultimate
size of standing crop is attained. In the third situation the same
period of time is required to reach equilibrium as in the second, but
a lower equilibrium level is established. If a census of the standing
crop is taken before the populations have reached their maximum
equilibrium levels, the larger standing crop will clearly occur in the
area in which the rate of production has been the greatest. Usually,

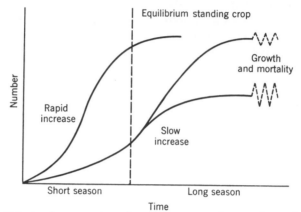

Fig. 13.8.   Relation between size of standing crop and rate of growth of population.   (Clarke, 1946.)

however, the observer will enter a natural area long after the initial
growth of the population has been completed and will measure the
standing crop at or near its equilibrium level. At this point the
magnitude of the standing crop is not an index of growth rate. The
size of the population at any moment is the result of the accumulation
of production minus the amount of destruction which has taken place
up to the time of observation.

In the initial growth of the population the length of life of the individuals influences the steepness of the population curve because, the
longer each individual lives, the faster will the total numbers increase.
Once equilibrium has been reached, however, individual length of
life has no effect upon the size of the standing crop. As discussed
in Chapter 9, natality is equal to mortality at equilibrium, or $A = M$.
If 50 animals are born per unit of time, 50 animals will die in the same
period, and it makes no difference whether those animals have lived
5 days or 5 years. Similarly, the size of the population is not determined by the magnitudes of A and M. As indicated in the diagram, a population with a large standing crop may exhibit a low

natality and a low mortality, whereas another population of smaller equilibrium size may display high birth and death rates. In analogous fashion the level of water in a tank (the standing crop) gives no clue to the rate of inflow (natality) or the rate of outflow (mortality). A high level of water in the tank may be maintained by a trickle of water running in and out, or, in another instance, a low water level may exist with a large inflow and a large outflow.

Determination of Equilibrium Level. What then does determine the magnitude of the standing crop at equilibrium? The total biomass of organisms inhabiting an area always tends to increase. This is due to the numerical increase of the population and to the growth in size of the individuals, or both. In some kinds of organisms, such as fish or trees, the individuals continue to grow larger all their lives, but in others, such as rodents and insects, full size is attained as soon as adult condition is reached. Although the number of trees in a forest stand tends to decrease due to competition, the increase in size of the individuals, for a time at least, more than makes up for the loss in numbers so that here also the total biomass of the population tends to grow larger. Since the size of the standing crop is not limited by factors intrinsic within the population, the increase in total biomass must be stopped by external factors. The biomass of the population will eventually reach the maximum size possible for the circumstances regardless of the speed of increase. The maximum standing crop that can maintain itself indefinitely in an area is spoken of as the *carrying capacity* of the area.

The ultimate limit to the growth of the population is determined by the supply of nutrient materials and energy. If the supply of these needs is large and if no other factor interferes, the population will grow to a large size. If food and energy continue to be provided at a rapid rate, the large population can be continuously maintained. A clear example of such a situation is found where a continuous upwelling of deep water supplies nutrients for the growth of the marine organisms in the area. Conditions of this sort account in part for the large carrying capacity of certain fishing banks.

When a population lives up to the limit of its food supply, it is living dangerously. Should the food supply be curtailed or should the population increase still further, large-scale destruction of the inhabitants would ensue. If populations of animals were checked by food supply only, critical conditions would be widespread because we know that animals can destroy their food supply faster than it can grow. The essence of this idea in relation to man was pointed out by an early "ecologist" by the name of Malthus. Because of the inefficiencies of feeding and digestion and because of the great amount of energy used for the various life processes, each animal destroys a much larger mass of food than its growth increment.

These facts clearly indicate that animals could quickly eat themselves out of house and home. Temporarily unchecked populations of insects or rodents sometimes increase to such numbers that every green thing within the area of their abundance is destroyed. Plagues of locusts in the Middle East have been known to consume all vegetation over areas as great as 600 sq km. Even deer, which reproduce relatively slowly, when protected from other checks, soon multiply to a point where the population needs more food than can grow within their home range.

When one realizes the fact that animals are able to destroy their food supply faster than it can grow, the question arises why the herbivores of the world have not destroyed all the vegetation, and why carnivores have not killed all of their prey and thus brought about their own destruction. One reason is that climate and other conditions vary locally, so that the animals do not find conditions suitable for maximal increase everywhere at once within their geographical ranges. If a local population does completely destroy itself by starvation, the area can be repopulated from neighboring regions. Another reason that extinction is usually avoided is that other factors frequently stop the increase in the population before the entire food supply is exhausted. For example, excessive grazing tends to change the species composition of the vegetation, and this condition, recognized as range deterioration, curtails the growth of the herbivores.

Increase of some animals is checked by accumulation of metabolites, by disease, or by intensified predation, as discussed in previous chapters, long before a food shortage is threatened. In special instances lack of breeding sites may be the chief factor limiting population growth. A striking illustration of the operation of this factor is provided by studies of the wood duck made at the Great Meadows Wildlife Refuge in Massachusetts. In an area of 120 hectares, including a large swamp, 13 tree holes were located that appeared to be suitable for nest sites in regard to size, shape, and location, and 6 of these were occupied by breeding ducks. After wildlife managers had put up 65 nesting boxes in the area, ducks built nests in 43 of these, thus revealing the extent of the previous underpopulation; the number of wood ducks had been much smaller than could have been supported by the supply of food and other necessities in the area.

The tendency for some species to limit themselves to home ranges or territories and thus avoid excessive concentration of the population has already been pointed out. Furthermore it should be noted that the biotic potential of prey species of animals is usually much higher than that of the predatory species. This relationship helps to retard the growth of the more remote links of the food chain. As prey becomes scarcer, predators have more and more difficulty in finding them so that their rate of feeding is automatically reduced. Often predators turn to other species at this time, relieving the pressure on the species originally used as a source of food.

This type of check also applies to man as a predator to some extent. When deer become scarce, sportsmen may voluntarily desist from hunting sufficiently to allow the population to recover. In some managed fish ponds unrestricted fishing by hook and line can be permitted. After the number of fish in the pond has been greatly reduced by the anglers, so much food is available for the remaining fish that they are too well fed to take bait. When the depletion of an oceanic fishery reaches the point where fishing for this species is no longer profitable, fishermen turn to other species. In such instances, if the population has not been reduced below the point of recovery, as discussed in Chapter 9, and if the habitat has not deteriorated in the meantime, the population may be able to return to its former abundance.

Regional Differences. The total quantity of life that can be supported in an area at its full carrying capacity may be made up of a few individuals of a large number of species or many individuals of a few species. Generally speaking tropical communities tend to exhibit the former condition and non-tropical communities the latter, but there are many exceptions. The fauna and flora of tropical biotopes are typically very rich in species but an observer often has difficulty in finding more than one or two specimens of each kind of animal or plant. The diversified nature of tropical vegetation is illustrated by the results of a transect 2 m wide and 150 m long run from the edge to the center of Castellow Hammock near Miami, Florida, in which 111 species of flowering plants were found belonging to 98 genera and 48 families (Phillips, 1940).

In contrast, the vegetation in high latitudes may be very monotonous from the point of view of species composition. The great spruce forest extending across the North American continent and Eurasia consists of but a few species of trees with a relatively small number of subordinate plants. The same general contrast in relation to numbers of species and individuals occurs among the land animals and also in the biota of aquatic areas (Table 21). Tropical marine areas, for example, support hundreds of species of fish with relatively small

TABLE 21

GENERAL DECREASE IN ABUNDANCE OF SPECIES WITH INCREASING LATITUDE
IN NORTH AMERICA AS INDICATED BY REPRESENTATIVE DATA FROM
VARIOUS SOURCES

| | *Approximate Number of Species* | | | |
	Florida	Massachusetts	Labrador	Baffin Land
Beetles	4000	2000	169	90
Land snails	250	100	25	0
Mollusks (tidal zone)	425	175	60	—
Reptiles	107	21	5	0
Amphibia	50	21	17	0
Fresh-water fish	—	75	20	1
Coastal marine fish	650	225	75	—
Flowering plants	2500	1650	390	218
Ferns and clubmosses	—	70	31	11

numbers of each, whereas in northern waters many fewer kinds of fish are found but some of them exist in huge populations. It is no accident that most of the large commercial fisheries are located in high latitudes. Enough cod are found among the Lofoten Islands off Norway during the early spring to keep 4000 fishing vessels busy, and 100 tons of cod may be taken with one cast of the purse seine. Many other illustrations of this generality may be found in faunal and floral lists for regions of contrasting latitude, such as those of Russell (1935).

Although this typical difference between tropical and non-tropical populations has been recognized for a long time, opinion differs as to its cause. One explanation lies in the fact that, since climatic conditions are more favorable at low latitudes, many different kinds of species can survive; and, because the total quantity of life in an area is limited, each species can be represented by only a few individuals. Furthermore, at high temperatures, with higher rates of reproduction, mutations probably occur more frequently so that in the course of evolution a larger variety of species has originated and more mutants would be expected to survive under the favorable conditions of the tropics. At high latitudes the reverse situation exists, and in addition the repeated expansion of the polar climate may have reduced the number of species as well as the time available for evolution. The relatively few species that do survive in colder regions find little competition and hence can develop large populations that exploit the environment to the limit.

In addition to this general reciprocal relationship between abundance of species and individuals, the standing crop in marine environments tends to be absolutely larger in high latitudes than in regions nearer the equator. This difference is particularly prominent if the standing crop in the tropics, which often remains uniformly small throughout the year, is compared with the standing crop in temperate or polar regions at the height of the growing season following the winter replenishment of nutrients. For instance, the standing crop of zooplankton in the antarctic summer was observed to be about 10 times greater than that in the tropical Atlantic. Again many exceptions exist in local areas—as in the Great Barrier Reef lagoon, where the standing crop was found to be as great as in temperate coastal regions. Under tropical conditions organisms grow faster and, after death, their tissues are decomposed and nutrients regenerated at a more rapid rate, but as already explained this difference in growth rate does not in itself account for the difference in the standing crop.

Part of the explanation of the latitudinal difference in total abundance of marine life is the fact that at low temperatures the metabolism of poikilotherms generally is much reduced. This means that a larger total number of organisms can be supported on the same amount of food. However, regional differences in metabolism are by no means simple and clear cut, as pointed out by Riley, Stommel, and Bumpus, (1949). Evidence exists that the rate of supply of nutrients to the surface in temperate and polar regions is usually greater than in the tropics owing to the nature of the vertical circulation of the ocean. Nutrients may thus be supplied more rapidly in relation to their use in the cooler water, with the result that a larger standing crop can be supported. However, in tropical regions with exceptionally great upwelling—as along the Peruvian coast—an enormous standing crop of plankton exists and supports the food chain leading to the production of guano, as described in Chapter 8. These regional differences in abundance of marine organisms are discussed in further detail by Sverdrup et al. (1942, Ch. 19).

Material Removed

Various aspects of the material removed from an area, as the second concept of productivity, are of interest to both the theoretical and the practical ecologist. Some may believe that the yield to man is the only component of the material removed that concerns farmers, fishermen, hunters, and foresters, but losses from the area in the form of emigration and organic deposits must also be considered. For the purpose of maintaining the yield to best advantage other concepts of productivity must also be understood and applied. In subsistence farming or hunting in which products are not taken to the market, the human agent may be regarded as an integral part of the local ecosystem; but in most farming, fishing, hunting, and forestry operations a large part of the organisms harvested is carried away, and hence the material of which the plants or animals are composed is permanently removed from the area.

Permanent emigration of animal or plant life similarly represents a loss of material from the ecosystem. Organisms may leave the area by their own locomotion or they may be carried away by wind or water currents. When the activity of natural predators results in the one-way transfer of organic material from one ecosystem to another—as when a fish hawk removes fish from a pond—the loss of material from the ecosystem under consideration is also to be included in this category. Another type of loss is represented by dead organic matter that is buried in the soil or in the mud of an aquatic biotope in such a way that it is functionally removed from the system. Also included is material that has gone into an inert chemical form and thus is essentially unrecoverable during the period under consideration.

If a community is to maintain itself, material in some form must be supplied to it in an amount at least equal to the total amount of material removed from the area in the various ways discussed. The supply in the form of nutrients and immigrants usually must be considerably larger than the removal because of the inevitable loss of energy and of material from the system at each level in the food chain. Ordinarily, man's harvest, which is only one portion of the total amount of material removed from the area, is very much smaller than the total supply to the area from all sources. The ratio of yield to supply gives one measure of the efficiency of the use of the area. Such a measure can show whether a needlessly low utilization is taking place or overexploitation is under way.

The yield to man may be improved in one or more of several ways. Although practical limitations must be considered in each specific situation, a summary of the theoretical possibilities is desirable as a basis for realistic procedure. A *maintained yield* can never average larger than the supply. However, the natural supply of materials entering the area may be augmented artificially by adding fertilizers or by stocking; and the amount of materials removed or lost in ways other than man's harvest may be curtailed. In addition, the degree of crowding of the desired species may be adjusted to the optimal level, and the competitors of this species may be removed.

The foregoing points will be illustrated by a schematic consideration of the interdependencies of a natural pasture from which it is desired to obtain the maximal yield of sheep (Fig. 13.9). Increased growth of the plant producers will result from the addition of fertilizers, but it is essential that this added supply of nutrients reaches the grass rather than the undesirable weeds. The grass supports a flock of sheep but it usually also supports a population of field rodents. If the rodents are excessively abundant, a reduction in their number would allow a larger portion of the grass to be consumed by the sheep.

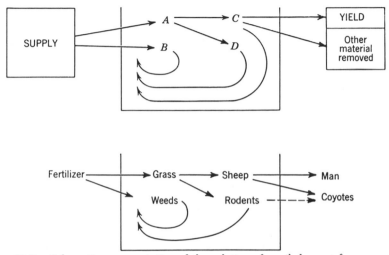

Fig. 13.9. Schematic representation of the relation of man's harvest from an area, such as a natural pasture, to the supply of materials and to the reduction of the product in various ways.

Often the best method of controlling the rodents is to allow the presence of predators such as coyotes, but should the coyotes become too numerous they would compete with man for the sheep and their numbers might have to be reduced. A suitable balance must be maintained among all the members of the ecosystem. The population of the species to be harvested should also be adjusted to the level of abundance at which its growth rate will be as great as possible without disturbing the equilibrium of the community. Study of the materials entering and leaving the area should reveal whether the area is being managed to the best advantage from the point of view of its desired use. The *maximum potential yield* is the largest maintained harvest that can be removed from an area under the best population and environmental conditions.

An aspect of the yield of great practical importance is the *yield per unit effort*. This may be measured in terms of man power, cost, or other basis, and depends among other things upon the size of the standing crop. Thus one aspect of productivity affects another aspect. These relationships may be illustrated by data for the total yield of haddock caught on the Icelandic fishing grounds in comparison with the catch per unit effort (as measured by the landings per day's absence from port) and the total hours of fishing by British trawlers (Fig. 13.10). The total yield of haddock declined slowly

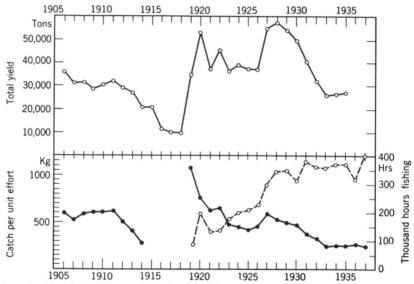

FIG. 13.10. (*Upper*) Total catch of haddock from Icelandic Fishing Grounds by all countries. (*Lower*) Catch per day's absence from port (solid line) and total hours of fishing (broken line) by British First Class Trawlers. (Modified from Russell, 1942, *The Overfishing Problem,* Cambridge Univ. Press.)

from 1905 to 1915, and the catch per unit effort declined regularly after 1911. During the war period 1914–1918 the haddock population had an opportunity to recover, and, with the resumption of fishing by the British trawlers in 1919, the catch per unit effort reached an all-time high. The total yield reached a peak in 1920 and a somewhat higher peak during 1927–1929, owing in part to the increase in fishing time and in part to the adoption of a new type of trawl. From 1924 to 1937 the hours of fishing were doubled, but the catch per unit effort exhibited a downward trend to a value in 1937 less than one quarter of that obtained in 1919. The explanation is found in the fact that the standing crop of haddock in Icelandic waters became progressively depleted, as a result of the intense fishing, and consequently a smaller and smaller catch was obtained from each day of fishing. A similar study of the drop in the catch per unit effort following depletion of the stock has been made for the Antarctic whales by Ruud (1952).

Production Rate

A knowledge of the standing crop of an area or of the yield from the area does not give a complete picture of productivity; in addition the rates at which the different constructive and destructive processes are going forward within the area must be considered. Since the plant producers, herbivores, carnivores, and other components of the ecosystem are all transforming energy and material simultaneously, the evaluation of production rates is extremely complex. For an understanding of the interdependencies of the entire ecosystem we should know the production rate for each of the trophic levels, that is, the amount of material formed by each link in the food chain per unit of time per unit area or volume, and we must distinguish between gross and net production. To disentangle these relations the analytical approach will again be adopted.

Let us consider first a very much simplified case such as an isolated pond in which no gain or loss of materials occurs during the period under consideration. The transformations going on within such an area are indicated schematically in Fig. 13.11. At the left of the diagram the energy represented by the standing crop at the beginning of the period is indicated. To keep the problem simple the food chain is considered to have only three links. The size of the rectangles for the green plants, herbivores, and carnivores are progressively smaller to indicate the typically reduced energy content of the standing crop as a pyramid of biomass. In the main part of the diagram the energy absorbed at each level of the food chain and its transformations are shown.

The largest rectangle at the bottom represents the total amount of incident light reaching the area during the period under consideration. Not all of the radiation is absorbed by the green plants. In the aquatic environment the lion's share of the light energy is absorbed by the water, and in the desert most of the sunlight falls on bare ground. In regions where the vegetation forms a complete cover, however, a large fraction of the incident radiation is absorbed. Thus the various rectangles of the diagram are not drawn to scale but simply illustrate the relations of the energy transformations among the various components. Of the light energy actually absorbed by the plants only a small fraction is used in photosynthesis and appears as carbohydrate formed since the process is far from 100 per cent efficient especially under natural conditions.

The energy of the carbohydrate formed represents the *gross plant production* and therefore the gross production of the producer component of the ecosystem. Not all the energy present in the photosynthetic product takes part in the realized growth of the plants since

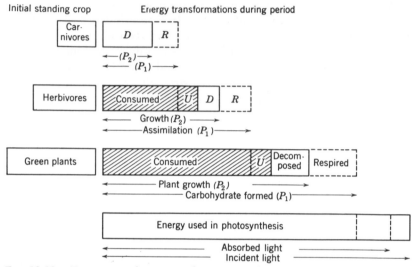

Fɪɢ. 13.11. Energy transformations during unit of time in an idealized ecosystem with no net increase or decrease (not drawn to scale). P_1 = gross production; P_2 = net production; R = respired; D = decomposed. Cross hatching indicates total portion of food organisms killed by consumers; a fraction, U, of this is unassimilated. (Clarke, 1946.)

the growth process also is not 100 per cent efficient. The accompanying catabolism of the plant is measured by the amount of respiration. Actual plant growth is represented by an amount of energy equal to the total carbohydrate formed minus the respiration and is designated as the *net plant production*. Since the formation of additional links in the food chain depend upon the elaboration of organic compounds by the green plants, the photosynthesis of plants in the ecosystem is sometimes referred to as "primary production" or "total production," but the more specific terms used here are preferable.

Part of the plant material formed in the ecosystem is consumed by herbivores, and part dies from other causes and undergoes direct decomposition. Only a portion of the plants designated as "consumed" is actually assimilated by the herbivores, for a certain amount of food that is eaten remains undigested and frequently more food is destroyed than is actually eaten. Sometimes this unassimilated portion is the greater of the two. A colony of beavers, for example, may cut down large numbers of aspens, but the bark that they consume is obviously only a very small fraction of the total biomass of the trees. Similarly, as mentioned earlier, the grazing activities of copepods often result in the destruction of a quantity of diatoms far greater than that actually assimilated.

We have assumed that in our simplified ecosystem the new plant growth was entirely removed by being consumed or by decomposing. Under natural conditions the net plant production per unit of time would rarely be exactly balanced by the loss due to herbivore feeding and to death of the plants from other causes. Any portion of the net production remaining at the end of the period constitutes a *net increase* to the standing crop. Under other circumstances the amount of foraging and of other destruction may exceed the amount of new growth during the period, with the result that a *net decrease* will take place in the standing crop.

We can apply the same line of reasoning to an analysis of the energy transformations at the herbivore level. The plant material assimilated is equal to the *gross herbivore production*. This amount, less that lost in respiration, is a measure of the actual growth of the herbivores, or the *net herbivore production*. At the end of the time unit one portion of the new herbivore growth has died and decomposed, and all of the other portion may have been destroyed by carnivores, as indicated in the diagram—or part of the growth increment may remain as a net increase in the population.

At the third trophic level the primary carnivores often eat only part of the prey that they kill, and, of course, only a fraction of the material is digested and assimilated. The *gross carnivore production* is equal to the total assimilation, and the *net carnivore production* is equal to the actual growth increment of these animals. Since the primary carnivores are at the top of the production pyramid in this assumed three-link food chain, no part of the carnivore production is consumed by predators, but all decomposes and goes back into the system after death. In most natural situations secondary and tertiary carnivores and other high-level consumers would also be present. The same types of relation apply to the gross and net production of these further links in the food chain.

In this simplified example the standing crop at all trophic levels at the end of the period is the same as it was at the beginning of the period, and there has been no yield or other material removed. Nevertheless, productive activity has been going on—the wheels of the factory have been turning—but the products of the factory have been taken in again as raw materials. An analytical scrutiny of the ecosystem reveals what processes are going on and at what rates, and how they are interdependent. A basis is also obtained for judging the productive capacity of the area and for deciding on the best procedure for the continued or improved use of the area for human needs. In an unfished lake, for example, the yield to man is zero. If fishing is to be initiated, information on the production rates of the various living components of the lake is desirable in order to understand the factors that would control the size of the fishery that could be permanently supported by the lake.

In areas in which rates of production are higher than rates of destruction a net increase in one or more of the components will occur. The surplus material may be removed by man, thus constituting a yield, or it may be removed in other ways described in the previous section, or it may be permanently added to the system. In the last case an increase in the organic components of the ecosystem will be experienced, but such an increase can take place only to the extent to which an equivalent supply of materials is added to the area. The amount of organisms and of nutrients in a lake, for example, are frequently seen to increase in this way over a period of time with the result that the lake becomes more eutrophic; the process is known as *eutrophication*. Similar increase of the living and non-living components of the ecosystem occurs in other types of habitat.

Turnover. In our discussion of production rate nothing has been said thus far about the length of the period considered. The time required for each type of organism to complete its growth, to die and decompose, and to start the cycle over again is known as its period of *turnover*. The length of the turnover period usually differs widely for the organisms at different trophic levels in the production pyramid, and may differ for the same level in different situations and at different seasons of the year. Herbaceous plants in a temperate terrestrial area usually have only one turnover per year, whereas the phytoplankton of an aquatic area may turn over within a few days or a few weeks. In the latter instance the same material may be used again several times during the year, and it would thus have little meaning to add up the increments of growth for the whole year in an attempt to reach a "total" annual value. If the growth of the plants is measured as energy, it is permissible to sum up the amount of energy which has been transformed during the year since the energy can be used by the plants only once. A comparison may thus be made between the annual incident radiation and the energy content of the plants produced. In the organisms at successively higher trophic levels, both the materials and the energy are used again one or more times. A summation of amounts of production at all trophic levels for a long period, such as a year, therefore, similarly has little meaning.

The procuring of significant measurements of production rate is further complicated by the fact that growth, consumption, and decomposition may all be going on simultaneously. This difficulty may be dealt with by reducing the period considered to such a small size that instantaneous rates for the various processes are obtained; in other words, by obtaining the differentials of the curves describing these processes (Clarke, 1946). The productive activity of an ecosystem is therefore best measured as a set of rates applying to the gross production, net production, and net increase for each category of organism or each trophic level. The term "productivity" has sometimes been used specifically for the rate at which assimilation (gross productivity) or growth (net productivity) is taking place since it is a measure of the rate at which the wheels of the system are turning. In view of the fact that this term is used in various broader senses it is preferable to employ the more explicit term, "production rate," and to specify the units of time and area considered.

Efficiencies. In ecosystems in which the magnitudes of the rates of production at the different trophic levels can be measured, calculations may be made of the quantitative relationships of the various steps in the production. The ratios, or efficiencies, on page 498 are of interest. In addition ratios including several or all of the steps within a trophic level, or embracing more than one trophic level, may be calculated. For example, the efficiency of the growth of a plant or animal component may be obtained as a percentage of the incident radiation.

Where the rates of the processes involved in the ecosystem have been measured, the various ratios, or efficiencies, can be calculated. Very few accurate measurements are available for organisms under natural conditions, but the order of magnitude is suggested by the following generalities. In ponds with dense algal blooms as much as 14 per cent of the light incident on the water surface may reach and be absorbed by the plant cells; in the open ocean less that 1 per cent of light energy is absorbed by the phytoplankton. Complete forest canopies absorb up to 99 per cent of the sunlight, but desert vegetation obviously captures a far lower percentage. The efficiency of the photosynthetic process, that is, of plant assimilation, for *Chlorella* cultures was found to be 12–20 per cent in moderate light and 2–3 per cent in the full light of summer, and higher plants are reported to display efficiencies of the same order (Wassink, Kok, and van Oorschot, 1953). When the small amount of light reaching the algae in a series of lakes was combined with their average photosynthetic efficiency, values for the rate of utilization of light incident on the water surface in the manufacture of carbohydrate ranged from 0.043 to 0.38 per cent (Clarke, 1939).

For the plant:

$$\text{Absorption} = \frac{\text{absorbed light}}{\text{incident light}}$$

$$\text{Assimilation} = \frac{\text{carbohydrates formed}}{\text{absorbed light}}$$

$$\text{Growth} = \frac{\text{plant growth}}{\text{carbohydrates formed}}$$

$$\text{Increase} = \frac{\text{net increase of plants}}{\text{plant growth}}$$

For the herbivore:

$$\text{Consumption} = \frac{\text{plants consumed}}{\text{plant growth}}$$

$$\text{Assimilation} = \frac{\text{plants assimilated}}{\text{plants consumed}}$$

$$\text{Growth} = \frac{\text{herbivore growth}}{\text{herbivore assimilation}}$$

$$\text{Increase} = \frac{\text{net increase of herbivore}}{\text{herbivore growth}}$$

For the carnivore:

$$\text{Consumption} = \frac{\text{herbivores consumed}}{\text{herbivore growth}}$$

$$\text{Assimilation} = \frac{\text{herbivores assimilated}}{\text{herbivores consumed}}$$

$$\text{Growth} = \frac{\text{carnivore growth}}{\text{carnivore assimilation}}$$

$$\text{Increase} = \frac{\text{net increase of carnivore}}{\text{carnivore growth}}$$

For the animals of the ecosystem, sample values may be given for herbivore and for carnivore production. It is said that 40 kg of grass are required to make 1 kg of beef. This is a value involving 2 steps in our analysis—the ratios of herbivore assimilation and of growth—and represents a net production for the herbivore equal to 2½ per cent of the food consumed. Obviously in the case of a mammal a large part of the food energy goes into heat production, and any active animal burns up considerable fuel in its locomotory activities, including foraging for food. Fish culturists have found that about 1 kg of fish can be produced for every 5 kg of meat consumed—or an efficiency of about 20 per cent for this highly digestible type of food. Measurements of the efficiencies of various steps in production for pond communities have been made by Lindeman (1942), for oceanic plankton by Riley, Stommel, and Bumpus (1949), and for certain farm crops by Transeau (1926). A schematic representation of the chief components in the ecosystem of Georges Bank, a fishing area off the coast of Massachusetts, shown in Fig. 13.12, summarizes our present knowledge of the quantitative relations involved. The blanks indicate the gaps

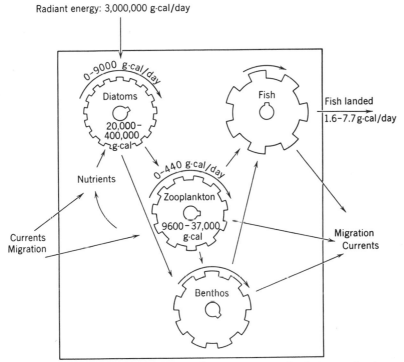

Fig. 13.12. Principal components and processes involved in production on Georges Bank, off Massachusetts. Values are averages for the whole bank per square meter of sea surface. Maximum and minimum values within the cogwheels are for the standing crop; those over the wheels are for net production rate. Average yield during 1923 to 1945 is indicated at right. (Clarke, 1946.)

in our information, and the large range in values draws attention to the variability in the abundance of the organisms, in the yield, and in the production rates. It will be observed that an average of 3 million g-cal of radiant energy fall on each square meter of sea surface over the Bank per day and that the energy content of the fish landed per day averages about 5 g-cal per sq m, or an overall efficiency of 0.00015 per cent. This very low value is due to the small fraction of the sun's radiation actually absorbed by the plant producers and the losses at each step in the long food chains involved (Clarke, 1946).

PRODUCTIVITY OF LAND AND WATER

Let us conclude our consideration of the ecosystem with a general comparison of the circumstances and efficiencies of its operation on land and in the water. The terrestrial environment clearly has certain advantages. More light is usually available, and large plants are ordinarily much more abundant. For this reason food chains can be shorter with correspondingly greater efficiency of production. Because the soil does not have the mobility of the water medium, nutrients are typically more concentrated, and products of decomposition tend to be retained as a humus near the surface of the ground where they can be immediately used again. On the other hand, the lack of water and the extreme changes in temperature are prominent among the disadvantages of the land as a place to live.

In the littoral zone of the ocean and of lakes, light is sufficiently intense for the growth of both planktonic and benthic plants. Since the water in this zone is continually mixed, nutrients are rapidly redistributed and food particles are carried in abundance to sessile animals. The disadvantages of the littoral zone include excessive molar action, considerable temperature change, and other special dangers near the water's edge. Beyond the littoral zone the replenishment of nutrients to the surface and of oxygen to the depths must await seasonal stirring. In the open sea and in the deepest lakes the euphotic zone represents only a tiny fraction of the entire depth, and effective wind stirring never extends below the permanent thermocline. The result is that nutritive materials sinking into deep water are regenerated only very slowly. Although organisms inhabiting large water bodies enjoy such advantages as relatively stable temperatures, they are handicapped by a restricted nutrient supply at the surface and by a lack of light at greater depths.

In relation to the distribution and availability of the critical materials in the major environments of the world we realize that the run-off from the land, including river and sewage discharge, represents a transfer of nutrients from the terrestrial environment to inland waters and thence to the ocean. Much of the nutrient material is utilized by the marine community, but, as we have seen, a portion of it is being permanently removed from the system as inert dissolved compounds, as submarine deposits, and as additions to the reservoir in the ocean abyss. The land is therefore continuously losing nutrient materials to fresh water and finally to the sea, and very little return movement of these materials to the terrestrial environment takes place.

Relatively few channels exist by which the crucial nutritive substances are being restored to the land. The use of fish, shellfish, and algae as food by land animals and the harvesting of marine products by man for fertilizers and for industrial uses, as well as for food, represent a return movement of materials to the land. A large fraction of the world's photosynthesis takes place in the sea. Estimates differ as to whether the average annual growth of the phytoplankton per unit area is as great as that of the land vegetation (Riley, 1944) or somewhat lower (Steeman Nielsen, 1952). Nevertheless, since the oceans cover about 70 per cent of the earth and since phytoplankton exists in all surface waters, perhaps half or more of the primary synthesis of organic matter for our globe is carried out by marine plant producers. Yet less than 1 per cent of man's food comes from the marine environment! From the point of view of conservation whatever increase can be made in man's use of marine resources will help to restore the balance and will represent a gain from the point of view of the inhabitants of the land (Clarke, 1950).

In view of the widely varying ecological conditions found in the major environments it is of interest to compare all aspects of their productivities in so far as this is possible. Characteristic differences in the standing crop of various areas have already been discussed. Far more difficult is a comparison of the production rates in view of the complexity of the relations between the various trophic levels in each ecosystem. Very few data exist for comparative purposes in natural environments. In general we may say that the efficiency of plant growth is usually greater than that of animal growth, and the efficiency of animal production is greater in the terrestrial than in the aquatic environment because of the shorter food chains.

Of particular interest to man is the yield which may be obtained from different types of environment. As we have seen, the magnitude of a sustained yield depends upon the supply of energy and of material and upon the production rates and efficiencies of the various links in the food chain. Table 22 gives some sample values for man's annual harvest per unit area.   As would be expected from the previous discussion, the yield is greater for organisms at lower trophic levels than for those further along in the food chain.   The highest yields are obtained when man can harvest the plant producers directly.   The value given for corn is a maximum crop after a growing period of 100 days (Transeau, 1926).   The solar energy reaching the cornfield during the rest of the year is lost as far as this crop is concerned.   The figure given for sugar cane in Hawaii, where a growing season of 11 months exists, represents one of the largest annual yields obtainable from any crop.

TABLE 22

COMPARISON OF ANNUAL YIELD TO MAN FROM VARIOUS ENVIRONMENTS
Values (from various sources) are in pounds per acre (roughly, kilograms per hectare) for fresh weight of whole organism.

Grass	Rich pasture	30,000
Corn	Ohio	40,000
Sugar cane	Hawaii (max.)	200,000
Cattle and sheep	Range	150
	Rich pasture	700
Fish	Georges Bank, Massachusetts	20
	Lake Mendota, Wisconsin	19
	Fertilized ponds, Alabama	300
	Milkfish, Philippines	700
	Cultivated ponds, India and China	3,000
Mollusks	Clams, Cape Cod (max.)	2,000
	Mussels, Europe	4,000

Since cattle, sheep, and other farm animals are products of a two-link food chain that are raised in a relatively advantageous environment, it is not surprising that the yields are considerably higher than those ordinarily found for animals in uncultivated aquatic environments.   The harvest taken from natural populations of fishes such as those from Georges Bank and Lake Mendota is thus much below the yields obtainable from the growth of farm animals, but probably it does not compare unfavorably with man's take from wild animal populations on land.

In the fertilized fish ponds of southeastern United States an average of 300 kg of fish per hectare per year may be produced.   An excellent example of the effect of the length of the food chain is furnished by the sizes of the yields of fishes of differing ecological position in these ponds.   When goldfish, which are herbivores, are raised a yield of 500 kg per hectare is obtained, but the yield for bluegill sunfish, a primary carnivore, is 250 kg per hectare, and that for bass, a secondary carnivore, is only 100 kg per hectare per year. The herbivorous milkfish in the Philippines, raised under very favorable tropical conditions, provides an annual yield of 500 to 1000 kg per hectare without the addition of fertilizer (Frey, 1947), and even larger harvests are reported from ponds in India and China. The very high yields of shellfish in the littoral zone are partially due to the fact that these animals act as food concentrators. They feed on plankton and detritus brought to them by currents from regions far beyond the area in which they are harvested. The efficiency of their production is thus not exactly comparable to the other items in Table 22, but the harvesting of these shellfish is clearly a very efficient use of marine resources by man.

CONCLUSION

The comparative productivity of land and water is a fitting topic with which to close our discussion of the elements of ecology. In this chapter we have shown how the individual physical and biological influences of the environment interact in the functioning of the ecological complex. We have considered the availability of solar energy for green plants in various habitats and the circumstances under which organic compounds can be synthesized by these primary producers. We have traced the transfer of materials and energy through successive links in the food chain and have discussed the qualitative and quantitative restrictions placed on the various plant and animal components of the ecosystem by the specific conditions of each habitat and each type of dependency. Thus the concept, with which we began, of the living community and its environment as a reciprocating system in dynamic balance has been analyzed and illustrated. We have seen how the intricate relations between the organism and the environment underlie the striking differences in the abundance and kind of plants and animals that populate contrasting habitats, in the harvest of living material that may be removed, and in the rates of production that are displayed. An understanding of these ecological relations enables man to live in adjustment with his natural environment, to preserve and develop it, and to derive the greatest benefit from it.

REFERENCES

Ackerman, E. A., 1941, *New England's Fishing Industry*, University of Chicago Press.

Aldrich, J., 1945, Birds of a deciduous forest aquatic succession, *Wilson Bull. 57:* 243–245.

Algéus, S., 1950, Further studies on the utilization of aspartic acid, succinamide, and asparagin by green algae, *Physiologia Plantarum, 3:* 370–375.

Allard, H. A., and W. W. Garner, 1940, Further observations on the responses of various species of plants to length of day, *U. S. Dept. Agr., Tech Bull. 727.*

Allee, W. C., 1926, Distribution of animals in a tropical rainforest with relation to environmental factors, *Ecology, 7:* 445–468.

Allee, W. C., 1931, *Animal Aggregations*, University of Chicago Press.

Allee, W. C., 1951, *Cooperation among Animals*, Henry Schumann, New York.

Allee, W. C., A. E. Emerson, O. Park, T. Park, and K. P. Schmidt, 1949, *Principles of Animal Ecology*, Saunders, Philadelphia.

Allen, J. A., 1870, Eared seals, *Bull. Museum of Comparative Zoology 2:* 1–89.

American Association for the Advancement of Science, 1939, The migration and conservation of salmon, *Publ. Am. Assoc. Advance. Sci. 8,* 1939.

Anderson, E., 1936, The species problem in *Iris, Ann. Missouri Botan. Garden, 23:* 457–509.

Anderson, E., 1949, Introgressive Hybridization, Wiley, New York.

Andrewartha, H. G., 1952, Diapause in relation to the ecology of insects, *Biol. Rev. Cambridge Phil. Soc. 27:* 1, 50–107.

Andrews, H. L., 1945, The kelp beds of the Monterey Region, *Ecology, 26:* 24–37.

Arey, L. B., and W. J. Crozier, 1921, Natural History of *Onchidium, J. Exptl. Zool., 22:* 443–502.

Baer, J. G., 1951, The ecology of animal parasites, University of Illinois Press.

Bajkov, A. D., 1949, Do fish fall from the sky? *Science, 109:* 402.

Baker, J. R., 1938, Latitude and egg-seasons in old world birds, *Proc. Zool. Soc. London, Ser. A, 108:* 557–582.

Baldwin, E., 1948, *An Introduction to Comparative Biochemistry*, Cambridge University Press.

Bartholomew, G. A., 1942, The fishing activities of double-crested cormorants on San Francisco Bay, *Condor, 44:* 13–21.

Bartholomew, G. A., 1949, The effect of light intensity and day length on reproduction in the English sparrow, *Bull. Mus. Comp. Zool. Harvard College, 101:* 433–476.

Barton, L. V., 1944, Some seeds showing special dormancy, *Contribs. Boyce Thompson Inst., 13:* 259–271.

Bates, M., 1950, *The Nature of Natural History*, Scribner, New York.

Beard, J. S., 1953, The Savanna vegetation of northern tropical America, *Ecol. Monographs, 23:* 149–215.

Bélehrádek, J., 1935, Temperature and living matter, *Protoplasma—Monographien, 8.*

Benson, S. B., 1933, Concealing coloration among some desert rodents of the southwestern United States, *Univ. Calif. Publs. Zoöl., 40:* 1–70.

Bessey, E. A., 1950, *Morphology and Taxonomy of the Fungi*, Blakiston Co., Philadelphia.

Bevelander, G., 1952, Calcification in molluscs, *Biol. Bull. 102:* 9–15.

Bigelow, H. B., 1926, Plankton of the Offshore Waters of the Gulf of Maine *U. S. Bur. Fish Bull. 40:* Part 2 (Doc. 968).

Birch, L. C., 1953, Experimental background to the study of the distribution and abundance of insects. III. The relation between innate capacity for increase and survival of different species of beetles living together on the same food, *Evolution, 7:* 136–145.

Birch, L. C., T. Park, and M. B. Frank, 1951, The effect of intraspecies and inter-species competition on the fecundity of two species of flour beetles, *Evolution, 5:* 116–132.

Bird, R. D., 1930, Biotic communities of the aspen parkland of central Canada, *Ecology, 11* (2): 356–442.

Birge, E. A., and C. Juday, 1911, The inland lakes of Wisconsin. The dissolved gases of the water and their biological significance, *Wisconsin Geol. Natural Hist. Survey, Bull. 22.*

Birge, E. A., and C. Juday, 1914, The Inland lakes of Wisconsin. The hydrography and morphometry of the lakes, *Wisconsin Geol. Natural Hist. Survey, Bull. 27,* Sc. Ser. 9.

Bissonette, T. H., 1936, Sexual photoperiodicity, *Quart. Rev. Biol., 11:* 371–386.

Bodenheimer, F. S., 1938, *Problems of Animal Ecology,* Oxford University Press, New York.

Borradaile, L. A., 1923, *The Animal and Its Environment,* Henry Frowde and Hodder and Stoughton, London.

Bousfield, E. L., 1954, Ecological control of the occurrence of barnacles in the Miramichi estuary, Ph.D. thesis, Harvard University.

Boyce, S. G., 1954, The salt spray community, *Ecol. Monographs, 24:* 29–67.

Braarud, T., 1951, Salinity as an ecological factor in marine phytoplankton, *Physiologia Plantarum, 4:* 28–34.

Brand, T. von, H. W. Rakestraw, and C. E. Renn, 1937, The experimental decomposition and regeneration of nitrogenous organic matter in sea water, *Biol. Bull., 72:* 165–175.

Brand, T. von, 1946, Anaerobiosis in invertebrates, *Biodynamica,* Normandy, Mo.

Brooks, J. L., 1946, Cyclomorphosis in Daphnia. I. An analysis of *D. retrocurva* and *D. galeata, Ecol. Monographs, 16:* 409.

Brooks, J. L., 1950, Speciation in ancient lakes, *Quart. Rev. Biol., 25:* 30–60; 131–176.

Brues, C. T., 1927, Animal life in hot springs. *Quart. Rev. Biol., 2:* 181–203.

Brues, C. T., 1939, Studies on the fauna of some thermal springs in the Dutch East Indies, *Proc. Am. Acad. Arts Sci., 73:* 71–95.

Brues, C. T., 1946, *Insect Dietary,* Harvard University Press.

Buchsbaum, R., 1937, *Readings in Ecology,* University of Chicago Press.

Buck, L. J., 1949, Association of plants and minerals, *J. N. Y. Bot. Garden, 50:* 265–269.

Burger, J. W., 1949, A review of experimental investigations on seasonal reproduction in birds, *The Wilson Bull. 61:* 209–256.

Burkholder, P. R., 1952, Cooperation and conflict among primitive organisms, *Am. Scientist, 40:* 601–631.

Burlew, J. S. (ed.), 1953, Algal culture from laboratory to pilot plant, *Carnegie Inst. Wash. Publ. 600.*

Cain, S. A., 1944, *Foundations of Plant Geography*, Harper, New York.

Cain, S. A., 1947, Characteristics of natural areas and factors in their development, *Ecol. Monographs*, *17:* 185–200.

Calhoun, J. B., and W. L. Webb, 1953, Induced emigrations among small mammals, *Science, 117:* 358–360.

Carpenter, C. R., 1942, Sexual behaviour of free-ranging Rhesus monkeys, *J. Comp. Psychol. 33:* 413–417.

Carpenter, J. R., 1935, Fluctuations in biotic communities. I. Prairie-forest ecotone of central Illinois, *Ecology, 16:* 203–212.

Carriker, M. R., 1951, Ecological observations on the distribution of oyster larvae in New Jersey estuaries, *Ecol. Monographs, 21* (1): 19–38.

Chamberlin, W. J., 1939, *The Bark and Timber Beetles of North America*, Oregon State College Cooperative Association, Corvallis, Oregon.

Chandler, A. C., 1944, *Introduction to Parasitology*, Wiley, New York.

Chapman, H. H., and W. H. Meyer, 1949, *Forest Mensuration*, McGraw-Hill, New York.

Chapman, R. N., 1931, *Animal Ecology with Especial Reference to Insects*, McGraw-Hill, New York.

Clarke, G. L., 1933, Diurnal migration of plankton in the Gulf of Maine and its correlation with changes in submarine irridation, *Biol. Bull., 65:* 402–436.

Clarke, G. L., 1934, Factors affecting the vertical distribution of copepods, *Ecol. Monographs, 4:* 530–540.

Clarke, G. L., 1936, On the depth at which fish can see, *Ecology, 17:* 452–456.

Clarke, G. L., 1938, Seasonal changes in the intensity of submarine illumination off Woods Hole, *Ecology, 19:* 89–106.

Clarke, G. L., 1939, The Utilization of solar energy by aquatic organisms, Problems in Lake Biology, *Publs. Am. Assoc. Advance. Sci., 10:* 27–38.

Clarke, G. L., 1940, Comparative richness of zooplankton in coastal and offshore areas of the Atlantic, *Biol. Bull., 78:* 226–255.

Clarke, G. L., 1946, Dynamics of production in a marine area, *Ecol. Monographs, 16:* 321–335.

Clarke, G. L., 1950, Conservation and the productivity of the sea, *Gamma Alpha Rec., 40:* 95–101.

Clarke, G. L., and D. W. Bishop, 1948, The nutritional value of marine zooplankton with a consideration of its use as an emergency food, *Ecology, 29:* 54–71.

Clarke, G. L., and S. S. Gellis, 1935, The nutrition of copepods in relation to the food-cycle of the sea, *Biol. Bull., 68:* 231–246.

Clarke, G. L., E. L. Pierce, and D. F. Bumpus, 1943, The distribution and reproduction of *Sagitta elegans* on Georges Bank in relation to the hydrographical conditions, *Biol. Bull., 85:* 201–226.

Clements, F. E., 1936, Nature and structure of the climax, *J. Ecol., 24:* 252–284.

Clements, F. E., and V. E. Shelford, 1939, *Bio-Ecology*, Wiley, New York.

Coblentz, W. W., 1939, Physical aspects of ultraviolet radiation in vitamin D therapy, *The Vitamins, Am. Med. Assoc.* (Chicago).

Coe, W. R., 1948, Nutrition, environmental conditions and growth of marine bivalve molluscs, *J. Marine Research* (*Sears Foundation*) 7: 586–601.

Coker, R. E., 1938, Functions of an ecological society, *Science, 87:* 309–315.

508 *References*

Cole, L. C., 1951, Population cycles and random oscillations, *J. Wildlife Management, 15:* 233–252.

Collias, N. E., 1944, Aggressive behavior among vertebrate animals, *Physiol. Zoöl., 17:* 83–123.

Collias, N. E., 1952, The development of social behaviour in birds, *The Auk, 69:* 127–159.

Collins, G. B., 1952, Factors influencing the orientation of migrating anadromous fishes, *U. S. Fish Wildlife Service, 52: Fishery Bull.* 375–396.

Cott, H. B., 1940, *Adaptive Coloration in Animals,* Oxford University Press, New York.

Crafts, A. S., H. B. Currier, and C. R. Stocking, 1949, *Water in the Physiology of Plants,* Chronica Botanica Co., Waltham, Mass.

Craighead, F. C., 1950, Insect enemies of eastern forests. Butterflies and Moths, by J. V. Schaffner, Jr., *U. S. Dept. Agr., Misc. Publ. 657.*

Crocker, R. L., 1952, Soil genesis and the pedogenic factors, *Quart. Rev. Biol., 27:* 139–168.

Crombie, A. C., 1947, Interspecific competition, *J. Animal Ecol., 16:* 44–73.

Crozier, W. J., 1929, The study of living organisms, Ch. 2 in *The Foundation of Experimental Psychology,* pp. 45–127, Clarke Univ. Press.

Cushing, D. H., 1951, The vertical migration of planktonic Crustacea, *Biol. Revs. Cambridge Phil. Soc., 26:* 158–192.

Dahl, E., 1951, On the relation between summer temperature and the distribution of alpine vascular plants in the lowlands of Fennoscandia, *Oikos, 3:* 22–52.

Dansereau, P., 1951, Description and recording of vegetation upon a structural basis, *Ecology, 32:* (2) 172–250.

Darling, F. F., 1937, *A Herd of Red Deer. A Study in Animal Behavior,* Oxford University Press, N. Y.

Darling, F. F., 1938, *Bird Flocks and the Breeding Cycle. A Contribution to the Study of Avian Sociality,* Cambridge University Press,

Darlington, P. J., Jr., 1938, The origin of the fauna of the Greater Antilles with discussion of dispersal of animals over water and through the air, *Quart. Rev. Biol., 13:* 274.

Darlington, P. J., Jr., 1943, Carabidae of mountains and islands: data on the evolution of isolated faunas, and on atrophy of wings, *Ecol. Monographs, 13:* 37.

Daubenmire, R. F., 1938, Merriam's life zones of North America, *Quart. Rev. Biol., 13:* 327–332.

Daubenmire, R. F., 1947, *Plants and Environment,* Wiley, New York.

Davenport, D., 1950, Studies in the physiology of commensalism, *Biol. Bull., 98:* 81–93.

Davis, J. H., 1940, The ecology and geologic role of mangroves in Florida. *Carnegie Inst. Wash. Publ. 517, Papers from Tortugas Lab., 32:* 305–414.

Debach, P., and H. S. Smith, 1947, Effects of parasite population density on rate of change of host and parasite populations, *Ecology, 28:* 290–298.

Deevey, E. S., 1947, Life tables for natural populations of animals, *Quart. Rev. Biol., 22:* 283–314.

Deevey, E. S., 1949, Biogeography of the Pleistocene. *Bull. Geol. Soc. Amer., 60:* 1315–1416.

Deevey, E. S., 1950, The probability of death, *Sci. American, 182:* 58–60.

Dexter, R. W., 1947, The marine communities of a tidal inlet at Cape Ann, Massachusetts; a study in bio-ecology, *Ecol. Monographs, 17:* 261–294.

Dice, L. R., 1952, *Natural Communities,* University of Michigan Press.

Dodds, G. S., and F. L. Hisaw, 1925, Ecological studies on aquatic insects. III. Adaptations of caddis-fly larvae to swift streams, *Ecology, 6:* 123–137.

Douglass, A. E., 1936, Climatic cycles and tree growth. III. A study of cycles *Carnegie Inst. Wash. Publ. 289,* 3, 171 pp.

Drury, W. H., Jr., 1952, The cyclic development of bog flats in interior Alaska, Ph.D. thesis, Harvard University.

Dutton, H. J., and C. Juday, 1944, Chromatic adaptation in relation to color and depth distribution of freshwater phytoplankton and large aquatic plants, *Ecology, 25:* 273–282.

Dye, J. F., 1952, Calculation of effect of temperature on *p*H, free carbon dioxide, and the three forms of alkalinity, *J. Am. Water Works Assoc., 44:* 356.

Edminster, F. C., 1947, *Fish Ponds for the Farm,* Scribner, New York.

Edmondson, W. T., 1945, Ecological studies of sessile Rotatoria. II. Dynamics of populations and social structures, *Ecol. Monographs, 15:* 141–172.

Edmondson, W. T., 1946, Factors in the dynamics of rotifer populations, *Ecol. Monographs, 16:* 357–372.

Edwards, G. A., and L. Irving, 1943, The influence of temperature and season upon the oxygen consumption of the sand crab *Emerita talpoida* Say., *J. Cellular Comp. Physiol., 21:* 169–182.

Ekman, S., 1953, *Zoogeography of the Sea,* Sidgwick & Jackson, Ltd., London.

Elton, C., 1930, *Animal Ecology and Evolution,* Oxford University Press, New York.

Elton, C., 1932, Territory among wood ants (*Formica rufa* L.) at Picket Hill, *J. Animal Ecol., 1:* 69–78.

Elton, C., 1939, *Animal Ecology,* Macmillan, New York.

Elton, C., 1942, *Voles, Mice, and Lemmings. Problems in Population Dynamics,* Clarendon Press, Oxford.

Elton, C., 1946, Competition and the structure of ecological communities, *J. Animal Ecol., 15:* 54–68.

Emerson, R., and L. Green, 1938, Effect of hydrogen-ion concentration on *Chlorella* photosynthesis, *Plant Physiol., 13:* 157–168.

Errington, P. L., 1945, Some contributions of a fifteen-year local study of the northern bob-white to a knowledge of population phenomena, *Ecol. Monographs, 15:* 1–34.

Evans, M. W., and H. H. Allard, 1934, The relation of length of day to growth of timothy, *J. Agr. Research, 48:* 571–586.

Farner, D. S., 1950, The annual stimulus for migration, *Condor, 52:* 104–122.

Farner, D. S., L. R. Mewaldt, and S. D. Irving, 1953, The roles of darkness and light in the photoperiodic response of the testes of white-crowned sparrows, *Biol. Bull., 105:* 434–442.

Fish, C. J., and M. W. Johnson, 1937, The biology of the zooplankton population in the Bay of Fundy and Gulf of Maine with special reference to production and distribution, *J. Biol. Board Can., 3:* 189–322.

Fish, M. P., 1954, The character and significance of sound production among fishes of the Western North Atlantic, *Bull. Bingham Oceano. Collec., 14*(3): 1–109.

Fisher, J., and H. G. Vevers, 1944, The changes in the world numbers of the gannet in a century, *J. Animal Ecol., 13:* 49–62.

Foerster, R. E., and W. E. Ricker, 1941, The effect of reduction of predaceous fish on survival of young sockeye salmon at Cultus Lake, *J. Fisheries Research Board Can., 5:* 315–336.

Foggie, A., 1947, Some ecological observations on a tropical forest type in the Gold Coast, *J. Ecol., 34:* 88–106.

Forbes, S. A., 1887, The lake as a microcosm, *Bull. Sc. A. Peoria,* 1887: 77–87. [Reprinted with emendations in *Illinois Nat. Hist. Survey, Bull. 15* (1925): 537–550. 1925].

Fowle, F. E., 1927, Smithsonian physical tables *Smithsonian Misc. Collections, Publ.* 2539.

Fraenkel, G. S., and D. L. Gunn, 1940, *The Orientation of Animals,* Clarendon Press, Oxford.

Frank, P. W., 1952, A laboratory study of intraspecies and interspecies competition in *Daphnia pulicaria* (Forbes) and *Simocephalus vetulus* O. F. Müller, *Physiol. Zoöl., 25:* 178–204.

Frey, D. G., 1947, The pond fisheries of the Philippines, *J. Marine Research* (Sears Foundation), *6:* 247–258.

Von Frisch, K., 1950, *Bees: Their Chemical Sense, Vision and Language,* Comstock, Ithaca, N. Y.

Frobisher, M., 1944, *Fundamentals of Bacteriology,* Saunders, Philadelphia.

Galambos, R., and D. R. Griffin, 1942, Obstacle avoidance by flying bats: the cries of bats, *J. Exptl. Zool., 89:* 475–490.

Gardiner, J. S., 1931, Coral reefs and atolls., Macmillan, London.

Garrett-Jones, C., 1950. A dispersion of mosquitoes by wind, *Nature, 165:* 285.

Gause, G. F., 1935, Experimental demonstration of Volterra's periodic oscillations in the numbers of animals, *J. Exptl. Biol., 12:* 44–48.

Gavin, A., 1945, Notes on mammals observed in the Perry River district, Queen Maud Sea, *J. Mammology, 26:* 226–230.

Geiger, R., 1950, *The Climate near the Ground* (Translated by Stewart), Harvard University Press.

Gellis, S. S., and G. L. Clarke, 1935, Organic matter in dissolved and in colloidal form as food for *Daphnia magna, Physiol. Zoöl., 8:* 127–137.

Gislen, T., 1948, Aerial plankton and its conditions of life, *Biol. Revs.* Cambridge *Phil. Soc., 23:* 109–126.

Gleason, H. A., 1926, The individualistic concept of the plant association, *Bull. Torrey Botan. Club, 53:* 7–26.

Graham, E. H., 1937, Botanical studies in the Uinta Basin of Utah and Colorado, *Annals Carnegie Museum, 26.*

Graham, E. H., 1944, *Natural Principles of Land Use,* Oxford University Press, New York.

Graham, M., 1938, The trawl fisheries: a scientific and national problem, *Nature, 142:* 1143–1146.

Griffin, D. R., 1952, Bird navigation, *Biol. Revs. Cambridge Phil. Soc., 27* (4): 359–400.

Griffin, D. R., 1953, Sensory physiology and the orientation of animals, *Am. Scientist, 41:* 209–244.

Griggs, R. F., 1946, The timberlines of Northern America and their interpretation, *Ecology, 27:* 275–289.

Griscom, L., 1945, *Modern Bird Study*, Harvard University Press.

Griscom, L., 1947, An ornithologist looks at waterfowl, *Audubon Mag.*, 49: 37–46.

Gross, A. O., 1928, The heath hen, *Mem. Boston Soc. Natural Hist.*, 6: 491–588.

Gross, A. O., 1947, Cyclic invasions of the snowy owl and the migration of 1945–1946, *Auk*, 64: 584–601.

Gross, F., 1947, An experiment in marine fish cultivation: V. Fish growth in a fertilized sea-loch (Loch Craiglin), *Proc. Roy. Soc. Edinburgh, B.*, 63: 56–95.

Gross, F., and J. C. Smyth, 1946, The decline of oyster populations, *Nature*, 157: 540–545.

Grundfest, H. E., 1932, The sensibility of the sunfish, *Lepomis*, to monochromatic radiation of low intensities, *J. Gen. Physiol.*, 15: 307–328.

Gunter, G., R. H. Williams, C. C. Davis, and F. G. W. Smith, 1948, Catastrophic mass mortality of marine animals and coincident phytoplankton bloom on the west coast of Florida, Nov. 1946 to August 1947, *Ecol. Monographs*, 18: 309–324.

Gustafson, A. F., C. H. Guise, W. J. Hamilton, and H. Ries, 1949, *Conservation in the United States*, Third Edition, Comstock, Ithaca, N. Y.

Hall, F. G., 1930, The ability of the common mackerel and certain other marine fishes to remove dissolved O_2 from sea water, *Am. J. Physiol.*, 93: 417–421.

Hamilton, W. J., Jr., 1939, *American Mammals*, McGraw-Hill, New York.

Hardy, A. C., 1936, Plankton ecology and the hypothesis of animal exclusion, *Proc. Linnean Soc. London, 148th Session:* 64–70.

Hartley, P. H. T., 1947, Predation by sparrow-hawk populations. Review of "De Sperwer als Roofvijand van Zangvogels" by L. Tinbergen, *Ecology*, 28: 326–328.

Harvey, E. N., 1952, *Bioluminescence*, Academic Press, New York, 632 pp.

Harvey, H. W., 1928, *Biological Chemistry and Physics of Sea Water*, Macmillan, New York.

Harvey, H. W., 1945, *Recent Advances in the Chemistry and Biology of Sea Water*, Cambridge University Press, 157 pp.

Harvey, H. W., 1949, On manganese in sea and fresh waters, *J. Marine Biol. Assoc. United Kingdom*, 28: 155–164.

Harvey, H. W., 1950, On the production of living matter in the sea off Plymouth, *J. Marine Biol. Assoc. United Kingdom*, 29: 97–137.

Harvey, H. W., L. H. N. Cooper, M. V. Lebour, and F. S. Russell, 1935, Plankton production and its control, *J. Marine Biol. Assoc. United Kingdom*, 20: 407–442.

Hasler, A. D., 1954, Odour perception and orientation in fishes, *J. Fisheries Research Board Can.*, 11: 107–129.

Hasler, A. D., and W. J. Wisby, 1951, Discrimination of stream odors by fish and its relation to parent stream behavior, *Am. Naturalist*, 85: 823.

Heape, W., 1932, Emigration, Migration, and Nomadism, Heffer, Cambridge.

Henderson, L. J., 1924, The fitness of the environment, Macmillan, New York.

Herman, C. M., 1937, A case of super-parasitism, *Bird Banding*, 8: 127.

Hesse, R., W. C. Allee, K. P. Schmidt, 1951, *Ecological Animal Geography*, Wiley, New York.

Hess, A. D., and A. Swartz, 1940, The forage ratio and its use in determining the food grade of streams, *Trans. Fifth North American Wildlife Conference*, pp. 162–164, Am. Wildlife Institute, Washington, D. C.

Hewitt, E. J., 1952, Sand and water culture methods used in the study of plant nutrition, *Commonwealth Bur. Horti. Plantation Crops, Tech. Commun. 22.*

Hjort, J., 1937, The story of whaling, *Sci. Monthly, 45:* 19–34.

Hobbs, H. H., Jr., 1942, The Crayfishes of Florida, Univ. Florida Publs., *Biol. Sci. Ser. 3* (2): 1–179.

Hopkins, D. M., and R. S. Sigafoos, 1951, Frost action and vegetation patterns on Seward Peninsula, Alaska, *U. S. Geol. Survey, Bull. 974–C:* 51–101.

Howard, W. E., 1949, Dispersal, amount of inbreeding, and longevity in a local population of prairie deermice on the George Reservation, southern Michigan, *Contribs. Laboratory Vertebrate Biol., 43:* 1–43, University of Michigan.

Hubbs, C. L., and R. W. Eschmeyer, 1938, The improvement of lakes for fishing, *Univ. Mich. Inst. Fisheries Research, Bull. 2.*

Hunter, G. W., III, 1942, Studies on the parasites of fresh-water fishes of Connecticut, *State Geol. and Nat. Hist. Survey (Connecticut) Bull. 63:* 228–288.

Hunter, G. W., and W. S. Hunter, 1929, Further experimental studies of the bass tapeworm, *Proteocephalus ambloplitis* (Leidy). *Supp. 18th Ann. Rept. N. Y. State Conservation Dept. Biol. Survey, Erie-Niagara System, 1928:* 198–207.

Hunter, G. W., and W. S. Hunter, 1935, Further studies on fish and bird parasites, *N. Y. State Conservation Dept., Biol. Survey, 24,* The Mohawk-Hudson watershed, *Suppl. Ann. Rept. 9.*

Huntsman, A. G., 1938, North American Atlantic Salmon *J. Conseil permanent intern. exploration mer* (Extrait du rapports et procès-verbaux) *4:* 11–15.

Huntsman, A. G., 1948, *Odontosyllis* at Bermuda and lunar periodicity, *J. Fisheries Research Board Can., 7:* 363–369.

Hutchins, L. W., 1947, The bases for temperature zonation in geographical distribution, *Ecol. Monographs, 17:* 325–335.

Hutchins, L. W., and M. Scharff, 1947, Maximum and minimum monthly mean sea surface temperatures charted from the "World Atlas of Sea Surface Temperatures," *J. Marine Research (Sears Foundation), 6:* 265–268.

Hutchinson, G. E., 1941, Ecological aspects of succession in natural populations, *Am. Naturalist, 75:* 406–418.

Hutchinson, G. E., 1944, Nitrogen in the biogeochemistry of the atmosphere, *Am. Scientist, 32:* 178–195.

Hutchinson, G. E., 1948, Circular causal systems in ecology, *Ann. N. Y. Acad. Sci., 50* (Art. 4): 221–246.

Hutchinson, G. E., 1950, Survey of contemporary knowledge of biogeochemistry. 3. The biogeochemistry of vertebrate excretion, *Bull. Am. Museum Nat. Hist., 96:* 1–554.

Hutchinson, G. E., and E. S. Deevey, Jr., 1949, *Ecological Studies in Populations. Survey of Biological Progress,* G. S. Avery, Editor, *1:* 325–371, Academic Press, New York.

Hutchinson, G. E., E. S. Deevey, Jr., and A. Wollack, 1939, The oxidation-reduction potentials of lake waters and their ecological significance, *Proc. Natl. Acad. Sci., 25:* 87–90.

Iselin, C. O' D., 1936, A study of the circulation of the western North Atlantic, *Papers Phys. Oceanog. Meteorol., 4* (4): 1–101.

Iversen, J., 1944, *Viscum, Hedera, Ilex* as climate indicators, *Geol. Fören. i Stockholm Förh., 66:* 463–483.

Jaeger, E. C., 1949, Further observations on the hibernation of the poor-will, *Condor,* May–June.

Jenkin, P. M., 1937, Oxygen production by the diatom *Coscinodiscus excentricus* Ehr. in relation to submarine illumination in the English Channel, *J. Marine Biol. Assoc. United Kingdom, 22:* 301–342.

Jenner, C. E., 1951, Photoperiodism in the fresh-water pulmonate snail, *Lymnaea palustris,* Ph.D. thesis, Harvard University.

Jerlov, N. G., 1951, Optical studies of ocean waters, *Repts. Swedish Deep-Sea Expedition, 3,* Physics and Chemistry, No. 1: 1–59.

Johnson, M. W., and O. B. Olson, 1948, The life history and biology of a marine harpacticoid copepod, *Tisbe furcata* (Baird), *Biol, Bull. 95:* 320–332.

Johnson, V. R., 1947, Breeding birds of the forest edge in Illinois, *Condor, 49* (2): 45–53.

Johnston, I. M., 1941, Gypsophily among Mexican desert plants, *J. Arnold Arboretum* (Harvard Univ.), *22:* 145–170.

Jones, F. R. H., 1952, The swim bladder and the vertical movements of Teleostean fishes. I. Physical factors. II The restriction to rapid and slow movements, *J. Exptl. Biol., 28:* 553–566; *29:* 94–109.

Juday, C., 1943, The summer standing crop of plants and animals in four Wisconsin lakes, *Trans. Wisconsin Acad. Sci., 34:* 103–135.

Keeble, F. W., 1910, *Plant-animals: A Study in Symbiosis,* Cambridge University Press.

Kellogg, C. E., 1941, *The Soils That Support Us,* Macmillan, New York.

Kellogg, W. N., R. Kohler, and H. N. Morris, 1953, Porpoise sounds as sonar signals, *Sci., 117:* 239–243.

Kendeigh, S. C., 1944, Measurement of bird populations, *Ecol. Monographs, 14:* 67–106.

Kendeigh, S. C., 1947, Bird population studies in the coniferous forest biome during a spruce budworm outbreak, *Dept. Lands Forests, Ontario, Canada, Division of Research, Biol. Bull. 1.*

Kendrew, W. G., 1930, *Climate, a Treatise on the Principles of Weather and Climate,* Oxford University Press.

Kendrew, W. G., 1949, *Climatology,* Oxford University Press.

Kessel, B., 1953, Distribution and migration of European starling in North America, *Condor, 55:* 49–67.

Ketchum, B. H., 1947, The biochemical relations between marine organisms and their environment, *Ecol. Monographs, 17:* 309–315.

Ketchum, B. H., 1951, The flushing of tidal estuaries. *Sewage and Ind. Wastes, 23:* 198–209.

Ketchum, B. H., and A. C. Redfield, 1949, Some physical and chemical characteristics of algae grown in mass culture, *J. Cellular Comp. Physiol., 33:* 281–300.

Kimball, H. H., 1928, Amount of solar radiation that reaches the surface of the earth on the land and on the sea, and methods by which it is measured, *Monthly Weather Rev., 56:* 393–399.

Korringa, P., 1947, The relations between the moon and periodicity in the breeding of marine animals, *Ecol. Monographs, 17:* 347–381.

Kramer, G., 1952, Experiments on bird orientation, *Ibis, 94:* 265–285.

Krauss, R. W., 1953, Inorganic nutrition of algae, *Carnegie Inst. Wash. Publ. 600:* 85–102.

Krecker, F. H., and L. Y. Lancaster, 1933, Bottom shore fauna of western Lake Erie; a population study to a depth of six feet, *Ecol., 14:* 79–93.

Krogh, A., 1931, Dissolved substances as food of aquatic organisms, *Biol. Revs.*, 6: 412–442.

Krogh, A., 1939, *Osmotic Regulation in Aquatic Animals*, Cambridge University Press.

Kuenen, Ph. H., 1950, *Marine Geology*, Wiley, New York.

Lack, D., 1947, *Darwin's Finches*, Macmillan, New York.

Lack, D., and E. Lack, 1951, Further changes in bird-life caused by afforestation, *J. Animal Ecol.*, 20: 173–179.

Ladd, Harry S., 1951, Brackish-water and marine assemblages of the Texas coast with special reference to mollusks, *Publ. Inst. Marine Science*, 2: 125–164.

Ladd, H. S., and J. I. Tracey, 1949, The problem of coral reefs, *Sci. Monthly* 69: 297.

Lauzier, L., R. W. Trites, and H. B. Hachey, 1951, Some features of the surface layer of the Gulf of St. Lawrence, *Rept. Joint Committee on Oceanography, Atlantic Oceanographic Group*, St. Andrews, N. B.

Leake, D. V., 1939, Preliminary note on the production of motile cells in *Basicladia*, *Proc. Oklahoma Acad. Sci.*, 19: 109–110.

van Leeuwen, W. M. D., 1936, *Krakatau–1883–1933*, A. Botany, E. J. Brill, Leiden.

Lehr, J. J., 1942, Importance of sodium for plant nutrition, *Soil Sci.*, 53: 399.

Leopold, A., 1943, Deer irruptions, *Wisconsin Conserv. Dept. Publ. 321*: 1–11.

Leopold, A., 1947, *Game Management*, Scribner, New York.

Leopold, A. C., 1951, Photoperiodism in plants, *Quart. Rev. Biol.*, 26: 247.

Leopold, A. C., and C. M. Kirkpatrick, 1952, The role of darkness in sexual activity of the quail, *Science, 116*: 280–281.

Lincoln, F. C., 1933, State distribution of returns from banded ducks, No. 5, *Bird-Banding*, IV-4: 177–189.

Lindeman, R. L., 1942, The trophic-dynamic aspect of ecology, *Ecology, 23*: 399–418.

Livingston, B. E., and F. Shreve, 1921, The distribution of vegetation in the United States as related to climatic conditions, *Carnegie Inst. Wash. Publ. 284*.

Loeb, J., 1918, Forced movements, tropisms, and animal conduct, Lippincott, New York.

Lotka, A. J., 1934, Theorie analytique des associations biologiques, *Actualités sci. et indus.*, 187: 1–45.

Lucas, C. E., 1949, External metabolites and ecological adaptation, *Symposia Soc. Exptl. Biol.*, 3, Growth: 336–356.

Lundegårdh, H., 1931, *Environment and Plant Development* (Translated by Eric Ashby), E. Arnold & Co., London, 302 pp.

Lüscher, M., 1953, The termite and the cell, *Sci. American, 188* (5): 74–81.

Lyman, C., 1942, Control of coat color in the varying hare, *Lepus americanus* Erxleben, Ph.D. thesis, Harvard University.

Lyman, C. P., and P. O. Chatfield, 1950, Hibernation, *Sci. American, 183* (6): 18–21.

Lyon, T. L., H. O. Buckman, and N. C. Brady, 1952, *The Nature and Properties of Soils*, Macmillan Co., New York.

MacArthur, J. W., and W. H. T. Baillie, 1929, Metabolic activity and duration of life, *J. Exptl. Zool.*, 53: 243–268.

MacGinitie, G. E., and N. MacGinitie, 1949, Natural history of marine animals, McGraw-Hill, New York.

MacLulich, D. A., 1937, Fluctuations in the numbers of the varying hare (*Lepus americanus*), *Univ. Toronto Studies, Biol. Ser., 43.*

Maéda, H., 1951, Analytical studies on marine lamp-communities, *Publ. Seto Marine Biol. Lab., 1* (4): 196–213.

Marshall, S. M., A. G. Nicholls, and A. P. Orr, 1934, On the biology of *Calanus finmarchicus.* V. Seasonal distribution, size, weight and chemical composition in Loch Striven in 1933 and their relation to phytoplankton, *J. Marine Biol. Assoc. United Kingdom, 19:* 793–828.

Marsland, D., and C. R. Plunkett, 1945, *Principles of Modern Biology*, Henry Holt, New York, 745 pp.

Mast, S. O., and D. M. Pace, 1946, The nature of the growth-substance produced by *Chilomonas paramecium, Physiol. Zoöl., 19:* 223–235.

Matthews, G. V. T., 1950, The experimental investigation of navigation in homing pigeons, *J. Exptl. Biol., 28:* 508–536.

Matthews, H. D., 1942, On the stridulations of insects, *Science, 95:* 324–325.

Mayr, E., 1942, *Systematics and the Origin of Species*, Columbia University Press, New York.

McDougall, Eric, 1925, The moisture belts of North America, *Ecology, 6:* 325–332.

McDougall, W. B., 1949, *Plant Ecology*, Lea & Febiger, Philadelphia.

Meehean, O. L., 1952, Problems of farm fish pond management. Symposium on farm fish ponds and management, *J. Wildlife Man., 16:* 3, 233–288.

Meyer, B. S., and D. B. Anderson, 1952, *Plant Physiology*, Van Nostrand, New York.

Miller, R. S., 1951, Activity patterns in small mammals with special reference to their use of natural resources, Ph.D. thesis, Oxford University.

Miner, R. W., 1934, The kingdom of the tides, *Am. Museum Natural History, Guide Leaflet Ser., 83.*

Möbius, K., 1883, The oyster and oyster-culture, *Rept. U. S. Fish Comm. 1880, Pt. 8:* 683–824.

Moore, H. B., 1950, The relation between the scattering layer and the Euphausiacea, *Biol. Bull., 99:* 181–212.

Morgan, A. H., 1930, *Fieldbook of Ponds and Streams*, Putnam, New York.

Morrison, P. E., 1932, A report on the molluscs of the northeastern Wisconsin lake district, *Trans. Wisconsin Acad. Sci., 27:* 359–396.

Murie, A., 1944, Wolves of Mt. McKinley, *Fauna of the National Parks of the U. S., Fauna Ser. 5.*

Murie, O. J., 1951, *The Elk of North America*, Stackpole Company, Harrisburg, Pa., and Wildlife Management Institute, Washington, D. C.

Murphy, R. C., 1926, Oceanic and climatic phenomena along the west coast of South America during 1925, *Geograph. Rev. 16:* 26–54.

Murphy, R. C., 1936, *Oceanic Birds of South America*, American Museum of Natural History, New York.

Murray, J., and J. Hjort, 1912, Depths of the ocean, Macmillan, London.

Naylor, A. W., 1952, The control of flowering, *Sci. American 186,* 5: 49–58.

Needham, J. G., and J. T. Lloyd, 1937, *The Life of Inland Waters*, Comstock, Ithaca, N. Y.

Neville, W. C., and A. Perlmutter, 1941, *A Study of Certain Marine Fishery Problems of Suffolk County, Long Island, New York*, Board of Supervisors, Suffolk County, New York.

Nicholls, A. G., 1933, On the biology of *Calanus finmarchicus*. III. Vertical distribution and diurnal migration in the Clyde Sea area, *J. Marine Biol. Assoc. United Kingdom, 19:* 139–164.

Nielsen, A., 1950, The torrential invertebrate fauna, *Oikos, 2:* 176–196.

Nielsen, C. O., 1949, Studies on the soil microfauna. II. The soil inhabiting nematodes, *Natura Jutlandica, 2:* 1–127.

Niering, W. A., 1953, The past and present vegetation of High Point State Park, New Jersey, *Ecol. Monographs, 23:* 127–148.

Odum, E. P., 1953, *Fundamentals of Ecology*, Saunders, Philadelphia.

Oosting, H. J., 1948, The Study of Plant Communities, W. H. Freeman & Co., San Francisco.

Oosting, H. J., and W. D. Billings, 1942, Factors affecting vegetational zonation on coastal dunes, *Ecology, 23:* 131.

Osborn, F., 1948, *Our Plundered Planet*, Little, Brown & Co., Boston.

Park, O., 1931, The measurement of daylight in the Chicago area and its ecological significance, *Ecol. Monographs, 1:* 189–230.

Park, O., 1940, Nocturnalism—the development of a problem, *Ecol. Monographs, 10:* 485–536.

Park, O., 1941, Quantitative determination of rhythmicity in organisms, *Ohio J. Sci., 41:* 39–45.

Park, O., W. C. Allee, and V. E. Shelford, 1939, *A Laboratory Introduction to Animal Ecology and Taxonomy*, University of Chicago Press.

Park, T., 1941, The laboratory population as a test of a comprehensive ecological system, *Quart. Rev. Biol., 16:* 274–293, 440–461.

Parkins, A. E., and J. R. Whitaker, 1939, *Our Natural Resources and Their Conservation*, Wiley, New York.

Parr, A. E., 1939, Quantitative observations on the pelagic sargassum vegetation of western North Atlantic, *Bull. Bingham Oceanographic Collection, 6*, Art. 7.

Patrick, Ruth, 1948, Factors affecting the distribution of diatoms, *Botan. Rev., 14:* 473–524.

Pearl, R., and S. L. Parker, 1922, Experimental studies on the duration of life. IV, Data on the influence of density of population on the duration of life in *Drosophila, Am. Naturalist, 56:* 312–321.

Pearl, R., L. J. Reed, and J. F. Kish, 1940, The logistic curve and the census count of 1940, *Science, 92:* 486–488.

Pearse, A. S., 1939, *Animal Ecology*, McGraw-Hill, New York.

Pearse, A. S., 1942, *Introduction to Parasitology*, Thomas, Springfield.

Pearse, A. S., 1950, *The Emigrations of Animals from the Sea*, Sherwood Press, Dryden, N. Y.

Pennak, R. W., 1939, The microscopic fauna of the sandy beaches, *Publ. Am. Assoc. Advanc. Sci., 10:* 94.

Pennak, R. W., 1942, Ecology of some copepods inhabiting intertidal beaches near Woods Hole, Mass., *Ecology, 23:* 446–456.

Petrides, G. A., 1950, The determination of sex and age ratios in fur animals, *Am. Midland Naturalist, 43:* 355–382.

Petrunkevitch, A., 1952, The spider and the wasp, *Sci. American, 187* (2): 20–23.

Phillips, W. S., 1940, A tropical hammock on the Miami (Fla.) limestone, *Ecology, 21:* 166–175.

Pitelka, F. A., 1941, Distribution of birds in relation to major biotic communities. *Am. Midland Naturalist, 25:* 113–137.

Pittendrigh, C. S., 1948, The Bromeliad—Anopheles—Malaria Complex in Trinidad. I. The Bromeliad Flora, *Evolution*, 2: 58–89.

Potzger, J. E., 1939, Microclimate and a notable case of its influence on a ridge in Central Indiana, *Ecology*, 20: 29–37.

Pratt, D. M., 1943, Analysis of population development in *Daphnia* at different temperatures, *Biol. Bull.*, 85: 116–140.

Pratt, D. M., 1950, Experimental study of the phosphorus cycle in fertilized salt water, *J. Marine Research (Sears Foundation)*, 9: 29–54.

Pratt, D. M., 1953, Abundance and growth of *Venus mercenaria* and *Callocardia morrhuana* in relation to the character of bottom sediments, *J. Marine Research (Sears Foundation)*, 12: 60–74.

Prescott, G. W., 1939, Some relationships of phytoplankton to limnology and aquatic biology, Problems of Lake Biology, *Pub. Am. Assoc. Advance Sci.*, 10: 65–78.

Prescott, G. W., 1948, Objectionable algae with reference to the killing of fish and other animals, *Hydrobiol.*, 1: 1–13.

Prosser, C. L. (Ed), 1950, *Comparative Animal Physiology*, Saunders, Philadelphia.

Rakestraw, N. W., 1950, The conception of alkalinity or excess base of sea water, *J. Marine Research (Sears Foundation)*, 8: 14–20.

Rasquin, P., 1947, Progressive pigmentary regression in fishes associated with cave environments, *Zoologica*, 32 (1): 35–41.

Raunkiaer, Christen, 1934, The life forms of plants and statistical plant geography, The Clarendon Press, Oxford.

Raup, H. M., 1951, Vegetation and cryoplanation, *Ohio J. Sci.*, 51: 105–116.

Ray, H., and M. Chakraverty, 1934, Lunar periodicity in the conjugation of *Conchophthirius lamellidens* Ghosh, *Nature*, 134: 663–664.

Raymont, J. E. G., 1950, A fish cultivation experiment in an arm of a sea-loch. IV. The bottom fauna of Kyle Scotnish, *Proc. Roy. Soc. Edinburgh, B, 64*: 65–108.

Raymont, J. E. G., and F. Gross, 1942, On the feeding and breeding of *Calanus finmarchicus* under laboratory conditions, *Proc. Roy. Soc. Edinburgh, B, 61*: 267–287.

Redfield, A. C., 1934, On the proportions of organic derivatives in sea water and their relation to the composition of plankton, *James Johnstone Memorial Volume, Univ. Liverpool*, pp. 176–192.

Redfield, A. C., 1941, The physiology of the environment, *Lowell Institute Lectures*, Boston, Mass. (Unpublished.)

Redfield, A. C., H. P. Smith, and B. H. Ketchum, 1937, The cycle of organic phosphorus in the Gulf of Maine, *Biol. Bull.*, 73: 421–443.

Rice, T. R., 1949, The effect of nutrients and metabolites on populations of planktonic algae, Ph.D. thesis, Harvard University, Biology Dept.

Rice, T. R., 1954, Biotic influences affecting population growth of planktonic algae, *U. S. Fish Wildlife Service, Fishery Bull. 87*.

Richards, P. W., 1952, The tropical rain forest: an ecological study, Cambridge University Press.

Riley, G. A., 1944, The carbon metabolism and photosynthetic efficiency of the earth, *Am. Scientist*, 32: 132–134.

Riley, G. A., 1952, Biological Oceanography, *Survey of Biological Progress*, G. S. Avery, Jr., Editor, 2: 79–103, Academic Press, New York.

Riley, G. A., H. Stommel, and D. F. Bumpus, 1949, Quantitative ecology of the plankton of the western North Atlantic, *Bull. Bingham Oceanog. Coll., 12* (3): 1–169.

Robertson, F. W., and J. H. Sang, 1944, The ecological determinants of population growth in a *Drosophila* culture. I. Fecundity of adult flies, *Proc. Roy. Soc. London, B, 132:* 258–277.

Robertson, J. D., 1941, The function and metabolism of calcium in the invertebrates, *Biol. Rev., 16:* 106–133.

Rowan, W., 1938, Light and seasonal reproduction in animals, *Biol. Rev., 13:* 374–402.

Rubey, W. W., 1951, Geologic history of sea water, *Bull. Geol. Soc. Amer., 62:* 1111–1147.

Russell, F. S., 1942, *The Overfishing Problem,* Cambridge University Press.

Russell, F. S., 1935, A review of some aspects of zooplankton research, *Rapports et proces verbaux, Conseil permanent intern. l'exploration mer, 45:* 1–30.

Russell, F. S., 1939, Hydrographical and biological conditions in the North Sea as indicated by plankton organisms, *J. conseil, Conseil permanent intern. l'exploration mer, 14:* 171–192.

Russell, F. S., and C. M. Yonge, 1928, *The Seas,* Warne, New York.

Ruttner, F., 1953, *Fundamentals of Limnology* (Translated by D. G. Frey and F. E. J. Fry), University of Toronto Press.

Ruud, J. T., 1952, Modern whaling and its prospects, *Food and Agr. Organization U. N., Fisheries Bulletin 5* (5): 2–21.

Ryther, J. H., 1954a, The ecology of phytoplankton blooms in Moriches Bay and Great South Bay, Long Island, New York, *Biol. Bull. 106:* 198–209.

Ryther, J. H., 1954b, Inhibitory effects of phytoplankton upon the feeding of *Daphnia magna,* with reference to growth, reproduction, and survival, *Ecology, 35:* in press.

Salt, G. F., F. S. J. Hollick, F. Raw, and M. V. Brian, 1948, The arthropod population of pasture soil, *J. Animal Ecol., 17:* 139–150.

Schallek, W., 1943, The Reaction of certain Crustacea to direct and to diffuse light, *Biol. Bull. 84:* 98–105.

Scheer, B. T., 1945, The development of marine fouling communities, *Biol. Bull. 89:* 103–121.

Scheer, B. T., 1948, *Comparative Physiology,* Wiley, New York.

Schmidt, Johannes, 1925, The breeding places of the eel, *Smithsonian Inst. Ann. Rept. 1924,* p. 279.

Schmidt-Nielsen, B. and K., 1950, Evaporative water loss in desert rodents in their natural habitat, *Ecology, 31:* 75–80.

Scholander, P. F., 1940, Experimental investigation on the respiratory function in diving mammals and birds, *Norske Videnskaps-Akad. Oslo, Hvalrådets Skrifter, 22:* 1–131.

Scholander, P. F., W. Flagg, V. Walters, and L. Irving, 1953, Climatic adaptation in arctic and tropical poikilotherms, *Physiol. Zoöl., 26:* 67–92.

Schuett, F., 1934, Studies in mass physiology. The activities of goldfishes under different conditions of aggregation, *Ecology, 15:* 258–282.

Schulman, E., 1948, Dendrochronology in northeastern Utah, *Tree-Ring Bull. 14:* 1–14.

Sears, M., and G. L. Clarke, 1940, Annual fluctuations in the abundance of marine zooplankton, *Biol. Bull. 79:* 321–328.

Sears, P. B., 1935, *Deserts on the March,* University of Oklahoma Press, Norman, Okla.

Sears, P. B., 1937, *This Is Our World,* University of Oklahoma Press, Norman.

Sears, P. B., 1939, *Life and Environment,* Teachers College, Columbia University, New York.

Sears, P. B., 1950, *Charles Darwin—the Naturalist as a Cultural Force,* Scribner, New York.

Sette, O. E., 1943, Biology of the Atlantic mackerel, *Scomber scombris.* Part I. Early Life History, *U. S. Fish Wildlife Service, Fishery Bull.* 38.

Sette, O. E., and A. W. H. Needler, 1934, Statistics of the mackerel fishery off the east coast of North America 1804 to 1930, *U. S. Bur. Fisheries, Investigational Rept. 1* (19): 1–48.

Shapley, H. (editor), 1953, *Climatic Change; Evidence Causes, and Effects,* Harvard University Press.

Shelford, V. E., 1951, Fluctuation of non-forest animal populations in the upper Mississippi Basin, *Ecol. Monographs, 21:* 149–181.

Shelford, V. E., 1951a, Fluctuation of forest animal populations in East Central Illinois, *Ecol. Monographs, 21:* 183–214.

Shipley, A. E., 1925, *Life,* Macmillan, New York.

Siggins, H. W., 1933, Distribution and rate of fall of conifer seeds, *J. Agr. Research, 47:* 119.

Siivanen, L., 1948, Structure of short-cyclic fluctuations in numbers of mammals and birds in the northern parts of the Northern hemisphere, *Finnish Foundation for Game Preservation, Papers on Game Research, 1,* Helsinki.

Sinnott, E. W., 1929, *Botany, Principles and Problems,* McGraw-Hill, New York.

Smith, F. E., 1952, Experimental methods in population dynamics, a critique, *Ecology, 33:* 441–450.

Smith, Guy-Harold, 1950, *Conservation of Natural Resources,* Wiley, New York.

Smith, G. M. (Editor), 1951, *Manual of Phycology,* Chronica Botanica Co., Waltham, Mass., Chapter B. Pigments (H. H. Strain).

Smith, H. W., 1936, The retention and physiological role of urea in the Elasmobranchii, *Biol. Revs, 11:* 49–82.

Smith, V. G., 1928, Animal communities of a deciduous forest succession, *Ecology, 9:* 479–500.

Solomon, M. E., 1949, The natural control of animal populations, *J. Animal Ecol., 18:* 1–35.

Spurway, C. H., 1941, Soil reaction (pH) preference of plants, *Mich. Agr. Expt. Sta., Spec. Bull. 306.*

Stauffer, R. C., 1937, Changes in the invertebrate community of a lagoon after disappearance of eelgrass, *Ecology, 18:* 427–431.

Steemann Nielsen, E., 1952, Experimental CO_2 curves in photosynthesis, *Physiol. Plantarum, 5:* 145–159.

Steemann Nielsen, E., 1952, The use of radio-active carbon (C_{14}) for measuring organic production in the sea, *J. conseil, Conseil permanent intern. l'exploration mer, 18:* 117–139.

Steemann Nielsen, E., 1953, Carbon dioxide concentration, respiration during photosynthesis, and maximum quantum yield of photosynthesis, *Physiologia Plantarum, 6:* 316–332.

Steinhaus, E. A., 1946, *Insect Microbiology,* Comstock, Ithaca, New York.

Stephenson, T. A., and A. Stephenson, 1949, The universal features of zonation between tide-marks on rocky coasts, *J. Ecol., 37:* 289–305.

Stewart, R. E., and J. W. Aldrich, 1951, Removal and repopulation of breeding birds in a spruce-fir forest community, *Auk, 68:* 471–482.

Stickel, L. F., 1950, Populations and home range relationships of the box turtle, *Terrapene c. Carolina* (Linnaeus), *Ecol. Monographs, 20:* 351–378.

Stiles, W., 1946, *Trace Elements in Plants and Animals*, Cambridge University Press.

Strandine, E. J., 1940, A quantitative study of the periodical *Cicada* with respect to soil of three forests, *Am. Midland Naturalist, 24:* 177–183.

Strohecker, H. F., 1938, Measurement of solar ultra-violet in the Chicago area, *Ecology, 19:* 57–80.

Sumner, F. B., 1935, Protective value of fish color change, *Am. Naturalist, 69:* 245–266.

Sverdrup, H. U., 1953, On conditions for the vernal blooming of phytoplankton, *J. conseil, Conseil permanent intern. l'exploration mer, 18* (3): 287–295.

Sverdrup, H. U., M. W. Johnson, and R. H. Fleming, 1942, *The Oceans*, Prentice-Hall, New York.

Swingle, H. S., and E. V. Smith, 1942, Management of farm fish ponds, *Ala. Agr. Expt. Sta. Bull. 254.*

Talbot, M., and C. H. Kennedy, 1940, The slave-making ant *Formica sanguinea subintegra* Emery. Its raids, nuptial flights and nest structure, *Ann. Entomol. Soc. Amer., 33:* 560–577.

Tansley, A. G., 1939, *Practical Plant Ecology*, G. Allen and Unwin. Ltd., London.

Taylor, W. P., 1936, What is ecology and what good is it? *Ecology, 17:* 333.

Thompson, D'Arcy W., 1942, *On Growth and Form*, Cambridge University Press.

Thornthwaite, C. W., 1931, The climates of North America according to a new classification, *Geograph. Rev., 21:* 633–655.

Thorpe, W. H., and F. G. W. Jones, 1937, Olfactory conditioning in a parasitic insect and its relation to the problem of host selection, *Proc. Roy. Soc. London, B., 124:* 56–81.

Thorson, G., 1950, Reproductive and larval ecology of marine bottom invertebrates, *Biol. Revs., 25:* 1–45.

Todd, V., 1949, The habits and ecology of the British harvestmen (Arachnida, opiliones) with special reference to those of the Oxford district, *J. Animal Ecol., 18:* 209–216.

Transeau, E. N., 1926, The accumulation of energy by plants, *Ohio J. Sci., 26:* 1–10.

Tressler, W. L., L. H. Tiffany, and W. P. Spencer, 1940, Limnological studies of Buckeye Lake, Ohio, *Ohio J. Sci., 40:* 261–290.

Trippensee, R. E., 1954, *Wildlife Management*, McGraw-Hill, New York.

Turner, W. I., and V. M. Henry, 1939, Growing plants in Nutrient Solutions, Wiley, New York.

Twenhofel, W. H., 1939, *Principles of Sedimentation*, McGraw-Hill, New York.

Utida, S., 1950, On the equilibrium state of the interacting populations of an insect and its parasite, *Ecology, 31:* 165–175.

Uvarov, B. P., 1931, Insects and climate, *Trans. Entomol. Soc. London, 79:* 1–247.

Vogt, W., 1948, *Road to Survival*, Wm. Sloane Assoc., New York.

Volterra, V., 1931, Variation and fluctuation of the number of individuals in animal species living together, in R. N. Chapman, *Animal Ecology*, McGraw-Hill, New York, pp. 409–448.

Waksman, S. A., 1932, *Principles of Soil Microbiology*, Williams and Wilkins, Baltimore.

Waksman, S. A., 1936, *Humus—Origin, Chemical Composition, and Importance in Nature*, Williams and Wilkins, Baltimore.

Walker, Boyd W., 1949, Periodicity of spawning by the grunion *Leuresthes tenuis*, an atherine fish, Ph.D. thesis, University of California at Los Angeles.

Walker, B. W., 1952, A guide to the grunion, *Calif. Fish Game*, 38: 409–420.

Warburg, O., 1948, Assimilation quotient and photochemical yield, *Am J. Botany*, 35: 194–204.

Warburg, O., D. Burk, and V. Shocken, 1950, The quantum efficiency of photosynthesis, *Biochim. et Biophys. Acta*, 4: 335–346.

Warfel, H. E., and D. Merriman, 1944, Studies of the marine resources of southern New England. I. An analysis of the fish population of the shore zone, *Bull. Bingham Oceanog. Collection*, 9 (2): 1–83.

Wassink, E. C., B. Kok, and J. L. P. van Oorschot, 1953, The efficiency of light-energy conversion in Chlorella cultures as compared with higher plants, *Carnegie Inst. Wash. Publ. 600:* 55–62.

Waterman, T. H., R. F. Nunnemacher, F. A. Chace, Jr., and G. L. Clarke, 1939, Diurnal vertical migrations of deep-water plankton, *Biol. Bull. 76:* 256–279.

Weaver, J. E., 1947, Rate of decomposition of roots and rhizomes of certain range grasses in undisturbed prairie soil, *Ecology*, 28: 221–240.

Weaver, J. E., and F. E. Clements, 1938, *Plant Ecology*, McGraw-Hill, New York.

Welch, Paul S., 1952, *Limnology*, McGraw-Hill, New York.

Wells, H. G., J. S. Huxley, G. P. Wells, 1939, *The Science of Life*, Book 6, Part V, Garden City Publishing Co., Garden City, L. I.

Welsh, J. H., 1932, Temperature and light as factors influencing the rate of swimming of larvae of the mussel crab, *Pinnotheres maculatus Say*, *Biol. Bull. 63:* 310–326.

Welsh, J. H., 1938, Diurnal rhythms, *Quart. Rev. Biol., 13:* 123–139.

Welty, J. C., 1934, Experiments in group behaviour of fishes, *Physiol. Zoöl.*, 7: 85–128.

Went, F. W., 1950, Climatic control of flowering and fruit set, *Am. Naturalist*, 84: 161–170.

Went, F. W., 1950, The response of plants to climate, *Science, 112:* 489–494.

Wesenberg-Lund, C., 1910, Summary of our knowledge regarding various limnological problems, in Murray and Pullar's *Bathymetrical Survey of the Scottish Fresh-Water Lochs, 1:* 374.

Weston, W. H., Jr., 1923, Production and dispersal of conidia in the Philippine *Sclerosporas* of Maize, *J. Agr. Research*, 23: 239–278.

Wheeler, W. M., 1923, *Social Life among the Insects*, Harcourt, New York.

Wheeler, W. M., 1926, *Ants*, Columbia University Press, New York.

Wherry, E. T., 1932, Ecological studies of serpentine-barren plants: I. Ash composition, *Proc. Pennsylvania Acad. Sci.*, 6: 32–38.

Whitney, R. J., 1942, Diurnal fluctuations of oxygen and *p*H in two small ponds and a stream, *J. Exptl. Biol., 19:* 92–99.

Whittaker, R. H., 1953, A consideration of climax theory: the climax as a population and pattern, *Ecol. Monographs*, 23: 41–78.

Wilbur, K. M., and L. H. Jodrey, 1952, Studies on shell formation, *Biol. Bull. 103:* 269–276.

Williams, C. B., G. F. Cockbill, M. E. Gibbs, and J. A. Downes, 1942, Studies in the migration of Lepidoptera, *Trans. Roy. Entomol. Soc. London*, 92: 101–283.

Wilson, C. C., 1948, Fog and atmospheric CO_2 as related to apparent photosynthetic rate of some broadleaf evergreens, *Ecology, 29:* 507–508.

Wilson, D. P., 1951, *Life of the Shore and Shallow Sea,* Nicholson & Watson, London.

Wilson, E. O., 1953, The origin and evolution of Polymorphism in ants, *Quart. Rev. Biol., 28:* 136–156.

Wilson, L. R., 1939, Rooted aquatic plants and their relation to the limnology of fresh-water lakes, in *Problems of Lake Biology, Publ. Am. Assoc. Advance. Sci. 10.*

Wolcott, R. H., 1946, *Animal Biology,* McGraw-Hill, New York.

Wolfanger, L. A., 1950, The Great Soil Groups and Their Utilization, pp. 25–62, in *Conservation of Natural Resources,* Guy-Harold Smith (Editor), Wiley, New York.

Wolfenbarger, D. O., 1946, Dispersion of small organisms. Distance dispersion rates of bacteria, spores, seeds, pollen and insects; incidence rates of diseases and injuries, *Am. Midland Naturalist, 35:* 1.

Woods Hole Oceanographic Institution, 1952, *Marine Fouling and its Prevention,* Washington, D. C., Naval Institute.

Yonge, C. M., 1944, Experimental analysis of the association between invertebrates and unicellular algae, *Biol. Rev., 19:* 68–80.

Yonge, C. M., 1949, *The Sea Shore,* Collins, London.

ZoBell, C. E., 1946, *Marine Microbiology,* Chronica Botanica Co., Waltham, Mass.

ZoBell, C. E., and C. H. Oppenheimer, 1950, Some effects of hydrostatic pressure on the multiplication and morphology of marine bacteria, *J. Bacteriol., 60:* 771–781.

GUIDE TO NEW REFERENCES

Chapter 1. Viewpoint of Modern Ecology

The Meaning of Ecology: Farb et al., 1963; Platt and Wolfe, 1964.
The Meaning of Environment (pp. 3–13).
  The Critical Environment: Greenway, 1958; Street, 1963; Thomas, 1956.
  Application to Conservation: Clawson, 1964; Dasmann, 1959, 1964; Landsberg, 1963; LeCren and Holdgate, 1962; Parson, 1964.
The Development of Ecology (pp. 13–18): Stauffer, 1957.
  The Ecological Complex: Billings, 1965; Macfadyen, 1963; Odum, 1963.
The Scope of Ecology: Margalef, 1963; Sears, 1962.

Chapter 2. The Medium

Pressure (pp. 27–32).
  Pressure Reduction with Altitude: Dorst, 1963; Swan, 1961.
  Pressure Increase with Depth: Bainbridge, 1961; Dietz, 1963; Hardy, 1959, Ch. 15; Idyll, 1964; Marshall, 1961; Scholander, 1963; Wollf, 1960; Zobell and Morita, 1959.
Support and Resistance to Motion (pp. 32–41).
  Effects on Structure and Size; Denton, 1960, 1963.
  Effects on Locomotion through Medium: Bainbridge, 1958; Gray, 1957; Meinertzhagen, 1955.
  Existence of Plankton: Hardy, 1956; Palmer, 1962; Raymont, 1963; Ruttner, 1963; Yentsch, 1962.
Transportation by Medium (pp. 42–52).
  Sessile Existence: Hardy, 1959; Macan, 1963, Ch. 4, 7; Moore, 1958; Thorson, 1957.
  Distribution by Medium.
    Transport by Air: Andrewartha, 1961; Brown et al., 1964; Darlington, 1957; Gregory, 1962.
    Transport by Water: Bousfield, 1955; Bruun, 1963; Dunbar, 1963; Johnson and Brinton, 1963; King, 1963; Maguire, 1963; Pickard, 1964; Southward, 1961–2; Von Arx, 1962.
Abrasive Action of Medium (pp. 53–58): Daubenmire, 1959, Ch. 6; Kingsbury, 1962; Southward, 1958; Weaver, 1963; Wilson, 1959.

Chapter 3. The Substratum

Significance of the Substratum (pp. 59–66).
  Attainment of the Substratum: Crisp and Meadows, 1962.
  Reactions to the Substratum: Dunning and Roeder, 1965; Griffin, 1958; Kellogg, 1961; Lissmann, 1963; Pye, 1963.
  The Variety of Substrata: Clements, 1963; Nair, 1962; Ray, 1959; Wisely, 1963.
Rock, Sand, and Mud in Aquatic Environment (pp. 66–71).
  Influence of the Aquatic Substrata: Bruun, 1957; Hedgpeth, 1957; Lewis, 1964; Ruttner, 1963; Scheltema, 1961; Swedmark, 1964; Thorson, 1957.

Breakdown and Build-Up of the Substratum: Deevey, 1958; Goreau and Hartman, 1963; Phleger, 1960; Sognnaes, 1963; Wells, 1957.
Rock, Sand, and Soil in Terrestrial Environment (pp. 71–84).
Influence of the Land Substrata.
Land Surfaces and Animals: Amos, 1959; Coulianos and Johnels, 1963; Miller, 1964; Pruitt, 1960.
Soil and Its Action on Plants: Daubenmire, 1959, Ch. 2; Eyre, 1963.
Action of Organisms on Soil.
Abundance of Organisms in Soil: Kevan, 1962; Murphy, 1962.
Soil Formation: Buckman and Brady, 1960; Griffin, 1963; Kühnelt, 1961; Lyford, 1963; Satchell, 1960; United States Department of Agriculture, 1957.
Soil-Group Divisions: Smith, 1963.

Chapter 4.   Water

Water Problem in the Aquatic Environment (pp. 91–128).
Composition of Natural Waters: Goldberg, 1963; Hutchinson, 1957; Redfield et al., 1963; Reid, 1961; Ruttner, 1963.
Methods of Meeting Osmotic Problem: Guillard, 1962; Potts and Parry, 1964; Prosser and Brown, 1961, Ch. 2; Segal and Burbanck, 1963; Schmidt-Nielsen and Kim, 1964.
Limiting Effects of Salinity: Carpelon, 1964; Gunter, 1961; Hedgpeth, 1957, Ch. 7, 23; Jeffries, 1964; Kinne, 1964; Lance, 1963; Macan, 1963, Ch. 10; Smith, 1959; Strogonov, 1964; Whittaker and Fairbanks, 1958.
Amphibious Situations (pp. 99–106).
Swamps, Marshes, Estuaries, and Tidal Zone: Chapman, 1960; Connecticut Arboretum, 1961; Kendeigh, 1961, Ch. 7; Lauff, 1965; Lewis, 1964; Ray, 1958; Ricketts and Calvin, 1962; Savage, 1961; Southward, 1958.
Water Problem in the Terrestrial Environment (pp. 107–128).
Occurrence of Water in Land Environment: Greenshields, 1964; Revelle, 1963.
Moisture in the Soil and in the Air: Childs, 1964; Lyford, 1964; Thomas and Leopold, 1964.
Microclimates: Geiger, 1964; Ross, 1958.
Meeting Water Problem on Land: Bartholomew and Cade, 1963; Daubenmire, 1959, Ch. 3; Kozlowski, 1964; Rutter and Whitehead, 1963; Schmidt-Nielsen, 1964.
Influence of Moisture on Growth and Distribution: Coupland, 1958; Evans, 1963; Kozlowski, 1962.

Chapter 5.   Temperature

Distribution of Temperature (pp. 129–140).
Extremes of Temperature and of Tolerance: Gunter, 1957; Leopold et al., 1962.
Changes in Temperature: Bjerknes, 1961; Kendrew, 1961; Kristensen, 1959; Lewis, 1963; Macan, 1963, Ch. 8; Raymont, 1963, Ch. 1; Ruttner, 1963; Williams, 1962.
Biological Action of Temperature (pp. 141–158).
Extreme Temperatures: Kempner, 1963; Smith, 1958.

Methods of Meeting Temperature Extremes: Prosser and Brown, 1961, Ch. 9.

Morphological and Physiological Adaptations: Bartholomew and Hudson, 1960; Hardy, 1961; Lasiewski, 1964; Lyman, 1963; Lyman and Dawe, 1960; Mayer, 1964; Read, 1964; Scholander et al., 1957.

Thermal Migrations: Amos, 1959; Dorst, 1963; Geiger, 1964; Pruitt, 1960; Schmidt-Nielsen, 1964.

Action within Effective Range: Andrewartha, 1961; Ch. 5; Daubenmire, 1959, Ch. 4; Fraenkel and Gunn, 1961, Ch. 14; Kinne, 1963; Lee and Badham, 1963; Mani, 1962; Ray, 1960.

Action of Temperature on Distribution (pp. 159–184).

Mode of Temperature Limitation: Mayer and Poljakoff-Mayber, 1963; Norris, 1963; Prosser and Brown, 1961, Ch. 9.

Results of Temperature Limitation: Bary, 1963; Billings, 1964; Greig-Smith, 1964; Hadley and Bliss, 1964; Oosting, 1956, Ch. 5.

Temperature and Moisture Acting Together: Gleason and Cronquist, 1964; Dansereau, 1957, Ch. 2; Kendrew, 1961.

Chapter 6. Light

Distribution of Light (pp. 185–197).

Light on Land and in Water: Clarke and Denton, 1962; Gates, 1962; Jerlov, 1963; Landsberg, 1963; Spurr, 1964, Ch. 2.

Biological Effects of Light (pp. 198–241).

General Effects: Brower, et al., 1963; Clarke and Sheppard, 1960; Giese, 1964; Gohor, 1963; Hamilton and Barth, 1962; Kettlewell, 1961; Mayr, 1963; McElroy and Glass, 1961; Moore, 1963, p. 143; Prosser and Brown, 1961, Ch. 12, 18, 19.

Activity, Vision, and Bioluminescence: Clarke and Kelly, 1965; Hardy and Kay, 1964; McElroy and Seliger, 1962; Nicol, 1962, 1963; Seliger et al., 1964; Waterman, 1961.

Orientation: Autrum, 1963; Cold Spring Harbor Symposium, 1960; Fraenkel and Gunn, 1961; Griffin, 1964; Jander, 1963; Jander et al., 1963; Kramer, 1961; Moore, 1963, p. 338; Ortlele and Sexton, 1964; Papi and Pardi, 1963.

Periodicity,

Diurnal Periodicity: Brown, 1962; Brünning, 1964; Clarke and Backus, 1964; Cloudsley-Thompson, 1961; Dietz, 1962; Kruuk, 1963; McNaught and Hasler, 1964; Pittendrigh, 1962.

Lunar Periodicity: Korringa, 1957; Barnwell, 1963.

Seasonal Periodicity: Butler and Downs, 1960; Danilevskii, 1965; Farner, 1964a,b; Hillman, 1962; McLeod and Beck, 1963.

Ultraviolet Light: Armstrong and Boalch, 1961; Cumming, 1964; Halldal, 1964.

Ecological Aspects of Photosynthesis. Billings, 1965, Daubenmire, 1959, Ch. 5; Evans, 1963, Ch. 6, 8, 14; Fogg, 1963; Lewin, 1962, Ch. 1, 52, 53; Mohr, 1964; Raymont, 1963, Ch. 8.

Chapter 7. Oxygen and Carbon Dioxide

Oxygen (pp. 242–258).

Availability of Oxygen: Cooper, 1961; Daubenmire, 1959, Ch. 6; Eberly, 1964; Hutchinson, 1957, Ch. 9, 11; Reid, 1961, Ch. 9; Raymont, 1963, Ch. 2.

Effects of Oxygen Availability: Blazka, 1958; Evans, 1963, Ch. 7; Macan, 1963, Ch. 9; Prosser and Brown, 1961, Ch. 7, 8; Ruttner, 1963; Stiles, 1960; Turner and Brittain, 1962.

Carbon Dioxide (pp. 259–276).

Carbon Dioxide and pH in Terrestrial Environment: Bray, 1959; Darling, 1963; Daubenmire, 1959, Ch. 6; Evans, 1963, Ch. 7.

Carbon Dioxide and pH in Aquatic Environment: Hasler, 1960; Kanwisher, 1960; Prosser and Brown, 1961, Ch. 8; Reid, 1961, Ch. 9; Ruttner, 1963; Steemann-Nielsen, 1963; Wright, 1960.

Calcium Carbonate: Ashby, 1961; Bé and Ericson, 1962; Boolootian, 1963; Macan, 1963, Ch. 11; Miller, 1955, Ch. 5, 10; Sognnaes, 1960; Stross and Hasler, 1960; Wells, 1957; Wien, 1962; Yonge, 1963.

Chapter 8.   Nutrients

Nutrients and the Environment (pp. 277–296).

Influence of Nutrients on Green Plants

Nutrients Required: Bear, 1964; Hood, 1963; Hutchinson, 1957, Ch. 12–17; Lewin, 1962, Ch. 6, 8–10, 12, 17; Meyer et al., 1960, Ch. 15; Schutte, 1964; Taylor, 1964.

Law of the Minimum: Arnon, 1958; Menzel et al., 1963; Odum, 1963, Ch. 4, 5; Ruttner, 1963, p. 99; Sacki, 1962; Talling, 1962.

Limitation by Nutrients in Nature: Goldman, 1960; Harvey, 1957; Provasoli, 1963; Raymont, 1963, Ch. 7, 9, 16; Spurr, 1964, Ch. 7; Tryon and Hartman, 1960; Walker, 1954.

Influence of Nutrients on Animals: Anderson and Underwood, 1959; Bennett, 1962; Conover, 1964; Dendy, 1963; Mullin, 1963; Prosser and Brown, 1961, Ch. 3–6; Talbot and Talbot, 1963; Thorson, 1958; Underwood, 1962.

Decomposition and Regeneration (pp. 297–308).

Processes of Decomposition and Transformation: Daubenmire, 1959, Ch. 2; Heukelekian and Dondero, 1964; Kriss, 1963, Chap. 4, 8; Nicholas, 1963; Scholes and Shewan, 1964; Parsons, 1963; Watson, 1963; Witkamp, 1963; Wood, 1963.

Regeneration: Alexander, 1964; Cooper, 1961; Grill and Richards, 1964; Ketchum, 1963; Nye, 1961; Redfield, 1958; Redfield et al., 1963; Tyurin and Kononova, 1962.

Chapter 9.   Relations within the Species

Origin of Groups (pp. 309–316).

Reproduction: Darling, 1964; Mowat, 1963; Murie, 1962; Schaller, 1963.

Passive Transport: Bainbridge, 1957.

Active Locomotion.

Common Orientation: Fraenkel and Gunn, 1960.

Mutual Attraction: Bonner, 1963; Collias, 1964; Frings and Frings, 1964; Koo, 1962; Lilly, 1963; Schevill et al., 1962; Sebeok, 1962; Shaw, 1961, 1962; Wilson, 1963a; Wynne-Edwards, 1962.

Effects of Increased Numbers (pp. 316–332).

Harmful Effects: Calhoun, 1962; Lucas, 1961; Watt, 1960.

Beneficial Effects: Thorpe and Zangwill, 1961.

Protection: Lindauer, 1961.

Influence on Reproduction: Errington, 1963; Hailman, 1964; Lack, 1954; Mayr, 1963; Meyerriecks, 1962.

Division of Labor: Etkin, 1964; Guhl, 1956; Miller, 1964; Southwick, 1963; von Frisch, 1955, 1962; Wenner, 1964.

Population Development (pp. 333–347).

Form of Population Growth: Andrewartha, 1961; Slobodkin, 1961.

Equilibrium and Fluctuation: Colebrook, 1963; Dasmann, 1964; Davis, 1963; Hazen, 1964; Knipling, 1960; Mudd, 1964; Wynne-Edwards, 1964.

Optimal Yield: Hardy, 1959; LeCren and Holdgate, 1962.

Spatial Relations of Populations (pp. 348–361).

Home range and Territory; Calhoun, 1963; Carpenter, 1958; Frank, 1964; King, 1959; Lin, 1963; McNale, 1963; Meyerriecks, 1960; Pitelka, 1959; Tinbergen, 1959.

Homing and Return Migration: Autrum, 1963; Carr, 1962; Dorst, 1963; Griffin, 1964; Hasler, 1960; Johnson, 1963; Rawson and Hartline, 1964; Robinson and Falls, 1965; Southwood, 1962.

Emigration: Curry-Lindahl, 1963; Dempster, 1963; Nielsen, 1964.

Chapter 10.   Relations between Species

General References: Daubenmire, 1959, Ch. 7; Hedgpeth, 1957, Ch. 15; Henry, 1965; Kendeigh, 1961, Ch. 12; Nicol, 1960, Ch. 14; Nutman and Mosse, 1963; Odum, 1963, Ch. 6.

Symbiosis (pp. 364–380).

Mutualism: Ahmadjian, 1963; Lamb, 1959; Limbaugh et al., 1961; McLaughlin and Zahl, 1962; Way, 1963; Wilson, 1963b.

Commensalism: Davenport, 1965; Kozlowski, 1962, Ch. 15.

Antagonism (pp. 381–400).

Antibiosis: Collier, 1958; Dragovich and May, 1962; Garb, 1961; Lee and Monsi, 1963; Lucas, 1961; Nigrelli, 1963; Oppenheimer, 1963, Ch. 52, 53; Tryon and Hartman, 1960, pp. 22–55.

Exploitation.

Parasitism: Bocquet and Stock, 1963; Chandler and Read, 1961; Cheng, 1964; Debach, 1964; Rogers, 1962.

Predation: Duddington, 1956; Errington, 1963; Evans, 1963; Ivlev, 1961; Klopfer, 1962; Maio, 1958; Thorsteinson, 1960; Tinbergen and Klomp, 1960.

Competition: Burnett, 1960; Clatworthy and Harper, 1962; Connell, 1961; Hardin, 1960; Huffaker, 1958; Hutchinson, 1961; MacArthur, 1958; MacArthur and Connell, 1965; Mayr, 1963, Ch. 4; Park, 1962; Symposium Soc. Exp. Biol., No. 15, 1961; Wynne-Edwards, 1962, Ch. 12.

Chapter 11.   The Community

General References: Bodenheimer, 1958, Ch. 5; Frey, 1963; Gleason and Cronquist, 1964; Glover, 1961; Hanson and Churchill, 1961; Neill, 1964; Shelford, 1963.

Community Concept: Fager, 1963; Hanson, 1958; Kendeigh, 1961, Ch. 3, 20; Odum, 1959, Ch. 8; Poore, 1962; Whittaker, 1962.

Community Dominance and Species Diversity: Brewer, 1963; Fager and Mc-Gowan, 1963; Hairston, 1959; Hutchinson, 1959; MacArthur, 1960; Norris, 1960; Paine, 1963; Patten, 1963; Whittaker, 1965.

Community Composition: Cassie, 1963; Lamprey, 1963; Hulburt, 1964; Moore and Nicholas, 1964; Whittaker and Fairbanks, 1958; Williams, 1960, 1964.

Structure and Stratification: Bider, 1962; Dansereau, 1957 (pp. 147–154); Margalef, 1963; Oosting, 1956, Ch. 4; Spurr, 1964, Ch. 14.

Chapter 12.   Succession and Fluctuation

Ecological Succession (pp. 425–446).

Dispersal and Invasion: Andrewartha, 1961, Ch. 4, 10; Gleason and Cronquist, 1964; Elton, 1958; Howard, 1960.

Succession and Climax: Benton and Werner, 1958, Ch. 5, 6; Churchill and Hanson, 1958; Kendeigh, 1961, Ch. 10, 16, 17; Kershaw, 1964, Ch. 3, 4; Oosting, 1956, Ch. 10.

Types of Succession: Cooper, 1961; Daubenmire, 1959, Ch. 8; Eggler, 1963; Ellison, 1960; Humphrey, 1962 Ch. 9, 10; Lamb and Zimmerman, 1964; Lippert and Jameson, 1964; Margalef, 1958; Oppenheimer, 1963; Ch. 27, 58; Redfield, 1964; Spurr, 1964, Ch. 12; Taylor, 1957.

Community Classification (pp. 447–450).

Community Types and Biomes: Dansereau, 1957; Hanson and Churchill, 1961, Ch. 6; Kendeigh, 1961, Ch. 20–28; Oosting, 1956, Ch. 11, 12; Shelford, 1963; Thorson, 1957.

Fluctuation Within the Community (pp. 451–464).

Irruptive and Cyclic Fluctuations: Cold Spring Harbor Symposium, 1957; Christian and Davis, 1964; Glock and Agerter, 1963; Hewitt, 1954; Keith, 1963; Lack, 1954, Ch. 19, 20; Nikolsky, 1963; Parrish and Craig, 1957; Pieper, 1964.

Chapter 13.   Dynamics of the Ecosystem

Fundamental Operation (pp. 465–481).

Principal Steps and Components: Davis, 1963; Macfadyen, 1963, Ch. 15–17; Odum, 1959, Ch. 2, 3; Odum, 1963, Ch. 2; Riley, 1963; Slobodkin, 1960.

Ecological Cycle in the Ocean.

Producers: Provasoli, 1963; Raymont, 1963; Steele, 1961; Steeman Nielsen, 1964; Strickland, 1960; Yentsch, 1963.

Herbivores and Carnivores: Conover, 1964; Cowey and Corner, 1963; Lagler et al., 1962; Lee, 1964; Nikolsky, 1963; Raymont and Carrie, 1964.

Decomposers and Transformers: Baylor and Sutcliffe, 1963; Krey, 1961; Wood, 1963.

Productivity of the Ecosystem (pp. 481–499).

Standing Crop, Yield and Production Rate.

Terrestrial Environment: Odum, 1960; Ovington, 1962; Niering, 1963; Talbot, 1964; Scott and Billings, 1964.

Aquatic Environment: Cushing, 1959; Doty, 1961; Elgmork, 1964; Fogg, 1965; Goldman, 1960b; Gordon and Kelly, 1962; Jackson, 1964; Nauwerck, 1963; Odum et al., 1963.

Energetics of Production: Beyers, 1963; Engelmann, 1961; Gates, 1965; Golley, 1960; Olson, 1963; Slobodkin, 1962; Wiegert, 1964; Wright, 1964.

Productivity of Land and Water (pp. 500–503). Cole, 1958; Fosberg, 1963; Odum, 1963, Ch. 3; Ovington et al., 1963; Ryther, 1963; Teal and Teal, 1964; Thorne, 1963; Westlake, 1963.

Pesticides and Radioactivity: American Institute of Biological Sciences, 1964; Carson, 1962; Cole, 1964; DeBach, 1964; Egler, 1964; Rudd, 1964; Schultz and Klement, 1963; Woodwell, 1963.

NEW REFERENCES FOR 1965 PRINTING

Ahmadjian, V., 1963, The fungi of lichens, *Sci. American, 208*(2): 123–132.

Alexander, M., 1964, Biochemical ecology of soil microorganisms, *Ann. Rev. Microbiol., 18:* 217–251.

American Institute of Biological Science, 1964, Special issue on the pesticide problem., *Bioscience, 14:* 15–46.

Amos, W. H., 1959, The life of a sand dune, *Sci. American, 201*(1): 91–99.

Anderson, A. J., and E. J. Underwood, 1959, Trace-element deserts, *Sci. American, 200*(1): 97–106.

Andrewartha, H. G., 1961, *Introduction to the Study of Animal Populations,* The University of Chicago Press, Chicago.

Armstrong, F. A. J., and G. T. Boalch, 1961, The ultra-violet absorption of sea water, *J. Marine Biol. Assoc., 41:* 591–597.

Arnon, D. I., 1958, Some functional aspects of inorganic micronutrients in the metabolism of green plants, *Perspectives in Marine Biology,* Buzzati-Traverso (ed.), 351–384, University of California Press, Los Angeles.

Ashby, M., 1961, *Introduction to Plant Ecology,* Macmillan, New York.

Autrum, H. (ed.), 1963, Animal orientation, *Ergeb. Biol., 26:* 1–303.

Bainbridge, R., 1957, The size, shape and density of marine phytoplankton concentrations, *Biol. Revs. 32:* 91–115.

Bainbridge, R., 1958, The speed of swimming fish as related to size and to the frequency and amplitude of the tail beat, *J. Exp. Biol., 35:* 109–133.

Bainbridge, R., 1961, Migrations, Chap. 12, in *The Physiology of Crustacea,* Vol. 2, T. H. Waterman, (ed.) Academic Press, New York.

Barnwell, F. H., 1963, Observations on daily and tidal rhythms in some fiddler crabs from equatorial Brazil, *Biol. Bull., 125:* 399–415.

Bartholomew, G. A., and J. W. Hudson, 1960, Aestivation in the Mohave ground squirrel, *Citellus mohavensis, Bull. Museum Comp. Zool., 124:* 193–208.

Bartholomew, G. A., and T. J. Cade, 1963, The water economy of land birds, *The Auk, 80:* 504–539.

Bary, B. M., 1963, Temperature, salinity and plankton in the eastern North Atlantic and coastal waters of Britain, 1957. III. The distribution of zooplankton in relation to water bodies, *J. Fisheries Research Board Can. 20,* 6: 1519–1548.

Baylor, E. R., and W. H. Sutcliffe, Jr., 1963, Dissolved organic matter in seawater as a source of particulate food, *Limnol. Oceanogr. 8*(4): 369–371.

Bé, A. W. H., and D. B. Ericson, 1962, Aspects of calcifications in planktonic foraminifera (Sarcodina), (*Globorotalia truncatulinoides*), in: Comparative biology of calcified tissue, 1962, *Ann. N. Y. Acad. Sci., 109:* 65–81.

Bear, F. (ed.), 1964, *Chemistry of the Soil* (2nd ed.), Reinhold, New York.

Bennett, G. W., 1962, *Management of Artificial Lakes and Ponds,* Reinhold, New York.

Benton, A. H., and W. E. Werner, 1958, *Principles of Field Biology and Ecology,* McGraw-Hill, New York.

Beyers, R. J., 1963, The metabolism of twelve aquatic laboratory microecosystems, *Ecol. Monographs, 33:* 281–306.

Bider, J. R., 1962, Dynamics and the temporo-spatial relations of a vertebrate community, *Ecology, 43:* 634–646.

Billings, W. D., 1965, *Plants and the Ecosystem,* Wadsworth, Belmont, California.

Bjerknes, J., 1961, El Niño-study based on analysis of ocean surface temperatures 1935–57, *Inter-American Tropical Tuna Commission, Bull.*, 5(3): 219–303.

Blazka, P., 1958, The anaerobic metabolism of fish, *Physiol. Zool.*, *31:* 117–128.

Bocquet, C., and J. H. Stock, 1963, Some recent trends in work on parasitic copepods, *Oceanogr. Mar. Biol. Ann. Rev.*, *1:* 289–300.

Boden, B. P., and Kampa, E. M., 1964, Planktonic Bioluminescence, *Oceanogr. Mar. Biol. Ann. Rev.*, *2:* 341–371.

Bodenheimer, F. S., 1958, *Animal Ecology Today*, Junk, The Hague.

Bonner, J. T., 1963, How slime molds communicate, *Sci. American, 209*(2): 84–93.

Boolootian, R. A., 1963, *Biology of Coral Atolls*, Biological Science Curriculum Study, Pamphlet 10, D. C. Heath, Boston.

Bousfield, E. L., 1955, *Ecological Control of the Occurrence of Barnacles in the Miramichi Estuary*, National Museum of Canada Bulletin No. 137, 69 pp.

Bray, J. R., 1959, An analysis of the possible change in atmospheric carbon dioxide concentration, *Tellus 11:* 220–230.

Brewer, R., 1963, Ecological and reproductive relations of Black-capped and Carolina chickadees, *The Auk, 80:* 9–47.

Brower, L. P., J. V. Z. Brower, and C. T. Collins, 1963, Experimental studies of mimicry, *Zoologica, 48:* 65–80.

Brown, F. A., Jr., 1962, *Biological Clocks*, Biological Sciences Curriculum Study Pamphlet, No. 2. American Institute of Biological Sciences, 36 pp., Heath, Boston.

Brown, R. M., Jr., D. A. Larson, and H. C. Bold, 1964, Airborne algae; their abundance and heterogeneity, *Science, 143:* 583–585.

Bruun, A. F., 1957, Deep sea and abyssal depths, Chap. 22 in: *Treatise on Marine Ecology and Paleoecology*, J. W. Hedgpeth (ed.), The Geological Society of America Memoir 67, New York.

Bruun, A. F., 1963, The breeding of the North Atlantic fresh-water eels, in: *Advances in Mar. Biol., 1*, pp. 137–169, F. S. Russell, (ed.), Academic Press, New York.

Buckman, H. O., and N. C. Brady, 1960, *The Nature and Properties of Soils*, Macmillan, New York.

Bünning, E., 1964, *The Physiological Clock*, Academic Press, New York.

Burnett, T., 1960, Interactions in insect populations, *Am. Naturalist, 94:* 201–212.

Butler, W. L., and R. J. Downs, 1960, Light and Plant Development, *Sci. American, 203*(6): 56–63.

Calhoun, J. B., 1962, Population Density and Social Pathology, *Sci. American, 206*(2): 139–149.

Calhoun, J. B., 1963, The social use of space, in: *Physiological Mammalogy*, W. V. Mayer and R. G. Van Gelder, (eds.) Vol. 1, pp. 1–187, Academic Press, New York.

Carpelan, L. H., 1964, Effects of salinity on algal distribution, *Ecology, 45:* 70–77.

Carpenter, C. R., 1958, Territoriality, in: *Behavior and Evolution*, A. Roe and G. G. Simpson (eds.), pp. 224–250, Yale University, Press, New Haven.

Carr, A., 1962, *Guideposts of Animal Navigation*, Biological Sciences Curriculum Study, American Institute of Biological Sciences, Pamphlet No. 1, 36 pp., Heath, Boston.

Carson, R., 1962, *Silent Spring*, Houghton Mifflin, Boston.

532   New References for 1965 Printing

Cassie, R. M., 1963, Microdistribution of plankton, *Oceanogr. Mar. Biol. Ann. Rev.*, H. Barnes (ed.), Vol. I, pp. 223–252, George Allen and Unwin, Ltd., London.

Chandler, A. C., and C. P. Read, 1961, *Introduction to Parasitology*, Wiley, New York.

Chapman, V. J., 1960, *Salt Marshes and Salt Deserts of the World*, Interscience; Wiley, New York.

Cheng, T. C., 1964, *The Biology of Animal Parasites*, Saunders, Philadelphia.

Childs, E. C., 1964, The movement of soil water, *Endeavour*, 23(89): 81–84.

Christian, J. J., and D. E. Davis, 1964, Endocrines, Behavior and Population, *Science, 146:* 1550–1560.

Churchill, E. D., and H. C. Hanson, 1958, The concept of climax in arctic and alpine vegetation, *Bot. Rev., 24:* 127–191.

Clarke, C. A., and P. M. Sheppard, The evolution of mimicry in the butterfly, *Papilio dardanus, Heredity, 14:* 163–173.

Clarke, G. L., and R. H. Backus, 1964, Interrelations between the vertical migration of deep scattering layers, bioluminescence, and changes in daylight in the sea, *Bull. Inst. Oceanogr. Monaco, 64*(1318): 1–36.

Clarke, G. L., and E. J. Denton, 1962, Light and animal life, in: *The Sea,* M. N. Hill, (ed.), Vol. 1, p. 456–468, Interscience, New York.

Clarke, G. L., and M. G. Kelly, 1965, Measurements of diurnal changes in bioluminescence from the sea surface to 2000 meters using a new photometric device, *Limnol. Oceanogr., 10*(4) (in press).

Clatworthy, J. N., and J. L. Harper, 1962, The comparative biology of closely related species living in the same area, *J. Exp. Bot., 13:* 307–324.

Clawson, M., 1964, *Natural Resources and International Development*, Johns Hopkins Press, Baltimore.

Clements, A. N., 1963, *The Physiology of Mosquitoes*, Pergamon Press-Macmillan, New York.

Cloudsley-Thompson, J. L., 1961, *Rhythmic Activity in Animal Physiology and Behavior*, Academic Press, New York.

Cold Spring Harbor Symposia on Quantitative Zoology, 1957, Symposium No. 22, 1957, on Population studies: Animal Ecology and Demography.

Cold Spring Harbor Symposia on Quantitative Biology, 1960, Symposium No. 25, 1960 on Biological Clocks.

Cole, L. C., 1958, The Ecosphere, *Sci. American, 198*(4): 83–96.

Cole, L. C., 1962, Review of *Silent Spring* by R. Carson, *Sci. American, 207*(6): 173–180.

Cole, L. C., 1964, Pesticides: a hazard to nature's equilibrium, *Am. J. Public Health., 54*(1): 24–31.

Colebrook, J. M., 1963, Continuous plankton records: Annual variations in the abundance of *Calanus finmarchicus*, 1948–1959, *Bull. Mar. Ecol., 6:* 17–30.

Collias, N. E., 1964, *Animal Language*, Biological Sciences Curriculum Study Pamphlet No. 20, pp. 1–36, American Institute of Biological Sciences.

Collier, A., 1958, Some biochemical aspects of red tides and related oceanographic problems, *Limnol. Oceanogr., 3:* 33–39.

Connecticut Arboretum, 1961, Connecticut's Coastal Marshes, *The Connecticut Arboretum, Bull. No. 12:* 1–36, Connecticut College, New London.

Connell, J. H., 1961, The influence of interspecific competition and other factors in the distribution of the barnacle *Chthamalus stellatus, Ecology 42:* 710–723.

Conover, R. J., 1964, Food relations and nutrition of zooplankton, *Proc. Symposium on Experimental Marine Ecology* occ. Pub. No. 2, Graduate School of Oceanography University of Rhode Island.

Cooper, C. F., 1961, The Ecology of Fire, *Sci. American, 204*(4): 150–161.

Cooper, L. N. H., 1961, Vertical and Horizontal Movements in the Ocean, in *Oceanography*, Sears (ed.), pp. 599–621. American Association for the Advancement of Science.

Coulianos, C. C., and A. G. Johnels, 1963, Note on the subnivean environment of small mammals, *Arkiv. Zool., 15*(4): 363–370.

Coupland, R. T., 1958, The effects of fluctuations in weather upon the grasslands of the Great Plains, *Bot. Rev., 24*(5): 274–317.

Cowey, C. B., and E. D. S. Corner, 1963, On the nutrition and metabolism of zooplankton, *J. Marine Biol. Assoc. United Kingdom, 43:* 495–511.

Crisp, D. J., and P. Meadows, 1962, The chemical basis of gregariousness in cirripedes. *Proc. Roy. Soc. Ser. B, 156,* 500–520.

Cumming, K. B., 1964, On the origin of the vitamin D found in Blackback Flounder (*Pseudopleuronectes americanus*), Ph.D. Thesis, Harvard University, Cambridge.

Curry-Lindahl, K., 1963, New theory on a fabled exodus-endocrine malfunction may cause lemming psychosis, *Nat. Hist., 72*(7): 46–53.

Cushing, D. H., 1959, The seasonal variation in oceanic production as a problem in population dynamics, *J. Conseil, 24:* 455–463.

Danilevskii, A. S., 1965, *Photoperiodism and Seasonal Development of Insects*, Oliver and Boyd, London.

Dansereau, P., 1957, *Biogeography, an Ecological Perspective*, Ronald Press, New York.

Darling, F. F., 1963, *Implications of rising carbon dioxide content of the atmosphere*, The Conservation Foundation, New York.

Darling, F. F., 1964, *A Herd of Red Deer*, Doubleday, New York.

Darlington, P. J., Jr., 1957, *Zoogeography: The Geographic Distribution of Animals*, Wiley, New York.

Dasmann, R. F., 1959, *Environmental Conservation*. Wiley, New York.

Dasmann, R. F., 1964, *Wildlife Biology*. Wiley, New York.

Daubenmire, R. F., 1959, *Plants and Environment*. Wiley, New York.

Davenport, D., 1965, Cnidarian symbioses and the experimental analysis of behaviour. In Symposium: The Cnidaria and their Evolution, W. J. Rees (ed.), *Proc. Zool. Soc. London* (in press).

Davis, C., 1963, On questions of production and productivity in ecology, *Arch. Hydrobiol. 59*(2): 145–161.

Davis, D. H. S. (ed.), 1965, *Ecological Studies in Southern Africa*. Junk, The Hague.

Davis, K., 1963, Population, *Sci. American 209*(3): 62–71.

DeBach, P. (ed.), 1964, *Biological Control of Insect Pests and Weeds*, Reinhold, New York.

Deevey, E. S., Jr., 1958, Bogs, *Sci. American, 199*(4): 114–122.

Dempster, J. P., 1963, The population dynamics of grasshoppers and locusts, *Biol. Revs., 38*(4): 490–529.

Dendy, J. S., 1963, Farm Ponds, in: *Limnology in North America*, Frey (ed.), Chap. 22, pp. 595–620, University of Wisconsin Press, Madison.

Denton, E. J., 1960, The buoyancy of marine animals, *Sci. American, 203*(1): 119–128.

Denton, E. J., 1963, Buoyancy mechanisms of sea creatures, *Endeavour, 22*(85): 3–8.

Dietz, R. S., 1962, The sea's deep scattering layers, *Sci. American, 207*(2): 44–50.

Dietz, R. S., 1963, Bathyscaphes and other deep submersibles for oceanographic research, Chap. 23, in *The Sea*, Vol. 2, M. N. Hill (ed.), pp. 497–515, Interscience, New York.

Dorst, J., 1963, *The Migrations of Birds.* Houghton Mifflin, Boston.

Doty, M. S. (ed.), 1961, *Primary Productivity Measurement, Marine and Freshwater.* Proceedings of conference held at University of Hawaii, Honolulu, Aug. 21–Sept. 6, 1961, U. S. Atomic Energy Commission.

Dragovich, A., and B. Z. May, 1962, Hydrological characteristics of Tampa Bay tributaries, *Fishery Bulletin of the Fish and Wildlife Service, 62:* 163–175.

Duddington, C. L., 1956, The Predaceous Fungi: Zoopagales and Moniliales, *Biol. Rev. Cambridge Phil. Soc., 31:* 152–193.

Dunbar, M. D. (ed.), 1963, *Marine Distributions,* Royal Society of Canada Special Publications, No. 5, University of Toronto Press, Toronto.

Dunning, D. C., and K. D. Roeder, 1965, Moth Sounds and the Insect-Catching Behavior of Bats, *Science, 147:* 173–4.

Eberly, W. R., 1964, Further studies on the metalimnetic oxygen minimum with special reference to its occurrence throughout the world. *Invest. Indiana Lakes and Streams, 6*(3): 103–137.

Eggler, W. E., 1963, Plant life of Paracutin volcano, Mexico, eight years after activity ceased. *Am. Midland. Naturalist, 69:* 38–68.

Egler, F. E., 1964, Pesticides—in our ecosystem, *Am. Scientist, 52*(1): 110–136.

Elgmork, K., 1964, Dynamics of zooplankton communities in some small inundated ponds. *Folia Limnol. Scandinavica No. 12:* 9–80.

Ellison, L., 1960, Influence of grazing on plant succession of rangelands, *Bot. Rev., 26*(1): 1–78.

Elton, C. S., 1958, *The Ecology of Invasions by Animals and Plants,* Wiley, New York.

Engelmann, M. D., 1961, The role of soil arthropods in the energetics of an old field community, *Ecol. Monographs, 31:* 221–238.

Errington, P. L., 1963, The Phenomena of Predation, *Am. Scientist, 51*(2): 180–192.

Errington, P. L., 1963, *Muskrat Populations,* Iowa State University Press, Ames.

Etkin, W. (ed.), 1964, *Social Behavior and Organization Among Vertebrates,* University of Chicago Press, Chicago.

Evans, H. E., 1963, Predatory Wasps, *Sci. American, 208*(4): 145–154.

Evans, L. T., 1963, *Environmental Control of Plant Growth,* Academic Press, New York.

Eyre, S. R., 1963, *Vegetation and Soils,* Arnold, London.

Fager, E. W., 1963, Communities of Organisms, In *The Sea,* M. N. Hill (ed.), Vol. 2, Chap. 19, pp. 415–435, Interscience, New York.

Fager, E. W., and J. A. McGowan, 1963, Zooplankton species groups in the North Pacific, *Science, 140*(3566): 453–460.

Farb, P., and The Editors of *Life*, 1963, *Ecology,* Life Nature Library, Time Inc., New York.

Farner, D. S., 1964, The photoperiodic control of reproductive cycles in birds, *Am. Scientist, 52:* 137–156.

Farner, D. S., 1964, *Photoperiodism in Animals,* Biological Science Curriculum Study, Pamphlet No. 15, pp. 1–36, Heath, Boston.

Fogg, G. E., 1963, *The Growth of Plants,* Penguin Books, Baltimore.

Fogg, G. E., 1965, *Algal Cultures and Phytoplankton Ecology,* University of Wisconsin Press, Madison.

Fosberg, F. R. (ed.), 1963, *Man's Place in the Island Ecosystem: A Symposium,* Bishop Museum Press, Honolulu.

Fraenkel, G. S., and D. L. Gunn, 1961, *The Orientation of Animals,* Dover, New York.

Frank, P. W., 1964, On home range of limpets, *Am. Naturalist, 98(899):* 99–104.

Frey, D. G. (ed.), 1963, *Limnology in North America,* University of Wisconsin Press, Madison.

Frings, H., and M. Frings, 1964, *Animal Communication,* Blaisdell Scientific Paperbacks, Blaisdell, New York.

Garb, S., 1961, Differential growth inhibitors produced by plants, *Bot. Rev., 27* (3) 422–443.

Gates, D. M., 1962, *Energy Exchange in the Biosphere,* Harper and Row Biological Monographs, New York.

Gates, D. M., 1965, Energy, plants and ecology, *Ecology, 46:* 1–13.

Geiger, R., 1964, *The Climate Near the Ground* (4th ed.), Harvard University Press, Cambridge.

Giese, A. C. (ed.), 1964, *Photophysiology:* Vol. 1. General Principles; Action of Light on Plants, Vol. 2. Action of Light on Animals and Microorganisms. Academic Press, New York.

Gleason, H. A., and A. Cronquist, 1964, *The Natural Geography of Plants,* Columbia University Press, New York.

Glock, W. S., and S. Agerter, 1963, Anomalous patterns in tree rings, *Endeavour, 22:* 9–13.

Glover, R. S., 1961, Biogeographical boundaries: The shapes of distributions, in: *Oceanography,* M. Sears (ed.), Am. Assoc. Advan. Sci. Pub. No. 67.

Gohar, H. A. F., 1963, Light and tropical marine invertebrates, *Bull. Inst. Oceanog. Monaco, ID.* 91–104.

Goldberg, E. D., 1963, The oceans as a chemical system, Chap. 1, in *The Sea,* Vol. 2 M. N. Hill (ed.), pp. 3–25, Interscience, New York.

Goldman, C. R., 1960a, Molybdenum as a factor limiting primary productivity in castle lake, California. *Science, 132:* 1016–1017.

Goldman, C. R., 1960b, Primary productivity and limiting factors in three lakes of the Alaska Peninsula. *Ecol. Monographs, 30:* 207–230.

Golley, F. B., 1960, Energy dynamics of a food chain of an old-field community, *Ecol. Monographs, 30(2):* 187–206.

Gordon, M. S., and H. M. Kelly, 1962, Primary productivity of an Hawaiian coral reef, *Ecology, 43:* 473–480.

Goreau, T. F., and W. D. Hartman, 1963, Boring sponges as controlling factors in the formation and maintenance of coral reefs, in: *Mechanisms of Hard Tissue Destruction,* R. F. Sognnaes (ed.), Amer. Assoc. Adv. Sci., Symposium Volume No. 75, Washington, D. C.

Gray, J., 1957, How fishes swim. *Sci. American, 197(2):* 48–54.

Greenshields, E. L., 1964, Water has a key role, in: *Farmer's World: The Year-book of Agriculture*, 1964, pp. 75–96.

Greenway, J. C., Jr., 1958, *Extinct and Vanishing Birds of the World*, American Committee for International Wild Life Protection (Special Publication No. 13), New York.

Gregory, P. H., 1962, *The Microbiology of the Atmosphere*, Interscience, New York.

Griffin, D. M., 1963, Soil moisture and the ecology of soil fungi, *Biol. Revs.*, 38(2): 141–166.

Griffin, D. R., 1958, *Listening in the Dark: The Acoustic Orientation of Bats and Men*, Yale University Press, New Haven.

Griffin, D. R., 1964, *Bird Migration*, Anchor Books, Doubleday, New York.

Grill, E. V., and F. A. Richards, 1964, Nutrient regeneration from phytoplankton decomposing in seawater, *J. Mar. Res.*, 22: 51–69.

Guhl, A. M., 1956, Social order of chickens, *Sci. American*, 194(2): 42–46.

Guillard, R. R. L., 1962, Salt and osmotic balance, in: *Physiology and Biochemistry of Algae*, R. A. Lewin (ed.), Chap. 32, pp. 529–540. Academic Press, New York.

Gunter, G., 1957, Temperature, Chapter 8 in: *Treatise on Marine Ecology and Paleoecology*, Hedgpeth (ed.), Geological Society of America, Memoir 67, pp. 159–184.

Gunter, G., 1961, Some Relations of Estuarine Organisms to Salinity, *Limnol. Oceanogr.* 6: 182–190.

Hadley, E. B., and L. C. Bliss, 1964, Energy relationships of alpine plants on Mt. Washington, N. H., *Ecol. Monog.* 34: 331–357.

Hailman, J. P., 1964, Breeding synchrony in the equatorial swallow-tailed gull, *Am. Naturalist*, 98(899): 79–83.

Hairston, N. G., 1959, Species abundance and community organization, *Ecology*, 40: 404–416.

Halldal, P., 1964, Ultraviolet action spectra of photosynthesis and photosynthetic inhibition in a green and a red alga, *Physiologia Plantarum*, 17: 414–421.

Hamilton, T. H., and R. H. Barth, 1962, The biological significance of season change in male plumage appearance in some new world migratory bird species, *Am. Naturalist*, 96: 129–144.

Hanson, H. C., 1958, Principles concerned in the formation and classification of communities, *Bot. Rev.*, 24(2): 66–125.

Hanson, H. C., and E. D. Churchill, 1961, *The Plant Community*, Reinhold, New York.

Hardin, G., 1960, The competitive exclusion principle, *Science*, 131: 1291–1297.

Hardy, A. C., 1956, *The Open Sea, part I: The World of Plankton*, Collins, London.

Hardy, A. C., 1959, *The Open Sea, part II: Fish and Fisheries*, Houghton Mifflin, Boston.

Hardy, A. C., and R. H. Kay, 1964, Experimental studies of plankton luminescence, *J. Marine Biol. Assoc. United Kingdom*, 44(2): 435–484.

Hardy, J. D., 1961, Physiology of temperature regulation, *Physiol. Revs.*, 41: 521–606.

Harvey, H. W., 1957, *The Chemistry and Fertility of Sea Waters*, Cambridge University Press, Cambridge, England.

Hasler, A. D., 1960, Guideposts of Migrating Fishes, *Science*, 132: 785–792.

Hasler, A. D., 1960, Homing orientation in migrating fishes, *Ergeb. Biol.*, 23: 94–115.

Hazen, W. E. (ed.), 1964, *Readings in Population and Community Ecology*, Saunders, Philadelphia.

Hedgpeth, J. W. (ed.), 1957, *Treatise on Marine Ecology and Paleoecology*, Geological Society of America, Memoir 67, Vol. 1.

Henry, S. M. (ed.), *Biochemistry and Physiology of Symbiosis*, Academic Press, New York (in press).

Heukelekian, H., and N. Dondero (eds.), 1964, *Aquatic Microbiology*, Wiley, N. Y.

Hewitt, O. H. (ed.), 1964, Symposium on cycles in animal populations, *J. Wildlife Management*, 18: 1–112.

Hillman, W. S., 1962, *The Physiology of Flowering*, Holt, Rinehart and Winston, New York.

Hood, D. W., 1963, Chemical oceanography, in: *Oceanogr. Mar. Biol. Ann. Rev.*, H. Barnes (ed.), Vol. 1, pp. 129–155.

Howard, W. E., 1960. Innate and environmental dispersal of individual vertabrates, *Am. Midland Naturalist*, 63: 152–160.

Huffaker, C. B., 1958, Experimental studies on predation: dispersion factors and predator-prey oscillations, *Hilgardia*, 27: 343–383.

Hulburt, E. M., 1964, The diversity of phytoplanktonic populations in oceanic, coastal and estuarine regions, *J. Marine Research*, 21: 81–93.

Humphrey, R. R., 1962, *Range Ecology*, Ronald Press, N. Y.

Hutchinson, G. E., 1957, *A Treatise on Limnology*, Vol. 1, *Geography, Physics, and Chemistry*, Wiley, New York.

Hutchinson, G. E., 1959, Homage to Santa Rosalia, or Why are there so many kinds of animals? *Am. Naturalist*, 93: 145–159.

Hutchinson, G. E., 1961, The Paradox of the Plankton, *Am. Naturalist*, 95: 137–146.

Idyll, C. P., 1964, *The Deep Sea and the Creatures that Live in It*, Thomas Crowell, New York.

Ivlev, V. S., 1961, *Experimental Ecology of the Feeding of Fishes*, Yale University Press, New Haven.

Jackson, D. (ed.), 1964, *Algae and Man*, Plenum Press, New York.

Jander, R., 1963, Insect orientation, in: *Ann. Rev. Entom.*, R. F. Smith and T. E. Mittler (eds.), 8: pp. 95–114.

Jander, R., K. Daumer, and T. H. Waterman, 1963, Polarized light orientation by two Hawaiian decapod cephalopods, *Zeit. Vergleich. Physiol.*, 46: 383–394.

Jeffries, H. P., 1964, Comparative studies on estuarine zooplankton, *Limmol. Oceanogr.*, 9(3): 348–358.

Jerlov, N. G., 1963, Optical oceanography, in: *Oceanogr. Mar. Biol. Ann. Rev.*, H. Barnes (ed.), Vol. 1, pp. 89–114.

Johnson, C. G., 1963, The aerial migration of insects, *Sci. American*, 209(6): 132–138.

Johnson, M. W., and E. Brinton, 1963, Biological species, water-masses and currents, in *The Sea*, M. N. Hill (ed.), Vol. II, pp. 381–411. Interscience, New York.

Kanwisher, J., 1960, pCO_2 in sea water and its effect on the movement of CO_2 in nature, *Tellus*, 12: 209–215.

Keith, L. B., 1963, *Wildlife's Ten Year Cycle*, University of Wisconsin Press, Madison.

538 *New References for 1965 Printing*

Kellogg, W. N., 1961, *Porpoises and Sonar*, University of Chicago Press, Chicago.

Kempner, E. S., 1963, Upper temperature limit of life, *Science, 142:* 1318–1319.

Kendeigh, S. C., 1961, *Animal Ecology*, Prentice-Hall, Englewood-Cliffs, N. J.

Kershaw, K. A., 1964, *Quantitative and Dynamic Ecology*, American Elsevier, New York.

Ketchum, B. H., 1963, Some biological characteristics of the marine environment, Great Lakes Research Division, University of Michigan Publ. No. *10:* 236–244.

Kettlewell, H. B. D., 1961, The phenomenon of industrial melanism in Lepidoptera, *Ann. Rev. Entomol., 6:* 245–262.

Kevan, D. K. McE., 1962, *Soil Animals*, Philosophical Library, New York.

King, C. A. M., 1963, *An Introduction to Oceanography*, McGraw-Hill, New York.

King, J. A., 1959, Social Behavior of Prairie Dogs, *Sci. American*, 201(4): 128–140.

Kingsbury, J. M., 1962, The effect of waves on the composition of a population of attached marine algae, *Bull. Torrey Botan. Club, 89:* 143–160.

Kinne, O., 1963, The effect of temperature and salinity on marine and brackish water animals. Part I, Temperature, *Oceanogr. Mar. Biol. Ann. Rev.* H. Barnes (ed.), *1:* 301–340.

Kinne, O., 1964, The effects of temperature and salinity on marine and brackish water animals. Part II, Salinity. *Oceanography Mar. Biol. Ann. Rev.,* H. Barnes (ed.), *2:* 281–339.

Klopfer, P. H., 1962, *Behavioral Aspects of Ecology*, Prentice-Hall, Englewood Cliffs, N. J.

Knipling, E. F., 1960, The eradication of the screw-worm fly, *Sci. American*, 203(4): 54–61.

Koo, T. (ed.), 1962, *Studies of Alaska Red Salmon*, University of Washington Press, Seattle.

Korringa, P., 1957, Lunar periodicity, *Geol. Soc. Am. Mem. 67*, Hedgpeth (ed.), Vol. 1, 917–934.

Kozlowski, T. T., 1962, *Tree Growth*, Ronald Press, New York.

Kozlowski, T. T., 1964, *Water Metabolism in Plants*, Harper and Row, New York.

Kramer, G., 1961, Long-Distance Orientation, *Biology and Comparative Physiology of Birds*, Marshall (ed.), Vol. 2, Ch. 22, Academic Press, New York.

Krey, J., 1961, The balance between living and dead matter in the oceans, in *Oceanography*, M. Sears (ed.), *Am. Assoc. Advance. Sci.* Pub. No. 67, Washington, D. C.

Kriss, A. E., 1963, *Marine Microbiology (Deep Sea)*, Oliver and Boyd, Edinburgh and London.

Kristensen, K. T., 1959, Temperature and heat balance of soil, *Oikos, 10:* 103–120.

Kruuk, H., 1963, Diurnal periodicity in the activity of the common sole, *Solea Vulgaris* (Quensus). *Neth. J. Sea Res.,* 2(1): 1–28.

Kühnelt, W., 1961, *Soil Biology*, Faber and Faber, London.

Lack, D. L., 1954, *The Natural Regulation of Animal Numbers*, Cambridge University Press, Cambridge, England.

Lagler, K. F., J. E. Bardach, and R. L. Miller, 1962, *Icthyology*, Wiley, New York.

Lamb, J. M., 1959, Lichens, *Sci. American*, 201(4): 144–156.

Lamb, M., and M. H. Zimmerman, 1964, Marine vegetation of Cape Ann, Essex County, Massachusetts. *Rhodora, 66:* 218–253.

Lamprey, H. F., 1963, Ecological separation of the large mammal species in the Tarangire Game Reserve, Tanganyika, *E. African Wildlife J., 1:* 63–92.

Lance, J., 1963, Salinity tolerance of some estuarine planktonic copepods, *Limnol. Oceanogr., 8(4):* 440–449.

Landsberg, H. E., 1963, Global distribution of solar and sky radiation, in: *World Maps of Climatology,* H. E. Landsberg, *et al.,* pp. 1–4 & 3 maps. Springer-Verlag, Heidelberg.

Landsberg, H. H., *et al.,* 1963, *Resources in America's Future,* Johns Hopkins Press, Baltimore.

Lasiewski, R. C., 1964, Body temperatures, heart and breathing rate, and evaporative water loss in hummingbirds, *Physiol Zool., 37(2):* 212–223.

Lauff, G. H. (ed.), 1965, *Estuaries,* Am. Assoc. Advance. Sci., Symposium Volume, (in press).

LeCren, E. D., and M. W. Holdgate, 1962, *The Exploitation of Natural Animal Populations,* Wiley, New York.

Lee, A. K., and J. A. Badham, 1963, Body temperature, activity and behavior of the agamid lizard, *Amphilbolurus barbatus, Copeia, 2:* 387–394.

Lee, K. I., and M. Monsi, 1963, Ecological studies on *Pinus densiflora.* 1. Effects of plant substances on the floristic composition of the undergrowth, *Botan. Mag. Tokyo, 76:* 400–413.

Lee, M. O. (ed.), 1964, *Biology of the Antarctic Seas,* Antarctic Research Series, Vol. 1, Am. Geophys. Union, Pub. No. 1190.

Leopold, A. S., and The Editors of Life, 1962, *The Desert,* Time Inc., New York.

Lewin, R. A. (ed.), 1962, *Physiology and Biochemistry of Algae,* Academic Press, New York.

Lewis, J. B., 1963, Environmental and tissue temperatures of some tropical intertidal marine animals, *Biol. Bull., 124(3):* 277–284.

Lewis, J. R., 1964, *The Ecology of Rocky Shores,* English Universities Press, London.

Lilly, J. C., 1965, Vocal mimicry in *Tursiops:* ability to match numbers and durations of human vocal bursts, *Science, 147:* 300–301.

Limbaugh, C., Pederson, H., and Chace, F. H., Jr., 1961, Shrimps that clean fishes, *Bulletin of Marine Science of the Gulf and Carribean, 11(2):* 237–257.

Lin, N., 1963, Territorial behavior in the cicada killer wasp, *Sphecius speciosus* (Drury), *Behavior 20:* 115–133.

Lindauer, M., 1961, *Communication Among Social Bees,* Harvard University Press, Cambridge, Mass.

Lippert, B. E., and D. L. Jameson, 1964, Plant succession in temporary ponds of the Willamette Valley, Oregon, *Am. Midland Naturalist, 71:* 181–197.

Lissmann, H. W., 1963, Electric location by fishes, *Sci. American, 208(3):* 50–59.

Lucas, C. E., 1961, Interrelationships between aquatic organisms mediated by external metabolites, in: *Oceanography,* M. Sears (ed.), Am. Assoc. Advance Sci. Pub. No. 67, 499–517.

Lyford, W. H., 1963, The importance of ants to brown podzolic soil genesis in New England, *Harvard Forest Paper,* No. 7, Harvard University Forest, Petersham, Mass.

Lyford, W. H., 1964, Water table fluctuations in periodically wet soils of Central New England, *Harvard Forest Paper,* No. 8, pp. 1–15. Harvard University Forest, Petersham, Mass.

540 New References for 1965 Printing

Lyman, C. P., 1963, Hibernation in mammals and birds, *Am. Scientist,* 51(2): 127–138.

Lyman, C. P., and A. R. Dawe (eds.), 1960, Mammalian Hibernation, *Bull. Museum Comp. Zool.* (Harvard University) 124: 1–549.

Macan, T. T., 1963, *Freshwater Ecology,* Wiley, New York.

MacArthur, R. H., 1958, Population ecology of some warblers of northeastern coniferous forests, *Ecology,* 39: 599–619.

MacArthur, R. H., 1960, On the relative abundance of species, *Am. Naturalist,* 94: 25–36.

MacArthur, R., and J. Connell, 1965, *The Biology of Populations,* Wiley, N. Y.

Macfadyen, A., 1963, *Animal Ecology, Aims and Methods,* Pitman, New York.

Maguire, B., Jr., 1963, The passive dispersal of small aquatic organisms and their colonization of isolated bodies of water, *Ecol. Monographs,* 33(2): 161–185.

Maio, J. T., 1958, Predatory fungi, *Sci. American,* 199(1): 67–72.

Mani, M. S., 1962, *Introduction to High Altitude Entomology,* Methuen, London.

Margalef, R., 1958, Temporal succession and spacial heterogeneity in phytoplankton, in: *Perspectives in Marine Biology,* Buzzati-Traverso (ed.), pp. 323–350.

Margalef, R., 1963a, On certain unifying principles in ecology, *Am. Naturalist,* 97: 357–374.

Margalef, R., 1963b, Some regularities in the distribution of populations of phytoplankton on a small and medium scale, and in their functional properties. *Invest. Pesquera,* 23: 169–230.

Marshall, N. B., 1961, Swimbladder structure of deep-sea fishes in relation to their systematics and biology, *Discovery Repts.,* 31(1): 1–121, Cambridge University Press, Cambridge.

Mayer, A. M., and A. Poljakoff-Mayber, 1963, *The Germination of Seeds,* Macmillan, New York.

Mayer, W. V., 1964, *Hibernation,* Biol. Sci. Curriculum Study Pamphlet No. 19, Am. Inst. Biol. Sci., Heath, Boston.

Mayr, E., 1963, *Animal Species and Evolution,* Harvard University Press, Cambridge, Mass.

McElroy, W. D., and B. Glass, 1961, *Light and Life,* Johns Hopkins Press, Baltimore.

McElroy, W. D., and H. H. Seliger, 1962, Biological luminescence, *Sci. American,* 207(6): 76–87.

McLaughlin, J. J. A., and P. A. Zahl, 1962, Endozoic algae, Ch. 55 in: *Physiology and Biochemistry of Algae,* R. A. Lewin (ed.), Academic Press, New York.

McLeod, D. G. R., and S. D. Beck, 1963, Photoperiodic termination of diapause in an insect, *Biol. Bull,* 124(1): 84–96.

McNale, B. K., 1963, Bioenergetics and the determination of home range size, *Am. Naturalist,* 97: 133–140.

McNaught, D. C., and A. D. Hasler, 1964, Rate of movement of populations of *Daphnia* in relation to changes in light intensity, *J. Fisheries Research Board Can.,* 21: 291–318.

Meinertzhagen, R., 1955, Speed and altitude of bird flight, *Ibis,* 97: 81–117.

Menzel, D. W., E. M. Hulburt, and J. H. Ryther, 1963, The effects of enriching Sargasso sea water on the production and species composition of the phytoplankton, *Deep-Sea Research,* 10: 209–219.

Meyer, B. S., D. B. Anderson, and R. H. Böhning, 1960, *Introduction to Plant Physiology,* Van Nostrand, Princeton, N. J.

Meyerriecks, A. J., 1960, Comparative breeding behavior of four species of herons. *Nuttall Ornithological Club,* Pub. No. 2, Cambridge, Mass.

Meyerriecks, A. J., 1962, *Courtship in Animals,* Biol. Sci. Curriculum Study, Pamphlet No. 3, pp. 1–34. Am. Inst. Biol. Sci., Heath, Boston.

Miller, E. M., 1964, *Biology of Termites,* Biol. Sci. Curriculum Study, Pamphlet No. 17, pp. 1–36, Am. Inst. Biol. Sci., Heath, Boston.

Miller, R. S., 1964, Ecology and distribution of pocket gophers (*Geomyidae*) of Colorado, *Ecology,* 45(2): 256–272.

Mohr, H., 1964, The control of plant growth and development by light, *Biol. Revs.,* 39(1): 87–112.

Moore, G. W., and B. G. Nicholas, 1964, *Speleology: The Study of Caves,* Heath, Boston.

Moore, H. B., 1958, *Marine Ecology,* Wiley, New York.

Moore, J. A. (ed.), 1963, Specialized Symposia, *Proc. XVI Intern. Congr. Zool.,* 4: 1–383.

Mowat, F., 1963, *Never Cry Wolf,* The Canadian Publishers, Toronto.

Mudd, S. (ed.), 1964, *The Population Crisis and the Use of World Resources,* Junk, The Hague.

Mullin, M. M., 1963, Some factors affecting the feeding of marine copepods of the genus *Calanus. Limnol. Oceanogr.,* 8: 239–250.

Murie, A., 1962, On the Trail of Wolves, (from, *A Naturalist in Alaska*), *Nat. His.,* 71: 28–36.

Murphy, P. W. E. (ed.), 1962, *Progress in Soil Zoology,* Butterworth, London.

Nair, N. B., 1962, Ecology of marine fouling and wood-boring organisms of western Norway, *Sarsia,* 8: 1–88.

Nauwerck, A., 1963, The relations between zooplankton and phytoplankton in Lake Erken (Sweden), *Symbolae Botan. Upsalienses,* 17: 1–163.

Neill, W. T., 1964, *Biogeography,* Biol. Sci. Curriculum Study, Am. Inst. Biol. Sci., Pamphlet No. 18, p. 1–36, Heath, Boston.

Nicholas, D. J. D., 1963, The metabolism of inorganic nitrogen and its compounds in micro-organisms, *Biol. Revs.,* 38(4): 530–568.

Nicol, J. A. C., 1960, *The Biology of Marine Animals,* Pitman, London.

Nicol, J. A. C., 1962, Animal luminescence, in: *Advances Comp. Physiol. Biochem.,* Lowenstein (ed.), Vol. 1: 217–273.

Nicol, J. A. C., 1963, Some aspects of photoreception and vision in fishes, in: *Advances in Marine Biology,* F. S. Russell (ed.), Vol. 1, pp. 171–208, Academic Press, New York.

Nielsen, E. T., 1964, On the migration of insects, H. Autrum (ed.), *Ergeb. Biol.,* 27: 162–193, Springer-Verlag, Berlin.

Niering, W. A., 1963, Terrestrial ecology of Kapingamarangi Atoll, Caroline Islands, *Ecol. Monograph.,* 33: 131–160.

Nigrelli, R. F., 1963, *Metabolites of the Sea,* Biol. Sci. Curriculum Study, Am. Inst. Biol. Sci., Pamphlet No. 7, Heath, Boston.

Nikolsky, G. V., 1963, *The Ecology of Fishes,* Academic Press, London.

Norris, K. S., 1963, The Functions of Temperature in the Ecology of the Percoid Fish *Girella nigricans* (Ayres), *Ecol. Monographs,* 33(1): 23–62.

Norris, R. A., 1960, Density, racial composition, sociality, and selective predation in nonbreeding populations of Savannah sparrows, *Bird Banding, 31*(4): 173–216.

Nutman, P. S., and B. Mosse (eds.), 1963, *Symbiotic Associations,* Thirteenth Symposium of the Society for General Microbiology, Cambridge University Press, London.

Nye, P. H., 1961, Organic matter and nutrient cycles under moist tropical forest, *Plant and Soil, 13:* 333–346.

Odum, E. P., 1959, *Fundamentals of Ecology,* Saunders, Philadelphia.

Odum, E. P., 1960, Organic production and turnover in old field succession, *Ecology, 41:* 34–49.

Odum, E. P., 1963, *Ecology,* (Modern Biology Series), Holt, Rinehart and Winston, New York.

Odum, H. T., R. P. C. duRest, R. J. Beyers, and C. Allbaugh, 1963, Diurnal metabolism, total phosphorus, Ohle anomaly, and zooplankton diversity of abnormal marine ecosystems of Texas, *Publ. Inst. Marine Science, Texas, 9:* 404–453.

Olson, J. S., 1963, Energy storage and the balance of producers and decomposers in ecological systems, *Ecology, 44:* 322–331.

Oosting, H. J., 1956, *The Study of Plant Communities* (2nd ed.), Freeman, San Francisco.

Oppenheimer, C. O. (ed.), 1963, *Symposium on Marine Microbiology,* Charles C Thomas, Springfield, Ill.

Ortlele, Edmund P., and O. J. Sexton, 1964, Orientation of the painted turtle, *Chrysemys picta, Am. Midland Naturalist, 71*(2): 320–334.

Ovington, J. D., 1962, Quantitative ecology and the woodland ecosystem concept, in: *Advances in Ecological Research,* Vol. 1, J. B. Cragg (ed.), pp. 103–183. Academic Press, New York.

Ovington, J. D., D. Heitkamp, and D. B. Lawrence, 1963, Plant biomass and productivity of prairie, savanna, oakwood, and maize field ecosystems in Central Minnesota, *Ecology, 44:* 52–63.

Paine, R. T., 1963, Trophic relationships of eight sympatric predatory gastropods, *Ecology, 44:* 63–72.

Palmer, C. M., 1962, *Algae in Water Supplies,* U. S. Public Health Service Pub. No. 657, Washington, D. C.

Papi, F., and L. Pardi, 1963, On the lunar orientation of sandhoppers (*Amphipoda Talitridae*), *Biol. Bull., 124*(1): 97–105.

Park, T., 1962, Beetles, competition, and populations, *Science, 138:* 1369–1375.

Parrish, B. B., and R. E. Craig, 1957, Recent changes in the North Sea herring fisheries, *Rapp. Cons. Explor. Mer., 143:* 12–21.

Parson, R. L., 1964, *Conserving American Resources,* Prentice-Hall, Englewood-Cliffs, N. J.

Parsons, T. R., 1964, Suspended organic matter in sea water, pp. 203–242 in: *Progress in Oceanography,* Vol. 1, Sears (ed.), 1963, Macmillan, N. Y.

Patten, B. C., 1963, Plankton: Optimum diversity structure of a summer community, *Science, 140:* 894–898.

Phleger, F. B., 1960, *Ecology and Distribution of Recent Foraminifera,* The Johns Hopkins Press, Baltimore.

Pickard, G. L., 1964, *Descriptive Physical Oceanography, An Introduction,* Macmillan, New York.

Pieper, R. D., 1964, Production and chemical composition of arctic tundra vegetation in relation to the lemming cycle, *Dissertation Abstr. 24:* 3943.

Pitelka, F. A., 1959, Numbers, breeding schedule, and territory in Pectoral Sandpipers of northern Alaska; *Condor, 61:* 233–264.

Pittendrigh, C. S., 1962, On temporal organization in living systems, *The Harvey Lectures, Series 56:* 93–125, Academic Press, New York.

Platt, R., and J. Wolfe (eds.), 1964, "Special Issue on Ecology" with articles by Sears, Odum, Blair, Dansereau, Reed, Platt et al., Cole, Deevey, Hasler, and Kuchler, *Bioscience, 14:* 9–43.

Poore, M. E. D., 1962, The method of successive approximation in descriptive ecology, in: *Advances in Ecological Research,* Vol. 1, J. B. Cragg (ed.), pp. 35–68, Academic Press, New York.

Potts, W. T. W., and G. Parry, 1964, *Osmotic and Ionic Regulation in Animals,* International Series of Monographs on Pure and Applied Biology, Zoology Division, Vol. 19, Pergamon-Macmillan, New York.

Prosser, C. L., and F. A. Brown, Jr., 1961, *Comparative Animal Physiology,* (2nd ed.), Saunders, Philadelphia.

Provasoli, L., 1963, Organic regulation of phytoplankton fertility, in: *The Sea,* M. N. Hill, (ed.), Vol. II, Ch. 8. Interscience, New York.

Pruitt, W. O., 1960, Animals in the snow, *Sci. American, 202*(1): 60–68.

Pye, J. D., 1963, Mechanisms of echolocation, in: Animal Orientation, H. Autrum (ed.), *Ergeb. Biol., 26:* 12–20, Springer-Verlag, Berlin.

Rawson, K. S., and P. H. Hartline, 1964, Telemetry of homing behavior by the deermouse, *Peromyscus, Science, 146:* 1596–1597.

Ray, E., 1958, Desiccation in salamanders, *Ecology, 39:* 75–82.

Ray, C., 1960, The application of Bergmann's and Allen's rules to the poikilotherms, *J. Morphol., 106:* 85–108.

Ray, D. L. (ed.), 1959, *Marine Boring and Fouling Organisms,* University of Washington Press, Seattle.

Raymont, J. E. G., 1963, *Plankton and Productivity in the Oceans,* Pergamon, New York.

Raymont, J. E. G., and B. G. A. Carrie, 1964, The production of zooplankton in Southhampton water, *Intrn. Rev. ges. Hydrobiol, 49:* 185–232.

Read, K. R. H., 1964, Comparative biochemistry of adaptations of poikilotherms to the thermal environment, Symp. on Exp. Marine Ecol., Graduate School of Oceanography, University of Rhode Island. Occasional Pub. No. 2, pp. 39–47.

Redfield, A. C., 1958, The biological control of chemical factors in the environment, *Am. Scientist, 46*(3): 205–221.

Redfield, A. C., 1964, Ontogeny of a salt marsh estuary, *Science, 147:* 50–55.

Redfield, A. C., B. H. Ketchum, and F. A. Richards, 1963, The influence of organisms on the composition of seawater, in *The Sea,* M. N. Hill (ed.), 2: 26–77 Interscience, New York.

Reid, G. K., 1961, *Ecology of Inland Waters and Estuaries,* Reinhold, New York.

Revelle, R., 1963, Water, *Sci. American, 209*(3): 92–109.

Ricketts, E. F., and J. Calvin, 1962, *Between Pacific Tides,* Stanford University Press, Stanford.

Riley, G. A. (ed.), 1963, *Marine Biology* I; Proceedings of the First International Interdisciplinary Conference, Port City Press, Baltimore.

Robinson, W. L., and J. B. Falls, 1965, A study of homing in meadow mice, *Am. Midland Naturalist, 73:* 188–223.

Rogers, W. P., 1962, *The Nature of Parasitism,* Academic Press, New York and London.

Ross, P., 1958, Microclimatic and vegetational studies in a cold-wet deciduous forest, *Harvard Black Rock Forest Papers,* No. *24:* 1–89, Cornwall-on-the-Hudson, N. Y.

Rudd, R. L., 1964, *Insecticides and the Living Landscape,* University of Wisconsin Press, Madison.

Rutter, A. J., and F. H. Whitehead (eds.), 1963, *The Water Relations of Plants,* Wiley, New York.

Ruttner, F., 1963, *Fundamentals of Limnology,* University of Toronto Press, Toronto.

Ryther, J. H., 1963, Geographic variations in productivity, Chap. 17, in *The Sea,* M. N. Hill (ed.), Vol. 2, pp. 347–380, Interscience, New York.

Satchell, J. E., 1960, Earthworms and soil fertility, *The New Scientist, 7:* 79 et seq.

Savage, R. M., 1961, *The Ecology and Life History of the Common Frog* (Rana temporaria temporaria), Putman, London.

Schaller, G. B., 1963, *The Mountain Gorilla, Ecology and Behavior,* University of Chicago Press, Chicago.

Scheltema, R. S., 1961, Metamorphosis of the veliger larvae of *Nassarius obsoletus* (Gastropoda) in response to bottom sediment, *Biol. Bull., 120:* 92–109.

Schevill, W. E., R. H. Backus, and J. B. Hersey, 1962, Sound production by marine animals, in: *The Sea,* M. N. Hill (ed.), Vol. I, Chap. 14, pp. 540–566, Interscience, New York.

Schmidt-Nielsen, K., 1964, *Desert Animals,* Clarendon, Oxford.

Schmidt-Nielsen, K., and Y. T. Kim, 1964, The effect of salt intake on the size and function of the salt gland of ducks, *The Auk, 81:* 160–172.

Scholander, P. F., 1963, The master switch of life, *Sci. American, 209*(6): 92–106.

Scholander, P. F., L. van Dam, J. W. Kanwisher, H. T. Hammel, and M. S. Gordon, 1957, Supercooling and osmoregulation in Arctic fish, *J. Cellular Comp. Physiol, 49:* 5–24.

Scholes, R. B., and J. M. Shewan, 1964, The present status of some aspects of marine microbiology, in *Advances in Marine Biology,* F. S. Russell (ed.), Vol. 2, pp. 133–163, Academic Press, New York.

Schultz, V., and A. W. Klement, Jr. (eds.), 1963, *Radioecology,* Proc. of First Nat'l. Symposium on Radioecology, 1961. Reinhold, New York.

Schutte, Karl H., 1964, *The Biology of Trace Elements,* Lippincott, Philadelphia.

Scott, D., and W. D. Billings, 1964, Effects of environmental factors on standing crop and productivity of an alpine tundra, *Ecol. Monographs, 34:* 243–270.

Sears, P. S., 1962, *Where There is Life,* Dell, New York.

Sebeok, T. A., 1962, Coding in the Evolution of Signalling Behavior, *Behavioral Science, 7:* 430–442.

Sebeok, T. A., 1965, Animal communication, *Science, 147:* 1006–1013.

Segal, E., and W. D. Burbanck, 1963, Effects of salinity and temperature on osmoregulation in two latitudinally separated populations of an estuarine isopod, *Cyathura polita* (Stimpson), *Physiol. Zool., 36:* 250–263.

Seliger, H. H., J. B. Buck, W. G. Fastie, and W. D. McElroy, 1964, Flash patterns in Jamaican fireflies, *Biol. Bull.*, *127*: 159–172.

Shaw, E., 1961, The development of schooling in fishes, II, *Physiol. Zool.*, *34*(4): 263–272.

Shaw, E., 1962, The schooling of fishes, *Sci. American*, *206*(6): 128–138.

Shelford, V. E., 1963, *The Ecology of North America*, University of Illinois Press, Urbana.

Slobodkin, L. B., 1960, Ecological energy relationships at the population level, *Am. Naturalist*, *94*: 213–236.

Slobodkin, L. B., 1961, *Growth and Regulation of Animal Populations*, Holt, Rinehart and Winston, New York.

Slobodkin, L. B., 1962, Energy in animal ecology, in: *Advances in Ecological Research*, J. B. Cragg (ed.), Vol. 1, pp. 69–101. Academic Press, New York.

Smith, A. U., 1958, The resistance of animals to cooling and freezing, *Biol. Revs.*, *33*(2): 197–253.

Smith, G. D., 1963, Objectives and basic assumptions of the new soil classification system, *Soil Sci.*, *96*(1): 6–16.

Smith, R. I., 1959, Physiological and ecological problems of brackish waters, in: *Marine Biology—Proceedings of 20th Annual Biology Colloquium*, Oregon State College, Corvallis.

Sognnaes, R. F. (ed.), 1960, *Calification in Biological Systems*, Amer. Assoc. Advanc. Sci., Pub. No. 64, Washington, D. C.

Sognnaes, R. F. (ed.), 1963, *Mechanisms of Hard Tissue Destruction*, Am. Assoc. Advanc. Sci. Symposium, Volume 75, Washington, D. C.

Southward, A. J., 1958, The zonation of plants and animals of rocky seashores, *Biol. Rev. Cambridge Phil. Soc.*, *33*: 137–177.

Southward, A. J., 1961, 1962, The distribution of some plankton animals in the English Channel and Western approaches, I and II, *J. Marine Biol. Assoc. United Kingdom*, *41*: 17–35; *42*: 275–375.

Southwick, C. H., 1963, *Primate Social Behavior*, Van Nostrand, Princeton, N. J.

Southwood, T. R. E., 1962, Migration of terrestrial arthropods in relation to habitat, *Biol. Revs.*, *37*(2): 171–214.

Spurr, S. H., 1964, *Forest Ecology*, Ronald Press, New York.

Stauffer, R. C., 1957, Haeckel, Darwin, and Ecology, *Quart. Rev. Biol.*, *32*(2): 138–144.

Steele, J. H., 1961, Primary production, in *Oceanography*, M. Sears (ed.), *Am. Assoc. Advanc. Sci.*, Pub. No. 67, Washington, D. C.

Steemann-Nielsen, E., 1963, On bicarbonate utilization by marine phytoplankton in photosynthesis, *Physiol. Plantarum*, *16*: 466–469.

Steemann-Nielsen, E., 1964, Recent advances in measuring and understanding marine primary production, *J. Ecol.*, *52*, (Suppl.): 119–130.

Stiles, W., 1960, Respiration, *Bot. Rev.*, *26*(2): 209–260.

Street, P., 1963, *Vanishing Animals*, Dutton, New York.

Strickland, J. D. H., 1960, Measuring the Production of Marine Phytoplankton, Bull. No. 122, Fisheries Res. Bd. Canada, 172 pp.

Strogonov, B. P., 1964, *Physiological Basis of Salt Tolerance of Plants*, Daniel Davey, New York.

Stross, R. G., and A. D. Hasler, 1960, Some Lime-Induced Changes in Lake Metabolism, *Limnology and Oceanography*, *5*: 265–272.

546 *New References for 1965 Printing*

Swan, L. W., 1961, The ecology of the high Himalayas, *Sci. American, 205*(4): 68–78.

Swedmark, B., 1964, The interstitial fauna of marine sand, *Biol. Revs., 39*(1): 1–42.

Symposium of the Society for Experimental Biology, 1961, Number XV: *Mechanisms in Biological Competition,* Academic Press, New York.

Talbot, L. M., 1964, Biological productivity of the tropical savanna ecosystem, in: *The Ecology of Man in the Tropical Environment,* Intern. Union for Cons. of Nature and Nat. Res. No. 4, pp. 88–97.

Talbot, L. M., and M. H. Talbot, 1963, The wildebeest in western Masailand, East Africa, *Wildlife Monogr., 12:* 7–84.

Talling, J. F., 1962, Freshwater Algae, in: *Physiology and Biochemistry of Algae,* R. A. Lewin (ed.), Chap. 50, Academic Press, New York.

Taylor, B. W., 1957, Plant succession on recent volcanoes in Papua, *J. Ecol., 45:* 233–243.

Taylor, W. R., 1964, Inorganic nutrient requirements for marine phytoplankton organisms, in: *Symposium on Experimental Marine Ecology,* Graduate School of Oceanography, University of Rhode Island, Occasional Pub. No. 2: 17–24.

Teal, M., and J. Teal, 1964, *Portrait of an Island,* Atheneum, New York.

Thomas, H. E., and L. B. Leopold, 1964, Ground water in North America, *Science, 143*(3610): 1001–1006.

Thomas, W. L. (ed.), 1956, *Man's Role in Changing the Face of the Earth,* University of Chicago Press, Chicago.

Thorne, Wynne (ed.), 1963, *Land and Water Use* Am. Assos. Advanc. Sci., Symposium, Vol. No. 73, Washington, D. C.

Thorpe, W. H., and O. L. Zangwill (eds.), 1961, *Current Problems in Animal Behavior,* Cambridge University Press, Cambridge, England.

Thorson, G., 1957, Bottom communities, in: *Treatise on Marine Ecology and Paleoecology,* J. W. Hedgpeth (ed.), Geol. Soc. Am. Memoir 67, Vol. 1: 461–534.

Thorson, G., 1958, Parallel level-bottom communities, their temperature adaptation, and their balance between predators and food animals, in: *Perspectives in Marine Biology,* Buzzati-Traverso (ed.), pp. 67–86, University of California Press.

Thorsteinson, A. J., 1960, Host selection in phytophagous insects, *Ann. Rev. Entomol., 5:* 193–218.

Tinbergen, L., and H. Klomp, 1960, The natural control of insects in pine woods. II. Conditions for damping of Nicholson oscillations in parasite-host systems, *Arch. Néerl. Zoolo., Tome 13:* 344–380.

Tinbergen, N., 1959, Comparative studies of the behaviour of gulls (*Laridae*): a progress report, *Behaviour, 15:* 1–70.

Tryon, C. A., Jr., and R. T. Hartman (eds.), 1960, *The Ecology of Algae,* Pymatuning Laboratory of Field Biology, Special Pub. No. 2, University of Pittsburgh.

Turner, J. S., and E. G. Brittain, 1962, Oxygen as a factor in photosynthesis, *Biol. Revs., 37*(1): 130–170.

Tyurin, I. Y., and M. M. Kononova, 1962, Biology of Humus Formation and Questions of Soil Fertility, *Acad. Sci. USSR Rep.* Int. Conf. Soil Sci., New Zealand.

Underwood, E. J., 1962, *Trace Elements in Human and Animal Nutrition,* (2nd ed.), Academic Press, New York.

U. S. Department of Agriculture, 1957, *Soil:* The Yearbook of Agriculture, for 1957, U. S. Gov't Printing Office, Washington.

Von Arx, W. S., 1962, *An Introduction to Physical Oceanography,* Addison-Wesley, Reading, Mass.

Von Frisch, K., 1955, *The Dancing Bees: an Account of the Life and Senses of the Honey Bee* (5th ed.), Harcourt, Brace, New York.

Von Frisch, K., 1962, Dialects in the language of the bees, *Sci. American, 207*(2): 78–87.

Walker, R. B., 1954, The Ecology of Serpentine Soils, II. Factors Affecting Plant Growth on Serpentine Soils, *Ecology, 35:* 259–266.

Waterman, T. H. (ed.), 1961, *The Physiology of Crustacea,* Academic Press, New York.

Watson, S. W., 1963, Autotrophic nitrification in the ocean, Chap. 7 in: *Symposium on Marine Microbiology,* C. H. Oppenheimer (ed.), pp. 73–84, Charles C Thomas, Springfield, Ill.

Watt, K. E. F., 1960, The effect of population density on fecundity of insects, *Can. Entomologist, 92:* 674–695.

Way, M. J., 1963, Mutualism between ants and honeydew-producing Homoptera, *Ann. Review of Entomol., 8:* 307–344, R. F. Smith (ed.).

Weaver, Charles R., 1963, Influence of water velocity upon orientation and performance of adult migrating salmonids, *U. S. Fish Wildlife Serv. Fishery Bull., 63*(1): 97–122.

Wells, J. W., 1957, Coral Reefs, Chap. 20, in: *Treatise on Marine Ecology and Paleoecology,* Vol. I, J. W. Hedgpeth (ed.), Geological Soc. Amer., Memoir 67.

Wenner, A. M., 1964, Sound Communication in Honeybees, *Sci. American, 210*(4): 116–124.

Westlake, D. F., 1963, Comparisons of plant productivity, *Biol. Revs., 38*(3): 385–425.

Whittaker, R. H., 1962, Classification of natural communities, *Bot. Rev., 28*(1): 1–239.

Whittaker, R. H., 1965, Dominance and diversity in land plant communities, *Science, 147:* 250–260.

Whittaker, R. H., and C. W. Fairbanks, 1958, A study of plankton copepod communities in the Columbia Basin, Southeastern Washington, *Ecology, 39.* 40–65.

Wiegert, R. G., 1964, Population energetics of meadow spittlebugs (*Philaenus spurmarius* L.) as affected by migration and habitat, *Ecol. Monographs, 34:* 217–241.

Wien, H. J., 1962, *Atoll Environment and Ecology,* Yale University Press, New Haven.

Williams, C. B., 1960, The range and pattern of insect abundance, *Am. Naturalist, 94:* 137–151.

Williams, C. B., 1964, *Patterns in the Balance of Nature and Related Problems in Quantitative Ecology,* Academic Press, New York.

Williams, J., 1962, *Oceanography: An Introduction to the Marine Sciences,* Little, Brown, Boston.

Wilson, E. O., 1963a, Pheromones, *Sci. American, 208*(5): 100–114.

Wilson, E. O., 1963b, Social Biology of Ants, *Ann. Rev. Entomol., 8:* 345–368.

Wilson, E. O., 1965, The challenge from related species, in: *Genetics of Colonizing Species* H. G. Baker (ed.), Chap. 1, Academic Press, New York (in press).

Wilson, J. W., 1959, Notes on wind and its effects on arctic-alpine vegetation, *J. Ecol., 47:* 415–427.

Wisely, B., 1963, Detection and avoidance of a cuprous oxide antifouling paint by bivalve and gastropod larvae, *Australian J. Marine and Freshwater Research, 14*(1): 60–69.

Witkamp, M., 1963, Microbial populations of leaf litter in relation to environmental conditions and decomposition, *Ecology, 44:* 370–377.

Wollf, T., 1960, The hadal community, an introduction, *Deep-Sea Research, 6*(2): 95–124.

Wood, E. J. F., 1963, Heterotrophic microorganisms in the oceans, in: *Ann. Rev. Oceanogr. Marine Biol.,* H. Barnes (ed.), pp. 197–222, Allen and Unwin, London.

Woodwell, G. M., 1963, The ecological effects of radiation, *Sci. American, 208*(6): 40–49.

Wright, J. G., 1960, The Limnology of Canton Ferry reservoir. III. Some observations on the density dependence of photosynthesis and its cause, *Limnol. Oceanog., 5:* 356–361.

Wright, R. T., 1964, Dynamics of a phytoplankton community in an ice-covered lake, *Limnol. Oceanogr., 9:* 163–178.

Wynne-Edwards, V. C., 1962, *Animal Dispersion in Relation to Social Behavior,* Hafner, N. Y.

Wynne-Edwards, V. C., 1964, Population control in animals, *Sci. American, 211*(2): 66–74.

Yentsch, C. S., 1962, Marine plankton, Chap. 52 in: *Physiol. and Biochem. of Algae,* Lewin (ed.), Academic Press, New York.

Yentsch, C. S., 1963, Primary production, *Oceanography and Marine Biology Annual Review,* H. Barnes (ed.), *1:* 157–175.

Yonge, C. M., 1963, The biology of coral reefs, in: *Advances in Marine Biology,* F. S. Russell (ed.), Vol. 1, pp. 209–260, Academic Press, New York.

ZoBell, C. E., and R. Y. Morita, 1959, Deep-sea bacteria, *Galathea Rep., 1:* 139–154.

Index